MECHANICAL METALLURGY

Metallurgy and Metallurgical Engineering Series

ROBERT F. MEHL, *Consulting Editor*

MICHAEL B. BEVER, *Associate Consulting Editor*

Mechanical Metallurgy

GEORGE E. DIETER, JR.

*Professor and Head of Department of Metallurgical
    Engineering
Drexel Institute of Technology
Philadelphia 4, Pa.*

McGRAW-HILL BOOK COMPANY, INC.

New York   Toronto   London   1961

MECHANICAL METALLURGY

6 7 8 9 - M P - 9 8 7

16890   THE MAPLE PRESS COMPANY, YORK, PA.

79400

PREFACE

Mechanical metallurgy is the area of knowledge which deals with the behavior and response of metals to applied forces. Since it is not a precisely defined area, it will mean different things to different persons. To some it will mean mechanical properties of metals or mechanical testing, others may consider the field restricted to the plastic working and shaping of metals, while still others confine their interests to the more theoretical aspects of the field, which merge with metal physics and physical metallurgy. Still another group may consider that mechanical metallurgy is closely allied with applied mathematics and applied mechanics. In writing this book an attempt has been made to cover, in some measure, this great diversity of interests. The objective has been to include the entire scope of mechanical metallurgy in one fairly comprehensive volume.

The book has been divided into four parts. Part One, Mechanical Fundamentals, presents the mathematical framework for many of the chapters which follow. The concepts of combined stress and strain are reviewed and extended into three dimensions. Detailed consideration of the theories of yielding and an introduction to the concepts of plasticity are given. No attempt is made to carry the topics in Part One to the degree of completion required for original problem solving. Instead, the purpose is to acquaint metallurgically trained persons with the mathematical language encountered in some areas of mechanical metallurgy. Part Two, Metallurgical Fundamentals, deals with the structural aspects of plastic deformation and fracture. Emphasis is on the atomistics of flow and fracture and the way in which metallurgical structure affects these processes. The concept of the dislocation is introduced early in Part Two and is used throughout to provide qualitative explanations for such phenomena as strain hardening, the yield point, dispersed phase hardening, and fracture. A more mathematical treatment of the properties of dislocations is given in a separate chapter. The topics covered in Part Two stem from physical metallurgy. However, most topics are discussed in greater detail and with a different emphasis than when they are first covered in the usual undergraduate course in physical metallurgy. Certain topics that are more physical metallurgy than mechanical

v

metallurgy are included to provide continuity and the necessary background for readers who have not studied modern physical metallurgy.

Part Three, Applications to Materials Testing, deals with the engineering aspects of the common testing techniques of mechanical failure of metals. Chapters are devoted to the tension, torsion, hardness, fatigue, creep, and impact tests. Others take up the important subjects of residual stresses and the statistical analysis of mechanical-property data. In Part Three emphasis is placed on the interpretation of the tests and on the effect of metallurgical variables on mechanical behavior rather than on the procedures for conducting the tests. It is assumed that the actual performance of these tests will be covered in a concurrent laboratory course or in a separate course. Part Four, Plastic Forming of Metals, deals with the common mechanical processes for producing useful metal shapes. Little emphasis is given to the descriptive aspects of this subject, since this can best be covered by plant trips and illustrated lectures. Instead, the main attention is given to the mechanical and metallurgical factors which control each process such as forging, rolling, extrusion, drawing, and sheet-metal forming.

This book is written for the senior or first-year graduate student in metallurgical or mechanical engineering, as well as for practicing engineers in industry. While most universities have instituted courses in mechanical metallurgy or mechanical properties, there is a great diversity in the material covered and in the background of the students taking these courses. Thus, for the present there can be nothing like a standardized textbook on mechanical metallurgy. It is hoped that the breadth and scope of this book will provide material for these somewhat diverse requirements. It is further hoped that the existence of a comprehensive treatment of the field of mechanical metallurgy will stimulate the development of courses which cover the total subject.

Since this book is intended for college seniors, graduate students, and practicing engineers, it is expected to become a part of their professional library. Although there has been no attempt to make this book a handbook, some thought has been given to providing abundant references to the literature on mechanical metallurgy. Therefore, more references are included than is usual in the ordinary textbook. References have been given to point out derivations or analyses beyond the scope of the book, to provide the key to further information on controversial or detailed points, and to emphasize important papers which are worthy of further study. In addition, a bibliography of general references will be found at the end of each chapter. A collection of problems is included at the end of the volume. This is primarily for the use of the reader who is engaged in industry and who desires some check on his comprehension of the material.

The task of writing this book has been mainly one of sifting and sorting facts and information from the literature and the many excellent texts on specialized aspects of this subject. To cover the breadth of material found in this book would require parts of over 15 standard texts and countless review articles and individual contributions. A conscientious effort has been made throughout to give credit to original sources. For the occasional oversights that may have developed during the "boiling-down process" the author offers his apologies. He is indebted to many authors and publishers who consented to the reproduction of illustrations. Credit is given in the captions of the illustrations.

Finally, the author wishes to acknowledge the many friends who advised him in this work. Special mention should be given to Professor A. W. Grosvenor, Drexel Institute of Technology, Dr. G. T. Horne, Carnegie Institute of Technology, Drs. T. C. Chilton, J. H. Faupel, W. L. Phillips, W. I. Pollock, and J. T. Ransom of the du Pont Company, and Dr. A. S. Nemy of the Thompson-Ramo-Wooldridge Corp.

George E. Dieter, Jr.

CONTENTS

x   Contents

Part Two.   Metallurgical Fundamentals

4. Plastic Deformation of Single Crystals 81

5. Plastic Deformation of Polycrystalline Aggregates 118

6. Dislocation Theory 158

LIST OF SYMBOLS

A	Area
a	Linear distance
a_0	Interatomic spacing
B	Constant
b	Width or breadth
$\mathbf{b}$	Burgers vector of a dislocation
C	Generalized constant
C_{ij}	Elastic coefficients
c	Length of Griffith crack
D	Diameter, grain diameter
E	Modulus of elasticity for axial loading (Young's modulus)
e	Conventional, or engineering, strain
exp	Base of natural logarithms ($= 2.718$)
F	Force per unit length on a dislocation line
f	Coefficient of friction
G	Modulus of elasticity in shear (modulus of rigidity)
$\mathcal{G}$	Crack-extension force
H	Activation energy
h	Distance, usually in thickness direction
(h,k,l)	Miller indices of a crystallographic plane
I	Moment of inertia
J	Invariant of the stress deviator; polar moment of inertia
K	Strength coefficient
K_f	Fatigue-notch factor
K_t	Theoretical stress-concentration factor
k	Yield stress in pure shear
L	Length
l, m, n	Direction cosines of normal to a plane
ln	Natural logarithm
log	Logarithm to base 10
M_B	Bending moment
M_T	Torsional moment, torque

m	Strain-rate sensitivity
N	Number of cycles of stress or vibration
n	Strain-hardening exponent
n'	Generalized constant in exponential term
P	Load or external force
p	Pressure
q	Reduction in area; plastic-constraint factor; notch sensitivity index in fatigue
R	Radius of curvature; stress ratio in fatigue; gas constant
r	Radial distance
S	Total stress on a plane before resolution into normal and shear components
S_{ij}	Elastic compliance
s	Standard deviation of a sample
T	Temperature
T_m	Melting point
t	Time; thickness
t_r	Time for rupture
U	Elastic strain energy
U_0	Elastic strain energy per unit volume
u, v, w	Components of displacement in x, y, and z directions
$[uvw]$	Miller indices for a crystallographic direction
V	Volume
v	Velocity; coefficient of variation
W	Work
Z	Zener-Hollomon parameter
α	Linear coefficient of thermal expansion
$\alpha, \beta, \theta, \phi$	Generalized angles
Γ	Line tension of a dislocation
γ	Shear strain
Δ	Volume strain or cubical dilatation; finite change
δ	Deformation or elongation; deflection; logarithmic decrement
ϵ	Natural, or true, strain
$\bar{\epsilon}$	Significant, or effective, true strain
$\dot{\epsilon}$	True-strain rate
$\dot{\epsilon}_m$	Minimum creep rate
η	Efficiency; coefficient of viscosity
θ	Dorn time-temperature parameter
κ	Bulk modulus or volumetric modulus of elasticity
Λ	Interparticle spacing
λ	Lamé's constant
μ	Lode's stress parameter

ν	Poisson's ratio; Lode's strain parameter
ρ	Density
σ	Normal stress; the standard deviation of a population
σ_0	Yield stress or yield strength
σ_0'	Yield stress in plane strain
$\bar{\sigma}$	Significant, or effective, true stress
$\sigma_1, \sigma_2, \sigma_3$	Principal stresses
σ'	Stress deviator
σ''	Hydrostatic component of stress
σ_a	Alternating, or variable, stress
σ_m	Average principal stress; mean stress
σ_r	Range of stress
σ_u	Ultimate tensile strength
σ_w	Working stress
τ	Shearing stress; relaxation time
Φ	Airy stress function
ψ	Specific damping capacity

Part One
MECHANICAL FUNDAMENTALS

Chapter 1

INTRODUCTION

1-1. Scope of This Book

Mechanical metallurgy is the area of metallurgy which is concerned primarily with the response of metals to forces or loads. The forces may arise from the use of the metal as a member or part in a structure or machine, in which case it is necessary to know something about the limiting values which can be withstood without failure. On the other hand, the objective may be to convert a cast ingot into a more useful shape, such as a flat plate, and here it is necessary to know the conditions of temperature and rate of loading which minimize the forces that are needed to do the job.

Mechanical metallurgy is *not* a subject which can be neatly isolated and studied by itself. It is a combination of many disciplines and many approaches to the problem of understanding the response of materials to forces. On the one hand is the approach used in reference to strength of materials and in the theories of elasticity and plasticity, where a metal is considered to be a homogeneous material whose mechanical behavior can be rather precisely described on the basis of only a very few material constants. This approach is the basis for the rational design of structural members and machine parts, and the three topics of strength of materials, elasticity, and plasticity are covered in Part One of this book from a more generalized point of view than is usually considered in a first course in strength of materials. The material covered in Chaps. 1 to 3 can be considered the mathematical framework on which much of the remainder of the book rests. For students of engineering who have had an advanced course in strength of materials or machine design, it probably will be possible to skim rapidly over these chapters. However, for most students of metallurgy and for practicing engineers in industry, it is worth spending the time to become familiar with the mathematics presented in Part One.

The theories of strength of materials, elasticity, and plasticity lose much of their power when the structure of the metal becomes an important consideration and it can no longer be considered as a homogeneous medium. Examples of this are in the high-temperature behavior of metals, where the metallurgical structure may continuously change with time, or in the ductile-to-brittle transition, which occurs in plain carbon steel. The determination of the relationship between mechanical behavior and structure (as detected chiefly with microscopic and X-ray techniques) is the main responsibility of the mechanical metallurgist. When mechanical behavior is understood in terms of metallurgical structure, it is generally possible to improve the mechanical properties or at least to control them. Part Two of this book is concerned with the metallurgical fundamentals of the mechanical behavior of metals. Metallurgical students will find that some of the material in Part Two has been covered in a previous course in physical metallurgy, since mechanical metallurgy is part of the broader field of physical metallurgy. However, these subjects are considered in greater detail than is usually the case in a first course in physical metallurgy. In addition, certain topics which pertain more to physical metallurgy than mechanical metallurgy have been included in order to provide continuity and to assist nonmetallurgical students who may not have had a course in physical metallurgy.

The last three chapters of Part Two, especially Chap. 6, are concerned primarily with atomistic concepts of the flow and fracture of metals. Many of the developments in these areas have been the result of the alliance of the solid-state physicist with the metallurgist. This is an area where *direct* observation is practically impossible and definitive experiments of an indirect nature are difficult to conceive. Moreover, it is an area of intense activity in which the lifetime of a concept or theory may be rather short. Therefore, in writing these chapters an attempt has been made to include only material which is generally valid and to minimize the controversial aspects of the subject.

Basic data concerning the strength of metals and measurements for the routine control of mechanical properties are obtained from a relatively small number of standardized mechanical tests. Part Three, Applications to Materials Testing, considers each of the common mechanical tests, not from the usual standpoint of testing techniques, but instead from the consideration of what these tests tell about the service performance of metals and how metallurgical variables affect the results of these tests. Much of the material in Parts One and Two has been utilized in Part Three. It is assumed that the reader either has completed a conventional course in materials testing or will be concurrently taking a laboratory course in which familiarization with the testing techniques will be acquired.

Part Four considers the metallurgical and mechanical factors involved in the forming of metals into useful shapes. Attempts have been made to present mathematical analyses of the principal metalworking processes, although in certain cases this has not been possible, either because of the considerable detail required or because the analysis is beyond the scope of this book.   No attempt has been made to include the extensive specialized technology associated with each metalworking process, such as rolling or extrusion, although some effort has been made to give a general impression of the mechanical equipment required and to familiarize the reader with the specialized vocabulary of the metalworking field.   Major emphasis has been placed on presenting a fairly simplified picture of the forces involved in each process and how geometrical and metallurgical factors affect the forming loads and the success of the metalworking process.

1-2. Strength of Materials—Basic Assumptions

Strength of materials is the body of knowledge which deals with the relation between internal forces, deformation, and external loads.   In the general method of analysis used in strength of materials the first step is to assume that the member is in equilibrium.   The equations of static equilibrium are applied to the forces acting on some part of the body in order to obtain a relationship between the external forces acting on the member and the internal forces resisting the action of the external loads. Since the equations of equilibrium must be expressed in terms of forces acting external to the body, it is necessary to make the internal resisting forces into external forces.   This is done by passing a plane through the body at the point of interest.   The part of the body lying on one side of the cutting plane is removed and replaced by the forces it exerted on the cut section of the part of the body that remains.   Since the forces acting on the "free body" hold it in equilibrium, the equations of equilibrium may be applied to the problem.

The internal resisting forces are usually expressed by the *stress*[1] acting over a certain area, so that the internal force is the integral of the stress times the differential area over which it acts.   In order to evaluate this integral, it is necessary to know the distribution of the stress over the area of the cutting plane.   The stress distribution is arrived at by observing and measuring the strain distribution in the member, since stress cannot be physically measured.   However, since stress is proportional to strain for the small deformations involved in most work, the determination of the strain distribution provides the stress distribution.   The expression for the stress is then substituted into the equations of equi-

---

[1] For present purposes *stress* is defined as force per unit area.   The companion term *strain* is defined as the change in length per unit length.   More complete definitions will be given later.

librium, and they are solved for stress in terms of the loads and dimensions of the member.

Important assumptions in strength of materials are that the body which is being analyzed is continuous, homogeneous, and isotropic. A *continuous body* is one which does not contain voids or empty spaces of any kind. A body is *homogeneous* if it has identical properties at all points. A body is considered to be *isotropic* with respect to some property when that property does not vary with direction or orientation. A property which varies with orientation with respect to some system of axes is said to be *anisotropic*.

While engineering materials such as steel, cast iron, and aluminum may appear to meet these conditions when viewed on a gross scale, it is readily apparent when they are viewed through a microscope that they are anything but homogeneous and isotropic. Most engineering metals are made up of more than one phase, with different mechanical properties, such that on a micro scale they are heterogeneous. Further, even a single-phase metal will usually exhibit chemical segregation, and therefore the properties will not be identical from point to point. Metals are made up of an aggregate of crystal grains having different properties in different crystallographic directions. The reason why the equations of strength of materials describe the behavior of real metals is that, in general, the crystal grains are so small that, for a specimen of any macroscopic volume, the materials are statistically homogeneous and isotropic. However, when metals are severely deformed in a particular direction, as in rolling or forging, the mechanical properties may be anisotropic on a macro scale.

1-3. Elastic and Plastic Behavior

Experience shows that all solid materials can be deformed when subjected to external load. It is further found that up to certain limiting loads a solid will recover its original dimensions when the load is removed. The recovery of the original dimensions of a deformed body when the load is removed is known as *elastic behavior*. The limiting load beyond which the material no longer behaves elastically is the *elastic limit*. If the elastic limit is exceeded, the body will experience a permanent set or deformation when the load is removed. A body which is permanently deformed is said to have undergone *plastic deformation*.

For most materials, as long as the load does not exceed the elastic limit, the deformation is proportional to the load. This relationship is known as Hooke's law; it is more frequently stated as *stress is proportional to strain*. Hooke's law requires that the load-deformation relationship should be linear. However, it does not necessarily follow that all materials which behave elastically will have a linear stress-strain relationship. Rubber is an example of a material with a nonlinear stress-strain relationship that still satisfies the definition of an elastic material.

Elastic deformations in metals are quite small and require very sensitive instruments for their measurement. Ultrasensitive instruments have shown that the elastic limits of metals are much lower than the values usually measured in engineering tests of materials. As the measuring devices become more sensitive, the elastic limit is decreased, so that for most metals there is only a rather narrow range of loads over which Hooke's law strictly applies. This is, however, primarily of academic importance. Hooke's law remains a quite valid relationship for engineering design.

1-4. Average Stress and Strain

As a starting point in the discussion of stress and strain, consider a uniform cylindrical bar which is subjected to an axial tensile load (Fig. 1-1). Assume that two gage marks are put on the surface of the bar in

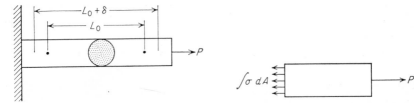

Fig. 1-1. Cylindrical bar subjected to axial load.   **Fig. 1-2.** Free-body diagram for Fig. 1-1.

its unstrained state and that L_0 is the gage length between these marks. A load P is applied to one end of the bar, and the gage length undergoes a slight increase in length and decrease in diameter. The distance between the gage marks has increased by an amount δ, called the deformation. The *average linear strain* e is the ratio of the change in length to the original length.

$$e = \frac{\delta}{L_0} = \frac{\Delta L}{L_0} = \frac{L - L_0}{L_0} \tag{1-1}$$

Strain is a dimensionless quantity since both δ and L_0 are expressed in units of length.

Figure 1-2 shows the free-body diagram for the cylindrical bar shown in Fig. 1-1. The external load P is balanced by the internal resisting force $\int \sigma \, dA$, where σ is the stress normal to the cutting plane and A is the cross-sectional area of the bar.   The equilibrium equation is

$$P = \int \sigma \, dA \tag{1-2}$$

If the stress is distributed uniformly over the area A, that is, if σ is constant, Eq. (1-2) becomes

$$P = \sigma \int dA = \sigma A$$
$$\sigma = \frac{P}{A} \tag{1-3}$$

In general, the stress will not be uniform over the area A, and therefore Eq. (1-3) represents an *average stress*.   For the stress to be absolutely uniform, every longitudinal element in the bar would have to experience exactly the same strain, and the proportionality between stress and strain would have to be identical for each element.   The inherent anisotropy between grains in a polycrystalline metal rules out the possibility of complete uniformity of stress over a body of macroscopic size.   The presence of more than one phase also gives rise to nonuniformity of stress on a microscopic scale.   If the bar is not straight or not centrally loaded, the strains will be different for certain longitudinal elements and the stress will not be uniform.   An extreme disruption in the uniformity of the stress pattern occurs when there is an abrupt change in cross section. This results in a stress raiser or stress concentration (see Sec. 2-13).

In engineering practice, the load is usually measured in pounds and the area in square inches, so that stress has units of pounds per square inch (psi).   Since it is common for engineers to deal with loads in the thousands of pounds, an obvious simplification is to work with units of 1,000 lb, called *kips*.   The stress may be expressed in units of kips per square inch (ksi).   (1 ksi = 1,000 psi.)   In scientific work stresses are often expressed in units of kilograms per square millimeter or dynes per square centimeter.   (1 kg/mm² = 9.81×10^7 dynes/cm².)

Below the elastic limit Hooke's law can be considered valid, so that the average stress is proportional to the average strain,

$$\frac{\sigma}{e} = E = \text{constant} \tag{1-4}$$

The constant E is the *modulus of elasticity*, or *Young's modulus*.

1-5. Tensile Deformation of Ductile Metal

The basic data on the mechanical properties of a ductile metal are obtained from a tension test, in which a suitably designed specimen is subjected to increasing axial load until it fractures.   The load and elongation are measured at frequent intervals during the test and are expressed

as average stress and strain according to the equations in the previous
section. (More complete details on the tension test are given in Chap. 9.)
   The data obtained from the tension test are generally plotted as a
stress-strain diagram. Figure 1-3 shows a typical stress-strain curve for

a metal such as aluminum or copper. The initial linear portion of
the curve OA is the elastic region
within which Hooke's law is
obeyed. Point A is the elastic
limit, defined as the greatest stress
that the metal can withstand without experiencing a permanent
strain when the load is removed.
The determination of the elastic
limit is quite tedious, not at all
routine, and dependent on the sensitivity of the strain-measuring

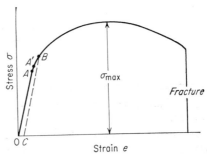

Fig. 1-3. Typical tension stress-strain
curve.

instrument. For these reasons it is often replaced by the *proportional
limit*, point A'. The proportional limit is the stress at which the stress-
strain curve deviates from linearity. The slope of the stress-strain curve
in this region is the modulus of elasticity.
   For engineering purposes the limit of usable elastic behavior is described
by the *yield strength*, point B. The yield strength is defined as the stress
which will produce a small amount of permanent deformation, generally
a strain equal to 0.2 per cent or 0.002 inches per inch. In Fig. 1-3
this permanent strain, or offset, is OC. Plastic deformation begins
when the elastic limit is exceeded. As the plastic deformation of the
specimen increases, the metal becomes stronger (strain hardening) so
that the load required to extend the specimen increases with further
straining. Eventually the load reaches a maximum value. The maximum load divided by the original area of the specimen is the *ultimate
tensile strength*. For a ductile metal the diameter of the specimen
begins to decrease rapidly beyond maximum load, so that the load
required to continue deformation drops off until the specimen fractures.
Since the average stress is based on the original area of the specimen,
it also decreases from maximum load to fracture.

1-6. Ductile vs. Brittle Behavior

   The general behavior of materials under load can be classified as ductile
or brittle depending upon whether or not the material exhibits the ability
to undergo plastic deformation. Figure 1-3 illustrates the tension stress-
strain curve of a ductile material. A completely brittle material would

fracture almost at the elastic limit (Fig. 1-4a), while a brittle metal, such as white cast iron, shows some slight measure of plasticity before fracture (Fig. 1-4b). Adequate ductility is an important engineering consideration, because it allows the material to redistribute localized stresses. When localized stresses at notches and other accidental stress concentrations do not have to be considered, it is possible to design for static situations on the basis of average stresses. However, with brittle materials, localized stresses continue to build up when there is no local yielding. Finally, a crack forms at one or more points of stress concentration, and it spreads rapidly over the section. Even if no stress concentrations are present in a brittle material, fracture will still occur suddenly because the yield stress and tensile strength are practically identical.

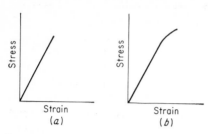

Fig. 1-4. (a) Stress-strain curve for completely brittle material (ideal behavior); (b) stress-strain curve for brittle metal with slight amount of ductility.

It is important to note that brittleness is not an absolute property of a metal. A metal such as tungsten, which is brittle at room temperature, is ductile at an elevated temperature. A metal which is brittle in tension may be ductile under hydrostatic compression. Furthermore, a metal which is ductile in tension at room temperature can become brittle in the presence of notches, low temperature, high rates of loading, or embrittling agents such as hydrogen.

1-7. What Constitutes Failure?

Structural members and machine elements can fail to perform their intended functions in three general ways:

1. Excessive elastic deformation
2. Yielding, or excessive plastic deformation
3. Fracture

An understanding of the common types of failure is important in good design because it is always necessary to relate the loads and dimensions of the member to some significant material parameter which limits the load-carrying capacity of the member. For different types of failure, different significant parameters will be important.

Two general types of excessive elastic deformation may occur: (1) excessive deflection under conditions of stable equilibrium, such as the deflection of beam under gradually applied loads; (2) sudden deflection, or *buckling*, under conditions of unstable equilibrium.

Excessive elastic deformation of a machine part can mean failure of the machine just as much as if the part completely fractured. For example, a shaft which is too flexible can cause rapid wear of the bearing, or the excessive deflection of closely mating parts can result in interference and damage to the parts. The sudden buckling type of failure may occur in a slender column when the axial load exceeds the Euler critical load or when the external pressure acting against a thin-walled shell exceeds a critical value. Failures due to excessive elastic deformation are controlled by the modulus of elasticity, not by the strength of the material. Generally, little metallurgical control can be exercised over the elastic modulus. The most effective way to increase the stiffness of a member is usually by changing its shape and increasing the dimensions of its cross section.

Yielding, or excessive plastic deformation, occurs when the elastic limit of the metal has been exceeded. Yielding produces permanent change of shape, which may prevent the part from functioning properly any longer. In a ductile metal under conditions of static loading at room temperature yielding rarely results in fracture, because the metal strain hardens as it deforms, and an increased stress is required to produce further deformation. Failure by excessive plastic deformation is controlled by the yield strength of the metal for a uniaxial condition of loading. For more complex loading conditions the yield strength is still the significant parameter, but it must be used with a suitable failure criterion (Sec. 3-4). At temperatures significantly greater than room temperature metals no longer exhibit strain hardening. Instead, metals can continuously deform at constant stress in a time-dependent yielding known as *creep*. The failure criterion under creep conditions is complicated by the fact that stress is not proportional to strain and the further fact that the mechanical properties of the material may change appreciably during service. This complex phenomenon will be considered in greater detail in Chap. 13.

The formation of a crack which can result in complete disruption of continuity of the member constitutes fracture. A part made from a ductile metal which is loaded statically rarely fractures like a tensile specimen, because it will first fail by excessive plastic deformation. However, metals fail by fracture in three general ways: (1) sudden brittle fracture; (2) fatigue, or progressive fracture; (3) delayed fracture. In the previous section it was shown that a brittle material fractures under static loads with little outward evidence of yielding. A sudden brittle type of fracture can also occur in ordinarily ductile metals under certain conditions. Plain carbon structural steel is the most common example of a material with a ductile-to-brittle transition.   A change from the ductile to the brittle type of fracture is promoted by a decrease in temperature, an increase in the rate of loading, and the presence of a complex state of stress due to a notch.   This problem is considered in Chap. 14.

Most fractures in machine parts are due to *fatigue*.   Fatigue failures occur in parts which are subjected to alternating, or fluctuating, stresses. A minute crack starts at a localized spot, generally at a notch or stress concentration, and gradually spreads over the cross section until the member breaks.   Fatigue failure occurs without any visible sign of yielding at *nominal* or average stresses that are well below the tensile strength of the metal.   Fatigue failure is caused by a critical *localized* tensile stress which is very difficult to evaluate, and therefore design for fatigue failure is based primarily on empirical relationships using nominal stresses. Fatigue of metals is discussed in greater detail in Chap. 12.

One common type of delayed fracture is *stress-rupture* failure, which occurs when a metal has been statically loaded at an elevated temperature for a long period of time.   Depending upon the stress and the temperature there may be no yielding prior to fracture.   A similar type of delayed fracture, in which there is no warning by yielding prior to failure, occurs at room temperature when steel is statically loaded in the presence of hydrogen.

All engineering materials show a certain variability in mechanical properties, which in turn can be influenced by changes in heat treatment or fabrication.   Further, uncertainties usually exist regarding the magnitude of the applied loads, and approximations are usually necessary in calculating the stresses for all but the most simple member. Allowance must be made for the possibility of accidental loads of high magnitude.   Thus, in order to provide a margin of safety and to protect against failure from unpredictable causes, it is necessary that the allowable stresses be smaller than the stresses which produce failure.   The value of stress for a particular material used in a particular way which is considered to be a safe stress is usually called the *working stress* σ_w.   For static applications the working stress of ductile metals is usually based on the yield strength σ_0 and for brittle metals on the ultimate tensile strength σ_u.   Values of working stress are established by local and Federal agencies and by technical organizations such as the American Society of Mechanical Engineers (ASME).   The working stress may be considered as either the yield strength or the tensile strength divided by a number called the *factor of safety*.

$$\sigma_w = \frac{\sigma_0}{N_0} \qquad \text{or} \qquad \sigma_w = \frac{\sigma_u}{N_u} \qquad\qquad (1\text{-}5)$$

where σ_w = working stress, psi

σ_0 = yield strength, psi

σ_u = tensile strength, psi

N_0 = factor of safety based on yield strength

N_u = factor of safety based on tensile strength

The value assigned to the factor of safety depends on an estimate of all the factors discussed above. In addition, careful consideration should be given to the consequences which would result from failure. If failure would result in loss of life, the factor of safety should be increased. The type of equipment will also influence the factor of safety. In military equipment, where light weight may be a prime consideration, the factor of safety may be lower than in commercial equipment. The factor of safety will also depend on the expected type of loading. For static loading, as in a building, the factor of safety would be lower than in a machine, which is subjected to vibration and fluctuating stresses.

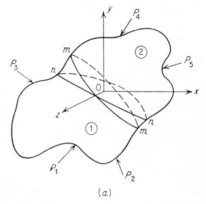

1-8. Concept of Stress and the Types of Stresses

Stress is defined as the internal resistance of a body to an external applied force, *per unit area*. In Sec. 1-4 the stress was considered to be uniformly distributed over the cross-sectional area of the member. However, this is not the general case. Figure 1-5a represents a body in equilibrium under the action of external forces P_1, P_2, . . . , P_5. There are two kinds of external forces which may act on a body, surface forces and body forces. Forces distributed over the surface of the body, such as hydrostatic pressure or the pressure exerted by one body on another, are called *surface forces*. Forces distributed over the volume of a body, such as gravitational forces, magnetic forces, or inertia forces (for a body in motion), are called *body forces*. The two most common types of body forces encountered in engineering practice are centrifugal

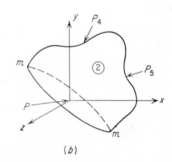

Fig. 1-5. (*a*) Body in equilibrium under action of external forces P_1, . . . , P_5; (*b*) forces acting on parts.

forces due to high-speed rotation and forces due to temperature differential over the body (thermal stress).

In general the force will not be uniformly distributed over any cross section of the body illustrated in Fig. 1-5a. To obtain the stress at some point O in a plane such as mm, part 1 of the body is removed and replaced by the system of external forces on mm which will retain each point in part 2 of the body in the same position as before the removal of part 1.

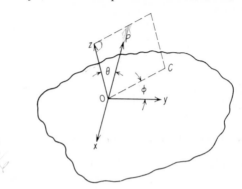

Fig. 1-6. Resolution of total stress into its components.

This is the situation in Fig. 1-5b. We then take an area ΔA surrounding the point O and note that a force ΔP acts on this area. If the area ΔA is continuously reduced to zero, the limiting value of the ratio $\Delta P/\Delta A$ is the stress at the point O on plane mm of body 2.

$$\lim_{\Delta A \to 0} \frac{\Delta P}{\Delta A} = \sigma \tag{1-6}$$

The stress will be in the direction of the resultant force P and will generally be inclined at an angle to ΔA. The same stress at point O in plane mm would be obtained if the free body were constructed by removing part 2 of the solid body. However, the stress will be different on any other plane passing through point O, such as the plane nn.

It is inconvenient to use a stress which is inclined at some arbitrary angle to the area over which it acts. The total stress can be resolved into two components, a *normal stress* σ perpendicular to ΔA, and a *shearing stress* (or shear stress) τ lying in the plane mm of the area. To illustrate this point, consider Fig. 1-6. The force P makes an angle θ with the normal z to the plane of the area A. Also, the plane containing the normal and P intersects the plane A along a dashed line that makes an angle ϕ with the y axis. The normal stress is given by

$$\sigma = \frac{P}{A} \cos \theta \tag{1-7}$$

The shear stress in the plane acts along the line OC and has the magnitude

$$\tau = \frac{P}{A} \sin \theta \qquad (1\text{-}8)$$

This shear stress may be further resolved into components parallel to the x and y directions lying in the plane.

x direction
$$\tau = \frac{P}{A} \sin \theta \sin \phi \qquad (1\text{-}9)$$

y direction
$$\tau = \frac{P}{A} \sin \theta \cos \phi \qquad (1\text{-}10)$$

Therefore, in general a given plane may have one normal stress and two shear stresses acting on it.

1-9. Concept of Strain and the Types of Strain

In Sec. 1-4 the average linear strain was defined as the ratio of the change in length to the original length of the same dimension.

$$e = \frac{\delta}{L_0} = \frac{\Delta L}{L_0} = \frac{L - L_0}{L_0}$$

where e = average linear strain
δ = deformation

By analogy with the definition of stress at a point, the strain at a point is the ratio of the deformation to the gage length as the gage length approaches zero.

Rather than referring the change in length to the original gage length, it often is more useful to define the strain as the change in linear dimension divided by the instantaneous value of the dimension.

$$\epsilon = \int_{L_0}^{L_f} \frac{dL}{L} = \ln \frac{L_f}{L_0} \qquad (1\text{-}11)$$

The above equation defines the *natural*, or *true*, *strain*. True strain, which is useful in dealing with problems in plasticity and metal forming, will be discussed more fully in Chap. 3. For the present it should be noted that for the very small strains for which the equations of elasticity are valid the two definitions of strain give identical values.[1]

Not only will the elastic deformation of a body result in a change in length of a linear element in the body, but it may also result in a change

---

[1] Considerable variance exists in the literature regarding the notation for average linear strain, true strain, and deformation. Linear strain is often denoted by ϵ, while true strain is sometimes denoted by δ or $\bar{\epsilon}$.

in the initial angle between any two lines. The angular change in a right angle is known as *shear strain*. Figure 1-7 illustrates the strain produced by the pure shear of one face of a cube. The angle at A, which was originally 90°, is decreased by the application of a shear stress by a small amount θ. The shear strain γ is equal to the displacement a

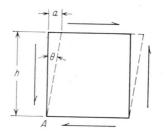

Fig. 1-7. Shear strain.

divided by the distance between the planes, h. The ratio a/h is also the tangent of the angle through which the element has been rotated. For the small angles usually involved, the tangent of the angle and the angle (in radians) are equal. Therefore, shear strains are often expressed as angles of rotation.

$$\gamma = \frac{a}{h} = \tan \theta = \theta \tag{1-12}$$

BIBLIOGRAPHY

Crandall, S. H., and N. C. Dahl (eds.): "An Introduction to the Mechanics of Solids," McGraw-Hill Book Company, Inc., New York, 1959.

Frocht, M. M.: "Strength of Materials," The Ronald Press Company, New York, 1951.

Seely, F. B., and J. O. Smith: "Resistance of Materials," 4th ed., John Wiley & Sons, Inc., New York, 1957.

——— and ———: "Advanced Mechanics of Materials," 2d ed., John Wiley & Sons, Inc., New York, 1952.

Shanley, F. R.: "Strength of Materials," McGraw-Hill Book Company, Inc., New York, 1957.

Chapter 2

STRESS AND STRAIN RELATIONSHIPS FOR ELASTIC BEHAVIOR

2-1. Introduction

The purpose of this chapter is to present the mathematical relationships for expressing the stress and strain at a point and the relationships between stress and strain in a rigid body which obeys Hooke's law. While part of the material covered in this chapter is a review of information generally covered in strength of materials, the subject is extended beyond this point to a consideration of stress and strain in three dimensions and to an introduction to the theory of elasticity. The material included in this chapter is important for an understanding of most of the phenomenological aspects of mechanical metallurgy, and for this reason it should be given careful attention by those readers to whom it is unfamiliar. In the space available for this subject it has not been possible to carry it to the point where extensive problem solving is possible. The material covered here should, however, provide a background for intelligent reading of the more mathematical literature in mechanical metallurgy.

2-2. Description of Stress at a Point

As described in Sec. 1-8, it is often convenient to resolve the stresses at a point into normal and shear components. In the general case the shear components are at arbitrary angles to the coordinate axes, so that it is convenient to resolve each shear stress further into two components. The general case is shown in Fig. 2-1. Stresses acting normal to the faces of the elemental cube are identified by the subscript which also identifies the direction in which the stress acts; that is, σ_x is the normal stress acting in the x direction. Since it is a normal stress, it must act on the plane perpendicular to the x direction. By convention, values of normal stresses greater than zero denote tension; values less than zero indicate compression. All the normal stresses shown in Fig. 2-1 are tensile.

Two subscripts are needed for describing shearing stresses. The first subscript indicates the plane in which the stress acts and the second the direction in which the stress acts. Since a plane is most easily defined by its normal, the first subscript refers to this normal. For example, τ_{yz} is the shear stress on the plane perpendicular to the y axis in the

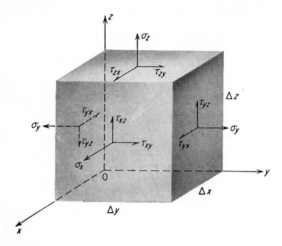

Fig. 2-1. Stresses acting on an elemental unit cube.

direction of the z axis. τ_{yx} is the shear stress on a plane normal to the y axis in the direction of the x axis. Shearing stresses oriented in the positive directions of the coordinate axes are positive if a tensile stress on the same cube face is in the positive direction of the corresponding axis. All the shear stresses shown in Fig. 2-1 are positive.

The notation given above is the one used by Timoshenko[1] and most American workers in the field of elasticity. The reader is reminded, however, that several other systems of notation are in use. Before attempting to read papers in this field it is important to become familiar with the notation which is used.

It can be seen from Fig. 2-1 that nine quantities must be defined in order to establish the state of stress at a point. They are σ_x, σ_y, σ_z, τ_{xy}, τ_{xz}, τ_{yx}, τ_{yz}, τ_{zx}, and τ_{zy}. However, some simplification is possible. If we assume that the areas of the faces of the unit cube are small enough so that the change in stress over the face is negligible, by taking the sum-

[1] S. P. Timoshenko and J. N. Goodier, "Theory of Elasticity," 2d ed., McGraw-Hill Book Company, Inc., New York, 1951.

mation of the moments of the forces about the z axis it can be shown that $\tau_{xy} = \tau_{yx}$.

$$(\tau_{xy} \, \Delta y \, \Delta z) \, \Delta x = (\tau_{yx} \, \Delta x \, \Delta z) \, \Delta y \qquad (2\text{-}1)$$
$$\therefore \ \tau_{xy} = \tau_{yx}$$

and in like manner

$$\tau_{xz} = \tau_{zx} \qquad \tau_{yz} = \tau_{zy}$$

Thus, the state of stress at a point is completely described by six components,[1] three normal stresses and three shear stresses, σ_x, σ_y, σ_z, τ_{xy}, τ_{xz}, τ_{yz}.

2-3. State of Stress in Two Dimensions (Plane Stress)

Many problems can be simplified by considering a two-dimensional state of stress. This condition is frequently approached in practice when

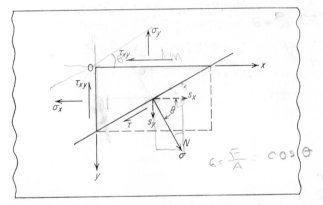

Fig. 2-2. Stress on oblique plane, two dimensions.

one of the dimensions of the body is small relative to the others. For example, in a thin plate loaded in the plane of the plate, there will be no stress acting perpendicular to the plate. The stress system will consist of two normal stresses σ_x and σ_y and a shear stress τ_{xy}. A stress condition in which the stresses are zero in one of the primary directions is called *plane stress*.

Figure 2-2 illustrates a thin plate with its thickness normal to the plane of the paper. In order to know the state of stress at point O in the plate, we need to be able to describe the stress components at O for any orientation of the axes through the point. To do this, consider an oblique plane normal to the plane of the paper at an angle θ between the

---

[1] For a more complete derivation see C. T. Wang, "Applied Elasticity," pp. 7–9, McGraw-Hill Book Company, Inc., New York, 1953.

x axis and the normal N to the plane. It is assumed that the plane shown in Fig. 2-2 is an infinitesimal distance from O and that the element is so small that variations in stress over the sides of the element can be neglected. The stresses acting on the oblique plane are the normal stress σ and the shear stress τ. The direction cosines between N and the x and y axes are l and m, respectively. From the geometry of Fig. 2-2, it follows that $l = \cos\theta$ and $m = \sin\theta$. If A is the area of the oblique plane, the areas of the sides of the element perpendicular to the x and y axes are Al and Am.

Let S_x and S_y denote the x and y components of the total stress acting on the inclined face. By taking the summation of the *forces* in the x direction and the y direction, we obtain

$$S_x A = \sigma_x Al + \tau_{xy} Am$$
$$S_y A = \sigma_y Am + \tau_{xy} Al$$

or

$$S_x = \sigma_x \cos\theta + \tau_{xy} \sin\theta$$
$$S_y = \sigma_y \sin\theta + \tau_{xy} \cos\theta$$

The components of S_x and S_y in the direction of the normal stress σ are

$$S_{xN} = S_x \cos\theta \qquad \text{and} \qquad S_{yN} = S_y \sin\theta$$

so that the normal stress acting on the oblique plane is given by

$$\sigma = S_x \cos\theta + S_y \sin\theta$$
$$\sigma = \sigma_x \cos^2\theta + \sigma_y \sin^2\theta + 2\tau_{xy} \sin\theta \cos\theta \tag{2-2}$$

The shearing stress on the oblique plane is given by

$$\tau = S_y \cos\theta - S_x \sin\theta$$
$$\tau = \tau_{xy}(\cos^2\theta - \sin^2\theta) + (\sigma_y - \sigma_x) \sin\theta \cos\theta \tag{2-3}$$

To aid in computation, it is often convenient to express Eqs. (2-2) and (2-3) in terms of the double angle 2θ. This can be done with the following identities:

$$\cos^2\theta = \frac{\cos 2\theta + 1}{2}$$

$$\sin^2\theta = \frac{1 - \cos 2\theta}{2}$$

$$2\sin\theta \cos\theta = \sin 2\theta$$
$$\cos^2\theta - \sin^2\theta = \cos 2\theta$$

Equations (2-2) and (2-3) now become

$$\sigma = \frac{\sigma_x + \sigma_y}{2} + \frac{\sigma_x - \sigma_y}{2} \cos 2\theta + \tau_{xy} \sin 2\theta \tag{2-4}$$

$$\tau = \frac{\sigma_y - \sigma_x}{2} \sin 2\theta + \tau_{xy} \cos 2\theta \tag{2-5}$$

Equations (2-2) and (2-3) and their equivalents, Eqs. (2-4) and (2-5), describe the normal stress and shear stress on any plane through a point in a body subjected to a plane-stress situation. Figure 2-3 shows

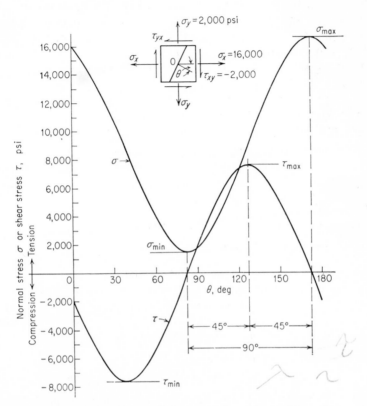

Fig. 2-3. Variation of normal stress and shear stress with angle θ.

the variation of normal stress and shear stress with θ for the biaxial-plane-stress situation given at the top of the figure. Note the following important facts about this figure:

1. The maximum and minimum values of normal stress on the oblique plane through point O occur when the shear stress is zero.

2. The maximum and minimum values of both normal stress and shear stress occur at angles which are 90° apart.

3. The maximum shear stress occurs at an angle halfway between the maximum and minimum normal stresses.

4. The variation of normal stress and shear stress occurs in the form of a sine wave, with a period of $\theta = 180°$. These relationships are valid for any state of stress.

For any state of stress it is always possible to define a new coordinate system which has axes perpendicular to the planes on which the maximum normal stresses act and on which no shearing stresses act. These planes are called the *principal planes*, and the stresses normal to these planes are the *principal stresses*. For two-dimensional plane stress there will be two principal stresses σ_1 and σ_2 which occur at angles that are 90° apart (Fig. 2-3). For the general case of stress in three dimensions there will be three principal stresses σ_1, σ_2, and σ_3. According to convention, σ_1 is the algebraically greatest principal stress, while σ_3 is the algebraically smallest stress. The directions of the principal stresses are the *principal axes* 1, 2, and 3. Although in general the principal axes 1, 2, and 3 do not coincide with the cartesian-coordinate axes x, y, z, for many situations that are encountered in practice the two systems of axes coincide because of symmetry of loading and deformation. The specification of the principal stresses and their direction provides a convenient way of describing the state of stress at a point.

Since by definition a principal plane contains no shear stress, its angular relationship with respect to the xy coordinate axes can be determined by finding the values of θ in Eq. (2-3) for which $\tau = 0$.

$$\tau_{xy}(\cos^2 \theta - \sin^2 \theta) + (\sigma_y - \sigma_x) \sin \theta \cos \theta = 0$$

$$\frac{\tau_{xy}}{\sigma_x - \sigma_y} = \frac{\sin \theta \cos \theta}{\cos^2 \theta - \sin^2 \theta} = \frac{\frac{1}{2}(\sin 2\theta)}{\cos 2\theta} = \frac{1}{2} \tan 2\theta$$

$$\tan 2\theta = \frac{2\tau_{xy}}{\sigma_x - \sigma_y} \qquad (2\text{-}6)$$

Since $\tan 2\theta = \tan (\pi + 2\theta)$, Eq. (2-6) has two roots, θ_1 and $\theta_2 = \theta_1 + n\pi/2$. These roots define two mutually perpendicular planes which are free from shear.

Equation (2-4) will give the principal stresses when values of $\cos 2\theta$ and $\sin 2\theta$ are substituted into it from Eq. (2-6). The values of $\cos 2\theta$ and $\sin 2\theta$ are found from Eq. (2-6) by means of the Pythagorean relationships.

$$\sin 2\theta = \pm \frac{\tau_{xy}}{[(\sigma_x - \sigma_y)^2/4 + \tau_{xy}^2]^{1/2}}$$

$$\cos 2\theta = \pm \frac{(\sigma_x - \sigma_y)/2}{[(\sigma_x - \sigma_y)^2/4 + \tau_{xy}^2]^{1/2}}$$

Substituting these values into Eq. (2-4) results in the expression for the maximum and minimum principal stresses for a two-dimensional (biaxial) state of stress.

$$\left.\begin{array}{c} \sigma_{max} = \sigma_1 \\ \sigma_{min} = \sigma_2 \end{array}\right\} = \frac{\sigma_x + \sigma_y}{2} \pm \left[\left(\frac{\sigma_x - \sigma_y}{2}\right)^2 + \tau_{xy}^2\right]^{\frac{1}{2}} \qquad (2\text{-}7)$$

2-4. Mohr's Circle of Stress—Two Dimensions

A graphical method for representing the state of stress at a point on any oblique plane through the point was suggested by O. Mohr. Figure 2-4 is a Mohr's circle diagram for a two-dimensional state of stress.

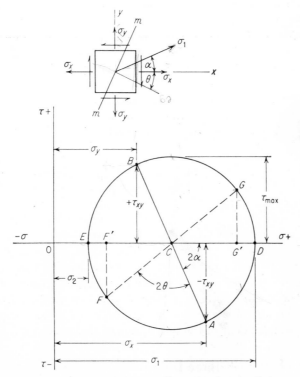

Fig. 2-4. Mohr's circle for two-dimensional state of stress.

Normal stresses are plotted along the x axis, shear stresses along the y axis.   The stresses on the planes normal to the x and y axes are plotted as points A and B.   The intersection of the line AB with the x axis determines the center of the circle.   At points D and E the shear stress is zero, so that these points represent the values of the principal stresses. The angle between the x axis and σ_1 is determined by angle ACD in Fig.

2-4. This angle on Mohr's circle is equal to twice the angle between σ_1 and the x axis on the actual stressed body.

From Fig. 2-4 it can be determined that

$$\sigma_1 = OC + CD = \frac{\sigma_x + \sigma_y}{2} + \left[\left(\frac{\sigma_x - \sigma_y}{2}\right)^2 + \tau_{xy}^2\right]^{1/2}$$

$$\sigma_2 = OC - CE = \frac{\sigma_x + \sigma_y}{2} - \left[\left(\frac{\sigma_x - \sigma_y}{2}\right)^2 + \tau_{xy}^2\right]^{1/2}$$

The radius of the circle is equal to

$$CD = \frac{\sigma_1 - \sigma_2}{2} = \tau_{max}$$

Thus, the radius of Mohr's circle is equal to the maximum shearing stress.

$$\tau_{max} = \frac{\sigma_1 - \sigma_2}{2} = \left[\left(\frac{\sigma_x - \sigma_y}{2}\right)^2 + \tau_{xy}^2\right]^{1/2} \tag{2-8}$$

This value is given by the maximum ordinate of the circle. Note that it acts on a plane for which $\theta = \pi/4$ ($2\theta = \pi/2$ on Mohr's circle); i.e., the plane on which τ_{max} acts bisects the angle between the principal stresses.

Mohr's circle can also be used to determine the stresses acting on any oblique plane mm. Using the convention that θ is positive when it is measured clockwise from the positive x axis, we find that to determine the stresses on the oblique plane whose normal is at an angle θ we must advance an angle 2θ from point A in the Mohr's circle. The normal and shearing stresses on the oblique plane are given by the coordinates of point F. The stresses on a plane perpendicular to mm would be obtained by advancing an additional 180° on the Mohr's circle to point G. This shows that the shearing stresses on two perpendicular planes are numerically equal. It can also be seen from Fig. 2-4 that $OF' + OG' = 2OC$. Therefore, the sum of the normal stresses on two perpendicular planes is a constant, independent of the orientation of the planes.

2-5. State of Stress in Three Dimensions

The general three-dimensional state of stress consists of three unequal principal stresses acting at a point. This is called a *triaxial state of stress*. If two of the three principal stresses are equal, the state of stress is known as *cylindrical*, while if all three principal stresses are equal, the state of stress is said to be *hydrostatic*, or *spherical*.

The determination of the principal stresses for a three-dimensional state of stress in terms of the stresses acting on an arbitrary cartesian-coordinate system is an extension of the method described in Sec. 2-3 for the two-dimensional case.   Figure 2-5 represents an elemental free body similar to that shown in Fig. 2-1 with a diagonal plane JKL of area A.   The plane JKL is assumed to be a principal plane cutting through the unit cube. σ is the principal stress acting normal to the plane JKL.   Let l, m, n be the direction cosines of σ, that is, the cosines

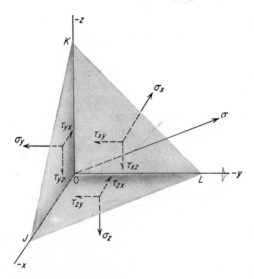

Fig. 2-5. Stresses acting on elemental free body.

of the angles between σ and the x, y, and z axes.   Since the free body in Fig. 2-5 must be in equilibrium, the forces acting on each of its faces must balance.   The components of σ along each of the axes are S_x, S_y, and S_z.

$$S_x = \sigma l \qquad\qquad S_y = \sigma m \qquad\qquad S_z = \sigma n$$
$$\text{Area } KOL = Al \qquad \text{Area } JOK = Am \qquad \text{Area } JOL = An$$

Taking the summation of the forces in the x direction results in

$$\sigma Al - \sigma_x Al - \tau_{yx} Am - \tau_{zx} An = 0$$

which reduces to

$$(\sigma - \sigma_x)l - \tau_{yx}m - \tau_{zx}n = 0 \qquad\qquad (2\text{-}9a)$$

Summing the forces along the other two axes results in

$$-\tau_{xy}l + (\sigma - \sigma_y)m - \tau_{zy}n = 0 \qquad\qquad (2\text{-}9b)$$
$$-\tau_{xz}l - \tau_{yz}m + (\sigma - \sigma_z) = 0 \qquad\qquad (2\text{-}9c)$$

Equations (2-9) are three homogeneous linear equations in terms of l,

m, and n. The only solution can be obtained by setting the determinant of the coefficients of l, m, and n equal to zero, since l, m, n cannot all equal zero.

$$
\begin{vmatrix}
\sigma - \sigma_x & -\tau_{yx} & -\tau_{zx} \\
-\tau_{xy} & \sigma - \sigma_y & -\tau_{zy} \\
-\tau_{xz} & -\tau_{yz} & \sigma - \sigma_z
\end{vmatrix} = 0
$$

Solution of the determinant results in a cubic equation in σ.

$$
\sigma^3 - (\sigma_x + \sigma_y + \sigma_z)\sigma^2 + (\sigma_x\sigma_y + \sigma_y\sigma_z + \sigma_x\sigma_z - \tau_{xy}^2 - \tau_{yz}^2 - \tau_{xz}^2)\sigma \\
- (\sigma_x\sigma_y\sigma_z + 2\tau_{xy}\tau_{yz}\tau_{xz} - \sigma_x\tau_{yz}^2 - \sigma_y\tau_{xz}^2 - \sigma_z\tau_{xy}^2) = 0 \quad (2\text{-}10)
$$

The three roots of Eq. (2-10) are the three principal stresses σ_1, σ_2, and σ_3. To determine the direction, with respect to the original x, y, z axes, in which the principal stresses act, it is necessary to substitute σ_1, σ_2, and σ_3 each in turn into the three equations of Eq. (2-9). The resulting equations must be solved simultaneously for l, m, and n with the help of the auxiliary relationship $l^2 + m^2 + n^2 = 1$.

Let S be the total stress before resolution into normal and shear components and acting on a plane (not a principal plane), and let l, m, and n be the direction cosines for the plane with respect to the three principal axes.

$$
S^2 = S_x^2 + S_y^2 + S_z^2 = \sigma_1^2 l^2 + \sigma_2^2 m^2 + \sigma_3^2 n^2 \quad (2\text{-}11)
$$

The normal stress σ acting on this plane is given by

$$
\sigma = S_x l + S_y m + S_z n = \sigma_1 l^2 + \sigma_2 m^2 + \sigma_3 n^2 \quad (2\text{-}12)
$$

Therefore, the shearing stress acting on the same plane is given by

$$
\tau^2 = S^2 - \sigma^2 = \sigma_1^2 l^2 + \sigma_2^2 m^2 + \sigma_3^2 n^2 - (\sigma_1 l^2 + \sigma_2 m^2 + \sigma_3 n^2)^2
$$

which reduces to

$$
\tau^2 = (\sigma_1 - \sigma_2)^2 l^2 m^2 + (\sigma_1 - \sigma_3)^2 l^2 n^2 + (\sigma_2 - \sigma_3)^2 m^2 n^2 \quad (2\text{-}13)
$$

Values of τ for the three particular sets of direction cosines listed below are of interest because they bisect the angle between two of the three principal axes. Therefore, they are the maximum shearing stresses or the *principal shearing stresses*.

l	m	n	τ	
0	$\pm\sqrt{\tfrac{1}{2}}$	$\pm\sqrt{\tfrac{1}{2}}$	$\tau_1 = \dfrac{\sigma_2 - \sigma_3}{2}$	
$\pm\sqrt{\tfrac{1}{2}}$	0	$\pm\sqrt{\tfrac{1}{2}}$	$\tau_2 = \dfrac{\sigma_1 - \sigma_3}{2}$	$(2\text{-}14)$
$\pm\sqrt{\tfrac{1}{2}}$	$\pm\sqrt{\tfrac{1}{2}}$	0	$\tau_3 = \dfrac{\sigma_1 - \sigma_2}{2}$	

Since according to convention σ_1 is the algebraically greatest principal normal stress and σ_3 is the algebraically smallest principal stress, τ_2 has the largest value of shear stress and it is called the *maximum shear stress* τ_{max}.

$$\tau_{max} = \frac{\sigma_1 - \sigma_3}{2} \qquad (2\text{-}15)$$

The maximum shear stress is important in theories of yielding and metal-forming operations. Figure 2-6 shows the planes of the principal shear

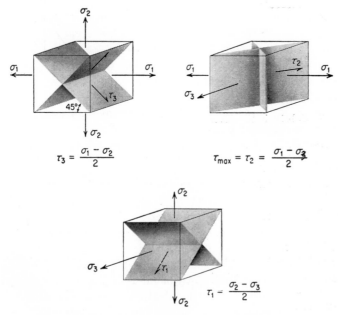

Fig. 2-6. Planes of principal shear stresses.

stresses for a cube whose faces are the principal planes. Note that for each pair of principal stresses there are two planes of principal shear stress, which bisect the principal directions for the normal stresses.

2-6. Mohr's Circle—Three Dimensions

The discussion given in Sec. 2-4 of the representation of a two-dimensional state of stress by means of Mohr's circle can be extended to three dimensions. Figure 2-7 shows how a triaxial state of stress, defined by the three principal stresses, can be represented by three Mohr's circles.

It can be shown[1] that all possible stress conditions within the body fall within the shaded area between the circles in Fig. 2-7.

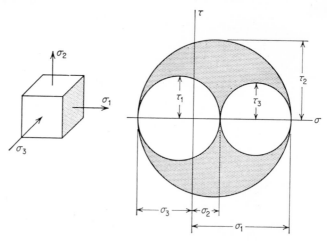

Fig. 2-7. Mohr's circle representation of a three-dimensional state of stress.

While the only physical significance of Mohr's circle is that it gives a geometrical representation of the equations that express the transformation of stress components to different sets of axes, it is a very convenient way of visualizing the state of stress. Figure 2-8 shows Mohr's circle for a number of common states of stress. Note that the application of a tensile stress σ_2 at right angles to an existing tensile stress σ_1 (Fig. 2-8c) results in a decrease in the principal shear stress on two of the three sets of planes on which a principal shear stress acts. However, the maximum shear stress is not decreased from what it would be for uniaxial tension, although if only the two-dimensional Mohr's circle had been used, this would not have been apparent. If a tensile stress is applied in the third principal direction (Fig. 2-8d), the maximum shear stress is reduced appreciably. For the limiting case of equal triaxial tension (hydrostatic tension) Mohr's circle reduces to a point, and there are no shear stresses acting on any plane in the body. The effectiveness of biaxial- and triaxial-tension stresses in reducing the shear stresses results in a considerable decrease in the ductility of the material, because plastic deformation is produced by shear stresses. Thus, brittle fracture is invariably associated with triaxial stresses developed at a notch or stress raiser. However, Fig. 2-8e shows that, if compressive stresses are applied lateral to a tensile stress, the maximum shear stress is larger than for the case of

[1] A. Nadai, "Theory of Flow and Fracture of Solids," 2d ed., pp. 96–98, McGraw-Hill Book Company, Inc., New York, 1950.

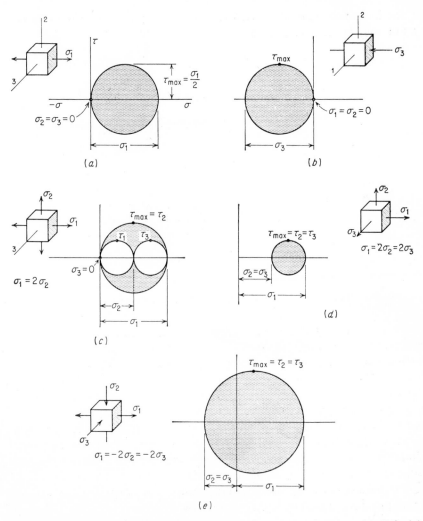

Fig. 2-8. Mohr's circles (three-dimensional) for various states of stress. (a) Uniaxial tension; (b) uniaxial compression; (c) biaxial tension; (d) triaxial tension (unequal); (e) uniaxial tension plus biaxial compression.

either uniaxial tension or compression. Because of the high value of shear stress relative to the applied tensile stress the material has an excellent opportunity to deform plastically without fracturing under this state of stress. Important use is made of this fact in the plastic working of metals. For example, greater ductility is obtained in drawing wire through a die than in simple uniaxial tension because the reaction of the metal with the die will produce lateral compressive stresses.

An important state of stress is *pure shear*.   Figure 2-9a illustrates Mohr's circle for a two-dimensional state of pure shear.   This state of stress is readily obtained by twisting a cylindrical bar in torsion.   The Mohr's circle for this state of stress shows that the maximum and minimum normal stresses are equal to the shear stress and occur at 45° to the

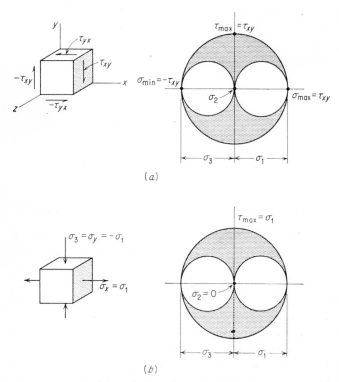

Fig. 2-9. Equivalent pure-shear conditions.   (a) Pure shear (plane stress); (b) equal biaxial tension and compression.

shear stresses.   The maximum shear stress is equal to the applied shear stress τ_{xy}, but it occurs only on the set of planes parallel to the z axis. On the other two sets of planes the principal shear stress is $\tau_{xy}/2$.   Note that for three-dimensional pure shear two out of the three sets of shear planes have a value of $\tau_{max} = \sigma_1$.   An identical state of stress to pure shear can be obtained when equal tensile and compressive stresses are applied to a unit cube (Fig. 2-9b).   Once again $\tau_{max} = \sigma_1$, but to obtain complete identity with a state of two-dimensional pure shear, the axes must be rotated 45° in space or 90° on the Mohr's circle.

2-7. Description of Strain at a Point

The brief description of linear strain and shear strain given in Sec. 1-9 can be expanded into a more generalized description of the strain at a point in a rigid body. For simplicity in illustration, Fig. 2-10 considers

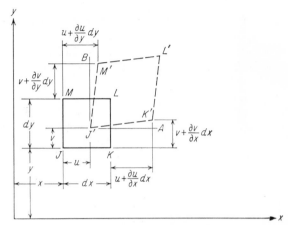

Fig. 2-10. Components of strain for plane strain.

a two-dimensional, or *plane-strain*, condition where all the deformation is confined to the xy plane. It is, however, a simple matter to generalize the relationship obtained from this figure to the three-dimensional case. Let the coordinates of a point in an unstrained rigid body be defined by x, y, and z. After strain is applied, the point will undergo *displacements* u, v, and w in the directions x, y, and z. In order that the displacement of the entire body be geometrically compatible, it is necessary that no two particles occupy the same point in space or that no voids be created within the body. In order to satisfy these requirements, the displacement components u, v, and w must vary continuously from point to point. This can be accomplished if their gradients with respect to x, y, and z have no discontinuities, and therefore the partial derivatives of u, v, and w with respect to x, y, and z enter into the analysis.

In Fig. 2-10 for the plane-strain condition, it can be seen that the x component of the displacement of K to K' is the displacement of J, given by u, *plus* the rate of change of u along the distance dx, given by $(\partial u/\partial x)\, dx$. The unit linear strain in the x direction, e_x, is given by

$$e_x = \frac{J'K' - JK}{JK} = \frac{[dx + (\partial u/\partial x)\, dx] - dx}{dx} = \frac{\partial u}{\partial x} \qquad (2\text{-}16a)$$

Similarly $$e_y = \frac{J'M' - JM}{JM} = \frac{dy + (\partial v/\partial y)\, dy - dy}{dy} = \frac{\partial v}{\partial y} \qquad (2\text{-}16b)$$

and if the z direction were being considered,

$$e_z = \frac{\partial w}{\partial z} \qquad (2\text{-}16c)$$

The shearing strain γ_{xy} at J' is given by the change in angle of the two elements originally parallel to the x and y axes.

$$\gamma_{xy} = \angle KJM - \angle K'J'M' = \angle BJ'M' + \angle AJ'K'$$

Since, for the small strains involved, the tangent of the angle equals the angle, from Fig. 2-10 it can be seen that

$$\gamma_{xy} = \frac{(\partial u/\partial y)\,dy}{dy} + \frac{(\partial v/\partial x)\,dx}{dx} = \frac{\partial u}{\partial y} + \frac{\partial v}{\partial x} \qquad (2\text{-}16d)$$

In the same way, it can be shown that

$$\gamma_{xz} = \frac{\partial u}{\partial z} + \frac{\partial w}{\partial x} \qquad (2\text{-}16e)$$

$$\gamma_{yz} = \frac{\partial y}{\partial z} + \frac{\partial w}{\partial y} \qquad (2\text{-}16f)$$

Thus, six terms are necessary completely to describe the state of strain at a point, e_x, e_y, e_z, γ_{xy}, γ_{yz}, γ_{xz}.

In complete analogy with stress, it is possible to define a system of coordinate axes along which there are no shear strains. These axes are the principal strain axes. For an isotropic body the directions of the principal strains coincide with those of the principal stresses.[1] An element oriented along one of these principal axes will undergo pure extension or contraction without any rotation or shearing strains. As with principal stresses, the largest and smallest linear strains at a point in the body are given by the values of the principal strains.

Methods similar to those used in Sec. 2-5, for the derivation of the equation for the values of the three principal stresses, and in Sec. 2-3, for the normal and shear stresses on any plane through a point in the body, can be used for the derivation[2] of similar quantities in terms of strain. However, these equations may be obtained much more easily by replacing σ and τ in the stress equation by e and $\gamma/2$. For example, the linear strain on any plane in a two-dimensional situation can, from Eq. (2-2), be expressed by

$$e_\theta = e_x \cos^2 \theta + e_y \sin^2 \theta + \gamma_{xy} \sin \theta \cos \theta \qquad (2\text{-}17)$$

The three principal strains $e_1 > e_2 > e_3$ are the three roots of the follow-

---

[1] For a derivation of this point see Wang, *op. cit.*, pp. 26–27.
[2] Timoshenko and Goodier, *op. cit.*, pp. 221–227.

ing equation [obtained from Eq. (2-10)]:

$$e^3 - (e_x + e_y + e_z)e^2 + [e_x e_y + e_y e_z + e_x e_z - \tfrac{1}{4}(\gamma_{xy}^2 + \gamma_{xz}^2 + \gamma_{yz}^2)]e \\ - e_x e_y e_z + \tfrac{1}{4}(e_x \gamma_{yz}^2 + e_y \gamma_{xz}^2 + e_z \gamma_{xy}^2 - \gamma_{xy}\gamma_{xz}\gamma_{yz}) = 0 \quad (2\text{-}18)$$

By following through with this analogy, the equations for the *principal shearing strains* can be obtained from Eq. (2-14).

$$\gamma_1 = e_2 - e_3$$
$$\gamma_{max} = \gamma_2 = e_1 - e_3 \qquad (2\text{-}19)$$
$$\gamma_3 = e_1 - e_2$$

The *volume strain*, or cubical dilatation, is the change in volume per unit of original volume.   Consider a rectangular parallelepiped with edges dx, dy, dz.   The volume in the strained condition is

$$(1 + e_1)(1 + e_2)(1 + e_3)\, dx\, dy\, dz$$

From its definition, the volume strain Δ is given by

$$\Delta = \frac{(1 + e_1)(1 + e_2)(1 + e_3)\, dx\, dy\, dz - dx\, dy\, dz}{dx\, dy\, dz}$$
$$= (1 + e_1)(1 + e_2)(1 + e_3) - 1$$

which for small strains, after neglecting the products of strains, becomes

$$\Delta = e_1 + e_2 + e_3 \qquad (2\text{-}20)$$

2-8. Measurement of Surface Strain

Except in a few cases involving contact stresses, it is not possible to measure stress directly.   Therefore, experimental measurements of stress are actually based on measured strains and are converted to stresses by means of Hooke's law and the more general relationships which are given in Sec. 2-10.   The most universal strain-measuring device is the bonded-wire resistance gage, frequently called the SR-4 strain gage.   These gages are made up of several loops of fine wire or foil of special composition, which are bonded to the surface of the body to be studied.   When the body is deformed, the wires in the gage are strained and their electrical resistance is altered.   The change in resistance, which is proportional to strain, can be accurately determined with a simple Wheatstone-bridge circuit.   The high sensitivity, stability, comparative ruggedness, and ease of application make resistance strain gages a very powerful tool for strain determination.

For practical problems of experimental stress analysis it is often important to determine the principal stresses.   If the principal directions are known, gages can be oriented in these directions and the principal stresses

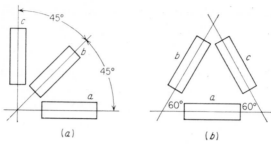

Fig. 2-11. Typical strain-gage rosettes.   (a) Rectangular; (b) delta.

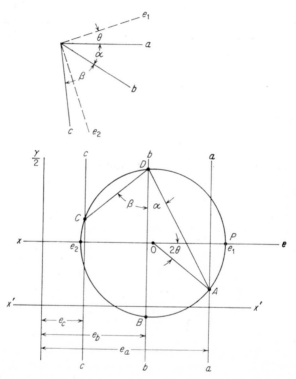

Fig. 2-12. Mohr's circle for determination of principal strains.

determined quite readily.   In the general case the direction of the principal strains will not be known, so that it will be necessary to determine the orientation and magnitude of the principal strains from the measured strains in arbitrary directions.   Because no stress can act perpendicular to a free surface, strain-gage measurements involve a two-dimensional state of strain.   The state of strain is completely determined if e_x, e_y, and γ_{xy} can be measured.   However, strain gages can make only direct readings of linear strain, while shear strains must be determined indirectly. Therefore, it is the usual practice to use three strain gages separated at fixed angles in the form of a "rosette," as in Fig. 2-11. Strain-gage readings at three values of θ will give three simultaneous equations similar to Eq. (2-17) which can be solved for e_x, e_y, and γ_{xy}. The two-dimensional version of Eq. (2-18) can then be used to determine the principal strains. Equations for directly converting strain-gage readings into principal stresses for the two rosettes shown in Fig. 2-11 will be found in Table 2-2.

A more convenient method of determining the principal strains from strain-gage readings than the solution of three simultaneous equations in three unknowns is the use of Mohr's circle. In constructing a Mohr's circle representation of strain, values of linear normal strain e are plotted along the x axis, and the shear strain divided by 2 is plotted along the y axis. Figure 2-12 shows the Mohr's circle construction[1] for the generalized strain-gage rosette illustrated at the top of the figure. Strain-gage readings e_a, e_b, and e_c are available for three gages situated at arbitrary angles α and β. The objective is to determine the magnitude and orientation of the principal strains e_1 and e_2.

1. Along an arbitrary axis $X'X'$ lay off vertical lines aa, bb, and cc corresponding to the strains e_a, e_b, and e_c.

2. From any point on the line bb (middle strain gage) draw a line DA at an angle α with bb and intersecting aa at point A. In the same way, lay off DC intersecting cc at point C.

3. Construct a circle through A, C, and D. The center of this circle is at O, determined by the intersection of the perpendicular bisectors to CD and AD.

4. Points A, B, and C on the circle give the values of e and $\gamma/2$ (measured from the new x axis through O) for the three gages.

5. Values of the principal strains are determined by the intersection of the circle with the new x axis through O. The angular relationship of e_1 to the gage a is one-half the angle AOP on the Mohr's circle ($AOP = 2\theta$).

2-9. Stress-Strain Relations

In the first chapter it was shown that uniaxial stress is related to uniaxial strain by means of the modulus of elasticity. This is Hooke's law in its simplest form,

$$\sigma_x = E e_x \tag{2-21}$$

where E is the modulus of elasticity in tension or compression. While a tensile force in the x direction produces a linear strain along that axis,

---

[1] G. Murphy, *J. Appl. Mech.*, vol. 12, p. A209, 1945; F. A. McClintock, *Proc. Soc. Exptl. Stress Analysis*, vol. 9, p. 209, 1951.

it also produces a contraction in the transverse y and z directions. The ratio of the strain in the transverse direction to the strain in the longitudinal direction is known as *Poisson's ratio*, denoted by the symbol ν.

$$e_y = e_z = -\nu e_x = -\frac{\nu \sigma_x}{E} \qquad (2\text{-}22)$$

Only the absolute value of ν is used in calculations. Poisson's ratio is 0.25 for a perfectly isotropic elastic material, but for most metals the values[1] are closer to 0.33.

The generalized description of Hooke's law says that for a body acted upon by a general stress system the strain along any principal axis is due to the stress acting along that axis *plus* the superimposed strain resulting from the Poisson effect of the principal stresses acting along the other two axes.

$$e_1 = \frac{1}{E}\sigma_1 - \frac{\nu}{E}\sigma_2 - \frac{\nu}{E}\sigma_3$$

$$= \frac{1}{E}[\sigma_1 - \nu(\sigma_2 + \sigma_3)]$$

and for the other two principal axes

$$e_2 = \frac{1}{E}[\sigma_2 - \nu(\sigma_1 + \sigma_3)]$$

$$e_3 = \frac{1}{E}[\sigma_3 - \nu(\sigma_1 + \sigma_2)] \qquad (2\text{-}23)$$

For a biaxial state of plane stress, $\sigma_3 = 0$, and Eqs. (2-23) reduce to

$$e_1 = \frac{1}{E}(\sigma_1 - \nu\sigma_2)$$

$$e_2 = \frac{1}{E}(\sigma_2 - \nu\sigma_1) \qquad (2\text{-}23a)$$

$$e_3 = -\frac{\nu}{E}(\sigma_1 + \sigma_2)$$

Note that, even when the stress along the third axis is zero, the strain along that axis is not zero (unless $\sigma_1 = -\sigma_2$).

In the case of plane strain, $e_3 = 0$, and the strain-stress relationships become

$$e_1 = \frac{1+\nu}{E}[(1-\nu)\sigma_1 - \nu\sigma_2]$$

$$e_2 = \frac{1+\nu}{E}[(1-\nu)\sigma_2 - \nu\sigma_1] \qquad (2\text{-}23b)$$

---

[1] A derivation which intuitively suggests that $\nu = 0.33$ has been presented by F. R. Shanley, "Strength of Materials," pp. 138–139, McGraw-Hill Book Company, Inc., New York, 1957.

Shear stress is related to shear strain by relationships similar to Eq. (2-21).

$$\tau_{xy} = G\gamma_{xy} \qquad \tau_{xz} = G\gamma_{xz} \qquad \tau_{yz} = G\gamma_{yz} \qquad (2\text{-}24)$$

The proportionality constant G is the *modulus of elasticity in shear*, or the *modulus of rigidity*.

Three material constants E, G, and ν are involved in the description of the elastic behavior of materials. It will be shown that these constants are related, so that for an isotropic material there are only two

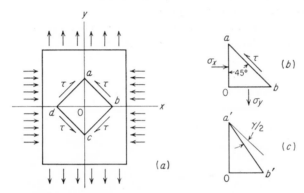

Fig. 2-13. (*a*) Element subjected to pure shear; (*b*) stresses on triangle Oab before deformation; (*c*) after deformation.

independent elastic constants. Consider a rectangular element which is subjected to a condition of pure shear (Fig. 2-13) (see the Mohr's circle in Fig. 2-9*b*). σ_x and σ_y are principal stresses since no shear stresses are present on the faces on which they act. The maximum shearing stress will lie on a 45° plane, and if $\sigma_y = -\sigma_x$, the value of τ_{max} will be σ_y. The shearing stresses distort the element in the manner shown in Fig. 2-13*c*. Oa is elongated, Ob is shortened, and ab does not change in length. Angle Oab is reduced by an amount $\gamma/2$.

$$\tan\left(\frac{\pi}{4} - \frac{\gamma}{2}\right) = \frac{Ob'}{Oa'} = \frac{1 + e_x}{1 + e_y}$$

Since, for elastic strains, γ is a small angle

$$\tan\left(\frac{\pi}{4} - \frac{\gamma}{2}\right) = \frac{\tan(\pi/4) - \tan(\gamma/2)}{1 + \tan(\pi/4)\tan(\gamma/2)} \approx \frac{1 - \gamma/2}{1 + \gamma/2}$$

For pure shear

$$\sigma_y = -\sigma_x = \tau$$

Substitution into Eq. (2-23) produces

$$e_y = -e_x = \sigma_y \frac{1+\nu}{E} = \tau \frac{1+\nu}{E}$$

Equating the two expressions for $\tan (\pi/4 - \gamma/2)$ and substituting the above equation gives

$$\tau = \frac{E}{2(1+\nu)} \gamma \tag{2-25}$$

Comparing this relation with the generalized form of Eq. (2-24) results in the general relationship between the three elastic constants. Typical values for a number of materials are given in Table 2-1.

$$G = \frac{E}{2(1+\nu)} \tag{2-26}$$

TABLE 2-1
TYPICAL ROOM-TEMPERATURE VALUES OF ELASTIC CONSTANTS
FOR ISOTROPIC MATERIALS

Material	Modulus of elasticity, 10^{-6} psi	Shear modulus, 10^{-6} psi	Poisson's ratio
Aluminum alloys	10.5	4.0	0.31
Copper	16.0	6.0	0.33
Steel (plain carbon and low-alloy)	29.0	11.0	0.33
Stainless steel (18-8)	28.0	9.5	0.28
Titanium	17.0	6.5	0.31
Tungsten	58.0	22.8	0.27

The addition of the three equations giving the strain produced by the three principal stresses [Eq. (2-23)] results in

$$e_1 + e_2 + e_3 = \frac{1-2\nu}{E} (\sigma_1 + \sigma_2 + \sigma_3) \tag{2-27}$$

The left-hand term of Eq. (2-27) is the volume strain Δ. Rewriting Eq. (2-27) results in

$$\Delta = \frac{3\sigma_m}{E} (1 - 2\nu) \tag{2-28}$$

where σ_m is the average of the three principal stresses. This can be written as

$$\kappa = \frac{\sigma_m}{\Delta} = \frac{E}{3(1-2\nu)} \tag{2-29}$$

The constant κ is the *volumetric modulus of elasticity*, or the *bulk modulus*.

The bulk modulus is therefore the ratio of the average stress to the volume strain. It is frequently evaluated for conditions of hydrostatic compression, where σ_m is equal to the hydrostatic pressure.

2-10. Calculation of Stresses from Elastic Strains

The general equations expressing stress in terms of strain are considerably more complicated than the equations giving strain in terms of stress [Eqs. (2-23)]. The simultaneous solution of these equations for σ_1, σ_2, and σ_3 results in

$$\sigma_1 = \frac{\nu E}{(1 + \nu)(1 - 2\nu)} \Delta + \frac{E}{1 + \nu} e_1$$

$$\sigma_2 = \frac{\nu E}{(1 + \nu)(1 - 2\nu)} \Delta + \frac{E}{1 + \nu} e_2 \qquad (2\text{-}30)$$

$$\sigma_3 = \frac{\nu E}{(1 + \nu)(1 - 2\nu)} \Delta + \frac{E}{1 + \nu} e_3$$

where $\Delta = e_1 + e_2 + e_3$. The term $\lambda = \nu E/(1 + \nu)(1 - 2\nu)$ is called Lamé's constant. By using this constant the above equations can be simplified to

$$\sigma_1 = \lambda\Delta + 2Ge_1$$
$$\sigma_2 = \lambda\Delta + 2Ge_2 \qquad (2\text{-}31)$$
$$\sigma_3 = \lambda\Delta + 2Ge_3$$

For the case of plane stress ($\sigma_3 = 0$) two simple and useful equations relating the stress to the strains may be obtained by solving the first two of Eqs. (2-23) simultaneously for σ_1 and σ_2.

$$\sigma_1 = \frac{E}{1 - \nu^2} (e_1 + \nu e_2)$$

$$\sigma_2 = \frac{E}{1 - \nu^2} (e_2 + \nu e_1) \qquad (2\text{-}32)$$

These equations can be very useful for determining the values of principal stress from strain-gage measurements. Note that even when a strain gage is oriented in the principal direction it is not correct to multiply the strain by the elastic modulus to get the stress in that direction. Because of the Poisson effect, corrections for lateral strains must be made by using Eqs. (2-32).

Usually the methods described in Sec. 2-8 will have to be employed to determine the values of principal strain before these equations can be used. A short-cut procedure is to use a strain-gage rosette with three gages at fixed orientations for which relationships have been worked out between the strains measured by each gage and the principal stresses. Table 2-2 gives the relationships between the principal stresses and the

TABLE 2-2

RELATIONSHIPS BETWEEN PRINCIPAL STRESS AND STRAIN-GAGE READINGS

See Fig. 2-11 for description of rosettes

	Formula	Rosette
Maximum normal stress σ_1	$\dfrac{E}{2}\left\{\dfrac{e_a+e_c}{1-\nu}+\dfrac{1}{1+\nu}\sqrt{(e_a-e_c)^2+[2e_b-(e_a+e_c)]^2}\right\}$	Rectangular
	$E\left[\dfrac{e_a+e_b+e_c}{3(1-\nu)}+\dfrac{1}{1+\nu}\sqrt{\left(e_a-\dfrac{e_a+e_b+e_c}{3}\right)^2+\left(\dfrac{e_b-e_c}{\sqrt{3}}\right)^2}\right]$	Delta
Minimum normal stress σ_2	$\dfrac{E}{2}\left\{\dfrac{e_a+e_c}{1-\nu}-\dfrac{1}{1+\nu}\sqrt{(e_a-e_c)^2+[2e_b-(e_a+e_c)]^2}\right\}$	Rectangular
	$E\left[\dfrac{e_a+e_b+e_c}{3(1-\nu)}-\dfrac{1}{1+\nu}\sqrt{\left(e_a-\dfrac{e_a+e_b+e_c}{3}\right)^2+\left(\dfrac{e_b-e_c}{\sqrt{3}}\right)^2}\right]$	Delta
Maximum shearing stress $\tau_{\max}$	$\dfrac{E}{2(1+\nu)}\sqrt{(e_a-e_c)^2+[2e_b-(e_a+e_c)]^2}$	Rectangular
	$\dfrac{E}{1+\nu}\sqrt{\left(e_a-\dfrac{e_a+e_b+e_c}{3}\right)^2+\left(\dfrac{e_b-e_c}{\sqrt{3}}\right)^2}$	Delta
Angle from axis of gage a to axis of σ_1	$\dfrac{1}{2}\tan^{-1}\dfrac{2e_b-(e_a+e_c)}{e_a-e_c}$	Rectangular
	$\dfrac{1}{2}\tan^{-1}\dfrac{(1/\sqrt{3})(e_b-e_c)}{e_a-(e_a+e_b+e_c)/3}$	Delta

strain readings e_a, e_b, and e_c for the three gages in the rectangular and delta rosettes shown in Fig. 2-11. The derivation of the equations and graphical solutions for these equations are discussed in texts[1] on strain-gage technology.

2-11. Generalized Stress-Strain Relationships

The stress-strain relationships given in the previous two sections contain three elastic constants E, G, and v. These are the only material constants needed to describe the elastic stress-strain behavior provided that the material can be considered isotropic. However, many materials are anisotropic; i.e., the elastic properties vary with direction. A metallic single crystal is an extreme example of an anisotropic elastic material, while cold-worked metals may also exhibit anisotropic elastic behavior. However, in the usual case with engineering materials the grain size is small enough and the grains are in a sufficiently random arrangement so that the equations based on isotropic conditions may be used.

In order to consider the possibility of elastic constants which vary with orientation in the material, Hooke's law can be written in completely general terms as a linear relationship between strain and stress.

$$
\begin{aligned}
e_x &= S_{11}\sigma_x + S_{12}\sigma_y + S_{13}\sigma_z + S_{14}\tau_{xy} + S_{15}\tau_{yz} + S_{16}\tau_{zx} \\
e_y &= S_{21}\sigma_x + S_{22}\sigma_y + S_{23}\sigma_z + S_{24}\tau_{xy} + S_{25}\tau_{yz} + S_{26}\tau_{zx} \\
e_z &= S_{31}\sigma_x + S_{32}\sigma_y + S_{33}\sigma_z + S_{34}\tau_{xy} + S_{35}\tau_{yz} + S_{36}\tau_{zx} \\
\gamma_{xy} &= S_{41}\sigma_x + S_{42}\sigma_y + S_{43}\sigma_z + S_{44}\tau_{xy} + S_{45}\tau_{yz} + S_{46}\tau_{zx} \\
\gamma_{yz} &= S_{51}\sigma_x + S_{52}\sigma_y + S_{53}\sigma_z + S_{54}\tau_{xy} + S_{55}\tau_{yz} + S_{56}\tau_{zx} \\
\gamma_{zx} &= S_{61}\sigma_x + S_{62}\sigma_y + S_{63}\sigma_z + S_{64}\tau_{xy} + S_{65}\tau_{yz} + S_{66}\tau_{zx}
\end{aligned}
\tag{2-33}
$$

The constants S_{11}, S_{12}, . . . , S_{ij} are the *elastic compliances*. Note that these equations indicate that a shear stress can produce a linear strain in an elastically anisotropic material. A similar set of six equations relates the stress to the strain in terms of the elastic coefficients C_{11}, C_{12}, . . . , C_{ij}.

$$
\sigma_x = C_{11}e_x + C_{12}e_y + C_{13}e_z + C_{14}\gamma_{xy} + C_{15}\gamma_{yz} + C_{16}\gamma_{zx}
$$
$$
\cdots\cdots\cdots\cdots\cdots\cdots\cdots\cdots\cdots\cdots\cdots \tag{2-34}
$$
$$
\tau_{xy} = C_{11}e_x + C_{42}e_y + C_{43}e_z + C_{44}\gamma_{xy} + C_{45}\gamma_{yz} + C_{46}\gamma_{zx}
$$
$$
\cdots\cdots\cdots\cdots\cdots\cdots\cdots\cdots\cdots\cdots\cdots
$$

Thus, in order to calculate the stress from the strain in the most general circumstances, it is necessary to know 6 strain components and 36 elastic coefficients. Fortunately, symmetry considerations can reduce considerably the number of necessary constants. The elastic constants

---

[1] C. C. Perry and H. R. Lissner, "The Strain Gage Primer," McGraw-Hill Book Company, Inc., New York, 1955.

with unequal subscripts are equivalent when the order of the subscripts is reversed.

$$S_{ij} = S_{ji} \qquad C_{ij} = C_{ji}$$

Therefore, even for the least symmetrical crystal structure (triclinic) the number of independent constants is reduced to 21. For metals, which all have crystal structures of relatively high symmetry, the maximum number of constants that need to be considered is 12. Thus, Eqs. (2-33) can be written as

$$
\begin{aligned}
e_x &= S_{11}\sigma_x + S_{12}\sigma_y + S_{13}\sigma_z & \gamma_{xy} &= S_{44}\tau_{xy} \\
e_y &= S_{21}\sigma_x + S_{22}\sigma_y + S_{23}\sigma_z & \gamma_{yz} &= S_{55}\tau_{yz} \\
e_z &= S_{31}\sigma_x + S_{32}\sigma_y + S_{33}\sigma_z & \gamma_{zx} &= S_{66}\tau_{zx}
\end{aligned}
\tag{2-35}
$$

By comparing these equations with Eqs. (2-23) and (2-24) it can be seen that S_{11} is the reciprocal of the modulus of elasticity in the x direction, that S_{21} determines the component of linear strain produced in the y

TABLE 2-3

ELASTIC COMPLIANCES FOR METAL CRYSTALS

Units of 10^{-12} cm^2/dyne

Metal	S_{11}	S_{12}	S_{44}	S_{13}	S_{33}
Aluminum...................	1.59	−0.58	3.52	S_{12}	S_{11}
Copper.....................	1.49	−0.62	1.33	S_{12}	S_{11}
Iron.......................	0.80	−0.28	0.80	S_{12}	S_{11}
Iron (polycrystalline)..........	0.48	−0.14	1.24	S_{12}	S_{11}
Tungsten...................	0.26	−0.07	0.66	S_{12}	S_{11}
Magnesium.................	2.23	−0.77	6.03	−0.49	1.98
Zinc.......................	0.82	+0.11	2.50	−0.66	2.64

direction due to σ_x, equivalent to ν/E, and that S_{31} represents the same thing for the z direction. Also, the compliance S_{44} is the reciprocal of the shear modulus.

For metals which exist in one of the cubic crystal structures $S_{11} = S_{22} = S_{33}$, $S_{12} = S_{13} = S_{21} = S_{23} = S_{31} = S_{32}$, and $S_{44} = S_{55} = S_{66}$. Therefore, Eq. (2-35) may be written as

$$
\begin{aligned}
e_x &= S_{11}\sigma_x + S_{12}(\sigma_y + \sigma_z) & \gamma_{xy} &= S_{44}\tau_{xy} \\
e_y &= S_{11}\sigma_y + S_{12}(\sigma_z + \sigma_x) & \gamma_{yz} &= S_{44}\tau_{yz} \\
e_z &= S_{11}\sigma_z + S_{12}(\sigma_x + \sigma_y) & \gamma_{zx} &= S_{44}\tau_{zx}
\end{aligned}
\tag{2-36}
$$

The identity between these equations and Eqs. (2-23) and (2-24) is apparent. Therefore, for a material with a cubic crystal structure there are three independent elastic constants, while for a truly isotropic material there are only two independent elastic constants. For an isotropic material the relationship between these constants is given by

$$S_{44} = 2(S_{11} - S_{12})$$

Table 2-3 lists some typical values for elastic compliance. By applying the above relationship compare the difference in isotropy between copper and tungsten.

2-12. Theory of Elasticity

The mathematic theory of elasticity entails a more detailed consideration of the stresses and strains in a loaded member than is required by

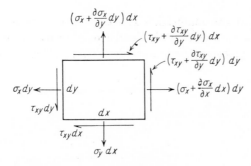

Fig. 2-14. Forces acting on volume element.

the ordinary methods of analysis of strength of materials. The solutions arrived at by strength of materials are usually made mathematically simpler by the assumption of a strain distribution in the loaded member which satisfies the physical situation but may not be mathematically rigorous. In the theory of elasticity no simplifying assumptions are made concerning the strain distribution.

As with strength of materials, the first requirement for a solution is to satisfy the conditions of equilibrium. Figure 2-14 illustrates the forces acting on an element of the body for a plane-stress situation. Taking the summation of forces in the x and y directions results in

$$\Sigma P_x = \frac{\partial \sigma_x}{\partial x} + \frac{\partial \tau_{xy}}{\partial y} = 0$$

$$\Sigma P_y = \frac{\partial \sigma_y}{\partial y} + \frac{\partial \tau_{xy}}{\partial x} + \rho g = 0$$

(2-37)

The term ρg arises from the consideration of the weight of the body, where ρ is the mass per unit volume and g is the acceleration of gravity. The above equations constitute the *equations of equilibrium* for plane stress. For a three-dimensional stress system there will be three equations,[1] each containing one partial derivative of the normal stress and two partial derivatives of the shear stresses.

Equations (2-37) must be satisfied at all points throughout the body. Note that these equilibrium equations do not give a relationship between the stresses and the external loads. Instead, they give the rate of change of the stresses at any point in the body. However, the relationship between stress and external load must be such that at the boundary of the body the stresses become equal to the surface forces per unit area; i.e., it must satisfy the boundary conditions.

One of the important requirements of the theory of elasticity is that the deformation of each element must be such that elastic continuity is preserved. Physically, this means that the stresses must vary so that no gaps occur in the material. The *equations of compatibility* for the two-dimensional case can be obtained from the definitions for strain in terms of the displacements u and v (Sec. 2-7).

$$e_x = \frac{\partial u}{\partial x} \tag{a}$$

$$e_y = \frac{\partial v}{\partial y} \tag{b}$$

$$\gamma_{xy} = \frac{\partial u}{\partial y} + \frac{\partial v}{\partial x} \tag{c}$$

These three equations show that there is a definite relationship between the three strains at a point, because they are expressed in terms of two displacements u and v. Differentiating Eq. (a) twice with respect to y, Eq. (b) twice with respect to x, and Eq. (c) with respect to both x and y results in

$$\frac{\partial^2 e_x}{\partial y^2} + \frac{\partial^2 e_y}{\partial x^2} = \frac{\partial^2 \gamma_{xy}}{\partial x \, \partial y} \tag{2-38}$$

Equation (2-38) is the *equation of compatibility* in two dimensions. If the strains satisfy this equation, they are compatible with each other and the continuity of the body is preserved. The equation of compatibility can be expressed in terms of stress by differentiating Eqs. (2-23) and (2-24) and substituting into Eq. (2-38).

$$\frac{\partial^2 \sigma_x}{\partial y^2} - \nu \frac{\partial^2 \sigma_y}{\partial y^2} + \frac{\partial^2 \sigma_y}{\partial x^2} - \nu \frac{\partial^2 \sigma_x}{\partial x^2} = 2(1 + \nu) \frac{\partial^2 \tau_{xy}}{\partial x \, \partial y} \tag{2-39}$$

If values of σ_x, σ_y, and τ_{xy} satisfy Eq. (2-39), it can be considered that the strains which accompany these stresses are compatible and that the continuity of the body will be preserved.

---

[1] Timoshenko and Goodier, *op. cit.*, chap. 9

Basically, the solution of a problem with the theory of elasticity requires the determination of an expression for the stresses σ_x, σ_y, τ_{xy} in terms of the external loads that satisfies the equations of equilibrium [Eqs. (2-37)], the equations of compatibility [Eq. (2-39)], and the boundary conditions. Such a solution generally involves considerable mathematical agility. Most of the complications attending the theory of elasticity arise out of the necessity for satisfying the requirement of continuity of elastic deformation. In solutions by strength of materials continuity of deformation is not always satisfied. Continuity is maintained by local plastic yielding. Generally, this does not have an important effect on the solution because the effects of yielding do not extend far beyond the region where they occur. In other problems, such as the determination of stresses at geometrical discontinuities (stress raisers), localized yielding is important, and the methods of the theory of elasticity must be used.

One method which is used for the solution of problems by the theory of elasticity is to find a function Φ in x and y which satisfies Eqs. (2-37) and (2-39) and also expresses the stresses in terms of the loads. Such a function is usually called the *Airy stress function*. Airy[1] showed that there will always exist a function in x and y from which the stresses at any point can be determined by the following equations:

$$\sigma_x = \frac{\partial^2 \Phi}{\partial y^2} - \rho g y \qquad \sigma_y = \frac{\partial^2 \Phi}{\partial x^2} - \rho g y \qquad \tau_{xy} = -\frac{\partial^2 \Phi}{\partial x\, \partial y} \qquad (2\text{-}40)$$

Equations (2-40) satisfy the equations of equilibrium. In order to satisfy the compatibility equation, Eqs. (2-40) are differentiated and substituted into Eq. (2-39).

$$\frac{\partial^4 \Phi}{\partial x^4} + 2 \frac{\partial^4 \Phi}{\partial x^2\, \partial y^2} + \frac{\partial^4 \Phi}{\partial y^4} = 0 \qquad (2\text{-}41)$$

If a stress function can be found for the problem which satisfies Eq. (2-41), the stresses are given by Eqs. (2-40) *provided* that Eqs. (2-40) also satisfy the boundary conditions of the problem. The discovery of a stress function which satisfies both Eq. (2-41) and the boundary conditions is usually not easy, and therefore only a fairly limited number of problems have been solved by this technique. For problems with complicated geometry and loading systems it is usually necessary to use finite-difference equations and relaxation methods[2] for the solution of the problem.

---

[1] G. B. Airy, *Brit. Assoc. Advance, Sci. Rept.*, 1862.

[2] R. V. Southwell, "Relaxation Methods in Theoretical Physics," Oxford University Press, New York, 1946.

2-13. Stress Concentration

A geometrical discontinuity in a body, such as a hole or a notch, results in a nonuniform stress distribution at the vicinity of the discontinuity. At some region near the discontinuity the stress will be higher than the average stress at distances removed from the discontinuity. Thus, a *stress concentration* occurs at the discontinuity, or *stress raiser*. Figure 2-15a shows a plate containing a circular hole which is subjected

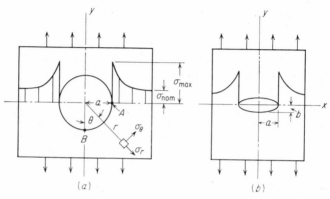

Fig. 2-15. Stress distributions due to (a) circular hole and (b) elliptical hole.

to a uniaxial load. If the hole were not present, the stress would be uniformly distributed over the cross section of the plate and it would be equal to the load divided by the cross-sectional area of the plate. With the hole present, the distribution is such that the axial stress reaches a high value at the edges of the hole and drops off rapidly with distance away from the hole.

The stress concentration is expressed by a theoretical stress-concentration factor K_t. Generally K_t is described as the ratio of the maximum stress to the nominal stress based on the net section, although some workers use a value of nominal stress based on the entire cross section of the member in a region where there is no stress concentrator.

$$K_t = \frac{\sigma_{max}}{\sigma_{nominal}} \qquad (2\text{-}42)$$

In addition to producing a stress concentration, a notch also creates a localized condition of biaxial or triaxial stress. For example, for the circular hole in a plate subjected to an axial load, a radial stress is produced as well as a longitudinal stress. From elastic analysis,[1] the stresses produced in an infinitely wide plate containing a circular hole and axially

[1] Timoshenko and Goodier, *op. cit.* pp. 78–81.

loaded can be expressed as

$$\sigma_r = \frac{\sigma}{2}\left(1 + \frac{a^2}{r^2}\right) + \frac{\sigma}{2}\left(1 + 3\frac{a^4}{r^4} - 4\frac{a^2}{r^2}\right)\cos 2\theta$$

$$\sigma_\theta = \frac{\sigma}{2}\left(1 + \frac{a^2}{r^2}\right) - \frac{\sigma}{2}\left(1 + 3\frac{a^4}{r^4}\right)\cos 2\theta \tag{2-43}$$

$$\tau = -\frac{\sigma}{2}\left(1 - 3\frac{a^4}{r^4} + 2\frac{a^2}{r^2}\right)\sin 2\theta$$

Examination of these equations shows that the maximum stress occurs at point A when $\theta = \pi/2$ and $r = a$. For this case

$$\sigma_\theta = 3\sigma = \sigma_{max} \tag{2-44}$$

where σ is the uniform tensile stress applied at the ends of the plate. The theoretical stress-concentration factor for a plate with a circular hole is therefore equal to 3. Further study of these equations shows that $\sigma_\theta = -\sigma$ for $r = a$ and $\theta = 0$. Therefore, when a tensile stress is applied to the plate, a compressive stress of equal magnitude exists at the edge of the hole at point B in a direction perpendicular to the axis of loading in the plane of the plate.

Another interesting case for which an analytical solution for the stress concentration is available[1] is the case of a small elliptical hole in a plate. Figure 2-15b shows the geometry of the hole. The maximum stress at the ends of the hole is given by the equation

$$\sigma_{max} = \sigma\left(1 + 2\frac{a}{b}\right) \tag{2-45}$$

Note that, for a circular hole ($a = b$), the above equation reduces to Eq. (2-44). Equation (2-45) shows that the stress increases with the ratio a/b. Therefore, a very narrow hole, such as a crack, normal to the tensile direction will result in a very high stress concentration.

Mathematical complexities prevent the calculation of elastic stress-concentration factors in all but the simplest geometrical cases. Much of this work has been compiled by Neuber,[2] who has made calculations for various types of notches. Stress-concentration factors for practical problems are usually determined by experimental methods.[3] Photoelastic analysis[4] of models is the most widely used technique. This method is especially applicable to plane-stress problems, although it is possible to make three-dimensional photoelastic analyses. Figure 2-16 shows typical

[1] C. E. Inglis, *Trans. Inst. Naval Architects*, pt. 1, pp. 219–230, 1913.

[2] H. Neuber, "Theory of Notch Stresses," English translation, J. W. Edwards, Publisher, Inc., Ann Arbor, Mich., 1946.

[3] M. Hetenyi, "Handbook on Experimental Stress Analysis," John Wiley & Sons, Inc., New York, 1950.

[4] M. M. Frocht, "Photoelasticity," John Wiley & Sons, Inc., New York, 1951.

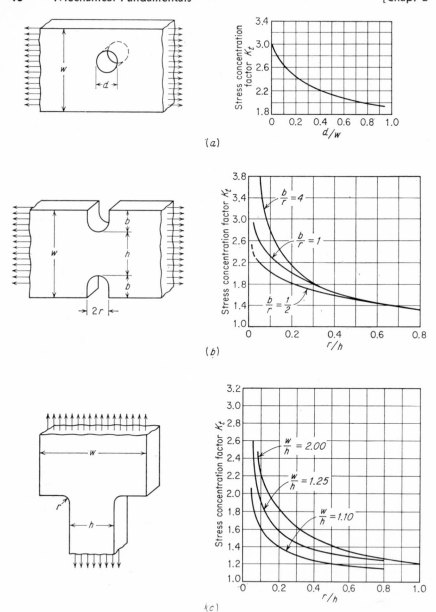

Fig. 2-16. Theoretical stress-concentration factors for different geometrical

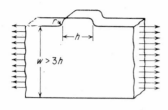

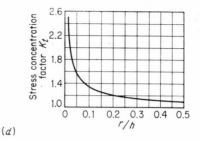

(d)

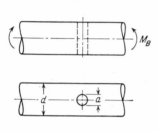

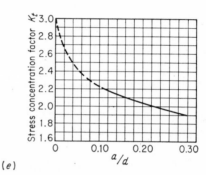

(e)

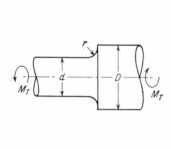

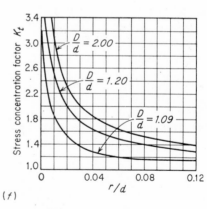

(f)

shapes.   (*After G. H. Neugebauer, Product Eng. vol.* 14, *pp.* 82–87, 1943.)

curves for the theoretical stress-concentration factor of certain machine elements that were obtained by photoelastic methods. Much of the information on stress concentrations in machine parts has been collected by Peterson.[1]

The effect of a stress raiser is much more pronounced in a brittle material than in a ductile material. In a ductile material, plastic deformation occurs when the yield stress is exceeded at the point of maximum stress. Further increase in load produces a local increase in strain at the critically stressed region with little increase in stress. Because of strain hardening, the stress increases in regions adjacent to the stress raiser, until, if the material is sufficiently ductile, the stress distribution becomes essentially uniform. Thus, a ductile metal loaded statically will not develop the full theoretical stress-concentration factor. However, redistribution of stress will not occur to any extent in a brittle material, and therefore a stress concentration of close to the theoretical value will result. Although stress raisers are not usually dangerous in ductile materials subjected to static loads, appreciable stress-concentration effects will occur in ductile materials under fatigue conditions of alternating stresses. Stress raisers are very important in the fatigue failure of metals and will be discussed further in Chap. 12.

2-14. Spherical and Deviator Components of Stress and Strain

Experiment shows that materials can withstand very large hydrostatic pressures (spherical state of stress) without undergoing plastic deformation. In many problems, particularly in the theory of plasticity, it is desirable to designate the part of the total stress which can be effective in producing plastic deformation. This is known as the *stress deviator σ'*. The other component is the *spherical*, or *hydrostatic, component of stress σ''*.

$$\sigma'' = \frac{\sigma_1 + \sigma_2 + \sigma_3}{3} = -p \tag{2-46}$$

The stress deviator is given by the following equations:

$$\sigma_1' = \sigma_1 - \sigma_1'' = \frac{2\sigma_1 - \sigma_2 - \sigma_3}{3}$$

$$\sigma_2' = \sigma_2 - \sigma_2'' = \frac{2\sigma_2 - \sigma_1 - \sigma_3}{3} \tag{2-47}$$

$$\sigma_3' = \sigma_3 - \sigma_3'' = \frac{2\sigma_3 - \sigma_1 - \sigma_2}{3}$$

It can be readily shown that $\sigma_1' + \sigma_2' + \sigma_3' = 0$.

[1] R. E. Peterson, "Stress-concentration Design Factors," John Wiley & Sons, Inc., New York, 1953.

The principal stress direction of the stress deviator is the same as that of the principal stress of the total stress. Thus, σ_1', has the same direction as σ_1. Since an incompressible isotropic body is not deformed by hydrostatic pressure, the deformation depends entirely on the stress deviator, the spherical component making no contribution.

In a completely analogous manner the strain at a point can be divided into a spherical component e'' and a strain deviator e'.

$$e'' = \frac{e_1 + e_2 + e_3}{3} \tag{2-48}$$

$$e_1' = e_1 - e'' = \frac{2e_1 - e_2 - e_3}{3}$$

$$e_2' = e_2 - e'' = \frac{2e_2 - e_1 - e_3}{3} \tag{2-49}$$

$$e_3' = e_3 - e'' = \frac{2e_3 - e_1 - e_2}{3}$$

Hooke's law may then be written in terms of the stress and strain deviators as follows:

$$\sigma_1' = 2Ge_1' \tag{2-50}$$

There are two analogous equations for the other two principal stresses and strains. Hooke's law in terms of the spherical components is given by

$$\sigma_1'' + \sigma_2'' + \sigma_3'' = 3\kappa(e_1'' + e_2'' + e_3'') \tag{2-51}$$

where κ is the volumetric modulus of elasticity.

When the stress deviator is referred to three arbitrary orthogonal axes x, y, z, the principal components may be found in a manner analogous to the method for determining the principal stresses of an arbitrary state of stress. The principal stress deviators are the roots of the cubic equation

$$(\sigma')^3 - J_2\sigma' - J_3 = 0 \tag{2-52}$$

The coefficients J_2 and J_3 are invariants of the stress deviator, i.e., their values are independent of the coordinate system in which the stress deviator is expressed. Expressions for J_2 and J_3 are found below. These quantities are frequently useful in the mathematical theory of plasticity.

$$
\begin{aligned}
J_2 &= -\tfrac{1}{2}[(\sigma_x')^2 + (\sigma_y')^2 + (\sigma_z')^2] + \tau_{xy}^2 + \tau_{xz}^2 + \tau_{yz}^2 \\
&= -\tfrac{1}{2}[(\sigma_1')^2 + (\sigma_2')^2 + (\sigma_3')^2] \\
&= -\tfrac{1}{6}[(\sigma_1 - \sigma_2)^2 + (\sigma_2 - \sigma_3)^2 + (\sigma_3 - \sigma_1)^2] \tag{2-53}
\end{aligned}
$$

$$
J_3 = \begin{vmatrix} \sigma_x' & \tau_{xy} & \tau_{xz} \\ \tau_{yx} & \sigma_y' & \tau_{yz} \\ \tau_{zx} & \tau_{zy} & \sigma_z' \end{vmatrix}
$$

$$
\begin{aligned}
&= \tfrac{1}{3}[(\sigma_1')^3 + (\sigma_2')^3 + (\sigma_3')^3] \\
&= \tfrac{1}{27}[(2\sigma_1 - \sigma_2 - \sigma_3)(2\sigma_2 - \sigma_3 - \sigma_1)(2\sigma_3 - \sigma_1 - \sigma_2)] \tag{2-54}
\end{aligned}
$$

2-15. Strain Energy

The *elastic strain energy* is the amount of energy expended by the action of external forces in deforming an elastic body.   Essentially all the work performed during elastic deformation is stored as elastic energy, and this energy is recovered on the release of the load.   Energy (or work) is equal to a force times the distance over which it acts.   In the deformation of an elastic body the force and deformation increase linearly from initial values of zero, so that the average energy is equal to one-half of their product.   This is also equal to the area under the load-deformation curve.

$$U = \tfrac{1}{2}P\delta \qquad (2\text{-}55)$$

For an elemental cube that is subjected to only a tensile stress along the x axis, the elastic strain energy is given by

$$\begin{aligned} U &= \tfrac{1}{2}P\delta = \tfrac{1}{2}(\sigma_x\, dA)(e_x\, dx) \\ &= \tfrac{1}{2}(\sigma_x e_x)(dA\ dx) \end{aligned} \qquad (2\text{-}56)$$

Equation (2-56) describes the total elastic energy absorbed by the element.   Since $dA\ dx$ is the volume of the element, the *strain energy per unit volume*, U_0, is given by

$$U_0 = \tfrac{1}{2}\sigma_x e_x = \frac{1}{2}\frac{\sigma_x{}^2}{E} = \tfrac{1}{2}e_x{}^2 E \qquad (2\text{-}57)$$

Note that the lateral strains which accompany deformation in simple tension do not enter in the expression for strain energy because no forces exist in the directions of the strains.

By the same reasoning, the strain energy per unit volume of an element subjected to *pure shear* is given by

$$U_0 = \tfrac{1}{2}\tau_{xy}\gamma_{xy} = \frac{1}{2}\frac{\tau_{xy}^2}{G} = \tfrac{1}{2}\gamma_{xy}^2 G \qquad (2\text{-}58)$$

The relationship for pure uniaxial deformation and pure shear can be combined by the principle of superposition to give the elastic strain energy for a general three-dimensional stress distribution.

$$U_0 = \tfrac{1}{2}(\sigma_x e_x + \sigma_y e_y + \sigma_z e_z + \tau_{xy}\gamma_{xy} + \tau_{xz}\gamma_{xz} + \tau_{yz}\gamma_{yz}) \qquad (2\text{-}59)$$

Substituting the equations of Hooke's law [Eqs. (2-23) and (2-24)] for the strains in the above expression results in an expression for strain energy per unit volume expressed solely in terms of the stress and the elastic constants.

$$U_0 = \frac{1}{2E} (\sigma_x{}^2 + \sigma_y{}^2 + \sigma_z{}^2) - \frac{\nu}{E} (\sigma_x\sigma_y + \sigma_y\sigma_z + \sigma_x\sigma_z)$$

$$+ \frac{1}{2G} (\tau_{xy}^2 + \tau_{xz}^2 + \tau_{yz}^2) \quad (2\text{-}60)$$

Also, by substituting Eqs. (2-31) into Eq. (2-59) the stresses are eliminated, and the strain energy is expressed in terms of strains and the elastic constants.

$$U_0 = \tfrac{1}{2}\lambda\Delta^2 + G(e_x{}^2 + e_y{}^2 + e_z{}^2) + \tfrac{1}{2}G(\gamma_{xy}^2 + \gamma_{xz}^2 + \gamma_{yz}^2) \quad (2\text{-}61)$$

It is interesting to note that the derivative of U_0 with respect to any strain component gives the corresponding stress component. Thus, $\partial U_0/\partial e_x = \lambda\Delta + 2Ge_x = \sigma_x$ [compare with Eqs. (2-31)].

BIBLIOGRAPHY

Love, A. E. H.: "A Treatise on the Mathematical Theory of Elasticity," 4th ed., Dover Publications, New York, 1949.

Southwell, R. V.: "An Introduction to the Theory of Elasticity," 2d ed., Oxford University Press, New York, 1941.

Timoshenko, S. P., and J. N. Goodier: "Theory of Elasticity," 2d ed., McGraw-Hill Book Company, Inc., New York, 1951.

Wang, C. T.: "Applied Elasticity," McGraw-Hill Book Company, Inc., New York, 1953.

Chapter 3

ELEMENTS OF
THE THEORY OF PLASTICITY

3-1. Introduction

The theory of plasticity deals with the behavior of materials in the region of strain beyond which Hooke's law is no longer valid. The mathematical description of the plastic deformation of metals is not nearly so well developed as the description of elastic deformation by means of the theory of elasticity because plastic deformation is much more complicated than elastic deformation. For example, in the plastic region of strain, there is no simple relationship between stress and strain as there is for elastic deformation. Moreover, elastic deformation depends only on the initial and final states of stress and is independent of the loading path, but for plastic deformation the plastic strain depends not only on the final load but also on the path by which it was reached.

The theory of plasticity is concerned with a number of different types of problems. From the viewpoint of design, plasticity is concerned with predicting the maximum load which can be applied to a body without causing excessive yielding. The yield criterion[1] must be expressed in terms of stress in such a way that it is valid for all states of stress. The designer is also concerned with plastic deformation in problems where the body is purposely stressed beyond the yield stress into the plastic region. For example, plasticity must be considered in designing for processes such as autofrettage, shrink fitting, and the overspeeding of rotor disks. The consideration of small plastic strains allows economies in building construction through the use of the theory of limit design.

The analysis of large plastic strains is required in the mathematical treatment of the plastic forming of metals. This aspect of plasticity

---

[1] The determination of the limiting load between elastic and plastic behavior is also generally covered in strength of materials. However, because it is necessary to adopt a yield criterion in the theories of plasticity, this topic is covered in the chapter on plasticity.

will be considered in Part Four. It is very difficult to describe, in a rigorous analytical way, the behavior of a metal under these conditions. Therefore, certain simplifying assumptions are usually necessary to obtain a tractable mathematical solution.

Another aspect of plasticity is concerned with acquiring a better understanding of the mechanism of the plastic deformation of metals. Interest in this field is centered on the imperfections in crystalline solids. The effect of metallurgical variables, crystal structure, and lattice imperfections on the deformation behavior are of chief concern. This aspect of plasticity is considered in Part Two.

3-2. The Flow Curve

The stress-strain curve obtained by uniaxial loading, as in the ordinary tension test, is of fundamental interest in plasticity when the curve is plotted in terms of true stress σ and true strain ϵ. True stress is given by the load divided by the instantaneous cross-sectional area of the specimen. True strain is discussed in the next section. The purpose of this section[1] is to describe typical stress-strain curves for real metals and to compare them with the theoretical flow curves for ideal materials.

The true stress-strain curve for a typical ductile metal, such as aluminum, is illustrated in Fig. 3-1a. Hooke's law is followed up to some yield

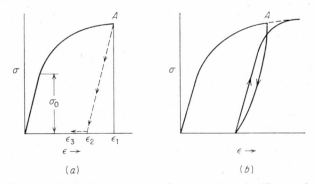

Fig. 3-1. Typical true stress-strain curves for a ductile metal.

stress σ_0. (The value of σ_0 will depend upon the accuracy with which strain is measured.) Beyond σ_0, the metal deforms plastically. Most metals strain-harden in this region, so that increases in strain require higher values of stress than the initial yield stress σ_0. However, unlike the situation in the elastic region, the stress and strain are not related by

---

[1] See Chap. 9 for a more complete discussion of the mathematics of the true stress-strain curve.

any simple constant of proportionality. If the metal is strained to point A, when the load is released the total strain will immediately decrease from ϵ_1 to ϵ_2 by an amount σ/E. The strain decrease $\epsilon_1 - \epsilon_2$ is the *recoverable elastic strain*. However, the strain remaining is not all permanent plastic strain. Depending upon the metal and the temperature, a small amount of the plastic strain $\epsilon_2 - \epsilon_3$ will disappear with time. This is known as anelastic behavior.[1] Generally the anelastic strain is neglected in mathematical theories of plasticity.

Generally the stress-strain curve on unloading from a plastic strain will not be exactly linear and parallel to the elastic portion of the curve (Fig. 3-1b). Moreover, on reloading the curve will generally bend over as the stress approaches the original value of stress from which it was unloaded. With a little additional plastic strain, the stress-strain curve becomes a continuation of what it would have been had no unloading taken place. The hysteresis behavior resulting from unloading and loading from a plastic strain is generally neglected in plasticity theories.

A true stress-strain curve is frequently called a *flow curve* because it gives the stress required to cause the metal to flow plastically to any given strain. Many attempts have been made to fit mathematical equations to this curve. The most common is a power expression of the form

$$\sigma = K\epsilon^n \qquad\qquad (3\text{-}1)$$

where K is the stress at $\epsilon = 1.0$ and n, the strain-hardening coefficient, is the slope of a log-log plot of Eq. (3-1). This equation can be valid only from the beginning of plastic flow to the maximum load at which the specimen begins to neck down.

Even the simple mathematical expression for the flow curve that is given by Eq. (3-1) can result in considerable mathematical complexity when it is used with the equations of the theory of plasticity. Therefore, in this field it is common practice to devise idealized flow curves which simplify the mathematics without deviating too far from physical reality. Figure 3-2a shows the flow curve for a *rigid, perfectly plastic* material. For this idealized material, a tensile specimen is completely rigid (zero elastic strain) until the axial stress equals σ_0, whereupon the material flows plastically at a constant flow stress (zero strain hardening). This type of behavior is approached by a ductile metal which is in a highly cold-worked condition. Figure 3-2b illustrates the flow curve for a perfectly plastic material with an elastic region. This behavior is approached by a material such as plain-carbon steel which has a pronounced yield-point elongation (see Sec. 5-5). A more realistic approach is to approximate the flow curve by two straight lines corresponding to

---

[1] Anelasticity is discussed in greater detail in Chap. 8.

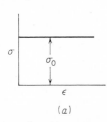
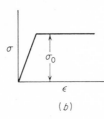
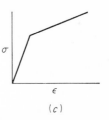

(a)   (b)   (c)

Fig. 3-2. Idealized flow curves. (a) Rigid ideal plastic material; (b) ideal plastic material with elastic region; (c) piecewise linear (strain-hardening) material.

the elastic and plastic regions (Fig. 3-2c). This type of curve results in somewhat more complicated mathematics.

3-3. True Strain

Equation (1-1) describes the conventional concept of unit linear strain, namely, the change in length referred to the original unit length.

$$e = \frac{\Delta L}{L_0} = \frac{1}{L_0} \int_{L_0}^{L} dL$$

This definition of strain is satisfactory for elastic strains where ΔL is very small. However, in plastic deformation the strains are frequently large, and during the extension the gage length changes considerably. Ludwik[1] first proposed the definition of true strain, or natural strain, ϵ, which obviates this difficulty. In this definition of strain the change in length is referred to the instantaneous gage length, rather than to the original gage length.

$$\epsilon = \sum \frac{L_1 - L_0}{L_0} + \frac{L_2 - L_1}{L_1} + \frac{L_3 - L_2}{L_2} + \cdots \qquad (3\text{-}2)$$

or

$$\epsilon = \int_{L_0}^{L} \frac{dL}{L} = \ln \frac{L}{L_0} \qquad (3\text{-}3)$$

The relationship between true strain and conventional linear strain follows from Eq. (1-1).

$$e = \frac{\Delta L}{L_0} = \frac{L - L_0}{L_0} = \frac{L}{L_0} - 1$$

$$e + 1 = \frac{L}{L_0}$$

$$\epsilon = \ln \frac{L}{L_0} = \ln (e + 1) \qquad (3\text{-}4)$$

[1] P. Ludwik, "Elemente der technologischen Mechanik," Springer-Verlag OHG. Berlin, 1909.

The two measurements of strain give nearly identical results up to strains of about 0.1.

Because the volume remains essentially constant during plastic deformation, Eq. (3-3) can be written in terms of either length or area.

$$\epsilon = \ln \frac{L}{L_0} = \ln \frac{A_0}{A} \tag{3-5}$$

Also, because of constancy of volume, the summation of the three principal strains is equal to zero.

$$\epsilon_1 + \epsilon_2 + \epsilon_3 = 0 \tag{3-6}$$

This relationship is not valid for the principal conventional strains.

The advantage of using true strain should be apparent from the following example: Consider a uniform cylinder which is extended to twice its original length.   The linear strain is then $e = (2L_0 - L_0)/L_0 = 1.0$, or a strain of 100 per cent.   To achieve the same amount of negative linear strain in compression, the cylinder would have to be squeezed to zero thickness.   However, intuitively we should expect that the strain produced in compressing a cylinder to half its original length would be the same as, although opposite in sign to, the strain produced by extending the cylinder to twice its length.   If true strain is used, equivalence is obtained for the two cases.   For extension to twice the original length, $\epsilon = \ln(2L_0/L_0) = \ln 2$.   For compression to half the original length, $\epsilon = \ln[(L_0/2)/L_0] = \ln \frac{1}{2} = -\ln 2$.

3-4. Yielding Criteria for Ductile Metals

The problem of deducing mathematical relationships for predicting the conditions at which plastic yielding begins when a material is subjected to a complex state of stress is an important consideration in the field of plasticity.   In uniaxial loading, plastic flow begins at the yield stress, and it is to be expected that yielding under a situation of combined stresses is related to some particular combination of the principal stresses.   A yield criterion can be expressed in the general form $F(\sigma_1, \sigma_2, \sigma_3, k_1, \ldots) = 0$, but there is at present no theoretical way of calculating the relationship between the stress components to correlate yielding in a three-dimensional state of stress with yielding in the uniaxial tension test.   The yielding criteria are therefore essentially empirical relationships.   At present, there are two generally accepted theories for predicting the onset of yielding in ductile metals.

Maximum-shear-stress Theory

The maximum-shear-stress theory, sometimes called the Tresca, Coulomb, or Guest yield criterion, states that yielding will occur when the maximum shear stress reaches a critical value equal to the shearing yield stress in a uniaxial tension test. From Eq. (2-15), the maximum shear stress is given by

$$\tau_{max} = \frac{\sigma_1 - \sigma_3}{2} \tag{3-7}$$

where σ_1 is the algebraically largest and σ_3 is the algebraically smallest principal stress.

For uniaxial tension $\sigma_1 = \sigma_0, \sigma_2 = \sigma_3 = 0$, where σ_0 is the yield strength in simple tension. Therefore, the *shearing* yield stress for simple tension τ_0 is equal to one-half of the tensile yield stress.

$$\tau_0 = \frac{\sigma_0}{2}$$

Substituting these values into the equation for the maximum shear stress results in

$$\tau_{max} = \frac{\sigma_1 - \sigma_3}{2} = \tau_0 = \frac{\sigma_0}{2} \tag{3-8}$$

or

$$\sigma_1 - \sigma_3 = \sigma_0 \tag{3-9}$$

This is sometimes written as

$$\sigma_1 - \sigma_3 = \sigma_1' - \sigma_3' = 2k \tag{3-10}$$

where σ_1' and σ_3' are the deviators of the principal stresses and k is the yield stress for pure shear, i.e., the stress at which yielding occurs in torsion, where $\sigma_1 = -\sigma_3$.

The maximum-shear-stress theory is in good agreement with experimental results, being slightly on the safe side, and is widely used by designers for ductile metals. It has replaced the older and far less accurate maximum-stress theory, Rankine's theory.

Prager and Hodge[1] have pointed out that in certain plasticity problems the simple relations of Eq. (3-9) or (3-10) cannot be used as the yielding conditions since it is not known which of the three principal stresses is the largest. In this case, the much more complicated general form of the equation, which is given below, must be used.

$$4J_2{}^3 - 27J_3{}^2 - 36k^2J_2{}^2 + 96k^4J_2 - 64k^6 = 0 \tag{3-11}$$

J_2 and J_3 are the invariants of the stress deviator (see Sec. 2-14). Obviously, such a complex relation will result in very cumbersome mathematics. It is for this reason that the yielding criterion that is discussed next is preferred in most theoretical work.

[1] W. Prager and P. G. Hodge, Jr., "Theory of Perfectly Plastic Solids," p. 23, John Wiley & Sons, Inc., New York. 1951.

Von Mises, or Distortion-energy, Theory

A somewhat better fit with experimental results is provided by the yield criterion given in Eq. (3-12).

$$\sigma_0 = \frac{1}{\sqrt{2}} [(\sigma_1 - \sigma_2)^2 + (\sigma_2 - \sigma_3)^2 + (\sigma_3 - \sigma_1)^2]^{1/2} \qquad (3\text{-}12)$$

According to this criterion, yielding will occur when the differences between the principal stresses expressed by the right-hand side of the equation exceed the yield stress in uniaxial tension, σ_0. The development of this yield criterion is associated with the names of Von Mises, Hencky, Maxwell, and Huber. Von Mises proposed this criterion in the invariant form given by Eq. (3-13) primarily because it was mathematically simpler than the invariant form of the maximum-shear-stress theory given by Eq. (3-11). Subsequent experiments showed that Eq. (3-13) provides better over-all agreement with combined stress-yielding data than the maximum-shear-stress theory.

$$J_2 - k^2 = 0 \qquad (3\text{-}13)$$

J_2 is the second invariant of the stress deviator, and k is the yield stress in pure shear.

A number of attempts have been made to provide physical meaning to the Von Mises yield criterion. One commonly accepted concept is that this yield criterion expresses the strain energy of distortion. On the basis of the distortion-energy concept, yielding will occur when the strain energy of distortion per unit volume exceeds the strain energy of distortion per unit volume for a specimen strained to the yield stress in uniaxial tension or compression. The derivation of Eq. (3-12) on the basis of distortion energy is given below. Another common physical interpretation of Eq. (3-12) is that it represents the critical value of the octahedral shear stress (see Sec. 3-7).

The total elastic strain energy per unit volume (see Sec. 2-15) can be divided into two components, the strain energy of distortion, U_0', and the strain energy of volume change, U_0''. To illustrate the resolution of total strain energy into its components, consider Fig. 3-3. This figure illustrates the point established in Sec. 2-14 that a general three-dimensional state of stress can be expressed in terms of a spherical or hydrostatic component of stress, σ'', and a stress deviator, σ'. Because experiments have shown[1] that up to rather large values of hydrostatic pressure a hydrostatic state of stress has no effect on yielding, it is valid to assume that only the stress deviator can produce distortion. Therefore, the

[1] P. W. Bridgman, "Studies in Large Plastic Flow and Fracture," McGraw-Hill Book Company, Inc., New York, 1952.

strain energy of distortion will be based on the stress deviator. It represents only the strain energy associated with changing the shape of the specimen and neglects the strain energy associated with changes in volume.

The strain energy of distortion will be determined by first calculating the strain energy of volume change and then subtracting this term from

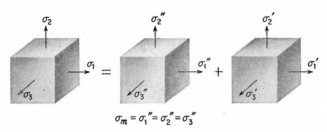

Fig. 3-3. Resolution of stress into hydrostatic stress and stress deviator.

the total strain energy. Referring again to Fig. 3-3, the strain energy per unit volume associated with a volume change will be

$$U_0'' = \tfrac{1}{2}\sigma_1'' e_1'' + \tfrac{1}{2}\sigma_2'' e_2'' + \tfrac{1}{2}\sigma_3'' e_3''$$

Referring to the definitions for the deviator component of strain given in Sec. 2-14 and letting σ_m equal the hydrostatic component of stress, or *average stress,*

$$U_0'' = \tfrac{1}{2}\sigma_m(e_1 + e_2 + e_3) = \tfrac{1}{2}\sigma_m\Delta \qquad (3\text{-}14)$$

However, from Eq. (2-29) $\Delta = \sigma_m/\kappa$, so that Eq. (3-14) becomes

$$U_0'' = \frac{1}{2}\frac{\sigma_m{}^2}{\kappa} \qquad (3\text{-}15)$$

Since $U_0' = U_0 - U_0''$, the strain energy of distortion can be determined by using Eq. (2-60) for the total strain energy U_0.

$$U_0' = \frac{1}{2E}(\sigma_1{}^2 + \sigma_2{}^2 + \sigma_3{}^2) - \frac{\nu}{E}(\sigma_1\sigma_2 + \sigma_2\sigma_3 + \sigma_1\sigma_3) - \frac{1}{2}\frac{\sigma_m{}^2}{\kappa} \qquad (3\text{-}16)$$

However, since $\sigma_m = (\sigma_1 + \sigma_2 + \sigma_3)/3$ and $\kappa = E/[3(1 - 2\nu)]$, Eq. (3-16) reduces to

$$U_0' = \frac{1 + \nu}{6E}[(\sigma_1 - \sigma_2)^2 + (\sigma_2 - \sigma_3)^2 + (\sigma_3 - \sigma_1)^2] \qquad (3\text{-}17)$$

For a uniaxial state of stress, $\sigma_1 = \sigma_0$, $\sigma_2 = \sigma_3 = 0$.

$$U_0' = \frac{1 + \nu}{3E}\sigma_0{}^2 \qquad (3\text{-}18)$$

Therefore, the distortion-energy yield criterion can be written

$$\frac{1 + \nu}{6E} 2\sigma_0{}^2 = \frac{1 + \nu}{6E} [(\sigma_1 - \sigma_2)^2 + (\sigma_2 - \sigma_3)^2 + (\sigma_3 - \sigma_1)^2]$$

or
$$\sigma_0 = \frac{1}{\sqrt{2}} [(\sigma_1 - \sigma_2)^2 + (\sigma_2 - \sigma_3)^2 + (\sigma_3 - \sigma_1)^2]^{1/2} \tag{3-19}$$

For a condition of pure shear, such as occurs in torsion, $\tau = \sigma$.

$$\sigma_1 = \sigma_0 \qquad \sigma_2 = 0 \qquad \sigma_3 = -\sigma_0$$

Therefore, the strain energy of distortion for this state of stress is given by

$$U_0' = \frac{1 + \nu}{E} \sigma^2 = \frac{1 + \nu}{E} \tau^2 \tag{3-20}$$

If for any type of stress system yielding begins when the strain energy of distortion reaches a critical value, the ratio between this critical value for uniaxial stress and pure shear can be obtained by equating Eqs. (3-18) and (3-20).

$$\frac{1 + \nu}{E} \tau_0{}^2 = \frac{1 + \nu}{3E} \sigma_0{}^2$$

$$\tau_0 = \frac{1}{\sqrt{3}} \sigma_0 = 0.577\sigma_0 \tag{3-21}$$

Thus, if the distortion-energy theory is a valid yielding criterion, the yield strength in shear, as determined from a torsion test, should be 0.577 times the tensile yield strength. Actual data show that the shear yield stress falls between 0.5 and 0.6 of the tensile yield stress, with the average occurring close to the predicted value. It should be noted that the maximum-shear-stress theory predicts that $\tau_0 = 0.50\sigma_0$. The better agreement shown by the distortion-energy theory for these two different types of tests is one reason for preferring the distortion-energy theory of yielding.

3-5. Combined Stress Tests

The conditions for yielding under states of stress other than uniaxial and torsion loading can be conveniently studied with thin-wall tubes. Axial tension can be combined with torsion to give various combinations of shear stress to normal stress intermediate between the values obtained separately in tension and torsion. For the combined axial tension and torsion, the principal stresses from Eq. (2-7) are

$$\sigma_1 = \frac{\sigma_x}{2} + \left(\frac{\sigma_x{}^2}{4} + \tau_{xy}^2\right)^{\frac{1}{2}}$$

$$\sigma_2 = 0 \qquad\qquad\qquad (3\text{-}22)$$

$$\sigma_3 = \frac{\sigma_x}{2} - \left(\frac{\sigma_x{}^2}{4} + \tau_{xy}^2\right)^{\frac{1}{2}}$$

Therefore, the maximum-shear-stress criterion of yielding is given by

$$\left(\frac{\sigma_x}{\sigma_0}\right)^2 + 4\left(\frac{\tau_{xy}}{\sigma_0}\right)^2 = 1 \qquad\qquad (3\text{-}23)$$

and the distortion-energy theory of yielding is expressed by

$$\left(\frac{\sigma_x}{\sigma_0}\right)^2 + 3\left(\frac{\tau_{xy}}{\sigma_0}\right)^2 = 1 \qquad\qquad (3\text{-}24)$$

Both equations define an ellipse. Figure 3-4 shows that the experimental results[1] agree best with the distortion-energy theory.

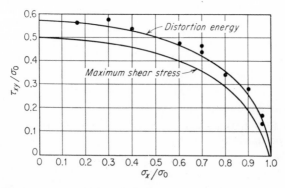

Fig. 3-4. Comparison between maximum-shear-stress theory and distortion-energy (Von Mises) theory.

Another type of combined stress test is to subject thin-wall tubes to axial load and internal hydrostatic pressure.[2] Since the stress in the radial direction is negligible ($\sigma_3 = 0$ at the outer free surface), this test provides a biaxial state of stress.

For the plane-stress condition, the distortion-energy theory of yielding can be expressed mathematically by

$$\sigma_1{}^2 + \sigma_2{}^2 - \sigma_1\sigma_2 = \sigma_0{}^2 \qquad\qquad (3\text{-}25)$$

[1] G. I. Taylor and H. Quinney, *Proc. Roy. Soc.* (*London*), vol. 230A, pp. 323–362, 1931.

[2] W. Lode, *Z. Physik*, vol. 36, pp. 913–939, 1926.

This is the equation of an ellipse whose major semiaxis is $\sqrt{2}\,\sigma_0$ and whose minor semiaxis is $\sqrt{\frac{2}{3}}\,\sigma_0$.

A convenient way of comparing yielding criteria for a two-dimensional state of stress is with a plot such as Fig. 3-5. Note that the maximum-shear-stress theory and the distortion-energy theory predict the same yield stress for conditions of uniaxial stress and balanced biaxial stress ($\sigma_1 = \sigma_2$). The greatest divergence between the two theories occurs for a state of pure shear ($\sigma_1 = -\sigma_2$). It has already been shown that for this state of stress the shear-stress law predicts a yield stress which is 15 per cent lower than the value given by the distortion-energy criterion.

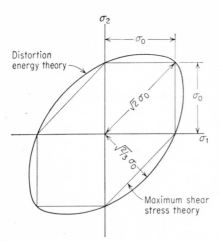

Fig. 3-5. Comparison of yield criteria for plane stress.

A very sensitive method of differentiating between the two yield criteria is the procedure adopted by Lode of determining the effect of the intermediate principal stress on yielding. According to the maximum-shear-stress law, there should be no effect of the value of the intermediate stress σ_2. Thus, $(\sigma_1 - \sigma_3)/\sigma_0 = 1$. For the distortion-energy theory, to account for the influence of the intermediate principal stress, Lode introduced the parameter μ, called *Lode's stress parameter*.

$$\mu = \frac{2\sigma_2 - \sigma_3 - \sigma_1}{\sigma_1 - \sigma_3} \tag{3-26}$$

Solving this equation for σ_2 and eliminating σ_2 from Eq. (3-12) results in

$$\frac{\sigma_1 - \sigma_3}{\sigma_0} = \frac{2}{(3 + \mu^2)^{1/2}} \tag{3-27}$$

Experimental data plot much better against Eq. (3-27) than against the maximum-shear-stress equation, indicating that the intermediate principal stress has an influence on yielding.

Another contribution of Lode was the introduction of a strain parameter ν.

$$\nu = \frac{2\,\Delta\epsilon_2 - \Delta\epsilon_3 - \Delta\epsilon_1}{\Delta\epsilon_1 - \Delta\epsilon_3} \tag{3-28}$$

where $\Delta\epsilon$ is a finite increment of strain. A plot of μ against ν should yield a straight line at 45° to the axis if the metal behaves according to the Levy–Von Mises equations of plasticity (see Sec. 3-9). Most metals show some slight but systematic deviation from Lode's relationship $\mu = \nu$.

3-6. Octahedral Shear Stress and Shear Strain

The octahedral stresses are a particular set of stress functions which are important in the theory of plasticity. They are the stresses acting on the faces of a three-dimensional octahedron which has the geometric property that the faces of the planes make equal angles with each of the three principal directions of stress. For such a geometric body, the angle between the normal to one of the faces and the nearest principal axis is 54°44', and the cosine of this angle is $1/\sqrt{3}$.

The stress acting on each face of the octahedron can be resolved[1] into a normal octahedral stress σ_{oct} and an octahedral shear stress lying in the octahedral plane, τ_{oct}. The normal octahedral stress is equal to the hydrostatic component of the total stress.

$$\sigma_{oct} = \frac{\sigma_1 + \sigma_2 + \sigma_3}{3} = \sigma'' \tag{3-29}$$

The octahedral shear stress τ_{oct} is given by

$$\tau_{oct} = \tfrac{1}{3}[(\sigma_1 - \sigma_2)^2 + (\sigma_2 - \sigma_3)^2 + (\sigma_3 - \sigma_1)^2]^{\frac{1}{2}} \tag{3-30}$$

Since the normal octahedral stress is a hydrostatic stress, it cannot produce yielding in solid materials. Therefore, the octahedral shear stress is the component of stress responsible for plastic deformation. In this respect, it is analogous to the stress deviator.

If it is assumed that a critical octahedral shear stress determines yielding, the failure criterion can be written as

$$\tau_{oct} = \frac{1}{3}[(\sigma_1 - \sigma_2)^2 + (\sigma_2 - \sigma_3)^2 + (\sigma_2 - \sigma_1)^2]^{\frac{1}{2}} = \frac{\sqrt{2}}{3}\sigma_0$$

or
$$\sigma_0 = \frac{1}{\sqrt{2}}[(\sigma_1 - \sigma_2)^2 + (\sigma_2 - \sigma_3)^2 + (\sigma_3 - \sigma_1)^2]^{\frac{1}{2}} \tag{3-31}$$

Since Eq. (3-31) is identical with the equation already derived for the distortion-energy theory, the two yielding theories give the same results. In a sense, the octahedral theory can be considered the *stress equivalent* of the distortion-energy theory. According to this theory, the octahedral

---

[1] A. Nadai, "Theory of Flow and Fracture of Solids," 2d ed., vol. I, pp. 99–105, McGraw-Hill Book Company, Inc., New York, 1950.

shear stress corresponding to yielding in uniaxial stress is given by

$$\tau_{oct} = \frac{\sqrt{2}}{3}\sigma_0 = 0.471\sigma_0 \tag{3-32}$$

Octahedral strains are referred to the same three-dimensional octahedron as the octahedral stresses. The octahedral linear strain is given by

$$\epsilon_{oct} = \frac{\epsilon_1 + \epsilon_2 + \epsilon_3}{3} \tag{3-33}$$

Octahedral shear strain is given by

$$\gamma_{oct} = \frac{2}{3}[(\epsilon_1 - \epsilon_2)^2 + (\epsilon_2 - \epsilon_3)^2 + (\epsilon_3 - \epsilon_1)^2]^{\frac{1}{2}} \tag{3-34}$$

3-7. Invariants of Stress and Strain

It is frequently useful to simplify the representation of a complex state of stress or strain by means of invariant functions of stress and strain. If the plastic stress-strain curve (the flow curve) is plotted in terms of invariants of stress and strain, approximately the same curve will be obtained regardless of the state of stress. For example, the flow curves obtained in a uniaxial-tension test and a biaxial-torsion test of a thin tube with internal pressure will coincide when the curves are plotted in terms of invariant stress and strain functions.

Nadai[1] has shown that the octahedral shear stress and shear strain are invariant functions which describe the flow curve independent of the type of test. Other frequently used invariant functions are the *effective*, or *significant*, stress and strain. These quantities are defined by the following equations for the case where the coordinate axes correspond to the principal directions:

Effective or significant stress

$$\bar{\sigma} = \frac{\sqrt{2}}{2}[(\sigma_1 - \sigma_2)^2 + (\sigma_2 - \sigma_3)^2 + (\sigma_3 - \sigma_1)^2]^{\frac{1}{2}} \tag{3-35}$$

Effective or significant strain

$$\bar{\epsilon} = \frac{\sqrt{2}}{3}[(\epsilon_1 - \epsilon_2)^2 + (\epsilon_2 - \epsilon_3)^2 + (\epsilon_3 - \epsilon_1)^2]^{\frac{1}{2}} \tag{3-36}$$

Note that both effective stress and effective strain reduce to the axial normal component of stress and strain for a tensile test. These values

[1] A. Nadai, *J. Appl. Phys.*, vol. 8, p. 205, 1937.

are also related to the octahedral shearing stress and strain, as can be seen by comparing Eqs. (3-30) and (3-34) with the above equations.

$$\tau_{\text{oct}} = \frac{\sqrt{2}}{3}\,\bar{\sigma} \qquad \gamma_{\text{oct}} = \sqrt{2}\,\bar{\epsilon} \tag{3-37}$$

Drucker[1] has pointed out that there are a large number of different functions of stress and strain which might serve as invariant stress and strain parameters. For example, he shows that combined stress data for aluminum-alloy tubes show better agreement when the equivalent shearing stress τ_{eq}, defined below, is plotted against octahedral shearing strain instead of τ_{oct} being plotted against γ_{oct}.

$$\tau_{\text{eq}} = \tau_{\text{oct}}\left(1 - 2.25\,\frac{J_3{}^2}{J_2{}^3}\right)^{\frac{1}{6}} \tag{3-38}$$

where J_2 and J_3 are invariants of the stress deviator. There appears to be no theoretical or experimental justification for choosing invariant stress and strain parameters other than the closeness of agreement with the data and mathematical convenience.

3-8. Basis of the Theories of Plasticity

The development of a generalized theory of plasticity, with the same wide applicability as the theory of elasticity, has not progressed rapidly because of the complexity of the problem. The inherent difficulty in developing a simple mathematical description of plasticity lies in the fact that plastic deformation is essentially an irreversible process. While elastic deformation depends only on the initial and final states of stress or strain and therefore the results are independent of the path along which the load is reached, in plastic deformation the total plastic strain depends not only on the final load but also on the path by which it was reached. Therefore, in plastic deformation, the type of load cycle determines the strain increment. The final value of a plastic-strain component is given by the integral of the increments of the plastic-strain component over the loading history that the material has undergone.

A particular condition of loading which simplifies the analysis is *proportional loading*. For proportional loading, the stress components increase in constant ratio to each other.

$$\frac{d\sigma_1}{\sigma_1} = \frac{d\sigma_2}{\sigma_2} = \frac{d\sigma_3}{\sigma_3} \tag{3-39}$$

For this type of loading, the strains can be expressed in terms of the final stress state because the final stress state specifies the stress history.

[1] D. C. Drucker, *J. Appl. Mech.*, vol. 16, pp. 349–357, 1949.

Mathematical theories of plasticity can be divided roughly into two types. *Deformation theories* relate the stress to the strain, while *flow theories* relate the stress to the strain rate, or the velocity of strain. Deformation theories utilize an averaging process over the entire deformation history and relate the total plastic strain to the final stress. This type of theory is valid when the material is subjected to proportional loading, but it is not generally considered to be reliable[1] when the direction of loading is changed during the test. Flow theories consider a succession of infinitesimal increments of distortion in which the instantaneous stress is related to the increment of the strain rate. Because a flow theory considers the instantaneous deformation, it is better able to describe large plastic deformations.

There are a number of general assumptions which are common to all plasticity theories. The metal is considered to be continuous and isotropic. The principal axes of plastic stress and strain are assumed to coincide at all times. Time effects are usually neglected, so that viscoelastic materials are excluded from the theories presented in this chapter. For the values of stress usually encountered, it is a very good assumption to consider that *volume remains constant*. This also leads to the useful relation that the sum of the principal true strains is equal to zero.

$$\epsilon_1 + \epsilon_2 + \epsilon_3 = 0$$

Constancy of volume also requires that Poisson's ratio must increase from its elastic value to a value of 0.5 for the plastic condition. Experiments show that Poisson's ratio increases with progressive plastic strain to this limiting value, but frequently the incorrect assumption is made that $\nu = 0.5$ for all values of plastic strain.

Unfortunately, there is no simple relationship between stress and strain in the plastic region such as exists with elastic deformation. An obvious simplification is to assume that plastic flow occurs at a constant value of flow stress, i.e., that there is no strain hardening. Plasticity theory based on ideal plastic behavior has been developed further than theories which consider the strain hardening of the metal. One way to take strain hardening into consideration is to use experimental data plotted as invariant stress-strain functions. In analyses of forming operations involving large plastic strains, it is common practice to allow for strain hardening by using an average value of yield stress.

The formation of many plasticity theories is based on the premise that the stress deviator is proportional to the strain increment. This is equivalent to saying that Lode's stress and strain parameters are equal,

---

[1] Arguments to show that deformation theories of plasticity should be valid for loading paths other than proportional loading have been given by B. Budiansky, *J. Appl. Mech.*, vol. 26, no. 2, pp. 259–264, 1959.

$\mu = \nu$.   Although deviations from Lode's relationship have been shown by experiment, it appears that the proportionality between stress deviator and strain increment is a reasonably good approximation.

To provide additional simplification to the analysis, it is often assumed that the body acts as a *rigid* plastic material. With this assumption, all elastic strain is neglected, and the total strain is considered to be entirely plastic. This is a suitable assumption when the plastic strain is large, so that the elastic strains are negligible by comparison. However, in many problems the body is strained only slightly beyond the yield stress, so that the elastic and plastic strains are of comparable magnitude. For this situation, it is necessary that the elastic strains be considered in the analysis. The total strain is then the sum of the elastic and plastic strain.

$$\epsilon_{ij} = \epsilon_{ij}^E + \epsilon_{ij}^P . \tag{3-40}$$

However, because of the assumption of constancy of volume, the plastic component of the hydrostatic component of strain must be equal to zero.

$$\epsilon^{P''} = \tfrac{1}{3}(\epsilon_1^P + \epsilon_2^P + \epsilon_3^P) = 0$$

Therefore, the plastic-strain deviator is equal to the plastic strain.

$$\epsilon_1^P = \epsilon_1^{P'} \qquad \epsilon_2^P = \epsilon_2^{P'} \qquad \epsilon_3^P = \epsilon_3^{P'} \tag{3-41}$$

3-9. Flow Theories

Rigid Ideal Plastic Material

A flow theory for a rigid ideal plastic material based on the proportionality between stress deviator and strain rate is the outgrowth of work by St. Venant, Levy, and Von Mises. The Levy–Von Mises equations are given below for a general coordinate system. λ is a proportionality constant, and σ_m is the hydrostatic component of stress. Note that a dot over the symbol for strain indicates the time derivative of strain, i.e., the strain rate.

$$\begin{aligned} \sigma_x - \sigma_m = \sigma_x' &= 2\lambda\dot{\epsilon}_x & \tau_{xy} &= \lambda\dot{\gamma}_{xy} \\ \sigma_y' &= 2\lambda\dot{\epsilon}_y & \tau_{yz} &= \lambda\dot{\gamma}_{yz} \\ \sigma_z' &= 2\lambda\dot{\epsilon}_z & \tau_{xz} &= \lambda\dot{\gamma}_{xz} \end{aligned} \tag{3-42}$$

In terms of the principal stresses, the Levy–Von Mises equations can be written

$$\sigma_1' = 2\lambda\dot{\epsilon}_1 \qquad \sigma_2' = 2\lambda\dot{\epsilon}_2 \qquad \sigma_3' = 2\lambda\dot{\epsilon}_3 \tag{3-43}$$

These equations are similar to the equations of viscosity for an incompressible fluid. The important difference is that for the case of the fluid the proportionality constant λ is a true material constant, the coefficient of viscosity.   For the case of the plastic body, the value of λ depends on the values of stress and strain. λ can be evaluated when the yield criterion is established.

The Von Mises yield criterion is given by

$$J_2 = k^2$$

or
$$2J_2 = (\sigma_1')^2 + (\sigma_2')^2 + (\sigma_3')^2 = \frac{2\sigma_0^2}{3} \qquad (3\text{-}44)$$

Substituting Eqs. (3-43) into Eq. (3-44) results in

$$\lambda^2(\dot{\epsilon}_1^2 + \dot{\epsilon}_2^2 + \dot{\epsilon}_3^2) = \frac{\sigma_0^2}{6} \qquad (3\text{-}45)$$

The quantity $\dot{\epsilon}_1^2 + \dot{\epsilon}_2^2 + \dot{\epsilon}_3^2$ is an invariant of strain rate.   Substituting Eq. (3-45) back into Eqs. (3-43) gives

$$\sigma_1' = \frac{\sqrt{2}\,\sigma_0\dot{\epsilon}_1}{[3(\dot{\epsilon}_1^2 + \dot{\epsilon}_2^2 + \dot{\epsilon}_3^2)]^{1/2}} \qquad (3\text{-}46)$$

Completely analogous equations follow for σ_2' and σ_3'.

Equations (3-43) can be written

$$2\sigma_1 - \sigma_2 - \sigma_3 = \frac{6\lambda}{dt}\, d\epsilon_1$$

$$2\sigma_2 - \sigma_1 - \sigma_3 = \frac{6\lambda}{dt}\, d\epsilon_2 \qquad (3\text{-}47)$$

$$2\sigma_3 - \sigma_1 - \sigma_2 = \frac{6\lambda}{dt}\, d\epsilon_3$$

Eliminating $6\lambda/dt$ from these equations results in

$$\frac{2\sigma_1 - \sigma_2 - \sigma_3}{2\sigma_2 - \sigma_3 - \sigma_1} = \frac{d\epsilon_1}{d\epsilon_2}$$

$$\frac{2\sigma_1 - \sigma_2 - \sigma_3}{2\sigma_3 - \sigma_1 - \sigma_2} = \frac{d\epsilon_1}{d\epsilon_3} \qquad (3\text{-}48)$$

The above two equations, plus the constancy-of-volume relationship $\epsilon_1 + \epsilon_2 + \epsilon_3 = 0$, constitute a system of differential equations that must be integrated over a particular stress path or strain path for the solution of a particular problem.

Elastic-Plastic Material

The extension of the Levy–Von Mises equations to the consideration of both elastic and plastic strains has been primarily the work of Prandtl and Reuss.   In discussing this theory it will be necessary to differentiate between the elastic strain ϵ^E and the plastic strain ϵ^P.   Assuming that the rate of change of plastic strain is proportional to the stress deviator results in

$$2G\dot{\epsilon}_1{}^{P'} = \lambda\sigma_1' \qquad 2G\dot{\epsilon}_2{}^{P'} = \lambda\sigma_2' \qquad 2G\dot{\epsilon}_3{}^{P'} = \lambda\sigma_3' \qquad (3\text{-}49)$$

The time derivative of Hooke's law expressed in terms of stress and strain deviators [Eq. (2-50)] gives the corresponding equations for elastic strain.

$$2G\dot{\epsilon}_1{}^{E'} = \dot{\sigma}_1' \qquad 2G\dot{\epsilon}_2{}^{E'} = \dot{\sigma}_2' \qquad 2G\dot{\epsilon}_3{}^{E'} = \dot{\sigma}_3' \qquad (3\text{-}50)$$

Combining Eqs. (3-49) and (3-50) results in expressions for the time derivative of *total strain.*

$$2G\dot{\epsilon}_1' = \dot{\sigma}_1' + \lambda\sigma_1' \qquad 2G\dot{\epsilon}_2' = \dot{\sigma}_2' + \lambda\sigma_2' \qquad 2G\dot{\epsilon}_3' = \dot{\sigma}_3' + \lambda\sigma_3' \qquad (3\text{-}51)$$

If it is assumed that the Von Mises criterion of yielding applies and that there is no strain hardening,

$$J_2 = k^2 \qquad \dot{J}_2 = 0$$

From Eq. (3-44)

$$\dot{J}_2 = \sigma_1'(\sigma_1')^2 + \sigma_2'(\sigma_2')^2 + \sigma_3'(\sigma_3')^2 = 0 \qquad (3\text{-}52)$$

This expression can be used to eliminate the proportionality constant λ from Eq. (3-51). However, to simplify the algebra, the quantity $\dot{U}_0'$ is introduced.[1] $\dot{U}_0'$ is the rate of change of strain energy involved in distortion, as opposed to the strain energy required for volume change.

$$\dot{U}_0' = \sigma_1'\dot{\epsilon}_1' + \sigma_2'\dot{\epsilon}_2' + \sigma_3'\dot{\epsilon}_3' \qquad (3\text{-}53)$$

By using Eqs. (3-52) and (3-53) and the yield criterion $J_2 = k^2$, it is possible to obtain the relationship

$$2G\dot{U}_0' = 2\lambda k^2 \qquad (3\text{-}54)$$

The stress-strain relations of Reuss's equations are obtained by substituting Eq. (3-54) into Eq. (3-52) and solving for the stress rate.

$$\dot{\sigma}_1' = 2G\left(\dot{\epsilon}_1' - \frac{3\dot{U}_0'}{2\sigma_0{}^2}\sigma_1'\right)$$

$$\dot{\sigma}_2' = 2G\left(\dot{\epsilon}_2' - \frac{3\dot{U}_0'}{2\sigma_0{}^2}\sigma_2'\right) \qquad (3\text{-}55)$$

$$\dot{\sigma}_3' = 2G\left(\dot{\epsilon}_3' - \frac{3\dot{U}_0'}{2\sigma_0{}^2}\sigma_3'\right)$$

These equations give the rate of change of the stress deviator as long as $J_2 = k^2$ and $\dot{U}_0' > 0$. To get the rate of change of stress, it is necessary to remember that $\dot{\sigma}_1 = \dot{\sigma}_1' + \dot{\sigma}_1''$. From Eq. (2-51)

$$\sigma'' = 3\kappa\epsilon^{E''} \qquad (3\text{-}56)$$

[1] This derivation follows the procedure given by Prager and Hodge, *op. cit.*, pp. 27–29.

When the stress is in the elastic range, or in unloading from the plastic region, Eqs. (3-55) do not apply. The proper equations are given by the elasticity equations like Eq. (2-50).

3-10. Deformation Theories

Hencky proposed that for small strains the stress deviator could be considered proportional to the strain deviator.

$$\sigma' = 2G_P\epsilon' \tag{3-57}$$

Elastic strains are neglected in Eq. (3-57). G_P is a plastic shear modulus which varies depending upon the values of stress and strain. Because of the assumption of constancy of volume, $\epsilon'' = 0$, and $\epsilon' = \epsilon$. Therefore, Eq. (3-57) can be expanded in terms of principal stresses and strains to give

$$\epsilon_1 = \frac{2\sigma_1 - \sigma_2 - \sigma_3}{6G_P} = \frac{1}{3G_P}\left[\sigma_1 - \frac{1}{2}(\sigma_2 + \sigma_3)\right] = \frac{1}{E_P}\left[\sigma_1 - \frac{1}{2}(\sigma_2 + \sigma_3)\right]$$

$$\epsilon_2 = \frac{2\sigma_2 - \sigma_1 - \sigma_3}{6G_P} = \frac{1}{3G_P}\left[\sigma_2 - \frac{1}{2}(\sigma_1 + \sigma_3)\right] = \frac{1}{E_P}\left[\sigma_2 - \frac{1}{2}(\sigma_1 + \sigma_3)\right]$$

$$\epsilon_3 = \frac{2\sigma_3 - \sigma_1 - \sigma_2}{6G_P} = \frac{1}{3G_P}\left[\sigma_3 - \frac{1}{2}(\sigma_1 + \sigma_2)\right] = \frac{1}{E_P}\left[\sigma_3 - \frac{1}{2}(\sigma_1 + \sigma_2)\right]$$

$$\tag{3-58}$$

The analogy is apparent between the right-hand side of Eqs. (3-58) and the familiar equations of elasticity expressing strain in terms of the principal stresses [Eqs. (2-23)]. For the plastic case, Poisson's ratio has been taken equal to $\frac{1}{2}$. E_P can be considered to be a *plastic modulus* that is actually a variable depending upon the stress and strain. The evaluation of E_P from an invariant stress-strain curve is shown in Fig. 3-6.

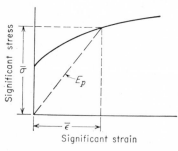

Fig. 3-6. Definition of E_p.

$$\frac{1}{E_P} = \frac{\bar{\epsilon}}{\bar{\sigma}} \tag{3-59}$$

Nadai[1] has developed relationships similar to Eqs. (3-58) based on the equality of Lode's stress and strain parameters. The fact that $\mu = \nu$ leads to the conclusion that the ratios of the principal shearing stresses to the principal shearing strains are equal,

---

[1] A. Nadai, "Plasticity," pp. 77–79, McGraw-Hill Book Company, Inc., New York, 1931.

and from these three relationships the equations can be derived. It is for this reason that relationships like Eqs. (3-58) are sometimes called Nadai's equations.

In a deformation theory, such as is given by the Hencky or Nádai equations, the total plastic strain is proportional to the stress deviator, while in a flow theory, such as is given by the Reuss equations, the increments of plastic strain are proportional to the stress deviator. The Hencky theory gives results in agreement with the incremental or flow theory provided that the principal axes of stress and strain remain coincident during the straining process and provided that proportional loading is maintained. The Hencky theory is not satisfactory for large deformations, but it is often used for small plastic strains because it offers certain mathematical conveniences.

3-11. Two-dimensional Plastic Flow—Plane Strain

In many practical problems, such as rolling and drawing, all displacements can be considered to be limited to the xy plane, so that strains in

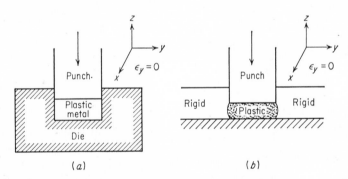

Fig. 3-7. Methods of developing plastic constraint.

the z direction can be neglected in the analysis. This is known as a condition of *plane strain*. When a problem is too difficult for an exact three-dimensional solution, a good indication of the deformation and forces required can often be obtained by consideration of the analogous plane-strain problem.

Since a plastic material tends to deform in all directions, to develop a plane-strain condition it is necessary to constrain the flow in one direction. Constraint can be produced by an external lubricated barrier, such as a die wall (Fig. 3-7a), or it can arise from a situation where only part of the material is deformed and the rigid material outside the plastic region prevents the spread of deformation (Fig. 3-7b).

Even though the strain in one of the principal directions is equal to zero for plane strain, it does not follow that there is zero stress in this direction. It can be shown[1] that for plane strain $\sigma_z = (\sigma_x + \sigma_y)/2$ or $\sigma_3 = (\sigma_1 + \sigma_2)/2$. If this value is substituted into the expression for the Von Mises criterion of yielding, the yield criterion for plane strain becomes

$$\sigma_1 - \sigma_2 = \frac{2}{\sqrt{3}}\sigma_0 = 1.15\sigma_0 \qquad (3\text{-}60)$$

The maximum-shear-stress criterion of yielding can be expressed by $\sigma_1 - \sigma_3 = \sigma_0 = 2k$. However, with the plane-strain condition defining the value of σ_3, the minimum principal stress will be σ_2 and the shear-stress criterion should be written

$$\sigma_1 - \sigma_2 = \sigma_0 = 2k \qquad (3\text{-}61)$$

In Eq. (3-61) k is the yield stress in pure shear. However, based on the Von Mises criterion of yielding the relationship between the tensile yield stress and the yield stress in shear [Eq. (3-21)] is given by $\sigma_0 = \sqrt{3}\,k$. Therefore, Eq. (3-60) becomes $\sigma_1 - \sigma_2 = 2k$. Thus, for plane-strain conditions, the two yield criteria are equivalent, and it can be considered that two-dimensional flow will occur when the shear stress reaches a critical value of k. Equation (3-61) is equally valid when written in terms of the stress deviator.

$$\sigma_1' - \sigma_2' = \sigma_0 = 2k \qquad (3\text{-}62)$$

3-12. Slip-field Theory

Consider a volume element in plane strain within a plastic region of a body. Figure 3-8a represents the two-dimensional state of stress with respect to arbitrary cartesian coordinates. It is possible to determine the principal planes such that the shear stresses vanish (Fig. 3-8b). The principal stresses are simply functions of the spherical component of stress, σ'', and the shearing stress k. k is a constant throughout the plastic region if strain hardening is neglected, but σ'' varies from point to point. The maximum shear stress will occur on planes 45° to the direction of the principal stresses. Thus, the critical shear stress k will first reach its value on these planes. This condition is shown in Fig. 3-8c, where it is seen that the maximum shear stress occurs in two orthogonal directions, designated α and β. These lines of maximum shear stress are called *slip lines*. The slip lines have the property that the shear strain is a maximum and the linear strain is zero tangent to their direction. However, it should be carefully noted that the slip lines just referred to

[1] O. Hoffman and G. Sachs, "Introduction to the Theory of Plasticity for Engineers," p. 118, McGraw-Hill Book Company, Inc., New York, 1953.

are not the slip lines, or slip bands, observed under the microscope on the surface of plastically deformed metal. This latter type of slip lines will be discussed more fully in the next chapter.

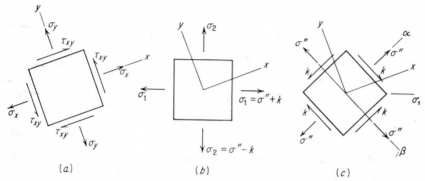

Fig. 3-8. Two-dimensional state of stress in plane strain.

By comparing Fig. 3-8b and c, it is seen that the principal stresses have a direction 45° to the slip lines. The values of the principal stresses can be determined if σ'' is known since

$$\sigma_1 = \sigma'' + k$$
$$\sigma_2 = \sigma'' - k$$

(3-63)

If σ'' is constant throughout the region, the slip lines will be straight lines.

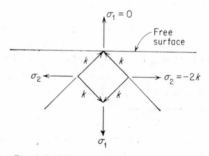

Fig. 3-9. Slip-line field at free surface.

However, if the slip lines curve by an angle ϕ, the following relationships hold:

$$\sigma'' + 2k\phi = \text{constant along } \alpha \text{ line}$$
$$\sigma'' - 2k\phi = \text{constant along } \beta \text{ line}$$

(3-64)

The slip lines at a free surface must make an angle of 45° with the surface (Fig. 3-9), since there can be no resultant tangential force at a free surface.   Since there is no resultant normal stress at a free surface, $\sigma_1 = 0$ and by Eqs. (3-63) $\sigma'' = -k$.   Therefore, $\sigma_2 = -2k$, and the transverse principal stress is compressive with a value of $2k$.

As a further example of the use of slip lines, consider the deformation of an ideal plastic metal by a flat punch.[1]   The friction between the face

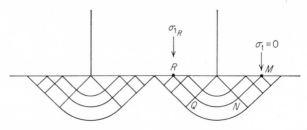

Fig. 3-10. Slip-line field produced by indentation of a punch.

of the punch and the metal is considered to be negligible.   Plastic deformation will first start at the corners of the punch and will result in a slip-line field such as is shown in Fig. 3-10.   Consider the point M. Since this is at a free surface, the normal stress is zero and $\sigma'' = k$.   In accordance with Eqs. (3-64), the equation of this slip line may be written $\sigma'' + 2k\phi = k$.   There is no change in the value of σ'' until we reach point N, where the slip line deviates from a straight line.   In going from N to Q, the slip line turns through an angle $\phi = -\pi/2$ so that its equation at point Q is $\sigma'' - 2k(\pi/2) = k$.   Since no further change takes place in ϕ in going to point R, the principal stress normal to the surface at R is

$$\sigma_{1_R} = \sigma'' + k = \left(k + 2k\frac{\pi}{2}\right) + k$$

or

$$\sigma_{1_R} = 2k\left(1 + \frac{\pi}{2}\right)$$

and

$$\sigma_{2_R} = 2k\frac{\pi}{2}$$

If we trace out any of the other slip lines, we shall find in the same way that the normal stress is $2k(1 + \pi/2)$.   Therefore, the pressure is uniform over the face of the punch and is equal to

$$\sigma_1 = 2k\left(1 + \frac{\pi}{2}\right) \tag{3-65}$$

[1] D. Tabor, "The Hardness of Metals," pp. 34–37, Oxford University Press, New York, 1951.

Since $k = \sigma_0/\sqrt{3}$,

$$\sigma_1 = \sigma_{max} = \frac{2\sigma_0}{\sqrt{3}}\left(1 + \frac{\pi}{2}\right) \approx 3\sigma_0 \qquad (3\text{-}66)$$

Thus, the theory predicts that full-scale plastic flow, with the resulting indentation, will occur when the stress across the face of the punch reaches three times the yield strength in tension.

The example described above is relatively simple and represents an overidealized situation. However, the method of slip fields, sometimes called the Hencky plastic-section method, is an important analytical tool for attacking difficult problems in plasticity. It has been used in the analysis of two-dimensional problems such as the yielding of a notched tensile bar[1] and the hot rolling of a slab.[2] Prager[3] and Thomsen[4] have given general procedures for constructing slip-line fields. However, there is no easy method of checking the validity of a solution. Partial experimental verification of theoretically determined slip-line fields has been obtained for mild steel by etching techniques[5] which delineate the plastically deformed regions.

BIBLIOGRAPHY

Hill, R.: "The Mathematical Theory of Plasticity," Oxford University Press, New York, 1950.

Hoffman, O., and G. Sachs: "Introduction to the Theory of Plasticity for Engineers," McGraw-Hill Book Company, Inc., New York, 1953.

Nadai, A.: "Theory of Flow and Fracture of Solids," 2d ed., vol. I, McGraw-Hill Book Company, Inc., New York, 1950.

Phillips, A.: "Introduction to Plasticity," The Ronald Press Company, New York, 1956.

Prager, W.: "An Introduction to Plasticity," Addison-Wesley Publishing Company, Reading, Mass., 1959.

—— and P. G. Hodge, Jr.: "Theory of Perfectly Plastic Solids," John Wiley & Sons, Inc., New York, 1951.

[1] R. Hill, *Quart. J. Mech. Appl. Math*, vol. 1, pp. 40–52, 1949.

[2] J. M. Alexander, *Proc. Inst. Mech. Engrs.*, *(London)*, vol. 169, pp. 1021–1030, 1955.

[3] W. Prager, *Trans. Roy. Inst. Technol.*, *Stockholm*, no. 65, 1953.

[4] E. G. Thomsen, *J. Appl. Mech.*, vol. 24, pp. 81–84, 1957.

[5] B. B. Hundy, *Metallurgia*, vol. 49, no. 293, pp. 109–118, 1954.

Part Two

METALLURGICAL FUNDAMENTALS

Chapter 4
PLASTIC DEFORMATION
OF SINGLE CRYSTALS

4-1. Introduction

The previous three chapters have been concerned with the phenomenological description of the elastic and plastic behavior of metals. It has been shown that formal mathematical theories have been developed for describing the mechanical behavior of metals based upon the simplifying assumptions that metals are homogeneous and isotropic. That this is not true should be obvious to anyone who has examined the structure of metals under a microscope. However, for fine-grained metals subjected to static loads within the elastic range the theories are perfectly adequate for design. Within the plastic range the theories describe the observed behavior, although not with the precision which is frequently desired. For conditions of dynamic and impact loading we are forced, in general, to rely heavily on experimentally determined data. As the assumption that we are dealing with an isotropic homogeneous medium becomes less tenable, our ability to predict the behavior of metals under stress by means of the theories of elasticity and plasticity decreases.

Following the discovery of the diffraction of X rays by metallic crystals by Von Laue in 1912 and the realization that metals were fundamentally composed of atoms arranged in specific geometric lattices there have been a great many investigations of the relationships between atomic structure and the plastic behavior of metals. Much of the fundamental work on the plastic deformation of metals has been performed with single-crystal specimens, so as to eliminate the complicating effects of grain boundaries and the restraints imposed by neighboring grains and second-phase particles. Techniques for preparing single crystals have been described in a number of sources.[1-3]

[1] R. W. K. Honeycombe, *Met. Reviews*, vol. 4, no. 13, pp. 1–47, 1959.
[2] A. N. Holden, *Trans. ASM*, vol. 42, pp. 319–346, 1950.
[3] W. D. Lawson and S. Nielsen, "Preparation of Single Crystals," Academic Press, Inc., New York, 1958.

The basic mechanisms of plastic deformation in single crystals will be discussed in this chapter.   This subject will be extended in the next chapter to a consideration of plastic deformation in polycrystalline specimens. Primary consideration will be given to tensile deformation.   The fundamental deformation behavior in creep and fatigue will be covered in chapters specifically devoted to these subjects.   The dislocation theory, which plays such an important part in present-day concepts of plastic deformation, will be introduced in this chapter to the extent needed to provide a qualitative understanding of modern concepts of plastic deformation.   A more detailed consideration of dislocation theory will be found in Chap. 6.   This will be followed by a chapter on the fundamental aspects of fracture and a chapter on internal friction and anelastic effects.

4-2. Concepts of Crystal Geometry

X-ray diffraction analysis shows that the atoms in a metal crystal are arranged in a regular, repeated three-dimensional pattern.   The atom arrangement of metals is most simply portrayed by a crystal lattice in which the atoms are visualized as hard balls located at particular locations in a geometrical arrangement.

The most elementary crystal structure is the simple cubic lattice (Fig. 4-1).   This is the type of structure cell found for ionic crystals, such as NaCl and LiF, but not for any of the metals.   Three mutually perpendicular axes are arbitrarily placed through one of the corners of the cell. Crystallographic planes and directions will be specified with respect to these axes in terms of *Miller indices*. A crystallographic plane is specified in terms of the length of its intercepts on the three axes, measured from the origin of the coordinate axes. To simplify the crystallographic formulas, the reciprocals of these intercepts are used.   They are reduced to a lowest common denominator to give the Miller indices (hkl) of the plane.   For example, the plane $ABCD$ in Fig. 4-1 is parallel to the x and z axes and intersects the y axis at one interatomic distance a_0.   Therefore, the indices of the plane are $1/\infty, 1/1, 1/\infty$, or $(hkl) = (010)$.   Plane $EBCF$ would be designated as the $(\bar{1}00)$ plane, since the origin of the coordinate system can be moved to G because every point in a space

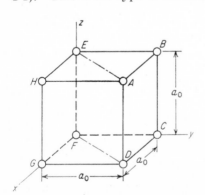

Fig. 4-1. Simple cubic structure.

lattice has the same arrangement of points as every other point. The bar over one of the integers indicates that the plane intersects one of the axes in a negative direction. There are six crystallographically equivalent planes of the type (100), any one of which can have the indices (100), (010), (001), ($\overline{1}$00), (0$\overline{1}$0), (00$\overline{1}$) depending upon the choice of axes. The notation {100} is used when they are to be considered as a group, or *family of planes.*

Crystallographic directions are indicated by integers in brackets: [uvw]. Reciprocals are not used in determining directions. As an example, the direction of the line FD is obtained by moving out from the origin a distance a_0 along the x axis and moving an equal distance in the positive y direction. The indices of this direction are then [110]. A family of crystallographically equivalent directions would be designated $\langle uvw \rangle$. For the cubic lattice only, a direction is always perpendicular to the plane having the same indices.

Many of the common metals have either a body-centered cubic (bcc) or face-centered cubic (fcc) crystal structure. Figure 4-2a shows a body-centered cubic structure cell with an atom at each corner and another atom at the body center of the cube. Each corner atom is surrounded by eight adjacent atoms, as is the atom located at the center of the cell.

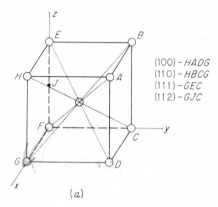

(100) – *HADG*
(110) – *HBCG*
(111) – *GEC*
(112) – *GJC*

(*a*)

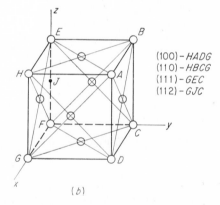

(100) – *HADG*
(110) – *HBCG*
(111) – *GEC*
(112) – *GJC*

(*b*)

Fig. 4-2. (*a*) Body-centered cubic structure; (*b*) face-centered cubic structure.

Therefore, there are two atoms *per structure cell* for the body-centered cubic structure ($\frac{8}{8} + 1$). Typical metals which have this crystal structure are alpha iron, columbium, tantalum, chromium, molybdenum, and tungsten. Figure 4-2b shows the structure cell for a face-centered cubic crystal structure. In addition to an atom at each corner, there is an atom at the center of each of the cube faces. Since these latter atoms belong to two unit cells, there are four atoms per structure cell in the face-centered cubic structure ($\frac{8}{8} + \frac{6}{2}$). Aluminum, copper, gold, lead, silver, and nickel are common face-centered cubic metals.

The third common metallic crystal structure is the hexagonal close-packed (hcp) structure (Fig. 4-3). In order to specify planes and directions in the hcp structure, it is convenient to use the Miller-Bravais system with four indices of the type $(hkil)$. These indices are based on four axes; the three axes a_1, a_2, a_3 are 120° apart in the basal plane, and the vertical c axis is normal to the basal plane. These axes and typical planes in the hcp crystal structure are given in Fig. 4-3. The third index is related to the first two by the relation $i = -(h + k)$.

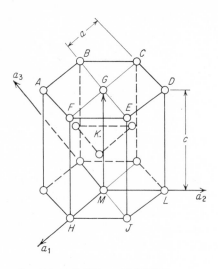

Basal plane (0001) − $ABCDEF$
Prism plane (10$\bar{1}$0) − $FEJH$
Pyramidal planes
    Type I, Order 1 (10$\bar{1}$1) − GHJ
    Type I, Order 2 (10$\bar{1}$2) − KJH
    Type II, Order 1 (11$\bar{2}$1) − GHL
    Type II, Order 2 (11$\bar{2}$2) − KHL
Digonal axis [11$\bar{2}$0] − FGC

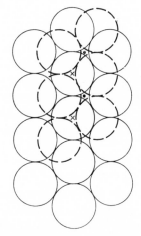

Fig. 4-3. Hexagonal close-packed structure.

Fig. 4-4. Stacking of close-packed spheres.

The face-centered cubic and hexagonal close-packed structures can both be built up from a stacking of close-packed planes of spheres. Figure 4-4 shows that there are two ways in which the spheres can be stacked. The first layer of spheres is arranged so that each sphere is surrounded by and just touching six other spheres. This corresponds to the solid circles in Fig. 4-4. A second layer of close-packed spheres can be placed over the bottom layer so that the centers of the atoms in the second plane cover one-half the number of valleys in the bottom layer (dashed circles in Fig. 4-4). There are two ways of adding spheres to give a third close-packed plane. Although the spheres in the third layer must fit into the valleys in the second plane, they may lie either over the valleys not covered in the first plane (the dots in Fig. 4-4) or directly above the atoms in the first plane (the crosses in Fig. 4-4). The first possibility results in a stacking sequence $ABCABC \cdots$, which is found for the

{111} planes of an fcc structure. The other possibility results in the stacking sequence $ABAB \cdots$, which is found for the (0001) basal plane of the hcp structure. For the ideal hcp packing, the ratio of c/a is $\sqrt{8/3}$, or 1.633. Table 4-1 shows that actual hcp metals deviate from the ideal c/a ratio.

TABLE 4-1
AXIAL RATIOS OF SOME HEXAGONAL METALS

Metal	c/a
Be	1.568
Ti	1.587
Mg	1.623
Ideal hcp	1.633
Zn	1.856
Cd	1.886

The fcc and hcp structures are both close-packed structures. Seventy-four per cent of the volume of the unit cell is occupied by atoms, on a hard sphere model, in the fcc and hcp structures. This is contrasted with 68 per cent packing for a bcc unit cell and 52 per cent of the volume occupied by atoms in the simple cubic unit cell.

Plastic deformation is generally confined to the low-index planes, which have a higher density of atoms per unit area than the high-index planes. Table 4-2 lists the atomic density per unit area for the common low-index planes. Note that the planes of greatest atomic density also are the most widely spaced planes for the crystal structure.

TABLE 4-2
ATOMIC DENSITY OF LOW-INDEX PLANES

Crystal structure	Plane	Atomic density, atoms per unit area	Distance between planes
Face-centered cubic	Octahedral {111}	$4/\sqrt{3}\ a_0^2$	$a_0/\sqrt{3}$
	Cube {100}	$2/a_0^2$	$a_0/2$
	Dodecahedral {110}	$2/\sqrt{2}\ a_0^2$	$a_0/2\ \sqrt{2}$
Body-centered cubic	Dodecahedral {110}	$2/\sqrt{2}\ a_0^2$	$a_0/\sqrt{2}$
	Cube {100}	$1/a_0^2$	$a_0/2$
	Octahedral {111}	$1/\sqrt{3}\ a_0^2$	$a_0/2\ \sqrt{3}$
Hexagonal close-packed	Basal {0001}	$1/3\ \sqrt{3}\ a_0^2$	c

4-3. Lattice Defects

Real crystals deviate from the perfect periodicity that was assumed in the previous section in a number of important ways. While the concept of the perfect lattice is adequate for explaining the *structure-insensitive* properties of metals, for a better understanding of the *structure-sensitive* properties it has been necessary to consider a number of types of lattice defects. The description of the structure-sensitive properties then reduces itself largely to describing the behavior of these defects.

Structure-insensitive	*Structure-sensitive*
Elastic constants	Electrical conductivity
Melting point	Semiconductor properties
Density	Yield stress
Specific heat	Fracture strength
Coefficient of thermal expansion	Creep strength

As is suggested by the above brief tabulation, practically all the mechanical properties are structure-sensitive properties. Only since the realization of this fact, in relatively recent times, have really important advances been made in understanding the mechanical behavior of materials.

The term *defect*, or *imperfection*, is generally used to describe any deviation from an orderly array of lattice points. When the deviation from the periodic arrangement of the lattice is localized to the vicinity of only a few atoms it is called a *point defect*, or *point imperfection*. However, if the defect extends through microscopic regions of the crystal, it is called a *lattice imperfection*. Lattice imperfections may be divided into *line defects* and *surface*, or *plane*, *defects*. Line defects obtain their name because they propagate as lines or as a two-dimensional net in the crystal. The edge and screw dislocations that are discussed in this section are the common line defects encountered in metals. Surface defects arise from the clustering of line defects into a plane. Low-angle boundaries and grain boundaries are surface defects (see Chap. 5). The *stacking fault* between two close-packed regions of the crystal that have alternate stacking sequences (Sec. 4-10) is also a surface defect.

Point Defects

Figure 4-5 illustrates three types of point defects. A *vacancy*, or vacant lattice site,[1] exists when an atom is missing from a normal lattice position (Fig. 4-5a). In pure metals, small numbers of vacancies are created by thermal excitation, and these are thermodynamically stable at temperatures greater than absolute zero. At equilibrium, the fraction of lattices that are vacant at a given temperature is given approximately by the equation

$$\frac{n}{N} = \exp \frac{-E_s}{kT} \tag{4-1}$$

[1] "Vacancies and Other Point Defects," Institute of Metals, London, 1958.

where n is the number of vacant sites in N sites and E_s is the energy required to move an atom from the interior of a crystal to its surface. Table 4-3 illustrates how the fraction of vacant lattice sites in a metal increases rapidly with temperature. By rapid quenching from close to the melting point, it is possible to trap in a greater than equilibrium

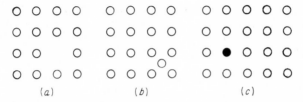

Fig. 4-5. Point defects.   (a) Vacancy; (b) interstitial; (c) impurity atom.

number of vacancies at room temperature. Higher than equilibrium concentrations of vacancies can also be produced by extensive plastic deformation (cold work) or as the result of bombardment with high-energy nuclear particles. When the density of vacancies becomes relatively large, it is possible for them to cluster together to form voids.

TABLE 4-3
EQUILIBRIUM VACANCIES IN A METAL

Temperature, °C	Approximate fraction of vacant lattice sites
500	1×10^{-10}
1000	1×10^{-5}
1500	5×10^{-4}
2000	3×10^{-3}

$$E_s \approx 1 \text{ ev}$$

An atom that is trapped inside the crystal at a point intermediate between normal lattice positions is called an *interstitial atom*, or interstitialcy (Fig. 4-5b). The interstitial defect occurs in pure metals as a result of bombardment with high-energy nuclear particles (radiation damage), but it does not occur frequently as a result of thermal activation.

The presence of an *impurity atom* at a lattice position (Fig. 4-5c) or at an interstitial position results in a local disturbance of the periodicity of the lattice, the same as for vacancies and interstitials.

Line Defects—Dislocations

The most important two-dimensional, or line, defect is the *dislocation*. The dislocation is the defect responsible for the phenomenon of slip, by which most metals deform plastically. Therefore, one way of thinking about a dislocation is to consider that it is the region of localized lattice disturbance separating the slipped and unslipped regions of a crystal. In Fig. 4-6, AB represents a dislocation lying in the slip plane, which is the plane of the paper. It is assumed that slip is advancing to the right. All the atoms above area C have been displaced one atomic distance in the slip direction; the atoms above D have not yet slipped. AB is then the boundary between the slipped and unslipped regions. It is shown

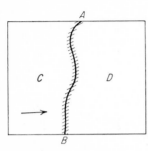

shaded to indicate that for a few atomic distances on each side of the dislocation line there is a region of atomic disorder in which the slip distance is between zero and one atomic spacing. As the dislocation moves, slip occurs in the area over which it moves. In the absence of obstacles, a dislocation can move easily on the application of only a small force; this helps explain why real crystals deform much more readily than would be expected for a crystal with a perfect lattice.

Fig. 4-6. A dislocation in a slip plane.

Not only are dislocations important for explaining the slip of crystals, but they are also intimately connected with nearly all other mechanical phenomena such as strain hardening, the yield point, creep, fatigue, and brittle fracture.

The two basic types of dislocations are the edge dislocation and the screw dislocation. The simplest type of dislocation, which was originally suggested by Orowan, Polanyi, and Taylor, is called the *edge dislocation*, or Taylor-Orowan dislocation. Figure 4-7 shows the slip that produces an edge dislocation for an element of crystal having a simple cubic lattice. Slip has occurred in the direction of the slip vector over the area $ABCD$. The boundary between the right-hand slipped part of the crystal and the left-hand part which has not yet slipped is the line AD, the edge dislocation. Note that the parts of the crystal above the slip plane have been displaced, in the direction of slip, with respect to the part of the crystal below the slip plane by an amount indicated by the shaded area in Fig. 4-7. All points in the crystal which were originally coincident across the slip plane have been displaced relative to each other by this same amount. The amount of displacement is equal to the *Burgers vector* **b** of the dislocation. For a pure edge dislocation such as is shown here, the magnitude of the Burgers vector is equal to the atomic spacing. A defining characteristic of an edge dislocation is that its Burgers vector is always perpendicular to the dislocation line.

Although the exact arrangement of atoms along AD is not known, it is generally agreed that Fig. 4-8 closely represents the atomic arrangement in a plane normal to the edge dislocation AD. The plane of the paper in this figure corresponds to a (100) plane in a simple cubic lattice and is equivalent to any plane parallel to the front face of Fig. 4-7. Note that the lattice is distorted in the region of the dislocation. There is one more vertical row of atoms above the slip plane than below it. The atomic arrangement results in a compressive stress above the slip plane and a tensile stress below the slip plane. An edge dislocation with the extra plane of atoms above the slip plane, as in Fig. 4-8, is called by convention a *positive edge dislocation* and is frequently indicated by the symbol ⊥.

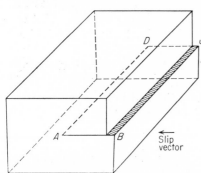

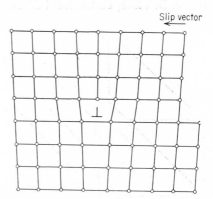

Fig. 4-7. Edge dislocation produced by slip in a simple cubic lattice. Dislocation lies along AD, perpendicular to slip direction. Slip has occurred over area $ABCD$. (*W. T. Read, Jr., "Dislocations in Crystals," p. 2, McGraw-Hill Book Company, Inc., New York, 1953.*)

Fig. 4-8. Atomic arrangement in a plane normal to an edge dislocation. (*W. T. Read, Jr., "Dislocations in Crystals," p. 3, McGraw-Hill Book Company, Inc., New York, 1953.*)

If the extra plane of atoms lies below the slip plane, the dislocation is a negative edge dislocation, ⊤.

A pure edge dislocation can glide or slip in a direction perpendicular to its length. However, it may move vertically by a process known as *climb*, if diffusion of atoms or vacancies can take place at an appreciable rate. Consider Fig. 4-8. For the edge dislocation to move upward (positive direction of climb), it is necessary to remove the extra atom directly over the symbol ⊥ or to add a vacancy to this spot. One such atom would have to be removed for every atomic spacing that the dislocation climbs. Conversely, if the dislocation moved down, atoms would have to be added. Atoms could be removed from the extra plane of atoms by the extra atom interacting with a lattice vacancy. Atoms are added to the extra plane for negative climb by the diffusion of an atom from the surrounding crystal, creating a vacancy. Since movement by climb is diffusion-controlled, motion is much slower than in glide and less likely except at high temperatures.

The second basic type of dislocation is the *screw*, or Burgers, dislocation. Figure 4-9 shows a simple example of a screw dislocation. The upper part of the crystal to the right of AD has moved relative to the lower part in the direction of the slip vector. No slip has taken place to the left of AD, and therefore AD is a dislocation line. Thus, the dislocation line is parallel to its Burgers vector, or slip vector, and by definition this must be a screw dislocation. Consider the trace of a circuit around the dislocation line, on the front face of the crystal. Starting at X and completing the circuit, we arrive at X', one atomic plane behind that containing X. In making this circuit we have traced the path of a right-handed screw. Every time a circuit is made around the dislocation line, the end point is displaced one plane parallel to the slip plane in the lattice. Therefore, the atomic planes are arranged around the dislocation in a spiral staircase or screw.

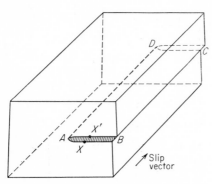

Fig. 4-9. Slip that produces a screw dislocation in a simple cubic lattice. Dislocation lies along AD, parallel to slip direction. Slip has occurred over the area $ABCD$. (*W. T. Read, Jr., "Dislocations in Crystals," p. 15, McGraw-Hill Book Company, Inc., New York, 1953.*)

The arrangement of atoms (in two dimensions) around a screw dislocation in a simple cubic lattice is shown in Fig. 4-10. In this figure we are looking down on the slip plane in Fig. 4-9. The open circles represent atoms just above the slip plane, and the solid circles are atoms just below the slip plane. A screw dislocation does not have a preferred slip plane, as an edge dislocation has, and therefore the motion of a screw dislocation is less restricted than the motion of an edge dislocation. However, movement by climb is not possible with a screw dislocation.

For the present, the discussion of dislocations will be limited to the geometrical concepts presented in this section. After a more complete discussion of the plastic deformation of single crystals and polycrystalline specimens, we shall return to a detailed discussion of dislocation theory in Chap. 6. Among the topics covered will be the effect of crystal structure on dislocation geometry, the experimental evidence for dislocations, and the interaction between dislocations.

4-4. Deformation by Slip

The usual method of plastic deformation in metals is by the sliding of blocks of the crystal over one another along definite crystallographic planes, called *slip planes*. As a very crude approximation, the slip, or glide, of a crystal can be considered analogous to the distortion produced in a deck of cards when it is pushed from one end. Figure 4-11 illustrates this classical picture of slip. In Fig. 4-11*a*, a shear stress is applied

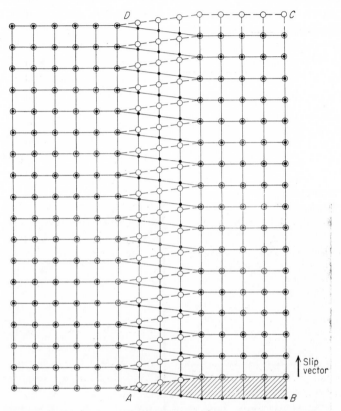

Fig. 4-10. Atomic arrangement around the screw dislocation shown in Fig. 4-9. The plane of the figure is parallel to the slip plane. *ABCD* is the slipped area, and *AD* is the screw dislocation. Open circles represent atoms in the atomic plane just above the slip plane, and the solid circles are atoms in the plane just below the slip plane. (*W. T. Read, Jr., "Dislocations in Crystals," p. 17, McGraw-Hill, Book Company, Inc., New York,* 1953.)

to a metal cube with a top polished surface. Slip occurs when the shear stress exceeds a critical value. The atoms move an integral number of atomic distances along the slip plane, and a step is produced in the polished surface (Fig. 4-11*b*). When we view the polished surface from above with a microscope, the step shows up as a line, which we call a *slip line*. If the surface is then repolished after slip has occurred, so that the step is removed, the slip line will disappear (Fig. 4-11*c*). The single crystal is still a single crystal after slip has taken place provided that the deformation was uniform.   Note that slip lines are due to changes in surface elevation and that the surface must be suitably prepared for

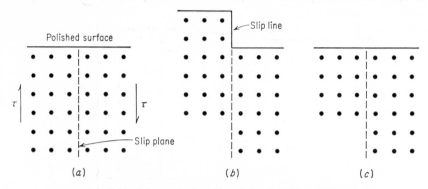

Fig. 4-11. Schematic drawing of classical idea of slip.

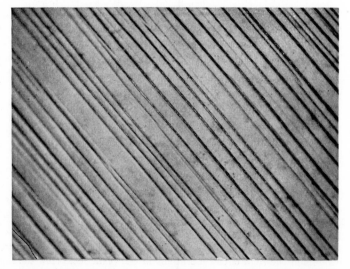

Fig. 4-12. Straight slip lines in copper, 500×.   (*Courtesy W. L. Phillips.*)

microscopic observation prior to deformation if the slip lines are to be observed.   Figure 4-12 shows straight slip lines in copper.

The fine structure of slip lines has been studied at high magnification by means of the electron microscope.   What appears as a line, or at best a narrow band, at 1,500 diameters' magnification in the optical microscope can be resolved by the electron microscope as discrete slip lamellae at 20,000 diameters, shown schematically in Fig. 4-13.   The situation where there are many slip lamellae comprising the slip band is found for aluminum and copper, but in alpha brass there is only one slip line, even when viewed at high magnification.

Slip occurs most readily in specific directions on certain crystallographic planes. Generally the slip plane is the plane of greatest atomic density (Table 4-2), and the slip direction is the closest-packed direction within the slip plane. Since the planes of greatest atomic density are also the most widely spaced planes in the crystal structure, the resistance to slip is generally less for these planes than for any other set of planes. The slip plane together with the slip direction establishes the *slip system*.

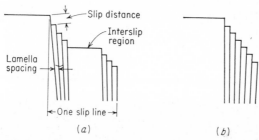

Fig. 4-13. Schematic drawing of the fine structure of a slip band. (*a*) Small deformation; (*b*) large deformation.

In the hexagonal close-packed metals, the only plane with high atomic density is the basal plane (0001). The digonal axes $\langle 11\bar{2}0 \rangle$ are the close-packed directions. For zinc, cadmium, magnesium, and cobalt slip occurs on the (0001) plane in the $\langle 11\bar{2}0 \rangle$ directions.[1] Since there is only one basal plane per unit cell and three $\langle 11\bar{2}0 \rangle$ directions, the hcp structure possesses three slip systems. The limited number of slip systems is the reason for the extreme orientation dependence of ductility in hcp crystals.

In the face-centered cubic structure, the {111} octahedral planes and the $\langle 110 \rangle$ directions are the close-packed systems. There are eight {111} planes in the fcc unit cell. However, the planes at opposite corners of the cube are parallel to each other, so that there are only four *sets* of octahedral planes. Each {111} plane contains three $\langle 110 \rangle$ directions (the reverse directions being neglected). Therefore, the fcc lattice has 12 possible slip systems.

The bcc structure is not a close-packed structure like the fcc or hcp structures. Accordingly, there is no one plane of predominant atomic density, as (111) in the fcc structure and (0001) in the hcp structure. The {110} planes have the highest atomic density in the bcc structure,

---

[1] Zirconium and titanium, which have low c/a ratios, slip primarily on the prism and pyramidal planes in the $\langle 11\bar{2}0 \rangle$ direction.

but they are not greatly superior in this respect to several other planes. However, in the bcc structure the ⟨111⟩ direction is just as close-packed as the ⟨110⟩ and ⟨11$\bar{2}$0⟩ directions in the fcc and hcp structures.   Therefore, the bcc metals obey the general rule that the slip direction is the close-packed direction, but they differ from most other metals by not having a definite single slip plane.   Slip in bcc metals is found to occur on the {110}, {112}, and {123} planes, while the slip direction is always the [111] direction.   There are 48 possible slip systems, but since the

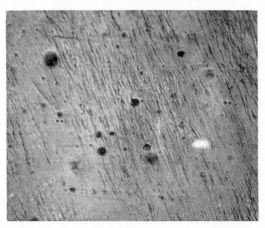

Fig. 4-14. Wavy slip lines in alpha iron, 150×.   (*Courtesy J. J. Cox.*)

planes are not so close-packed as in the fcc structure, higher shearing stresses are usually required to cause slip.

Slip in bcc alpha iron has been particularly well studied.[1]   It has been concluded that the slip plane in alpha iron may occupy any position in the [111] zone, its position being determined by the orientation of the stress axis with respect to the crystal axis and the variation in the shearing strengths of the planes in the slip zone.   These studies have shown that observed deviations from the low-index planes {110}, {112}, and {123} are real effects, which supports the belief that slip in alpha iron is noncrystallographic.   Further evidence for noncrystallographic slip is the fact that slip lines in alpha iron are wavy[2] (Fig. 4-14).

Certain metals show additional slip systems with increased temper-

---

[1] F. L. Vogel and R. M. Brick, *Trans. AIME*, vol. 197, p. 700, 1958; R. P. Steijn and R. M. Brick, *Trans. ASM*, vol. 46, pp. 1406–1448, 1954; J. J. Cox, G. T. Horne, and R. F. Mehl, *Trans. ASM*, vol. 49, 118–131, 1957.

[2] J. R. Low and R. W. Guard, *Acta Met.*, vol. 7, pp. 171–179, 1959, have shown that curved slip lines are produced in iron by screw components of the dislocation loop but that the slip lines are straight when viewed normal to the edge component of the dislocation.

ature. Aluminum deforms on 'he {100} plane at elevated temperature, while in magnesium the {10$\bar{1}$1} pyramidal plane plays an important role in deformation by slip above 225°C. In all cases the slip direction remains the same when the slip plane changes with temperature.

4-5. Slip in a Perfect Lattice

If slip is assumed to occur by the translation of one plane of atoms over another, it is possible to make a reasonable estimate[1] of the shear

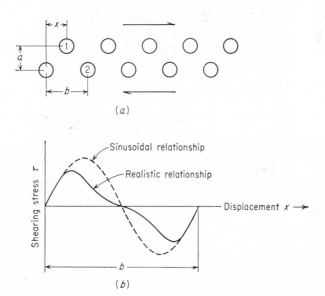

Fig. 4-15. (a) Shear displacement of one plane of atoms over another atomic plane; (b) variation of shearing stress with displacement in slip direction.

stress required for such a movement in a perfect lattice. Consider two planes of atoms subjected to a homogeneous shear stress (Fig. 4-15). The shear stress is assumed to act in the slip plane along the slip direction. The distance between atoms in the slip direction is b, and the spacing between adjacent lattice planes is a. The shear stress causes a displacement x in the slip direction between the pair of adjacent lattice planes. The shearing stress is initially zero when the two planes are in coincidence, and it is also zero when the two planes have moved one identity distance b, so that point 1 in the top plane is over point 2 on the bottom plane. The shearing stress is also zero when the atoms of the top plane are midway between those of the bottom plane, since this is a

[1] J. Frenkel, *Z. Physik*, vol. 37, p. 572, 1926.

symmetry position. Between these positions each atom is attracted toward the nearest atom of the other row, so that the shearing stress is a periodic function of the displacement.

As a first approximation, the relationship between shear stress and displacement can be expressed by a sine function

$$\tau = \tau_m \sin \frac{2\pi x}{b} \tag{4-2}$$

where τ_m is the amplitude of the sine wave and b is the period. At small values of displacement, Hooke's law should apply.

$$\tau = G\gamma = \frac{Gx}{a} \tag{4-3}$$

For small values of x/b, Eq. (4-2) can be written

$$\tau \approx \tau_m \frac{2\pi x}{b} \tag{4-4}$$

Combining Eqs. (4-3) and (4-4) provides an expression for the maximum shear stress at which slip should occur.

$$\tau_m = \frac{G}{2\pi} \frac{b}{a} \tag{4-5}$$

As a rough approximation, b can be taken equal to a, with the result that the theoretical shear strength of a perfect crystal is approximately equal to the shear modulus divided by 2π.

$$\tau_m \approx \frac{G}{2\pi} \tag{4-6}$$

The shear modulus for metals is in the range 10^6 to 10^7 psi (10^{11} to 10^{12} dynes/cm^2). Therefore, Eq. (4-6) predicts that the theoretical shear stress will be in the range 10^5 to 10^6 psi, while actual values of the shear stress required to produce plastic deformation are in the range 10^2 to 10^4 psi. Even if more refined calculations are used to correct the sine-wave assumption, the value of τ_m cannot be reduced by more than a factor of 5 from the value predicted by Eq. (4-6). Thus, it seems reasonable to expect that the theoretical shear strength of most metals lies between $G/10$ and $G/50$. This is still at least 100 times greater than the observed shear strengths of metal crystals. It can only be concluded that a mechanism other than the bodily shearing of planes of atoms is responsible for slip. In the next section, it is shown that dislocations provide such a mechanism.

4-6. Slip by Dislocation Movement

The concept of the dislocation was first introduced to explain the discrepancy between the observed and theoretical shear strengths of metals. For the concept to be useful in this field, it is necessary to demonstrate (1) that the passage of a dislocation through a crystal lattice requires far less than the theoretical shear stress and (2) that the movement of the dislocation through the lattice produces a step, or slip band, at the free surface.

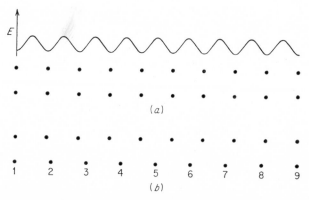

Fig. 4-16. Schematic diagram illustrating the fact that a dislocation moves easily through a crystal lattice. (a) Energy field in perfect crystal lattice; (b) lattice containing an edge dislocation. (*F. Seitz, "The Physics of Metals," p.* 91, *McGraw-Hill Book Company, Inc., New York,* 1943.)

To illustrate that the stress required to move a dislocation through a crystal is very low compared with the theoretical shear stress, we shall use Fig. 4-16. Figure 4-16a represents the atoms in two adjacent planes in a perfect crystal lattice which does not contain a dislocation. The top curve of the figure represents schematically the energy of an atom in the lower plane of atoms as a function of its position relative to the upper plane. For the normal arrangement of a perfect crystal, all the atoms in the lower plane are at minimum positions in the energy curve. Therefore, if the top row of atoms is displaced toward the right relative to the bottom row, each atom encounters the same force opposing the displacement. This is the situation described in Sec. 4-5. Now consider the situation when the crystal contains a dislocation (Fig. 4-16b). This illustrates a positive edge dislocation, with the extra plane of atoms between 4 and 5. The atoms at large distances from the center of the dislocation are at positions corresponding to the minimum of the energy curve; the atoms at the center are not. Now consider pairs of atoms, for example,

4 and 5, 3 and 6, etc., located symmetrically on opposite sides of the center of the dislocation. They encounter forces which are equal and opposite. As a result, if the atoms near the center of the dislocation are displaced by equal distances, one-half will encounter forces opposing the motion and one-half will encounter forces which assist the motion. Therefore, to a first approximation, the net work required to produce

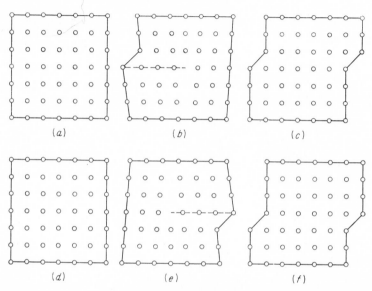

Fig. 4-17. Movement of edge dislocation in a simple cubic lattice. *(G. I. Taylor, Proc. Roy. Soc. (London), vol. 145A, p. 369, 1934.)*

the displacement is zero, and the stress required to move the dislocation one atomic distance is very small.

The lattice offers essentially no resistance to the motion of a dislocation *only* when the dislocation lies at a position of symmetry with respect to the atoms in the slip plane. In general, a small force, the Peierls-Nabarro force, is needed to drive a dislocation through the lattice. While it is well established that the value of the Peierls-Nabarro force is much smaller than the theoretical shear stress for a perfect lattice, the accurate calculation of this force is difficult because it depends strongly on the relatively uncertain atomic arrangement at the center of a dislocation.

Figure 4-17, based on the original work by Taylor,[1] illustrates that the movement of a dislocation results in a surface step, or slip band. The top series of sketches shows a positive edge dislocation moving to the right in a simple cubic lattice. The slip plane is shown dashed. When the dislocation reaches the right side of the crystal, assumed to be a free surface,

[1] G. I. Taylor, *Proc. Roy. Soc. (London)*, vol. 145A, p. 362, 1934.

it produces a shift with respect to the planes on each side of the slip plane of one Burgers vector, or one atomic distance for the simple cubic lattice. The bottom series of sketches shows that the same surface step is produced by the movement of a negative edge dislocation to the left.

4-7. Critical Resolved Shear Stress for Slip

The extent of slip in a single crystal depends on the magnitude of the shearing stress produced by external loads, the geometry of the crystal structure, and the orientation of the active slip planes with respect to the shearing stresses. Slip begins when the shearing stress on the slip plane in the slip direction reaches a threshold value called the *critical resolved shear stress*. This value[1] is really the single-crystal equivalent of the yield stress of an ordinary stress-strain curve. The value of the critical resolved shear stress depends chiefly on composition and temperature.

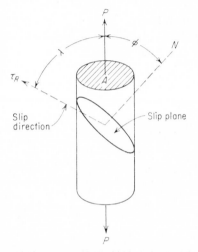

Fig. 4-18. Diagram for calculating critical resolved shear stress.

The fact that different tensile loads are required to produce slip in single crystals of different orientation can be rationalized by a critical resolved shear stress; this was first recognized by Schmid.[2] To calculate the critical resolved shear stress from a single crystal tested in tension, it is necessary to know, from X-ray diffraction, the orientation with respect to the tensile axis of the plane on which slip first appears and the slip direction. Consider a cylindrical single crystal with cross-sectional area A (Fig. 4-18). The angle between the *normal* to the slip plane and the tensile axis is ϕ, and the angle which the slip direction makes with the tensile axis is λ. The area of the slip plane inclined at the angle ϕ will be $A/\cos \phi$, and the component of the axial load acting in the slip plane in the slip direction is $P \cos \lambda$. Therefore, the critical resolved shear stress is given by

$$\tau_R = \frac{P \cos \lambda}{A/(\cos \phi)} = \frac{P}{A} \cos \phi \cos \lambda \qquad (4\text{-}7)$$

---

[1] In practice it is very difficult to determine the stress at which the first slip bands are produced. In most cases, the critical shear stress is obtained by the intersection of the extrapolated elastic and plastic regions of the stress-strain curve.

[2] E. Schmid, *Z. Elektrochem.*, vol. 37, p. 447, 1931.

The law of the critical resolved shear stress, also known as Schmid's law, is best demonstrated with hcp metals, where the limited number of slip systems allows large differences in orientation between the slip plane and the tensile axis (see Prob. 4-8). In fcc metals the high symmetry results in so many equivalent slip systems that it is possible to get a

TABLE 4-4

ROOM-TEMPERATURE SLIP SYSTEMS AND CRITICAL RESOLVED SHEAR STRESS
FOR METAL SINGLE CRYSTALS

Metal	Crystal structure	Purity, %	Slip plane	Slip direction	Critical shear stress, g/mm^2	Ref.
Zn.............	hcp	99.999	(0001)	[11$\bar{2}$0]	18	a
Mg.............	hcp	99.996	(0001)	[11$\bar{2}$0]	77	b
Cd.............	hcp	99.996	(0001)	[11$\bar{2}$0]	58	c
Ti.............	hcp	99.99	(10$\bar{1}$0)	[11$\bar{2}$0]	1,400	d
		99.9	(10$\bar{1}$0)	[11$\bar{2}$0]	9,190	d
Ag.............	fcc	99.99	(111)	[110]	48	e
		99.97	(111)	[110]	73	e
		99.93	(111)	[110]	131	e
Cu.............	fcc	99.999	(111)	[110]	65	e
		99.98	(111)	[110]	94	e
Ni.............	fcc	99.8	(111)	[110]	580	c
Fe.............	bcc	99.96	(110)	[111]	2,800	f
			(112)			
			(123)			
Mo.............	bcc	......	(110)	[111]	5,000	g

[a] D. C. Jillson, *Trans. AIME*, vol. 188, p. 1129, 1950.

[b] E. C. Burke and W. R. Hibbard, Jr., *Trans. AIME*, vol. 194, p. 295, 1952.

[c] E. Schmid, "International Conference on Physics," vol. 2, Physical Society, London, 1935.

[d] A. T. Churchman, *Proc. Roy. Soc. (London)*, vol. 226A, p. 216, 1954.

[e] F. D. Rosi, *Trans. AIME*, vol. 200, p. 1009, 1954.

[f] J. J. Cox, R. F. Mehl, and G. T. Horne, *Trans. ASM*, vol. 49, p. 118, 1957.

[g] R. Maddin and N. K. Chen, *Trans. AIME*, vol. 191, p. 937, 1951.

variation in the yield stress of only about a factor of 2 because of differences in the orientation of the slip plane with the tensile axis. The demonstration of the resolved-shear-stress law is even less favorable in bcc metals owing to the large number of available slip systems. However, available data indicate that Schmid's law is obeyed for cubic metals as well as hcp metals.

Table 4-4 gives values of critical resolved shear stress for a number of metals. The importance of small amounts of impurities in increasing the critical resolved shear stress is shown by the data for silver and copper.

Alloying-element additions have even a greater effect, as shown by the
data for gold-silver alloys in Fig. 4-19.   Note that a large increase in the
resistance to slip is produced by alloying gold and silver even though
these atoms are very much alike in size and electronegativity, and hence

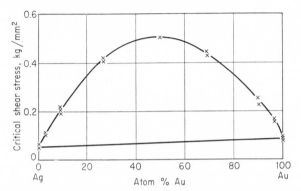

Fig. 4-19. Variation of critical resolved shear stress with composition in silver-gold-
alloy single crystals.   (*G. Sachs and J. Weerts, Z. Physik, vol. 62, p. 473, 1930.*)

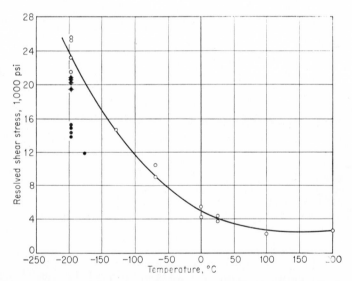

Fig. 4-20. Variation of critical resolved shear stress with temperature for iron single
crystals.   (*J. J. Cox, R. F. Mehl, and G. T. Horne, Trans. ASM, vol. 49, p. 123, 1957.*)

they form a solid solution over the complete range of composition.   In
solid solutions, where the solute atoms differ considerably in size from the
solvent atoms, an even greater increase in critical resolved shear stress
would be observed.

The magnitude of the critical resolved shear stress of a crystal is determined by the interaction of its population of dislocations with each other and with defects such as vacancies, interstitials, and impurity atoms. This stress is, of course, greater than the stress required to move a single dislocation, but it is appreciably lower than the stress required to produce slip in a perfect lattice. On the basis of this reasoning, the critical resolved shear stress should decrease as the density of defects decreases, provided that the total number of imperfections is not zero. When the last dislocation is eliminated, the critical resolved shear stress should rise abruptly to the high value predicted for the shear strength of a perfect crystal. Experimental evidence for the effect of decreasing defect density is shown by the fact that the critical resolved shear stress of soft metals can be reduced to less than one-third by increasing the purity. At the other extreme, micron-diameter single-crystal filaments, or whiskers, can be grown essentially dislocation-free. Tensile tests[1] on these filaments have given strengths which are approximately equal to the calculated strength of a perfect crystal.

4-8. Testing of Single Crystals

Most studies of the mechanical properties of single crystals are made by subjecting the crystal to simple uniaxial tension. While the stress-strain curves may be plotted in terms of average uniaxial stress vs. average linear strain ($\Delta L/L_0$), a more fundamental way of presenting the data is to plot resolved shear stress [Eq. (4-7)] against the shear strain or *glide strain*. Glide strain is the relative displacement of two parallel slip planes separated at a unit distance. If the orientation of the slip plane and the slip direction with respect to the tensile axis are known both before and after deformation, the glide strain γ can be obtained[2] from Eq. (4-8)

$$\gamma = \frac{\cos \lambda_1}{\sin \chi_1} - \frac{\cos \lambda_0}{\sin \chi_0} \tag{4-8}$$

where χ_0 and χ_1 are the initial and final angles between the slip plane and the tensile axis and λ_0 and λ_1 are the initial and final angles between the slip direction and the tensile axis. The glide strain can also be expressed in terms of the axial change in length and the original orientation, without requiring information on the final orientation of the glide elements.

$$\frac{L_1}{L_0} = (1 + 2\gamma \sin \chi_0 \cos \lambda_0 + \gamma^2 \sin^2 \chi_0)^{1/2} \tag{4-9}$$

or

$$\gamma = \left[\left(\frac{L_1}{L_0} \right)^2 - \sin^2 \lambda_0 \right]^{1/2} - \frac{\cos \lambda_0}{\sin \chi_0} \tag{4-10}$$

---

[1] S. S. Brenner, *J. Appl. Phys.*, vol. 27, pp. 1484–1491, 1956.

[2] For a derivation of Eqs. (4-8) and (4-9), see E. Schmid and W. Boas, "Plasticity of Crystals," English translation, pp. 58–60, F. A. Hughes & Co., London, 1950.

In the ordinary tension test, the movement of the crosshead of the testing machine constrains the specimen at the grips, since the grips must remain in line. Therefore, the specimen is not allowed to deform freely by uniform glide on every slip plane along the length of the specimen, as is pictured in Fig. 4-21a. Instead, the specimen deforms in the manner shown in Fig. 4-21b. Near the center of the gage length the

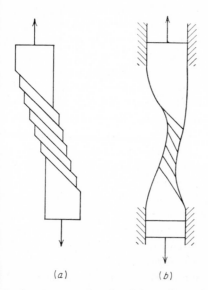

Fig. 4-21. (a) Tensile deformation of single crystal without constraint; (b) rotation of slip planes due to constraint.

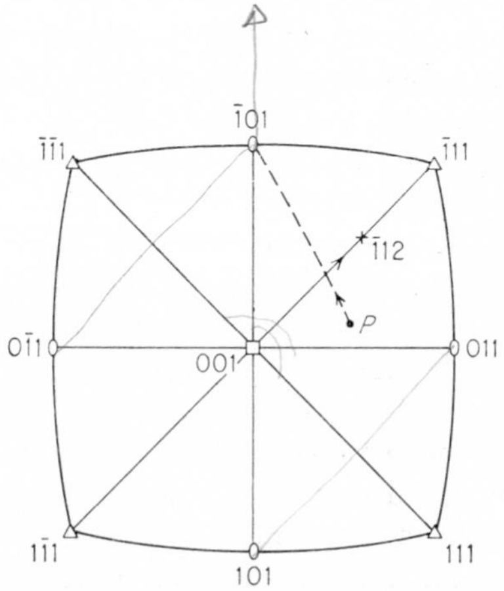

Fig. 4-22. Stereographic triangles showing lattice rotation of fcc metal during tensile elongation.

slip planes rotate, as the crystal is extended, so as to align themselves parallel with the tensile axis. Near the grips bending of the slip planes is superimposed on the rotation. The amount of rotation toward the tensile axis increases with the extent of deformation. In tensile deformation, the change in the angle between the slip plane and the tensile axis is related to the change in gage length in the axial direction by

$$\frac{L_1}{L_0} = \frac{\sin \chi_0}{\sin \chi_1} \qquad (4\text{-}11)$$

A convenient way of recording this reorientation is by following the axis of the specimen on the unit stereographic triangle.[1] In Fig. 4-22, the initial orientation of the axis of an fcc single-crystal tension specimen is plotted on the unit stereographic triangle at P. The slip plane is

[1] For a description of stereographic projection, see C. S. Barrett, "The Structure of Metals," 2d ed., chap. 2, McGraw-Hill Book Company, Inc., New York, 1952.

(111), and the slip direction is [$\bar{1}$01]. During elongation of the crystal, the specimen axis moves along a great circle passing through P and the slip direction [$\bar{1}$01]. As the deformation continues and rotation of the initial or *primary slip system* occurs, the value of cos ϕ cos λ for the primary slip system decreases. Therefore, even if strain hardening is neglected, a greater tensile load must be applied to maintain the value of the resolved shear stress on this slip system. While cos ϕ cos λ is decreasing on the primary slip system owing to rotation, it is increasing on another set of planes, which are being rotated closer to a position 45° to the tensile axis. When the resolved shear stress on the new slip system is equal or about equal to the shear stress on the old slip system, a new set of slip lines appear on the specimen surface and the axis rotates toward the [$\bar{1}$12]. In the fcc metals, the new slip lines occur on the *conjugate slip system* ($\bar{1}\bar{1}$1)-[011]. Under the microscope conjugate slip appears as another set of intersecting slip lines. *Cross slip* on the (1$\bar{1}$1)-[$\bar{1}$01] system may also occur. This slip system has the same slip direction as the primary slip system. In the microscope cross slip usually appears as short offsets to the primary slip lines. With even greater rotation, it is geometrically possible for a fourth slip system ($\bar{1}$11)-[0$\bar{1}$1] to become operative. However, this slip system is usually not found to be operative in fcc metals. The appearance of more than one slip system during deformation is often described under the general heading of *duplex* or *multiple* slip.

An excellent method of studying the deformation behavior of single crystals is by loading in shear. Parker and Washburn[1] have described a method of loading single crystals in pure shear so that the shear strain is applied by a couple acting parallel to the active slip system. This method of testing has the advantage that the crystal can be oriented so that the maximum shear stress occurs on any desired slip system. Resolved shear stress and shear strain are measured directly in this type of test.

4-9. Deformation by Twinning

The second important mechanism by which metals deform is the process known as twinning.[2] Twinning results when a portion of the crystal takes up an orientation that is related to the orientation of the rest of the untwinned lattice in a definite, symmetrical way. The twinned portion of the crystal is a mirror image of the parent crystal.

---

[1] E. R. Parker and J. Washburn, "Modern Research Techniques in Physical Metallurgy," American Society for Metals, Metals Park, Ohio, 1953.

[2] For a complete review of this subject, see E. O. Hall, "Twinning and Diffusionless Transformations in Metals," Butterworth & Co. (Publishers), Ltd., London, 1954, or R. W. Cahn, *Adv. in Phys.*, vol. 3, pp. 363–445, 1954.

The plane of symmetry between the two portions is called the *twinning plane*. Figure 4-23 illustrates the classical atomic picture of twinning. Figure 4-23*a* represents a section perpendicular to the surface in a cubic lattice with a low-index plane parallel to the paper and oriented at an angle to the plane of polish. The twinning plane is perpendicular to the paper. If a shear stress is applied, the crystal will twin about the twinning plane (Fig. 4-23*b*). The region to the right of the twinning plane is undeformed. To the left of this plane, the planes of atoms have sheared in such a way as to make the lattice a mirror image across the twin plane.

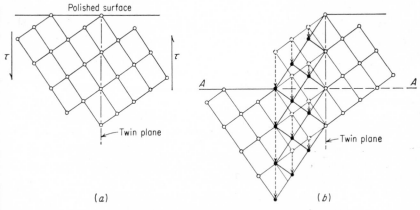

Fig. 4-23. Classical picture of twinning.

In a simple lattice such as this, each atom in the twinned region moves by a homogeneous shear a distance proportional to its distance from the twin plane. In Fig. 4-23*b*, open circles represent atoms which have not moved, dashed circles indicate the original positions in the lattice of atoms which change position, and solid circles are the final positions of these atoms in the twinned region. Note that the twin is visible on the polished surface because of the change in elevation produced by the deformation and because of the difference in crystallographic orientation between the deformed and undeformed regions. If the surface were polished down to section *A A*, the difference in elevation would be eliminated but the twin would still be visible after etching because it possesses a different orientation from the untwinned region.

It should be noted that twinning differs from slip in several specific respects. In slip, the orientation of the crystal above and below the slip plane is the same after deformation as before, while twinning results in an orientation difference across the twin plane. Slip is usually considered to occur in discrete multiples of the atomic spacing, while in twinning the atom movements are much less than an atomic distance. Slip occurs on relatively widely spread planes, but in the twinned region of a crystal every atomic plane is involved in the deformation.

Twins may be produced by mechanical deformation or as the result of annealing following plastic deformation. The first type are known as *mechanical twins;* the latter are called *annealing twins.* Mechanical twins are produced in bcc or hcp metals under conditions of rapid rate of loading (shock loading) and decreased temperature. Face-centered cubic metals are not ordinarily considered to deform by mechanical twinning, although gold-silver alloys twin fairly readily when deformed at low temperature, and mechanical twins have been produced in copper by tensile deformation at 4°K. Twins can form in a time as short as a few microseconds, while for slip there is a delay time of several milliseconds before a slip band is formed. Under certain conditions, twins can be heard to form with a click or loud report (tin cry). If twinning occurs during a tensile test, it produces serrations in the the stress-strain curve.

Twinning occurs in a definite direction on a specific crystallographic plane for each crystal structure. Table 4-5 lists the common twin planes

TABLE 4-5
TWIN PLANES AND TWIN DIRECTIONS

Crystal structure	Typical examples	Twin plane	Twin direction
bcc..........	α-Fe, Ta	(112)	[111]
hcp..........	Zn, Cd, Mg, Ti	$(10\bar{1}2)$	$[\bar{1}011]$
fcc..........	Ag, Au, Cu	(111)	[112]

and twin directions. It is not known whether or not there is a critical resolved shear stress for twinning. The shear stress at which twinning occurs is influenced by prior deformation. Figure 4-20 shows data for iron single crystals pulled in tension at −196°C. The solid circles show a resolved shear stress appreciably below that for slip. The crosses represent iron crystals prestrained 4 per cent at room temperature before testing at −196°C. Note that the resolved shear stress for twinning is increased by the prior deformation by slip. If the crystals are given even greater prestrain at room temperature (open circles), deformation by twinning is completely suppressed and the crystal deforms by slip at −196°C.

The lattice strains needed to produce a twin configuration in a crystal are small, so that the amount of gross deformation that can be produced by twinning is small. For example,[1] the maximum extension which it is possible to produce in a zinc crystal when the entire crystal is converted

---

[1] Barrett, *op. cit.*, p. 384.

into a twin on the {1012} plane is only 7.39 per cent. The important role of twinning in plastic deformation comes not from the strain produced by the twinning process but from the fact that orientation changes resulting from twinning may place new slip systems in a favorable orientation with respect to the stress axis so that additional slip can take place. Thus, twinning is important in the over-all deformation of metals with a low number of slip systems, such as the hcp metals. However, it should be understood that only a relatively small fraction of the total volume of

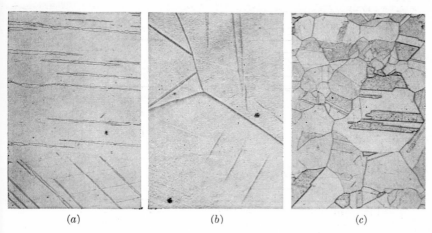

(a)   (b)   (c)

Fig. 4-24. Microstructures of twins. (a) Neumann bands in iron; (b) mechanical twins produced in zinc by polishing; (c) annealing twins in gold-silver alloy.

a crystal is reoriented by twinning, and therefore hcp metals will, in general, possess less ductility than metals with a greater number of slip systems.

Figure 4-24 shows some metallographic features of twins in several different systems. Figure 4-24a is an example of mechanical twins in iron (Neumann bands). Note that the width of the twins can be readily resolved at rather low magnification. The boundaries of the twins etch at about the same rate as grain boundaries, indicating that they are rather high-energy boundaries. Figure 4-24b shows the broad, lense-shaped twins commonly found in hcp metals. Note that twins do not extend beyond a grain boundary. Figure 4-24c shows annealing twins in an fcc gold-silver alloy. Annealing twins are usually broader and with straighter sides than mechanical twins. The energy of annealing twin boundaries is about 5 per cent of the average grain-boundary energy. Most fcc metals form annealing twins. Their presence in the microstructure is a good indication that the metal has been given mechanical deformation prior to annealing, since it is likely that they grow from twin nuclei produced during deformation.

4-10. Stacking Faults

In an earlier section, it was shown that the atomic arrangement on the {111} plane of an fcc structure and the {0001} plane of an hcp structure could be obtained by the stacking of close-packed planes of spheres. For the fcc structure, the stacking sequence of the planes of atoms is given by *ABC ABC ABC*. For the hcp structure, the stacking sequence is given by *AB AB AB*.

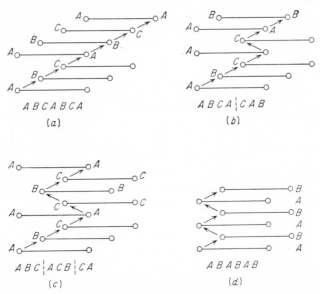

Fig. 4-25. Faulted structures. (*a*) Face-centered cubic packing; (*b*) deformation fault in fcc; (*c*) twin fault in fcc; (*d*) hcp packing.

Fairly recently it has been realized that errors, or faults, in the stacking sequence can be produced in most metals by plastic deformation.[1] Slip on the {111} plane in an fcc lattice produces a deformation stacking fault by the process shown in Fig. 4-25*b*. Slip has occurred between an *A* and a *B* layer, moving each atom layer above the slip plane one identity distance to the right. The stacking sequence then becomes *ABCA|CAB*. Comparison of this faulted stacking sequence (Fig. 4-25*b*) with the stacking sequence for an hcp structure without faults (Fig. 4-25*d*) shows that the deformation stacking fault contains four layers of an hcp sequence. Therefore, the formation of a stacking fault

---

[1] Very precise X-ray diffraction measurements are needed to detect the presence of stacking faults. For example, see B. E. Warren and E. P. Warekois, *Acta Met.*, vol. 3, p. 473, 1955.

in an fcc metal is equivalent to the formation of a thin hcp region. Another way in which a stacking fault could occur in an fcc metal is by the sequence[1] shown in Fig. 4-25c.   The stacking sequence $ABC{\mid}ACB{\mid}CA$ is called an extrinsic, or twin, stacking fault.   The three layers ACB constitute the twin.   Thus, stacking faults in fcc metals can also be considered as submicroscopic twins of nearly atomic thickness.   The reason why mechanical twins of microscopically resolvable width are not formed readily when fcc metals are deformed is that the formation of stacking faults is so energetically favorable.

The situation for the hcp structure is somewhat different from that found in fcc metals.   Figure 4-25d shows that, on going from an A layer to a B layer, if we continue in a straight line we will not come to another atom on the next A layer.   However, slip can occur between two of the planes so that the stacking sequence becomes $ABABA{\mid}CBCBC$.   As a result, four layers of atoms $BACB$ are in the straight-line fcc stacking order.   Thus, a stacking fault in

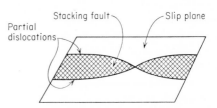

Fig. 4-26. Schematic model of a stacking fault.

an hcp metal is equivalent to the formation of a thin fcc region.   It is more difficult to form stacking faults in a bcc lattice than in the close-packed fcc and hcp structures.   The possibility of stacking faults in the {112} planes has been investigated theoretically and demonstrated by X-ray diffraction.[2]   Stacking faults have been observed with thin-film electron microscopy in columbium.[3]

Stacking faults occur most readily in fcc metals, and they have been most extensively studied for this crystal structure.   For example, it is now known that differences in the deformation behavior of fcc metals can be related to differences in stacking-fault behavior.   From the point of view of dislocation theory, a stacking fault in an fcc metal can be considered to be an *extended dislocation* consisting of a thin hexagonal region bounded by partial dislocations[4] (Fig. 4-26).   The nearly parallel dislocations tend to repel each other, but this is balanced by the surface tension of the stacking fault pulling them together.   The lower the *stacking-fault energy*, the greater the separation between the partial dis-

[1] C. N. J. Wagner, *Acta Met.*, vol. 5, pp. 427–434. 1957.

[2] P. B. Hirsch and H. M. Otte, *Acta Cryst.*, vol. 10, pp. 447–453, 1957; O. J. Guenter and B. E. Warren, *J. Appl. Phys.*, vol. 29, pp. 40–48, 1958.

[3] A. Fourdeux and A. Berghezen, *J. Inst. Metals*, vol. 89, pp. 31–32, 1960–1961.

[4] Partial dislocations will be considered in more detail in Chap. 6.   The splitting of dislocations into separated partials has been observed with the electron microscope in stainless-steel foils.

locations and the wider the stacking fault. Stacking-fault energies in fcc metals have been estimated on the assumption that the stacking-fault energy is equal to twice the energy of a coherent boundary of an annealing twin. On this basis, the stacking-fault energies for copper, nickel, and aluminum are approximately 40, 80, and 200 ergs/cm^2. Since the lower the energy of the twin boundary, the greater the tendency for the formation of annealing twins, the estimates of stacking-fault energy are in qualitative agreement with metallographic observations of the frequency of occurrence of annealing twins; e.g., aluminum rarely shows annealing twins. X-ray work has shown that the energy of stacking faults in brass decreases with zinc content, and this is in agreement with the fact that alpha brass forms a greater number of annealing twins than copper.

Stacking faults enter into the plastic deformation of metals in a number of ways. Metals with wide stacking faults strain-harden more rapidly, twin easily on annealing, and show a different temperature dependence of flow stress from metals with narrow stacking faults. Figure 4-26 helps to illustrate why cross slip is more difficult in metals with wide stacking-fault ribbons. Because dislocations in the slip plane are extended, it is not possible for them to transfer from one slip plane to another except at a point where the partial dislocations come together. Since it requires energy to produce a constriction in the stacking fault, the process of cross slip is more difficult in a metal with wide stacking faults than in a metal with narrow stacking faults. For example, the activation energy for cross slip is about 1 ev in aluminum and approximately 10 ev in copper.

4-11. Deformation Bands and Kink Bands

Inhomogeneous deformation of a crystal results in regions of different orientation called *deformation bands*. When slip occurs without restraint in a perfectly homogeneous fashion, the slip lines are removed by subsequent polishing of the surface. Deformation bands, however, can be observed even after repeated polishing and etching because they represent regions of different crystallographic orientation. In single crystals, deformation bands several millimeters wide may occur, while in polycrystalline specimens microscopic observation is needed to see them. The tendency for the formation of deformation bands is greater in polycrystalline specimens because the restraints imposed by the grain boundaries make it easy for orientation differences to arise in a grain during deformation. Deformation bands generally appear irregular in shape but are elongated in the direction of principal strain. The outline of the bands is generally indistinct and poorly defined, indicating a general fading out of the orientation difference.   Deformation bands have been observed in both fcc and bcc metals, but not in hcp metals.

Consideration of the equation for critical resolved shear stress shows that it will be difficult to deform a hexagonal crystal when the basal plane is nearly parallel to the crystal axis.   Orowan[1] found that if a cadmium crystal of this orientation were loaded in compression it would deform by a localized region of the crystal suddenly snapping into a tilted position with a sudden shortening of the crystal.   The buckling, or *kinking*, behavior is illustrated in Fig. 4-27.   The horizontal lines represent basal planes, and the

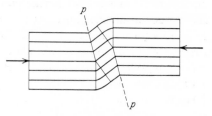

Fig. 4-27. Kink band.

planes designated p are the kink planes at which the orientation suddenly changes.   Distortion of the crystal is essentially confined to the kink band.   Further study of kink bands by Hess and Barrett[2] showed that they can be considered to be a simple type of deformation band. Kink bands have also been observed in zinc crystals tested in tension, where a nonuniform distribution of slip can produce a bending moment which can cause kink formation.

4-12. Strain Hardening of Single Crystals

One of the chief characteristics of the plastic deformation of metals is the fact that the shear stress required to produce slip continuously increases with increasing shear strain.   The increase in the stress required to cause slip because of previous plastic deformation is known as *strain hardening*, or *work hardening*.   An increase in flow stress of over 100 per cent from strain hardening is not unusual in single crystals of ductile metals.

Strain hardening is caused by dislocations interacting with each other and with barriers which impede their motion through the crystal lattice. Hardening due to dislocation interaction is a complicated problem because it involves large groups of dislocations, and it is difficult to specify group behavior in a simple mathematical way.   It is known that the number of dislocations in a crystal increases with strain over the number present in the annealed crystal.   Thus, the first requirement for understanding strain hardening was the development of a logical mechanism for the generation of dislocations.   F. C. Frank and W. T. Read conceived a

[1] E. Orowan, *Nature*, vol. 149, p. 643, 1942.

[2] J. A. Hess and C. S. Barrett, *Trans. AIME*, vol. 185, p. 599, 1949.

logical mechanism by which a large amount of slip could be produced by one dislocation. The Frank-Read source (see Chap. 6 for details) provides a method by which the dislocations initially present in the crystal as a result of growth can generate enough dislocations to account for the observed strain hardening. The mechanism is consistent with the experimental observation that slip is concentrated on a relatively few active slip planes and that the total slip on each slip plane is of the order of 1,000 atomic spacings. A method is also provided in the concept of the Frank-Read source for immobilizing the source after slip of this order of magnitude has occurred. Direct experimental evidence for the existence of the Frank-Read source in crystals has been developed in recent years.

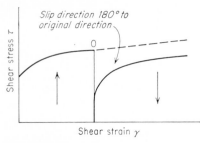

One of the earliest dislocation concepts to explain strain hardening was the idea that dislocations pile up on slip planes at barriers in the crystal. The pile-ups produce a *back stress* which opposes the applied stress on the slip plane. The existence of a back stress was demonstrated experimentally by shear tests on zinc single crystals.[1] Zinc crystals are ideal for

Fig. 4-28. Effect of complete reversal of slip direction on stress-strain curve. (*E. H. Edwards, J. Washburn, and E. R. Parker, Trans. AIME, vol., 197, p. 1526, 1953.*)

crystal-plasticity experiments because they slip only on the basal plane, and hence complications due to duplex slip are easily avoided. In Fig. 4-28, the crystal is strained to point O, unloaded, and then reloaded in the direction opposite to the original slip direction. Note that on reloading the crystal yields at a lower shear stress than when it was first loaded. This is because the back stress developed as a result of dislocations piling up at barriers during the first loading cycle is aiding dislocation movement when the direction of slip is reversed. Furthermore, when the slip direction is reversed, dislocations of opposite sign could be created at the same sources that produced the dislocations responsible for strain in the first slip direction. Since dislocations of opposite sign attract and annihilate each other, the net effect would be a further softening of the lattice. This explains the fact that the flow curve in the reverse direction lies below the curve for continued flow in the original direction. The lowering of the yield stress when deformation in one direction is followed by deformation in the opposite direction is called the *Bauschinger effect.*[2] While all metals exhibit a Bauschinger effect, it may not always be of

---

[1] E. H. Edwards, J. Washburn, and E. R. Parker, *Trans. AIME*, vol. 197, p. 1525, 1953.

[2] J. Bauschinger, *Zivilingur.*, vol. 27, pp. 289–347, 1881.

the magnitude shown here for zinc crystals. Moreover, the flow curve after reversal of direction does not fall below the original flow curve for all metals.

The existence of back stress and its importance to strain hardening in metals having been established, the next step is to identify the barriers to dislocation motion in single crystals. Microscopic precipitate particles and foreign atoms can serve as barriers, but other barriers which are effective in pure single crystals must be found. Such barriers arise from the fact that glide dislocations on intersecting slip planes may combine

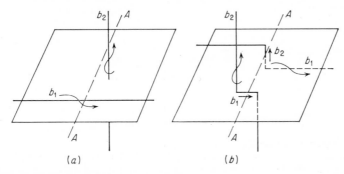

Fig. 4-29. Schematic representation of intersection of two screw dislocations. (*a*) Before intersection; (*b*) jogs formed after intersection.

with one another to produce a new dislocation that is not in a slip direction. The dislocation of low mobility that is produced by a dislocation reaction is called a *sessile dislocation*. Since sessile dislocations do not lie on the slip plane of low shear stress, they act as a barrier to dislocation motion until the stress is increased to a high enough level to break down the barrier. The most important dislocation reaction, which leads to the formation of sessile dislocations, is the formation of Cottrell-Lomer barriers in fcc metals by slip on intersecting {111} planes.

Another mechanism of strain hardening, in addition to that due to the back stress resulting from dislocation pile-ups at barriers, is believed to occur when dislocations moving in the slip plane cut through other dislocations intersecting the active slip plane. The dislocations threading through the active slip plane are often called a *dislocation forest,* and this strain-hardening process is referred to as the *intersection* of a forest of dislocations. Figure 4-29 shows that the intersection of dislocations results in the formation of *jogs,* or offsets, in the dislocation line. The jogs formed in this case are edge dislocations because their Burgers vectors are perpendicular to the original dislocation line. Any further movement of the screw dislocations along the line AA would require the newly formed edge components to move out of their slip planes. Thus, the formation of jogs in screw dislocations impedes their motion and may even lead to the formation of vacancies and interstitials if the jogs are forced to move nonconservatively. Jogs in edge dislocations do not impede their motion. All these processes require an increased expenditure of energy, and therefore they contribute to hardening.

Strain hardening due to a dislocation cutting process arises from short-range forces occurring over distances less than 5 to 10 interatomic distances. This hardening can be overcome at finite temperatures with the

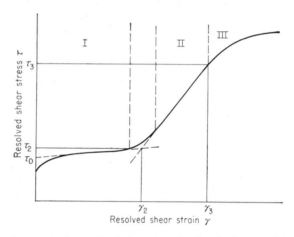

Fig. 4-30. Generalized flow curve for fcc single crystals.

help of thermal fluctuations, and therefore it is temperature- and strain-rate-dependent. On the other hand, strain hardening arising from dislocation pile-up at barriers occurs over longer distances, and therefore it is relatively independent of temperature and strain rate. Accordingly, data on the temperature and strain-rate dependence of strain hardening can be used[1] to determine the relative contribution of the two mechanisms.

When the stress-strain curves for single crystals are plotted as resolved shear stress vs. shear strain, certain generalizations can be made for all fcc metals. Following the notation proposed by Seeger,[2] the flow curve for pure-metal single crystals can be divided into three stages (Fig. 4-30). Stage I, the region of *easy glide*, is a stage in which the crystal undergoes little strain hardening. During easy glide, the dislocations are able to move over relatively large distances without encountering barriers. The low strain hardening produced during this stage implies that most of the dislocations escape from the crystal at the surface. During easy glide,

[1] Z. S. Basinski, *Phil. Mag.*, vol. 4, ser. 8, pp. 393–432, 1959.
[2] A. Seeger, "Dislocations and Mechanical Properties of Crystals," John Wiley & Sons, Inc., New York, 1957.

slip always occurs on only one slip system.   For this reason, stage I slip is sometimes called *laminar flow*.

Stage II is a nearly linear part of the flow curve where strain hardening increases rapidly.   In this stage, slip occurs on more than one set of planes.   The length of the active slip lines decreases with increasing strain, which is consistent with the formation of a greater number of Cottrell-Lomer barriers with increasing strain.   During stage II, the ratio of the strain-hardening coefficient (the slope of the curve) to the shear modulus is nearly independent of stress and temperature, and approximately independent of crystal orientation and purity.   The fact that the slope of the flow curve in stage II is nearly independent of temperature agrees with the theory that assumes the chief strain-hardening mechanism to be piled-up groups of dislocations.

Stage III is a region of decreasing rate of strain hardening.   The processes occurring during this stage are often called *dynamical recovery*.   In this region of the flow curve, the stresses are high enough so that dislocations can take part in processes that are suppressed at lower stresses.   Cross slip is believed to be the main process by which dislocations, piled up at obstacles during stage II, can escape and reduce the internal-strain field.   The stress at which stage III begins, τ_3, is strongly temperature-dependent.   Also, the flow stress of a crystal strained into stage III is more temperature-dependent than if it had been strained only into stage II.   This temperature dependence suggests that the intersection of forests of dislocations is the chief strain-hardening mechanism in stage III.

The curve shown in Fig. 4-30 represents a general behavior for fcc metals.   Certain deviations from a three-stage flow curve have been observed.   For example, metals with a high stacking-fault energy, like aluminum, usually show only a very small stage II region at room temperature because they can deform so easily by cross slip.   The shape and magnitude of a single-crystal flow curve, particularly during the early stages, depends upon the purity of the metal, the orientation of the crystal, the temperature at which it is tested, and the rate at which it is strained.   The easy-glide region is much more prominent in hcp crystals than in fcc metals.   A region of easy glide in the flow curve is favored by slip on a single system, high purity, low temperature, absence of surface oxide films, an orientation favorable for simple slip, and a method of testing which minimizes extraneous bending stresses.   Figure 4-31 shows that crystal orientation can have a very strong effect on the flow curve of fcc single crystals.   When the tensile axis is parallel to a $\langle 011 \rangle$ direction, one slip system is carrying appreciably more shear stress than any other and the flow curve shows a relatively large region of easy glide.   When the tensile axis is close to a $\langle 100 \rangle$ or $\langle 111 \rangle$ direction, the stress on several slip systems is not very different and the flow curves show rapid rates of strain hardening.

Starting as close to absolute zero as is practical, the value of the resolved shear stress at a given shear strain decreases with increasing temperature.   If fcc crystals are strained to the end of stage II at a temperature T_1 and then the temperature is increased to T_2 without any

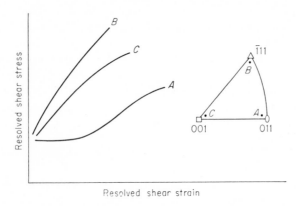

Fig. 4-31. Effect of specimen orientation on the shape of the flow curve for fcc single crystals.

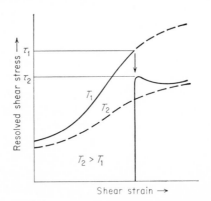

Fig. 4-32. Flow curves exhibiting work softening.

change in strain, the flow stress drops from τ_1 to τ_2 (Fig. 4-32).   The state of strain hardening reached at T_1 is unstable at T_2, and a recovery process sets in which tends to reduce the strain hardening to what it would have been if all the straining had been accomplished at T_2.   This behavior is called[1] *work softening.*   Work softening is the result of the release at T_2 of dislocation pile-ups produced at T_1.   The release of dislocations may be due to easier cross slip at the higher temperature or

[1] A. H. Cottrell and R. J. Stokes, *Proc. Roy. Soc. (London)*, vol. A233, p. 17, 1955.

the fact that the size of a stable dislocation pile-up is smaller at T_2 because of increased thermal fluctuations.

BIBLIOGRAPHY

Azároff, L. V.: "Introduction to Solids," McGraw-Hill Book Company, Inc., New York, 1960.

Barrett, C. S.: "The Structure of Metals," 2d ed., McGraw-Hill Book Company, Inc., New York, 1952.

Clarebrough, L. M., and M. E. Hargreaves: Work Hardening of Metals, in "Progress in Metal Physics," vol. 8, Pergamon Press, Ltd., London, 1959.

Cottrell, A. H.: "Dislocations and Plastic Flow in Crystals," Oxford University Press, New York, 1953.

Maddin, R., and N. K. Chen: Geometrical Aspects of the Plastic Deformation of Metal Single Crystals, in "Progress in Metal Physics," vol. 5, Pergamon Press, Ltd., London, 1954.

Schmid, E., and W. Boas: "Plasticity of Crystals," English translation, F. A. Hughes & Co., London, 1950.

Chapter 5
PLASTIC DEFORMATION
OF POLYCRYSTALLINE AGGREGATES

5-1. Introduction

The previous chapter considered the plastic deformation of metallic single crystals in terms of the movement of dislocations and the basic deformation mechanisms of slip and twinning. Single-crystal specimens represent the metal in its most ideal condition. The simplification which results from the single-crystal condition materially assists in describing the deformation behavior in terms of crystallography and defect structure. However, with the exception of electronic and semiconductor devices, single crystals are rarely used for practical purposes because of limitations involving their strength, size, and production. Commercial metal products are invariably made up of a tremendous number of small individual crystals or grains. The individual grains of the polycrystalline aggregate do not deform in accordance with the relatively simple laws which describe plastic deformation in single crystals because of the restraining effect of the surrounding grains. Therefore, there is a gap between fundamental deformation mechanisms determined from single crystals and the prediction of the plastic behavior of a polycrystalline aggregate from these basic concepts.

Grain boundaries exert a considerable influence on the plastic-deformation behavior of polycrystalline metals. Other factors which also have an important effect on mechanical properties are the presence of sub-grain boundaries within the grains, solid-solution alloying additions, and dispersion of second-phase particles. These factors will each be considered in this chapter, primarily in terms of how they influence the tensile-flow curve. Wherever possible, qualitative explanations of these processes will be given in terms of dislocation theory. Other topics covered in this chapter include yield-point behavior, strain aging, cold work, annealing, and the development of preferred orientations. It will be appreciated that not all these topics are solely restricted to polycrystalline materials. However, the bulk of the experimental data on these phenomena have been obtained from polycrystalline materials, and therefore they are considered in this chapter.

5-2. Grain Boundaries and Deformation

The boundaries between grains in a polycrystalline aggregate are a region of disturbed lattice only a few atomic diameters wide. In the general case, the crystallographic orientation changes abruptly in passing from one grain to the next across the grain boundary. The ordinary high-angle grain boundary represents a region of random misfit between the adjoining crystal lattices.[1] As the difference in orientation between the grains on each side of the boundary decreases, the state of order in the boundary increases. For the limiting case of a low-angle boundary where the orientation difference across the boundary may be less than 1° (see Sec. 5-3), the boundary is composed of a regular array of dislocations.

Ordinary high-angle grain boundaries are boundaries of rather high surface energy. For example, a grain boundary in copper has an interfacial surface energy of about 600 ergs/cm^2, while the energy of a twin boundary is only about 25 ergs/cm^2. Because of their high energy, grain boundaries serve as preferential sites for solid-state reactions such as diffusion, phase transformations, and precipitation reactions. An important point to consider is that the high energy of a grain boundary usually results in a higher concentration of solute atoms at the boundary than in the interior of the grain. This makes it difficult to separate the pure mechanical effect of grain boundaries on properties from an effect due to impurity segregation.

Grain boundaries may serve to either strengthen or weaken a metal, depending upon the temperature, rate of strain, and the purity of the metal. At temperatures below approximately one-half of the absolute melting point, and for relatively fast strain rates (so that recovery effects are not great), grain boundaries increase the rate of strain hardening and increase the strength. At high temperatures and slow strain rates (conditions of creep deformation) deformation is localized at the grain boundaries. Grain-boundary sliding and stress-induced migration can occur, and eventually fracture takes place at the grain boundary. The fairly narrow temperature region in which the grain boundaries become weaker than the interior of the grains, so that fracture occurs in an intergranular rather than transgranular fashion, is called the *equicohesive temperature.*

The principal difference between the room-temperature deformation of single-crystal and polycrystalline specimens is that polycrystalline

---

[1] For a review of the proposed models of grain boundaries see D. McLean, "Grain Boundaries in Metals," chap. 2, Oxford University Press, New York. 1957

material exhibits a higher rate of strain hardening. The stress-strain curve for polycrystalline material shows no stage I or easy-glide region. Only stage II and stage III deformation are obtained with polycrystalline specimens. Associated with the increased strain hardening is usually an increase in yield stress and tensile strength. The effects of grain boundaries on strength are due to two main factors. The first is the fact that

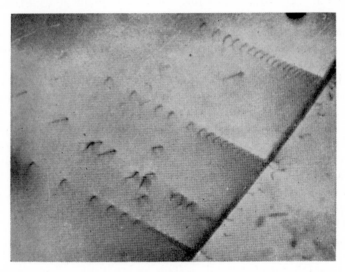

Fig. 5-1. Dislocations piled up against a grain boundary, as observed with the electron microscope in a thin foil of stainless steel, 17,500×. [*M. J. Whelan, P. B. Hirsch, R. W. Horne, and W. Bollman, Proc. Roy. Soc. (London), vol.* 240A, *p.* 524, 1957.]

grain boundaries are barriers to slip. Of greater importance is the fact that the requirement for continuity between grains during deformation introduces complex modes of deformation within the individual grains. Slip on multiple-slip systems occurs very readily in polycrystalline specimens.

The fact that slip lines stop at grain boundaries can be readily observed with the light microscope. However, by means of special etch-pit techniques (Sec. 6-2) and high-magnification electron microscopy of thin films it is possible to establish that dislocations pile up along the slip planes at the grain boundaries (Fig. 5-1). Dislocation pile-ups produce back stresses which oppose the generation of new dislocations at Frank-Read sources within the grains. With increasing applied stress more and more dislocations pile up at grain boundaries. High shear stresses are developed at the head of a dislocation pile-up, and eventually this becomes high enough to produce dislocation movement in the neighboring grain across the boundary. This will reduce the dislocation pile-up and minimize hardening from this effect. Hardening due to dislocation pile-up at grain boundaries is therefore important in the early stages of deformation, but not at large strains. It will be more effective in an hcp metal, with only one easy slip plane, than in fcc or bcc metals, with many equivalent slip planes. For the latter case, no grain can be very unfavorably oriented with respect to the applied stress, so that, on the average, slip can be initiated in a neighboring grain at only a little higher stress than was required to initiate slip in the most favorably oriented grains. However, for hcp metals, there may be a very unfavorable orientation difference between neighboring grains so that an appreciably higher stress is required to initiate slip in the neighboring grain. Therefore, polycrystalline hcp metals show a very much higher rate of strain hardening compared with single crystals. In fcc and bcc metals the difference in the flow curve between polycrystals and single crystals is not nearly so great.

The effect of crystal orientation on the flow curve of fcc single crystals was illustrated in Fig. 4-31. Orientations which produce many favorably oriented slip systems readily deform by multiple slip. Multiple slip always results in a high rate of strain hardening. From purely geometrical considerations the grains of a polycrystalline metal must remain in contact during deformation. Taylor[1] has shown that five independent slip systems must operate in each grain in order to maintain continuity. Since slip on only two or three systems, depending on orientation, occurs for multiple slip in single crystals, slip in polycrystals is more complex than in single crystals oriented for multiple slip. Greater strain hardening is usually observed in polycrystals than can be accounted for on the basis of multiple slip in single crystals and by grain-boundary barriers.[2]

Grain size has a measurable effect on most mechanical properties. For example, at room temperature, hardness, yield strength, tensile strength, fatigue strength, and impact resistance all increase with decreasing grain size. The effect of grain size is largest on properties which are related to the early stages of deformation, for it is at this stage that grain-boundary barriers are most effective. Thus, yield stress is more dependent on grain size than tensile strength. For the later stages of deformation the strength is controlled chiefly by complex dislocation interactions occurring within the grains, and grain size is not a controlling variable.

For most metals the yield stress is related to the grain size by

$$\sigma_0 = \sigma_i + K_y D^{-\frac{1}{2}} \qquad (5\text{-}1)$$

where σ_0 = yield stress

σ_i = friction stress opposing motion of a dislocation

K_y = measure of extent to which dislocations are piled up at barriers

D = grain diameter

[1] G. I. Taylor, *J. Inst. Metals*, vol. 62, p. 307, 1938.
[2] McLean, *op. cit.*, chap. 6.

Equation (5-1) was first proposed for low-carbon steel[1] and has been extensively applied to tests on this material. The slope of a plot of σ_0 versus $D^{-\frac{1}{2}}$ is K_y, a measure of the extent to which dislocations are piled up at grain boundaries. It is essentially independent of temperature. The intercept σ_i is a measure of the stress needed to drive a dislocation against the resistance of impurities, precipitate particles, subgrain boundaries, and the Peierls-Nabarro force. This term depends on both the composition and the temperature, but it is independent of the applied stress. Since the Peierls-Nabarro force is temperature-dependent and the other resistances to dislocation motion are approximately temperature-independent, it appears possible to obtain an estimate of the lattice resistance to dislocation motion from an analysis of the grain-size dependence of yield stress.[2]

The problem of determining the flow curve of polycrystalline material from single-crystal data is difficult. The analyses of this problem which have been made[3] consist essentially in averaging the single-crystal curves over different orientations. Only moderate agreement has been obtained.

Grain size is measured with a microscope by counting the number of grains within a given area, by determining the number of grains that intersect a given length of random line, or by comparison with standard charts. The average grain diameter D can be determined from measurements along random lines by the equation

$$D = \frac{L}{N} \tag{5-2}$$

where L is the length of the line and N is the number of intercepts which the grain boundary makes with the line. This can be related[4] to the ratio of the grain-boundary surface area S to the volume of the grains, V, by the equation

$$\frac{S}{V} = \frac{2N}{L} = \frac{4l}{\pi A} \tag{5-3}$$

where l is the total length of grain boundary on a random plane of polish and A is the total area of the grains on a random plane of polish. A very common method of measuring grain size in the United States is to compare the grains at a fixed magnification with the American Society for Testing Materials (ASTM) grain-size charts. The ASTM grain-size

[1] N. J. Petch, *J. Iron Steel Inst.* (*London*), vol. 173, p. 25, 1953; E. O. Hall, *Proc. Phys. Soc.* (*London*), vol. 64B, p. 747, 1951.

[2] J. Heslop and N. J. Petch, *Phil. Mag.*, vol. 1, p. 866, 1956.

[3] Taylor, *op. cit.*; J. F. W. Bishop, *J. Mech. and Phys. Solids*, vol. 3, pp. 259–266, 1955; U. F. Kocks, *Acta Met.*, vol. 8, pp. 345–352, 1960.

[4] C. S. Smith and L. Guttman, *Trans. AIME*, vol. 197, p. 81, 1953.

number n is related to N^*, the number of grains per square inch at a magnification of $100\times$ by the relationship

$$N^* = 2^{n-1} \qquad (5\text{-}4)$$

Table 5-1 compares the ASTM grain-size numbers with several other useful measures of grain size.

TABLE 5-1
COMPARISON OF GRAIN-SIZE MEASURING SYSTEMS†

ASTM No.	Grains/in.² at 100×	Grains/mm²	Grains/mm.³	Av. grain diam, mm
−3	0.06	1	0.7	1.00
−2	0.12	2	2	0.75
−1	0.25	4	5.6	0.50
0	0.5	8	16	0.35
1	1	16	45	0.25
2	2	32	128	0.18
3	4	64	360	0.125
4	8	128	1,020	0.091
5	16	256	2,900	0.062
6	32	512	8,200	0.044
7	64	1,024	23,000	0.032
8	128	2,048	65,000	0.022
9	256	4,096	185,000	0.016
10	512	8,200	520,000	0.011
11	1,024	16,400	1,500,000	0.008
12	2,048	32,800	4,200,000	0.006

† ASM Metals Handbook, 1948 ed.

5-3. Low-angle Grain Boundaries

It has been recognized only fairly recently that a definite substructure can exist within the grains surrounded by high-energy grain boundaries. The subgrains are low-angle boundaries in which the difference in orientation across the boundary may be only a few minutes of arc or, at most, a few degrees. Because of this small orientation difference, special X-ray techniques are required to detect the existence of a substructure network. Subgrain boundaries are lower-energy boundaries than grain boundaries, and therefore they etch less readily than grain boundaries. However, in many metals they can be detected in the microstructure by metallographic procedures (Fig. 5-2).

A low-angle boundary contains a relatively simple arrangement of dislocations. The simplest situation is the case of a tilt boundary. Figure 5-3a illustrates two cubic crystals with a common [001] axis. The slight difference in orientation between the grains is indicated by the angle θ. In Fig. 5-3b the two crystals have been joined to form a bicrystal containing a low-angle boundary. Along the boundary the atoms adjust their position by localized deformation to produce a smooth transition from one grain to the other. However, elastic deformation cannot accommodate all the misfit, so that some of the atom planes must end on the grain boundary. Where the atom planes end, there is an edge dislocation. Therefore, low-angle tilt boundaries can be considered to be

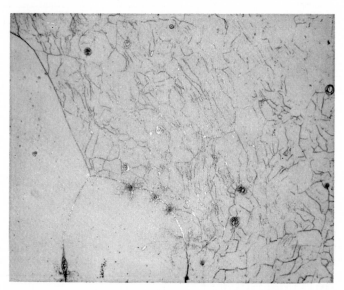

Fig. 5-2. Substructure network in iron–3 per cent silicon alloy, 250×.

an array of edge dislocations. From the geometry of Fig. 5-3b the relationship between θ and the spacing between dislocations is given by

$$\theta = 2 \tan^{-1} \frac{b}{2D} \approx \frac{b}{D} \qquad (5\text{-}5)$$

where b is the magnitude of the Burgers vector of the lattice.

The validity of the dislocation model of the low-angle boundary is found in the fact it is possible to calculate the grain-boundary energy as a function of the difference in orientation between the two grains. So long as the angle does not become greater than about 20°, good agreement is obtained between the measured values of grain-boundary energy and the values calculated on the basis of the dislocation model. Other evidence for the dislocation nature of low-angle boundaries comes from metallographic observations. If the angle is low, so that the spacing between dislocations is large, it is often possible to observe that the

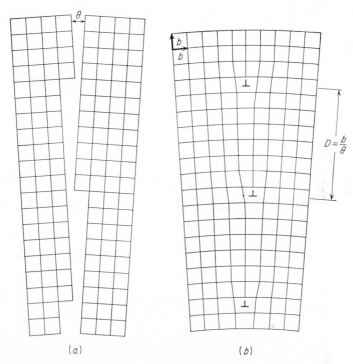

$D = \dfrac{b}{\theta}$

(a)   (b)

Fig. 5-3. Diagram of low-angle grain boundary. (a) Two grains having a common [001] axis and angular difference in orientation of θ; (b) two grains joined together to form a low-angle grain boundary made up of an array of edge dislocations. (W. T. Read, Jr., "Dislocations in Crystals," p. 157, McGraw-Hill Book Company, Inc., New York, 1953.)

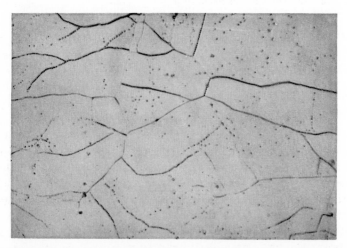

Fig. 5-4. Etch-pit structures along low-angle grain boundaries in iron-silicon alloy, $1,000\times$.

boundary is composed of a row of etch pits, with each pit corresponding to the site of an edge dislocation (Fig. 5-4).

Subboundaries or low-angle boundaries can be produced in a number

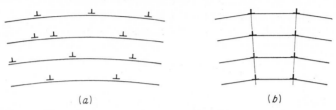

(a)   (b)

Fig. 5-5. Movement of dislocations to produce polygonization (schematic).

of ways.[1] They may be produced during crystal growth, during high-temperature creep deformation, or as the result of a phase transformation. The veining in ferrite grains is a well-known example of a substructure resulting from the internal stresses accompanying a phase transformation. Perhaps the most general method of producing a substructure network is by introducing a small amount of deformation (from about 1 to 10 per cent prestrain) and following this with an annealing treatment to rearrange the dislocations into subgrain boundaries. The amount of deformation and temperature must be low enough to prevent the formation of new grains by recrystallization (see Sec. 5-12). This process has been called recrystallization *in situ*, or polygonization.

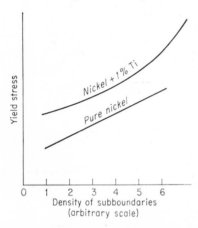

Fig. 5-6. Effect of density of subboundaries on yield stress. (*E. R. Parker and T. H. Hazlett, "Relation of Properties to Microstructure," American Society for Metals, Metals Park, Ohio,* 1954.)

The term *polygonization* was used originally to describe the situation that occurs when a single crystal is bent to a relatively small radius of curvature and then annealed. Bending results in the introduction of an excess number of dislocations of one sign. These dislocations are distributed along the bent-glide planes as shown in Fig. 5-5a. When the crystal is heated, the dislocations group themselves into the lower-energy configuration of a low-angle boundary by dislocation climb. The resulting structure is a polygonlike network of low-angle grain boundaries (Fig. 5-5b).

[1] R. W. Cahn, "Impurities and Imperfections," American Society for Metals, Metals Park, Ohio, 1955.

Since low-angle boundaries consist of simple dislocation arrays, a study of their properties should provide valuable information on dislocation behavior.   Parker and Washburn[1] demonstrated that a low-angle boundary moves as a unit when subjected to a shear stress, in complete agreement with what would be expected for a linear dislocation array.   It has also been found that the boundary angle decreases with increasing

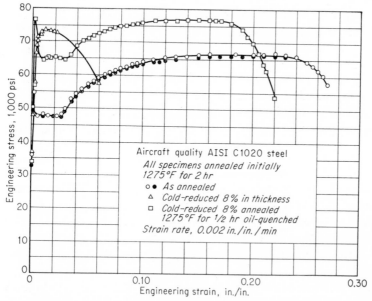

Fig. 5-7. Effect of a substructure of low-angle grain boundaries on the stress-strain curve of SAE 1020 steel.   (*E. R. Parker and J. Washburn, "Impurities and Imperfections," p. 155, American Society for Metals, Metals Park, Ohio, 1955.*)

distance of shear.   This means that the boundary loses dislocations as it moves, a fact which would be expected if dislocations are held up at imperfections such as foreign atoms, precipitated particles, and other dislocations.

The formation of subgrains in an annealed material results in a significant increase in strength.   Figure 5-6 shows the increase in the yield stress in nickel due to an increase in the density of subgrain boundaries produced by various prestraining and annealing treatments.   The fact that the curves for pure nickel and alloyed nickel are nearly parallel indicates that the strengthening due to substructure is additive to that produced by solid-solution hardening.   The effect of a substructure of low-angle grain boundaries on the stress-strain curve of 1020 steel is shown in Fig. 5-7.   Note that the material that was cold-reduced and

[1] E. R. Parker and J. Washburn, *Trans. AIME*, vol. 194, pp. 1076–1078, 1952.

annealed, so as to produce a substructure, has a higher yield point and tensile strength than both the annealed material and the material which was only cold-reduced.   Moreover, the ductility of the material containing a substructure is almost as good as the ductility of the annealed steel.

5-4. Solid-solution Hardening

The introduction of solute atoms into solid solution in the solvent-atom lattice invariably produces an alloy which is stronger than the pure metal.   There are two types of solid solutions.   If the solute- and solvent atoms are roughly similar, the solute atoms will occupy lattice points in the crystal lattice of the solvent atoms.   This is called *substitutional solid solution*.   If the solute atoms are much smaller than the solvent atoms, they occupy interstitial positions in the solvent lattice.   Carbon, nitrogen, oxygen, hydrogen, and boron are the elements which commonly form *interstitial solid solutions.*

The factors which control the tendency for the formation of substitutional solid solutions have been uncovered chiefly through the work of Hume-Rothery.   If the sizes of the two atoms, as approximately indicated by the lattice parameter, differ by less than 15 per cent, the size factor is favorable for solid-solution formation.   When the size factor is greater than 15 per cent, the extent of solid solubility is usually restricted to less than 1 per cent.   Metals which do not have a strong chemical affinity for each other tend to form solid solutions, while metals which are far apart on the electromotive series tend to form intermetallic compounds.   The relative valence of the solute and solvent also is important. The solubility of a metal with higher valence in a solvent of lower valence is more extensive than for the reverse situation.   For example, zinc is much more soluble in copper than is copper in zinc.   This relative-valence effect can be rationalized to a certain extent in terms of the electron-atom ratio.[1]   For certain solvent metals, the limit of solubility occurs at approximately the same value of electron-atom ratio for solute atoms of different valence.   Finally, for complete solid solubility over the entire range of composition the solute and solvent atoms must have the same crystal structure.

The acquisition of fundamental information about the causes of solid-solution hardening has been a slow process.   Early studies[2] of the increase in hardness resulting from solid-solution additions showed that the hard-

---

[1] For example, an alloy of 30 atomic per cent Zn in Cu has an electron-atom ratio of 1.3. $(3 \times 2) + (7 \times 1) = 13$ valence electrons per $3 + 7 = 10$ atoms.

[2] A. L. Norbury, *Trans. Faraday Soc.*, vol. 19, pp. 506–600, 1924; R. M. Brick, D. L. Martin, and R. P. Angier, *Trans. ASM*, vol. 31, pp. 675–698, 1943; J. H. Frye and W. Hume-Rothery, *Proc. Roy. Soc. (London)*, vol. 181, pp. 1–14, 1942.

ness increase varies directly with the difference in the size of the solute and solvent atoms, or with the change in lattice parameter resulting from the solute addition.   However, it is apparent that size factor alone cannot explain solid-solution hardening.   An improvement in correlation of data[1] results when the relative valence of the solute and solvent are considered in addition to the lattice-parameter distortion.   The importance of valence is shown in Fig. 5-8, where the yield stress of copper alloys of constant lattice parameter is plotted against the electron-atom ratio.[2]   Further results[3] show that alloys with equal grain size, lattice parameter, and electron-atom ratio have the same initial yield stress, but the flow curves differ at larger strains.

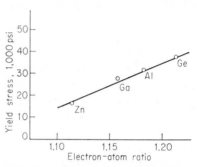

Systemic studies of the effect of solid-solution alloying additions on the flow curve in tension have been made for iron,[4] copper,[5] aluminum,[6] and nickel.[7]   For the case of iron the solid-solution-strengthened alloy is a power function of the alloy addition. Figure 5-9 shows the increase in tensile strength due to alloying additions

Fig. 5-8. Effect of electron-atom ratio on the yield stress of copper solid-solution alloys. (*W. R. Hibbard, Jr., Trans. Met. Soc. AIME, vol.* 212, *p.* 3, 1958.)

in iron.   For a given atomic per cent of solute the increase in strength varies inversely with the limit of solubility.

The distribution of solute atoms in a solvent lattice is not usually completely random.   There is growing evidence that solute atoms group preferentially at dislocations, stacking faults, low-angle boundaries, and grain boundaries.   However, even in a perfect lattice the atoms would not be completely random.   For a solid solution of A and B atoms, if B atoms tend to group themselves preferentially around other B atoms, the situation is called *clustering*.   However, if a given B atom is preferentially surrounded by A atoms, the solid solution exhibits *short-range order*. The tendency for clustering or short-range order increases with increasing solute additions.

[1] J. E. Dorn, P. Pietrokowsky, and T. E. Tietz, *Trans. AIME*, vol. 188, pp. 933–943, 1950.

[2] W. R. Hibbard, Jr., *Trans. Met. Soc. AIME*, vol. 212, pp. 1–5, 1958.

[3] N. G. Ainslie, R. W. Guard, and W. R. Hibbard, *Trans. Met. Soc. AIME*, vol. 215, pp. 42–48, 1959.

[4] C. E. Lacy and M. Gensamer, *Trans. ASM*, vol. 32, pp. 88–110, 1944.

[5] R. S. French and W. R. Hibbard, Jr., *Trans. AIME*, vol. 188, pp. 53–58, 1950.

[6] Dorn, Pietrokowsky, and Tietz, *op. cit.*

[7] V. F. Zackay and T. H. Hazlett, *Acta Met.*, vol. 1, pp. 624–628, 1953.

It is likely that solid-solution hardening is not simply the result of internal stresses due to the local lattice disturbance from randomly dispersed solute atoms. Consider a dislocation line in a perfectly random solid-solution lattice. On the average, there will be equal numbers of positive and negative stress fields, due to solute atoms, acting on the dislocation line. The net stress will be nearly zero, and the dislocation

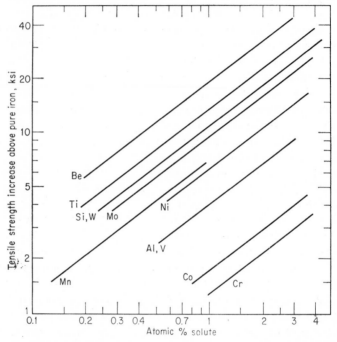

Fig. 5-9. Increase in tensile strength of iron due to solid-solution alloy additions vs. atomic per cent of alloy added. (*C. E. Lacy and M. Gensamer, Trans. ASM, vol. 32, p. 88, 1944.*)

will move through the lattice almost as easily as through the lattice of a pure metal.

Following the ideas of Cottrell,[1] it is generally held that hardening from solute atoms results from the interaction of solute atoms, in the form of "atmospheres," with dislocations. Since the atoms in the region above a positive edge dislocation are compressed and below the slip plane are stretched, the strain energy of distortion can be reduced by large atoms collecting in the expanded region and small atoms collecting in the compressed region. Interstitial atoms collect in the expanded

[1] A. H. Cottrell, "Dislocations and Plastic Flow in Crystals," Oxford University Press, New York, 1953.

region below the slip plane of a positive edge dislocation. Because the local energy is lower when a dislocation is surrounded by a solute atmosphere, a higher stress is required to make the dislocation move than would be required if there were no interaction between the dislocation and the solute atoms. If the stress becomes high enough, the dislocation can be torn away from its atmosphere. When this happens, the dislocation is free to move at a lower stress.

The best-known case of dislocation interaction with a solute-atom atmosphere is the existence of an upper and lower yield point in iron and other metals. The occurrence of a yield point in iron is known to be associated with interstitial solute atoms (see Sec. 5-5). The upper yield point corresponds to the stress required to tear dislocations away from their atmospheres of interstitial atoms.

A number of types of solute-atom interaction must be considered in explaining solid-solution strengthening.[1] Cottrell locking due to elastic interaction between the solute atoms and the dislocations, such as is described above for interstitial atoms, is certainly an important factor in solid-solution strengthening. In view of the valency effects observed in solid solutions, electrical interaction must also be considered. However, estimates show that electrical interaction is only about one-third to one-seventh as strong as elastic interaction. Suzuki[2] has pointed out the existence of a third type of interaction. Thermodynamic reasoning shows that the concentration of solute atoms at a stacking fault will be greater than the average bulk concentration. Thus, there is a "chemical interaction" between these regions and dislocations. While for most alloys this chemical interaction is weaker than the interaction force due to Cottrell locking, the force due to chemical interaction does not decrease with increasing temperature nearly so much as in the case of Cottrell locking. Fisher[3] has pointed out that the existence of short-range order or clustering in an alloy will produce a strengthening effect. Slip in a pure metal does not change the internal energy of the lattice, because the configuration of atoms across the slip plane is the same after slip as before. The same situation would exist for a completely random solid solution, but in an alloy with short-range order slip will partially destroy the

---

[1] Theories of solid-solution strengthening are reviewed by E. R. Parker and T. H. Hazlett, "Relation of Properties to Microstructure," pp. 50–53, American Society for Metals, Metals Park, Ohio, 1954. A fairly mathematical discussion of the interactions between dislocations and solute atoms is given by A. H. Cottrell, "Relation of Properties to Microstructure," pp. 131–162, American Society for Metals, Metals Park, Ohio, 1954.

[2] H. Suzuki, *Sci. Repts. Research Insts. Tohoku Univ.*, vol. 4A, no. 5, pp. 455–463, 1952; "Dislocations and Mechanical Properties of Crystals," p. 361, John Wiley & Sons, Inc., New York, 1957.

[3] J. C. Fisher, *Acta Met.*, vol. 2, p. 9, 1954.

pattern of order across the slip plane. An internal surface of increased energy is produced at the slip plane, and this results in an increase in the stress required to produce slip. The chemical interaction of Suzuki would be expected to predominate over short-range order in dilute solutions, where the stacking-fault energy decreases rapidly with concentration. In concentrated solid solutions strengthening from short-range order should predominate.

In a binary alloy with *long-range order* each of the constituent atoms occupies special sites in the lattice. In effect, this results in a superlattice with a larger unit cell and a new crystal structure. The interaction of dislocations with long-range order[1] results in a strengthening effect. An ordered crystal will contain domains within which the order is perfect, but which are out of step with the order in the neighboring domains. Since the domain boundaries are a high-energy interface, there is an interaction between dislocations and these antiphase boundaries. The stress required to produce slip varies inversely with the distance between domain boundaries. Because more domain boundaries are produced as slip continues, the rate of strain hardening is higher in the ordered condition than in the disordered state. Ordered alloys with a fine domain size (approximately 50 A) are stronger than the disordered state. Ordered alloys with a large domain size generally have a yield stress lower than that of the disordered state. This arises from the fact that the dislocations in a well-ordered alloy are grouped into pairs, each pair having a Burgers vector twice as large as that for the disordered lattice.

5-5. Yield-point Phenomenon

Many metals, particularly low-carbon steel, show a localized, heterogeneous type of transition from elastic to plastic deformation which produces a yield point in the stress-strain curve. Rather than having a flow curve with a gradual transition from elastic to plastic behavior, such as was shown in Fig. 3-1, metals with a yield point have a flow curve or, what is equivalent, a load-elongation diagram similar to Fig. 5-10. The load increases steadily with elastic strain, drops suddenly, fluctuates about some approximately constant value of load, and then rises with further strain. The load at which the sudden drop occurs is called the *upper yield point*. The constant load is called the *lower yield point*, and the elongation which occurs at constant load is called the *yield-point elongation*. The deformation occurring throughout the yield-point elon-

---

[1] N. Brown and M. Herman, *Trans. AIME*, vol. 206, pp. 1353–1354, 1954; A. H. Cottrell, "Relation of Properties to Microstructure," pp. 131–162, American Society for Metals, Metals Park, Ohio, 1954; N. Brown, *Phil. Mag.*, vol. 4, pp. 693–704, 1959; P. A. Flinn, *Trans. AIME*, vol. 218, pp. 145–154, 1960.

gation is heterogeneous.   At the upper yield point a discrete band of deformed metal, often readily visible with the eye, appears at a stress concentration such as a fillet, and coincident with the formation of the band the load drops to the lower yield point.   The band then propagates along the length of the specimen, causing the yield-point elongation.

In the usual case several bands will form at several points of stress concentration.   These bands are generally at approximately 45° to the tensile axis.   They are usually called *Lüders bands*, Hartmann lines, or stretcher strains, and this type of deformation is sometimes referred to as the Piobert effect. When several Lüders bands are formed, the flow curve during the yield-point elongation will be ir-regular, each jog corresponding to the formation of a new Lüders band.

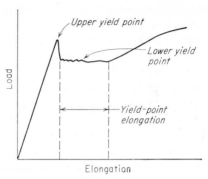

Fig. 5-10. Typical yield-point behavior.

After the Lüders bands have propagated to cover the entire length of the specimen test section, the flow will increase with strain in the usual manner.   This marks the end of the yield-point elongation.

The yield-point phenomenon was found originally in low-carbon steel. A pronounced upper and lower yield point and a yield-point elongation of over 10 per cent can be obtained with this material under proper condi-tions.   More recently the yield point has come to be accepted as a general phenomenon, since it has been observed in a number of other metals and alloys.   In addition to iron and steel, yield points have been observed in polycrystalline molybdenum, titanium, and aluminum alloys and in single crystals of iron, cadmium, zinc, alpha and beta brass, and alumi-num.   Usually the yield point can be associated with small amounts of interstitial or substitutional impurities.   For example, it has been shown[1] that almost complete removal of carbon and nitrogen from low-carbon steel by wet-hydrogen treatment will remove the yield point.   However, only about 0.001 per cent of either of these elements is required for a reappearance of the yield point.

A number of experimental factors affect the attainment of a sharp upper yield point.   A sharp upper yield point is promoted by the use of an elastically rigid (hard) testing machine, very careful axial alignment of the specimen, the use of specimens free from stress concentrations, high rate of loading, and, frequently, testing at subambient temperatures. If, through careful avoidance of stress concentrations, the first Lüders

[1] J. R. Low and M. Gensamer, *Trans. AIME*, vol. 158, p. 207, 1944.

band can be made to form at the middle of the test specimen, the upper yield point can be roughly twice the lower yield point. However, it is more usual to obtain an upper yield point 10 to 20 per cent greater than the lower yield point.

Cottrell's concept that the yield point is due to the interaction of solute atoms with dislocations was introduced in the previous section. Solute atoms diffuse to dislocations because this lowers the strain energy of the crystal. The dislocations are then anchored in position by an atmosphere of solute atoms. The original theory[1] considered that solute atoms would segregate only to edge dislocations, because a screw dislocation ordinarily has no tensile component. More recently the theory has been modified to show that there is a strong interaction between interstitial atoms and screw dislocations when the lattice is nonsymmetrically deformed by the solute atoms so that a tensile component of stress is developed.[2]

The local concentration of solute atoms near the dislocation, c, is related to the average concentration c_0 by the relationship

$$c = c_0 \exp \frac{-U}{kt} \qquad (5\text{-}6)$$

where U is the interaction energy. For carbon and nitrogen in iron the interaction energy has a value between 0.5 and 1.0 ev. As the temperature decreases, the solute atmosphere becomes more concentrated and below a critical temperature the atmosphere condenses into a line of solute atoms. These atoms occupy a position of maximum interaction energy just below the center of a positive edge dislocation running parallel to the length of the dislocation.

The shear stress required to tear away a dislocation from its atmosphere goes through a maximum when plotted against displacement. Therefore, a dislocation will tend to return to its atmosphere for small displacements, but when a certain breakaway stress has been reached, movement of the dislocation becomes easier with increasing distance from the atmosphere. The stress at which the dislocations break away from their atmosphere corresponds to the upper yield point. This releases an avalanche of dislocations into the slip plane, and these pile up at the grain boundary. The stress concentration at the tip of the pile-up combines with the applied stress in the next grain to unlock the dislocations in that grain, and in this way a Lüders band propagates over the specimen.

[1] A. H. Cottrell and B. A. Bilby, *Proc. Phys. Soc. (London)*, vol. 62A, pp. 49–62, 1949.

[2] A. W. Cochardt, G. Schoek, and H. Wiedersich, *Acta Met.*, vol. 3, pp. 533–537, 1955.

5-6. Strain Aging

Strain aging is a type of behavior, usually associated with the yield-point phenomenon, in which the strength of a metal is increased and the ductility is decreased on heating at a relatively low temperature after cold working. This behavior can best be illustrated by considering Fig. 5-11, which schematically describes the effect of strain aging on the

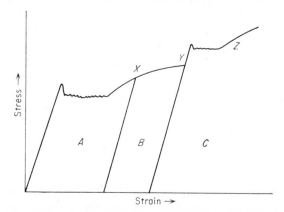

Fig. 5-11. Stress-strain curves for low-carbon steel showing strain aging. Region A, original material strained through yield point. Region B, immediately retested after reaching point X. Region C, reappearance and increase in yield point after aging at 300°F.

flow curve of a low-carbon steel. Region A of Fig. 5-11 shows the stress-strain curve for a low-carbon steel strained plastically through the yield-point elongation to a strain corresponding to point X. The specimen is then unloaded and retested without appreciable delay or any heat treatment (region B). Note that on reloading the yield point does not occur, since the dislocations have been torn away from the atmosphere of carbon and nitrogen atoms. Consider now that the specimen is strained to point Y and unloaded. If it is reloaded after aging for several days at room temperature or several hours at an aging temperature like 300°F, the yield point will reappear. Moreover, the yield point will be increased by the aging treatment from Y to Z. The reappearance of the yield point is due to the diffusion of carbon and nitrogen atoms to the dislocations during the aging period to form new atmospheres of interstitials anchoring the dislocations. Support for this mechanism is found in the fact that the activation energy for the return of the yield point on aging is in good agreement with the activation energy for the diffusion of carbon in alpha iron.

Nitrogen plays a more important role in the strain aging of iron than carbon because it has a higher solubility and diffusion coefficient and produces less complete precipitation during slow cooling. From a practical standpoint it is important to eliminate strain aging in deep-drawing steel because the reappearance of the yield point can lead to difficulties with surface markings or "stretcher strains" due to the localized heterogeneous deformation. To control strain aging, it is usually desirable to lower the amount of carbon and nitrogen in solution by adding elements which will take part of the interstitials out of solution in the form of stable carbides or nitrides. Aluminum, vanadium, titanium, columbium, and boron have been added for this purpose. While a certain amount of control over strain aging can be achieved, there is no commercial low-carbon steel which is completely non-strain aging. The usual industrial solution to this problem is to deform the metal to point X by roller leveling or a skin-pass rolling operation and use it immediately before it can age.

Just as the existence of a yield point has become recognized as a general metallurgical phenomenon, so the existence of strain aging has come to be recognized in metals other than low-carbon steel. In addition to the return of the yield point and an increase in the yield point after aging, it has been suggested[1] that a serrated flow curve and a minimum in the variation of strain-rate sensitivity with temperature are characteristics of strain aging. The strain-rate sensitivity is the change in stress required to produce a certain change in strain rate at constant temperature (see Chap. 9). The occurrence of serrations in the stress-strain curve is known as discontinuous, or repeated, yielding. It is also called the *Portevin–Le Châtelier effect*. This phenomenon is due to successive yielding and aging while the specimen is being tested. This results from the fact that in the range of temperature in which it occurs the time required for the diffusion of solute atoms to dislocations is much less than the time required for an ordinary tension test. Discontinuous yielding is observed in aluminum–3 per cent magnesium alloys, duralumin, alpha brass, and plain-carbon steel.

For plain-carbon steel discontinuous yielding occurs in the temperature region of 450 to 700°F. This temperature region is known as the *blue brittle region* because steel heated in this temperature region shows a decreased tensile ductility and decreased notched-impact resistance. This temperature range is also the region in which steels show a minimum in strain-rate sensitivity and a maximum in the rate of strain aging. All these facts point to the realization that blue brittleness is not a separate phenomenon but is just an accelerated strain aging.

The phenomenon of strain aging should be distinguished from a process

[1] J. D. Lubahn, *Trans. ASM*, vol. 44, pp. 643–666, 1952.

known as *quench aging*, which occurs in low-carbon steels. Quench aging is a type of true precipitation hardening that occurs on quenching from the temperature of maximum solubility of carbon and nitrogen in ferrite. Subsequent aging at room temperature, or somewhat above, produces an increase in hardness and yield stress, as in the age hardening of aluminum alloys. Plastic deformation is not necessary to produce quench aging.

5-7. Strengthening from Second-phase Particles

Only a relatively small number of alloy systems permit extensive solid solubility between two or more elements, and only a relatively small hardening effect can be produced in most alloy systems by solid-solution additions. Therefore, most commercial alloys contain a heterogeneous microstructure consisting of two or more metallurgical phases. A number of different conditions may be encountered.[1] The two phases may be ductile and present in the microstructure in relatively massive form, as in alpha-beta brass. On the other hand, the structure may consist of a hard, brittle phase in a ductile matrix, as in spheroidized steel or WC particles in a cobalt matrix in a cemented carbide cutting tool.

The strengthening produced by second-phase particles is usually additive to the solid-solution strengthening produced in the matrix. For two-phase alloys produced by equilibrium methods, the existence of a second phase ensures maximum solid-solution hardening because its presence resulted from supersaturation of the continuous phase. Moreover, the presence of second-phase particles in the continuous matrix phase results in localized internal stresses which modify the plastic properties of the continuous phase. Many factors must be considered for a complete understanding of strengthening from second-phase particles. These factors include the size, shape, number, and distribution of the second-phase particles, the strength, ductility, and strain-hardening behavior of the matrix and second phase, the crystallographic fit between the phases, and the interfacial energy and interfacial bonding between the phases. It is almost impossible to vary these factors independently in experiments, and it is very difficult to measure many of these quantities with any degree of precision. Therefore, our existing knowledge of the effect of second phases on mechanical properties is mainly empirical and incomplete.

In a multiphase alloy, each phase contributes certain things to the over-all properties of the aggregate. If the contributions from each

---

[1] A review of the effect of second-phase particles on mechanical properties has been given by J. E. Dorn and C. D. Starr, "Relation of Properties to Microstructure," pp. 71–94, American Society for Metals, Metals Park, Ohio, 1954.

phase are independent, then the properties of the multiphase alloy will be a weighted average of the properties of the individual phases. For example, the density of a two-phase alloy will be equal to the sum of the volume fraction of each phase times its density. However, for the structure-sensitive mechanical properties the properties of the aggregate are generally influenced by interaction between the two phases. Two simple hypotheses may be used to calculate the properties of a two-phase alloy from the properties of the individual phases. It it is assumed that

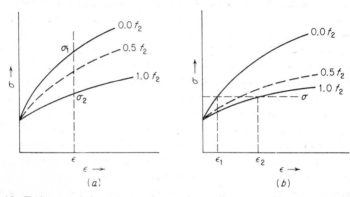

Fig. 5-12. Estimate of flow stress of two-phase alloy. (a) Equal strain; (b) equal stress. (*From J. E. Dorn and C. D. Starr, "Relation of Properties to Microstructure," pp. 77–78, American Society for Metals, Metals Park, Ohio, 1954.*)

the strain in each phase is equal, the average stress in the alloy for a given strain will increase linearly with the volume fraction of the strong phase.

$$\sigma_{avg} = f_1\sigma_1 + f_2\sigma_2 \tag{5-7}$$

The volume fraction of phase 1 is f_1, and $f_1 + f_2 = 1$. Figure 5-12a shows the calculation of the flow curve for an alloy with 0.5 volume fraction of phase 2 on the basis of the equal-strain hypothesis. An alternative hypothesis is to assume that the two phases are subjected to equal stresses. The average strain in the alloy at a given stress is then given by

$$\epsilon_{avg} = f_1\epsilon_1 + f_2\epsilon_2 \tag{5-8}$$

Figure 5-12b shows the flow curve for a 0.5-volume-fraction alloy on the basis of the equal-stress hypothesis. Both these hypotheses are simple approximations, and the strengths of alloys containing two ductile phases usually lie somewhere between the values predicted by the two models.

The deformation of an alloy consisting of two ductile phases depends upon the total deformation and the volume fractions of the phases. Slip will occur first in the weaker phase, and if very little of the stronger phase is present, most of the deformation will continue in the softer phase. At large deformations flow of the matrix will occur around the particles of the harder phase. If the volume fraction of the harder phase is less than about 0.3, the soft phase deforms more than the hard phase for reductions of up to 60 per cent. At greater reductions the two phases deform more uniformly. When the phases are present in about equal amounts, they deform to about the same extent.[1]

The mechanical properties of an alloy consisting of a ductile phase and a hard brittle phase will depend on how the brittle phase is distributed in the microstructure. If the brittle phase is present as a grain-boundary envelope, as in oxygen-free copper-bismuth alloys or hypereutectoid steel, the alloy is brittle. If the brittle phase is in the form of discontinuous particles at grain boundaries, as when oxygen is added to copper-bismuth alloys or with internally oxidized copper and nickel, the brittleness of the alloy is reduced somewhat. When the brittle phase is present as a fine dispersion uniformly distributed throughout the softer matrix, a condition of optimum strength and ductility is obtained. This is the situation in heat-treated steel with a tempered martensitic structure.

The strengthening produced by a finely dispersed insoluble second phase in a metallic matrix is known as *dispersion hardening*. A very similar strengthening phenomenon, *precipitation hardening*, or *age hardening*, is produced by solution treating and quenching an alloy in which a second phase is in solid solution at the elevated temperature but precipitates upon quenching and aging at a lower temperature. The age-hardening aluminum alloys and copper-beryllium alloys are common examples. For precipitation hardening to occur, the second phase must be soluble at an elevated temperature but must exhibit decreasing solubility with decreasing temperature. By contrast, the second phase in dispersion-hardening systems has very little solubility in the matrix, even at elevated temperatures. Usually there is atomic matching, or *coherency*, between the lattices of the precipitate and the matrix, while in dispersion-hardened systems there generally is no coherency between the second-phase particles and the matrix. The requirement of a decreasing solubility with temperature places a limitation on the number of useful precipitation-hardening alloy systems. On the other hand, it is at least theoretically possible to produce an almost infinite number of dispersion-hardened systems by mixing finely divided metallic powders and second-phase particles (oxides, carbides, nitrides, borides, etc.) and consolidating them by powder metallurgy techniques. Advantage has been taken of this method to produce dispersion-hardened systems which are thermally stable at very high temperatures. Because of the finely dispersed second-phase particles these alloys are much more resistant to recrystallization

[1] L. M. Clarebrough, *Australian J. Sci. Repts.*, vol. 3, pp. 72–90, 1950.

and grain growth than single-phase alloys. Because there is very little solubility of the second-phase constituent in the matrix, the particles resist growth or overaging to a much greater extent than the second-phase particles in a precipitation-hardening system.

The formation of a coherent precipitate in a precipitation-hardening system, such as Al-Cu, occurs in a number of steps. After quenching from solid solution the alloy contains regions of solute segregation, or clustering. Guiner and Preston first detected this local clustering with special X-ray techniques, and therefore this structure is known as a GP zone. The clustering may produce local strain, so that the hardness of GP[1] is higher than for the solid solution. With additional aging the hardness is increased further by the ordering of larger clumps of copper atoms on the {100} planes of the matrix. This structure is known as GP[2], or θ''. Next, definite precipitate platelets of $CuAl_2$, or θ', which are coherent with the matrix, form on the {100} planes of the matrix. The coherent precipitate produces an increased strain field in the matrix and a further increase in hardness. With still further aging the equilibrium phase $CuAl_2$, or θ, is formed from the transition lattice θ'. These particles are no longer coherent with the matrix, and therefore the hardness is lower than at the stage when coherent θ' was present. For most precipitation-hardening alloys the resolution with the light microscope of the first precipitate occurs after the particles are no longer coherent with the matrix. Continued aging beyond this stage produces particle growth and further decrease in hardness. Figure 5-13 illustrates the way in which strength varies with aging time or particle size. The sequence of events in the Al-Cu system is particularly complicated. Although other precipitation-hardening systems may not have so many stages, it is quite common for a coherent precipitate to form and then lose coherency when the particle grows to a critical size.

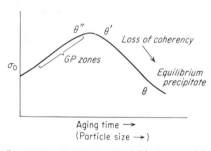

Fig. 5-13. Variation of yield stress with aging time (schematic).

Metallographic observations of deformation mechanisms in precipitation-hardening systems require very careful techniques.[1] In the as-quenched condition slip bands are broad and widely spaced. As aging continues, the slip bands become finer and more closely spaced. As GP[2] zones form and the alloy proceeds toward peak hardness, fewer and fewer slip bands can be observed with the electron microscope.

[1] G. Thomas and J. Nutting, *J. Inst. Metals*, vol. 86, pp. 7–14, 1957–1958; R. B. Nicholson, G. Thomas, and J. Nutting, *Acta Met.*, vol. 8, pp. 172–176, 1960.

When the alloy begins to overage and coherency breaks down, the slip lines once more can be observed. Electron-microscope studies have shown that dislocation motion is impeded by fully and partially coherent precipitates, but eventually the dislocations shear through the particles. For a noncoherent precipitate the slip lines do not cut through the particles. Instead, the dislocation lines bend to avoid the particles, probably by a process of cross slip.[1]

The degree of strengthening resulting from second-phase dispersions depends upon the distribution of particles in the soft matrix. In addition to shape, the second-phase dispersion can be described by specifying the volume fraction, average particle diameter, and mean interparticle spacing. These factors are all interrelated so that one factor cannot be changed without affecting the others (see Prob. 5-5). For example, for a given volume fraction of second phase, reducing the particle size decreases the average distance between particles. For a given size particle, the distance between particles decreases with an increase in the volume fraction of second phase. Quantitative relationships between strength and the geometrical factors have not been determined to any extent for real alloys.

However, the qualitative aspects of dispersion hardening can be considered, the common situation of carbide particles in ferrite being used as an example. In general, the hardness and strength increase with carbon content or volume fraction of the carbide phase. Further, for a given carbon content, the strength will be higher for a fine carbide spacing than with a coarse interparticle spacing. Particle shape has a less important effect on tensile properties, although for a given volume fraction of carbides lamellar carbides will be stronger than spheroidized carbides. Particle shape is of greater importance in notched impact, where a spheroidized structure will be tougher than a lamellar structure.

Detailed quantitative metallography on steels heat-treated to provide different interparticle spacings has shown the relationship between strength and structure. Gensamer and coworkers[2] found that the flow stress, at a true strain of 0.2, was inversely proportional to the logarithm of the mean interparticle spacing (mean free ferrite path) for pearlite and spheroidite structures (Fig. 5-14). Confirmation of this relationship has been found for tempered martensitic structures[3] and overaged Al-Cu alloys.[4] Figure 5-15 illustrates the marked strengthening produced by $CuAl_2$ particles in an Al-Cu alloy. The figure shows the variation of

[1] P. B. Hirsch, J. Inst. Metals, vol. 86, pp. 13–14, 1957–58.

[2] M. Gensamer, E. B. Pearsall, W. S. Pellini, and J. R. Low, Jr., Trans. ASM, vol. 30, pp. 983–1020, 1942.

[3] A. M. Turkalo and J. R. Low, Jr., Trans. Met. Soc. AIME, vol. 212, pp. 750–758, 1958.

[4] C. D. Starr, R. B. Shaw, and J. E. Dorn, Trans. ASM, vol. 46, pp. 1075–1088, 1954.

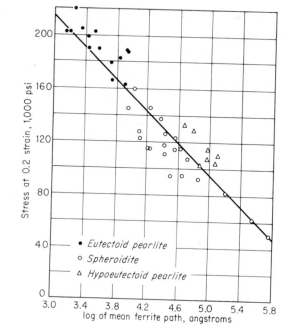

Fig. 5-14. Flow stress vs. logarithm of mean free ferrite path in steels with pearlitic and spheroidal distribution of carbides. (*M. Gensamer, E. B. Pearsall, W. S. Pellini, and J. R. Low, Trans. ASM, vol. 30, p. 1003, 1942.*)

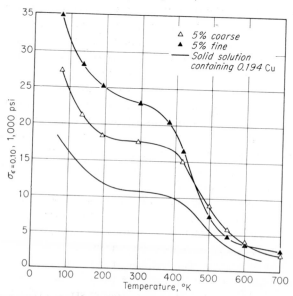

Fig. 5-15. Variation of flow stress with temperature for Al-Cu alloy containing 5 volume per cent fine and coarse second-phase particles. (*C. D. Starr, R. B. Shaw, and J. E. Dorn, Trans. ASM, vol. 46, p. 1085, 1954.*)

flow stress with temperature for an alloy containing 5 volume per cent of $CuAl_2$ in three conditions. The top curve is for a fine $CuAl_2$ dispersion, the middle curve for a coarse dispersion, and the bottom curve is for an alloy without dispersed particles which contains the same amount of copper in solid solution as the top two alloys.

Table 5-2 gives the variation of proportional limit and tensile strength

TABLE 5-2
VARIATION OF TENSILE PROPERTIES WITH VOLUME FRACTION
OF SECOND PHASE FOR Co-WC ALLOYS†

Volume fraction of WC	Mean interparticle path, μ	Proportional limit, psi $\times$ 10^{-3}	Tensile strength, psi $\times$ 10^{-3}
0.00	....	...	103
0.10	16.8	9	102
0.35	3.4	21	165
0.50	1.7	40	173
0.63	1.0	74	193
0.78	0.4	85	124
0.90	0.2	...	95

† C. Nishimatsu and J. Gurland, *Trans. ASM*, vol. 52, pp. 469–484, 1960.

with composition and mean interparticle spacing for a series of Co-WC alloys. These alloys were prepared by powder metallurgy and consisted of uniform dispersions of 2-μ WC particles in a cobalt matrix. The rapid increase in proportional limit with increasing volume fraction of second phase shows the effect of decreasing interparticle spacing in raising the flow stress of the ductile matrix. Tensile strength is much less sensitive. However, when the microstructure is nearly all tungsten carbide, the material fails in a brittle manner by fracture through the carbides. Fracture initiates in the brittle carbide phase but does not propagate readily through the surrounding cobalt envelope. However, with a high volume fraction of carbide many WC particles are touching, and the brittle fracture can propagate readily from carbide to carbide. This is reflected in a decrease in tensile strength.

Dislocation models of dispersion hardening and precipitation hardening consider that second-phase particles act as obstacles to the movement of dislocations. In making the first analysis of this problem, Mott and Nabarro[1] considered that a dislocation line would take on a smoothly curved form when moving through the lattice instead of moving as a straight line. Since different sections of the dislocation line can move partly independently of each other, the random stress fields in the matrix which interact with the dislocation line do not cancel out. Because a

[1] N. F. Mott and F. R. N. Nabarro, *Proc. Phys. Soc. (London)*, vol. 52, p. 86, 1940.

dislocation possesses *line tension*, which tends to keep it at its shortest length, any bending or increase in length of a dislocation line requires the expenditure of extra energy. The smallest radius of curvature to which a dislocation line can be bent under the influence of an internal stress field τ_i is given by

$$R = \frac{Gb}{2\tau_i} \qquad (5\text{-}9)$$

Orowan[1] suggested that the yield stress of an alloy containing a dispersion of fine particles is determined by the shear stress required to force a dislocation line between two particles separated by a distance Λ. In

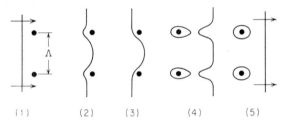

$$(1) \qquad (2) \qquad (3) \qquad (4) \qquad (5)$$

Fig. 5-16. Schematic drawing of stages in passage of a dislocation between widely separated obstacles—based on Orowan's mechanism of dispersion hardening.

Fig. 5-16, stage 1 shows a straight dislocation line approaching two particles separated by a distance Λ. At stage 2 the line is beginning to bend, and at stage 3 it has reached the critical stage. Since Λ equals twice the critical radius of curvature, from Eq. (5-9) the stress needed to force the dislocation line between the obstacles is given by

$$\tau = \frac{Gb}{\Lambda} \qquad (5\text{-}10)$$

At stage 4 the dislocation has passed between the obstacles, leaving them encircled by small loops of dislocations. Every dislocation gliding over the slip plane adds one loop around the obstacle. These dislocation loops exert a back stress which must be overcome by dislocations moving on the slip plane. This requires an increase in shear stress to continue deformation. Thus, the presence of dispersed particles leads to increased strain hardening during the period when loops are building up around the particles. This continues until the shear stress developed by the loops is high enough to shear the particles or the surrounding matrix. According to the theory developed by Fisher, Hart, and Pry,[2] the increase in shear

[1] E. Orowan, discussion in "Symposium on Internal Stresses," p. 451, Institute of Metals, London, 1947.

[2] J. C. Fisher, E. W. Hart, and R. H. Pry, *Acta Met.*, vol. 1, p. 336, 1953.

stress due to fine particles, τ_h, is related to the volume fraction of the second phase, f, and the shear strength of a dislocation-free matrix, τ_c, by the relationship

$$\tau_h = 3\tau_c f^n \tag{5-11}$$

where n is between 1 and 1.5.

Orowan's relationship between strength and particle spacing has been experimentally confirmed for most systems containing overaged or noncoherent particles. The Fisher, Hart, and Pry equation for the contribution to strain hardening from dispersed particles also appears to be approximately verified. According to Eq. (5-10) the shear strength of a dispersion-hardened alloy will have a maximum value when Λ has a value that makes it equally likely that dislocations will pass between the particles or cut through them. As the distance between particles is increased, the critical radius of curvature is increased and the stress required to bend the dislocation line is decreased. When the distance between particles is decreased, the dislocation line becomes more rigid. It is difficult for the dislocation line to bend sharply enough to pass between the particles, and so it shears through them instead. There are indications that in the region of small particle spacing the yield stress is a direct function of the radius of the particles.

5-8. Hardening Due to Point Defects

Vacancies and interstitials are produced by the bombardment of a metal with high-energy nuclear particles. The bombardment of the lattice with fast neutrons having energies up to 2 million ev knocks atoms into interstitial positions in the lattice, and vacancies are left behind. Neutron irradiation increases the hardness and yield strength of most metals. In copper single crystals a dose of 10^{18} neutrons per square centimenter increases the yield strength by a factor of 10 and changes the deformation characteristics so that they are similar to alpha brass.[1] In metals which show a ductile-to-brittle transition, such as steel, prolonged neutron irradiation can appreciably raise the transition temperature. The structural changes producing radiation hardening and radiation damage are difficult to study in detail because at least two point defects are acting simultaneously. Interstitials are even more mobile than vacancies, so that quite low temperatures are required to prevent them from interacting with other lattice defects.

A situation in which the only point defects are vacancies can be produced by rapidly quenching a pure metal (so that there can be no

[1] A. H. Cottrell, "Vacancies and Other Point Defects in Metals and Alloys," pp. 1–39, Institute of Metals, London, 1958.

precipitation of a second phase) from a temperature near its melting point. At room temperature or below the metal contains a super-saturated solution of most of the vacancies that existed in equilibrium at the higher temperature. Vacancy concentrations of up to about 10^{-4} can be achieved by quenching. Soft metals, such as aluminum, copper, and zinc, can be hardened by introducing a randomly distributed population of vacancies in this way. *Quench hardening* results in an increase in yield stress and a decrease in the rate of strain hardening, just as is produced by radiation hardening. Therefore, a dispersion of point defects can produce hardening, by analogy with the hardening produced by a dispersion of second-phase particles. The mechanism by which this occurs is not yet established. There is some evidence that at this stage the single vacancies have migrated into clusters. A greater quench hardening results if an aging treatment is interposed between the quench and the measurement of the tensile properties. It is likely that the aging permits the vacancies to migrate to dislocations, where they interact and impede the movement of dislocations (see Sec. 6-12). Much remains to be learned about the interaction of point defects with each other and with line defects and how these interactions affect the mechanical properties.

Plastic deformation produces point defects, chiefly vacancies. These point defects are created by the intersection of dislocations, and therefore, a discussion of this topic will be deferred until Chap. 6. Vacancy formation appears to be particularly important in the fatigue of metals, and it will be considered from this standpoint in Chap. 12. At elevated temperatures vacancies become very important in controlling diffusion and in making possible dislocation climb. Thus, vacancies are important in the creep of metals, and they will be considered in greater detail in Chap. 13.

5-9. Strain Hardening and Cold Work

In Chap. 4 strain hardening was attributed to the interaction of dislocations with other dislocations and with other barriers to their motion through the lattice. So long as slip takes place on only a single set of parallel planes, as with single crystals of hcp metals, only a small amount of strain hardening occurs. However, even with single crystals extensive easy glide is not a general phenomenon, and with polycrystalline specimens it is not observed. Because of the mutual interference of adjacent grains in a polycrystalline specimen multiple slip occurs readily, and there is appreciable strain hardening. Plastic deformation which is carried out in a temperature region and over a time interval such that the strain hardening is not relieved is called *cold work*.

Plastic deformation produces an increase in the number of dislocations, which by virtue of their interaction results in a higher state of internal stress. An annealed metal contains about 10^6 to 10^8 dislocations per square centimeter, while a severely plastically deformed metal contains about 10^{12} dislocations per square centimeter. Strain hardening or cold work can be readily detected by X-ray diffraction, although detailed analysis of the X-ray patterns in terms of the structure of the cold-worked state is not usually possible. In Laue patterns cold work produces a blurring, or *asterism*, of the spots. For Debye-Scherrer patterns the lines are broadened by cold work. X-ray line broadening can be due to both a decrease in size of the diffraction unit, as would occur if the grains were fragmented by cold work, and an increase in lattice strain due to dislocation interaction. Techniques for analyzing the entire peak profile of X-ray lines and separating out the contribution due to lattice strain and particle size have been developed.[1] It is likely that improvements in this

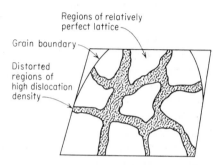

Fig. 5-17. Model of the structure of cold-worked metal (schematic).

method and more widespread application of the technique will result in better understanding of the structure of cold-worked metal.

A fairly reliable model of the structure of cold-worked metal has developed from microbeam X-ray studies[2] and from electron microscopy of thin films. Figure 5-17 is a schematic drawing of the cold-worked structure that occurs within a single grain. It is a cell-like structure consisting of relatively perfect regions of the lattice which are connected with each other by boundaries of dislocation networks. According to this model the dislocation density varies drastically from a high value in the distorted boundaries to a low value in the relatively perfect regions. The study of the dislocation structure of cold-worked metal with thin-film electron microscopy is a very active area of research which should provide valuable information about how these networks vary with composition, deformation, and temperature.

Most of the energy expended in deforming a metal by cold working is converted into heat. However, roughly about 10 per cent of the expended

[1] B. E. Warren and B. L. Averbach, *J. Appl. Phys.*, vol. 21, p. 595, 1950; B. E. Warren and B. L. Averbach, "Modern Research Techniques in Physical Metallurgy," American Society for Metals, Metals Park, Ohio, 1953; B. E. Warren, "Progress in Metal Physics," vol. 8, pp. 147–202, Pergamon Press, Ltd., London, 1959.

[2] P. Gay, P. B. Hirsch, and A. Kelly, *Acta Cryst.*, vol. 7, p. 41, 1954.

energy is stored in the lattice as an increase in internal energy. Reported values of stored energy[1] range from about 0.01 to 1.0 cal/g of metal. The magnitude of the stored energy increases with the melting point of the metal and with solute additions. For a given metal the amount of stored energy depends on the type of deformation process, e.g., wire drawing vs. tension. The stored energy increases with strain up to a limiting value corresponding to saturation. It increases with decreasing temperature of deformation. Very careful calorimeter measurements are required to measure the small amounts of energy stored by cold working.

The major part of the stored energy is due to the generation and interaction of dislocations during cold working. Vacancies account for part of the stored energy for metals deformed at very low temperature. However, vacancies are so much more mobile than dislocations that they readily escape from most metals deformed at room temperature. Stacking faults and twin faults are probably responsible for a small fraction of the stored energy. A reduction in short-range order during the deformation of solid solutions may also contribute to stored energy. Elastic strain energy accounts for only a minor part of the measured stored energy.

Strain hardening or cold working is an important industrial process that is used to harden metals or alloys that do not respond to heat treatment. The rate of strain hardening can be gaged from the slope of the flow curve. In mathematical terms, the rate of strain hardening can be expressed by the strain-hardening coefficient n in Eq. (3-1). Generally, the rate of strain hardening is lower for hcp metals than for cubic metals. Increasing temperature also lowers the rate of strain hardening. For alloys strengthened by solid-solution additions the rate of strain hardening may be either increased or decreased compared with the behavior for the pure metal. However, the final strength of a cold-worked solid-solution alloy is almost always greater than that of the pure metal cold-worked to the same extent.

Figure 5-18 shows the typical variation of strength and ductility

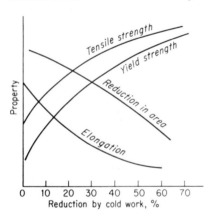

Fig. 5-18. Variation of tensile properties with amount of cold work.

[1] For a comprehensive review of the stored energy of cold work see A. L. Titchener and M. B. Bever, "Progress in Metal Physics," vol. 7, pp. 247–338, Pergamon Press, Ltd., London, 1958.

parameters with increasing amount of cold work. Since in most cold-working processes one or two dimensions of the metal are reduced at the expense of an increase in the other dimensions, cold work produces elongation of the grains in the principal direction of working. Severe deformation produces a reorientation of the grains into a preferred orientation (Sec. 5-11). In addition to the changes in tensile properties shown in Fig. 5-18, cold working produces changes in other physical properties. There is usually a small decrease in density of the order of a few tenths of a per cent, an appreciable decrease in electrical conductivity due to an increased number of scattering centers, and a small increase in the thermal coefficient of expansion. Because of the increased internal energy of the cold-worked state chemical reactivity is increased. This leads to a general decrease in corrosion resistance and in certain alloys introduces the possibility of stress-corrosion cracking.

5-10. Bauschinger Effect

In an earlier discussion of the strain hardening of single crystals it was shown that generally a lower stress is required to reverse the direction of slip on a certain slip plane than to continue slip in the original direction. The directionality of strain hardening is called the Bauschinger effect. Figure 5-19 is an example of the type of stress-strain curve that is obtained when the Bauschinger effect is considered.

The initial yield stress of the material in tension is A. If the same ductile material were tested in compression, the yield strength would be approximately the same, point B on the dashed curve. Now, consider that a new specimen is loaded in tension past the tensile yield stress to C along the path OAC. If the speci-men is then unloaded, it will follow the

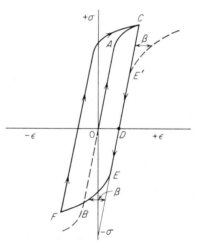

Fig. 5-19. Bauschinger effect and hysteresis loop.

path CD, small elastic-hysteresis effects being neglected. If now a compressive stress is applied, plastic flow will begin at the stress corresponding to point E, which is appreciably lower than the original compressive yield stress of the material. While the yield stress in tension was increased by strain hardening from A to C, the yield stress in compression was decreased. This is the *Bauschinger effect*. The phenomenon is reversible, for had the specimen originally been stressed plastically in compression, the yield stress in tension would have been decreased. One way of describing the amount of Bauschinger effect is by the Bauschinger strain β (Fig. 5-19). This is the difference in strain between the tension and compression curves at a given stress.

If the loading cycle in Fig. 5-19 is completed by loading further in compression to point F, then unloading, and reloading in tension, a mechanical-hysteresis loop is obtained. The area under the loop will depend upon the initial overstrain beyond the yield stress and the number of times the cycle is repeated. If the cycle is repeated many times, failure by fatigue is likely to occur.

Orowan[1] has pointed out that, if the Bauschinger effect is due solely to the effect of back stresses, the flow curve after reversal of strain ought always to be softer than the flow curve for the original direction of strain. However, not all metals show a permanent softening after strain reversal, and those which do show only a small effect. Therefore, Orowan considers that the Bauschinger effect can be explained by the same mechanism which he proposed for dispersion hardening (Sec. 5-7). Obstacles to dislocation motion are considered to be other dislocations, inclusions, precipitate particles, etc. The stress required to move a dislocation through these obstacles is given approximately by Eq. (5-10). For a given shear stress a dislocation line will move over the slip plane until it meets a row of obstacles that are strong enough to resist shearing and close enough to resist the dislocation loop from squeezing between them. Now, when the load is removed, the dislocation line will not move appreciably unless there are very high back stresses. However, when the direction of loading is reversed, the dislocation line can move an appreciable distance at a low shear stress because the obstacles to the rear of the dislocation are not likely to be so strong and closely packed as those immediately in front of the dislocation. As the dislocation line moves, it encounters, on the average, stronger and closer obstacles, so that the shear stress continuously increases with strain. This is in agreement with the type of flow curve usually observed for the Bauschinger effect.

5-11. Preferred Orientation

A metal which has undergone a severe amount of deformation, as in rolling or wire drawing, will develop a *preferred orientation*, or texture, in which certain crystallographic planes tend to orient themselves in a preferred manner with respect to the direction of maximum strain. The tendency for the slip planes in a single crystal to rotate parallel to the axis

[1] E. Orowan, Causes and Effects of Internal Stresses, in "Internal Stresses and Fatigue in Metals," Elsevier Publishing Company, New York, 1959.

of principal strain was considered in the previous chapter.   The same situation exists in a polycrystalline aggregate, but the complex interactions between the multiple slip systems makes analysis of the polycrystalline situation much more difficult.   Since the individual grains in a polycrystalline aggregate cannot rotate freely, lattice bending and fragmentation will occur.

Preferred orientations are determined by X-ray methods.   The X-ray pattern of a fine-grained randomly oriented metal will show rings corresponding to different planes where the angles satisfy the condition for Bragg reflections.   If the grains are randomly oriented, the intensity of the rings will be uniform for all angles, but if a preferred orientation exists, the rings will be broken up into short arcs, or spots.   The dense areas of the X-ray photograph indicate the orientation of the poles of the planes corresponding to the diffraction ring in question.   The orientation of the grains of a particular crystallographic orientation with respect to the principal directions of working is best shown by means of a *pole figure*.   For a description of the methods of determining pole figures and a compilation of pole figures describing the deformation textures in many metals, the reader is referred to Barrett.[1]   The current use of Geiger-counter X-ray diffractometer techniques[2] has made it possible to determine pole figures with greater accuracy and less labor than with older film methods.

A preferred orientation can be detected with X rays after about a 20 to 30 per cent reduction in cross-sectional area by cold working.   At this stage of reduction there is appreciable scatter in the orientation of individual crystals about the ideal orientation.   The scatter decreases with increasing reduction, until at about 80 to 90 per cent reduction the preferred orientation is essentially complete.   The type of preferred orientation, or deformation texture, which is developed depends primarily on the number and type of slip systems available and on the principal strains.   Other factors which may be important are the temperature of deformation and the type of texture present prior to deformation.

The simplest deformation texture is produced by the drawing or rolling of a wire or rod.   This is often referred to as a *fiber texture* because of its similarity to the arrangement in naturally fibrous materials.   It is important to note that a distinction should be made between the *crystallographic* fibering produced by crystallographic reorientation of the grains during deformation and *mechanical fibering*, which is brought about by the alignment of inclusions, cavities, and second-phase constituents in the

[1] C. S. Barrett, "Structure of Metals," 2d ed., chap. 9, McGraw-Hill Book Company, Inc., New York, 1952.

[2] A. H. Geisler, "Modern Research Techniques in Physical Metallurgy," American Society for Metals, Metals Park, Ohio, 1953.

main direction of mechanical working. Mechanical and crystallographic fibering are important factors in producing directional mechanical properties of plastically worked metal shapes such as sheet and rods. This will be discussed further in Chap. 9.

In an ideal wire texture a definite crystallographic direction lies parallel to the wire axis, and the texture is symmetrical around the wire or fiber axis. Several types of deviations from the ideal texture are observed. In face-centered cubic metals a double fiber texture is usually observed. The grains have either $\langle 111 \rangle$ or $\langle 100 \rangle$ parallel to the wire axis and have random orientations around the axis.[1] Body-centered cubic metals have a simple $\langle 110 \rangle$ wire texture. The wire texture in hcp metals is not so simple. For moderate amounts of deformation the hexagonal axis $\langle 0001 \rangle$ of zinc is parallel to the fiber axis, while for severe deformation the hexagonal axis is about 20° from the wire axis. For magnesium and its alloys $\langle 10\bar{1}0 \rangle$ is parallel to the wire axis for deformation below 450°C, while above this temperature $\langle 2\bar{1}\bar{1}0 \rangle$ is parallel to the fiber axis.

The deformation texture of a sheet produced by rolling is described by the crystallographic planes parallel to the surface of the sheet as well as the crystallographic directions parallel to the direction of rolling. There is often considerable deviation from the ideal texture, so that pole figures are useful for describing the degree of preferred orientation.[2] Precision determination of the rolling texture in fcc metals has shown that the texture may be described best by the {123} planes lying parallel to the plane of the sheet with the $\langle 112 \rangle$ direction parallel to the rolling direction.[3] This texture changes to the more common {110} $\langle 112 \rangle$ texture by the addition of solid-solution alloying elements. In bcc metals the {100} planes tend to be oriented parallel to the plane of the sheet with the $\langle 110 \rangle$ direction within a few degrees of the rolling direction. For hcp metals the basal plane tends to be parallel with the rolling plane with $\langle 2\bar{1}\bar{1}0 \rangle$ aligned in the rolling direction.

The preferred orientation resulting from deformation is strongly dependent on the slip and twinning systems available for deformation, but it is not generally affected by processing variables such as die angle, roll diameter, roll speed, and reduction per pass. The direction of flow is the most important process variable. For example, the same deformation texture is produced whether a rod is made by rolling, drawing, or swaging.

The formation of a strong preferred orientation will result in an

---

[1] It has been suggested that a $\langle 111 \rangle$ texture is favored by easy cross slip, which occurs most readily in metals with high stacking-fault energy. See N. Brown, *Trans. AIME*, vol. 221, pp. 236–238, 1961.

[2] A large number of pole figures for rolling textures are given by Barrett, *op. cit.*, chap. 18.

[3] R. E. Smallman, *J. Inst. Metals*, vol. 84, pp. 10–18, 1955–56.

anisotropy in mechanical properties. Although the individual grains of a metal are anisotropic with respect to mechanical properties, when these grains are combined in a random fashion into a polycrystalline aggregate the mechanical properties of the aggregate tend to be isotropic. However, the grain alignment that accounts for the preferred orientation again introduces an anisotropy in mechanical properties. Different mechanical properties in different directions can result in uneven response of the material during forming and fabrication operations.

5-12. Annealing of Cold-worked Metal

The cold-worked state is a condition of higher internal energy than the undeformed metal. Therefore, there is a tendency for strain-hardened

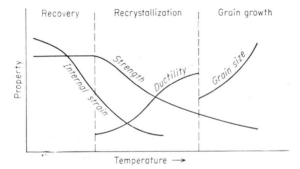

Fig. 5-20. Schematic drawing indicating recovery, recrystallization, and grain growth and the chief property changes in each region.

metal to revert to the strain-free condition. With increasing temperature the cold-worked state becomes more and more unstable. Eventually the metal softens and reverts to a strain-free condition. The over-all process by which this occurs is known as annealing.[1] Annealing is very important commercially because it restores the ductility to a metal that has been severely strain-hardened. Therefore, by interposing annealing operations after severe deformation it is possible to deform most metals to a very great extent.

The over-all process of annealing can be divided into three fairly distinct processes, recovery, recrystallization, and grain growth. Figure 5-20 will help to distinguish between these processes. *Recovery* is usually defined as the restoration of the physical properties of the cold-worked metal without any observable change in microstructure. Electrical con-

[1] For detailed reviews of annealing, see P. A. Beck, *Adv. in Phys.*, vol. 3, pp. 245–324, 1954; J. E. Burke and D. Turnbull, "Progress in Metal Physics," vol. 3, Interscience Publishers, Inc., New York, 1952.

ductivity increases rapidly toward the annealed value during recovery, and lattice strain, as measured with X rays, is appreciably reduced. The properties that are most affected by recovery are those which are sensitive to point defects. The strength properties, which are controlled by dislocations, are not affected at recovery temperatures. An exception to this is single crystals of hcp metals which have deformed on only one set of planes (easy glide). For this situation it is possible to recover completely the yield stress of a strain-hardened crystal without producing

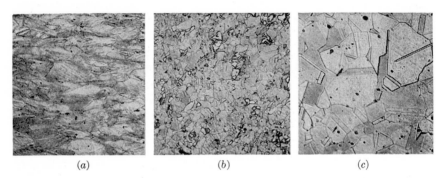

(a)   (b)   (c)

Fig. 5-21. Changes in microstructure of cold-worked 70-30 brass with annealing. (a) Cold-worked 40 per cent; (b) 400°C, 15 min; (c) 575°C, 15 min. 150×. (*Courtesy L. A. Monson.*)

recrystallization. *Recrystallization* is the replacement of the cold-worked structure by a new set of strain-free grains. Recrystallization is readily detected by metallographic methods and is evidenced by a decrease in hardness or strength and an increase in ductility. The density of dislocations decreases considerably on recrystallization, and all effects of strain hardening are eliminated. The stored energy of cold work is the driving force for both recovery and recrystallization. Polygonization (Sec. 5-3) can be considered an intermediate situation between recovery and recrystallization. If the new strain-free grains are heated at a temperature greater than that required to cause recrystallization, there will be a progressive increase in grain size. The driving force for grain growth is the decrease in free energy resulting from a decreased grain-boundary area due to an increase in grain size. Figure 5-21 shows the progression from a cold-worked microstructure to a fine recrystallized grain structure, and finally to a larger grain size by grain growth.

Recrystallization is the reversion by thermal activation of the cold-worked structure to its original strain-free condition. As the temperature is increased, the dislocation networks tend to contract and the regions of initially low dislocation density begin to grow. The fraction of the microstructure that has recrystallized in a time t can be represented by an equation of the form

$$X = 1 - \exp\left(-Bt^{n'}\right) \tag{5-12}$$

where B and n' are constants. Values of n' between 1 and 2 indicate one-dimensional recrystallization, while values between 2 and 3 denote two-dimensional recrystallization. It is convenient to consider the process of recrystallization in terms of the rate of nucleation N and the rate of growth G of new strain-free grains. The relative values of N and G determine the recrystallized grain size. If N is large with respect to G, there are many sites of nucleation and the grain size will be relatively small.

Six main variables influence recrystallization behavior. They are (1) amount of prior deformation, (2) temperature, (3) time, (4) initial grain size, (5) composition, and (6) amount of recovery or polygonization prior to the start of recrystallization. Because the temperature at which recrystallization occurs depends on the above variables, it is not a fixed temperature in the sense of a melting temperature. For practical considerations a recrystallization temperature can be defined as the temperature at which a given alloy in a highly cold-worked state completely recrystallizes in 1 hr. The relationship of the above variables to the recrystallization process can be summarized[1] as follows.

1. A minimum amount of deformation is needed to cause recrystallization.

2. The smaller the degree of deformation, the higher the temperature required to cause recrystallization.

3. Increasing the annealing time decreases the recrystallization temperature. However, temperature is far more important than time. Doubling the annealing time is approximately equivalent to increasing the annealing temperature 10°C.

4. The final grain size depends chiefly on the degree of deformation and to a lesser extent on the annealing temperature. The greater the degree of deformation and the lower the annealing temperature, the smaller the recrystallized grain size.

5. The larger the original grain size, the greater the amount of cold work required to produce an equivalent recrystallization temperature.

6. The recrystallization temperature decreases with increasing purity of the metal. Solid-solution alloying additions always raise the recrystallization temperature.

7. The amount of deformation required to produce equivalent recrystallization behavior increases with increased temperature of working.

8. For a given reduction in cross section, different metalworking processes, such as rolling, drawing, etc., produce somewhat different effective

[1] R. F. Mehl, Recrystallization, in "Metals Handbook," pp. 259–268, American Society for Metals, Metals Park, Ohio, 1948.

deformations.   Therefore, identical recrystallization behavior may not be obtained.

Because the driving force for grain growth is appreciably lower than the driving force for recrystallization, at a temperature at which recrystallization occurs readily grain growth will occur slowly.   However, grain growth is strongly temperature-dependent, and a grain-coarsening region will soon be reached in which the grains increase in size very rapidly. Grain growth is inhibited considerably by the presence of a fine dispersion of second-phase particles, which restricts grain-boundary movement. For the usual type of grain growth, where the grains increase in size uniformly, theory predicts that at a given temperature the grain size D at a time t is given by

$$D^2 - D_0{}^2 = Ct \qquad (5\text{-}13)$$

However, most experimental data agree best with an equation

$$D^{1/n} - D_0{}^{1/n} = Ct \qquad (5\text{-}14)$$

where n varies from about 0.2 to 0.5, depending on the metal and the temperature.

Under certain conditions, some of the grains of a fine-grained recrystallized metal will begin to grow rapidly at the expense of the other grains when heated at a higher temperature.   This phenomenon is known as exaggerated, or *abnormal, grain growth*.   The driving force for exaggerated grain growth is the decrease in surface energy, not stored energy, but because the phenomenon shows kinetics similar to those of recrystallization it is often called *secondary recrystallization*.

5-13. Annealing Textures

The recrystallization of a cold-worked metal may produce a preferred orientation which is different from that existing in the deformed metal. This is called an *annealing texture*, or *recrystallization texture*.   An outstanding example is the cube texture in copper, where the {100} plane lies parallel to the rolling plane with a $\langle 001 \rangle$ direction parallel to the direction of rolling.   The existence of a recrystallization texture depends on a preferential orientation of the nuclei of the recrystallized grains.   Annealing-texture formation depends on a number of processing variables, the amount and type of deformation preceding annealing, the composition of the alloy, the grain size, the annealing temperature and time, and the preferred orientation produced by the deformation.

Generally the factors which favor the formation of a fine recrystallized grain size also favor the formation of an essentially random orientation of recrystallized grains.   Moderate cold reductions and low annealing

temperatures are beneficial.   A good way of minimizing a recrystallization texture is first to produce a strong preferred orientation by a heavy
initial reduction and then use a high annealing temperature.   This is followed by enough added cold reduction to break up this orientation and
produce a fine recrystallized grain size at a low temperature.

Sometimes the formation of a strong recrystallization texture is beneficial.   The best example is cube-oriented silicon-iron transformer sheet,
where the grains are oriented in the easy direction of magnetization.   To
obtain a nearly perfect recrystallization texture, it is necessary to produce
a high degree of preferred orientation in the cold-worked metal.   This is
followed by long annealing at a high temperature to allow selective grain
growth to produce a strong texture.

BIBLIOGRAPHY

Barrett, C. S.: "Structure of Metals," 2d ed., chap. 15, McGraw-Hill Book Company,
    Inc., New York, 1952.
Birchenall, C. E.: "Physical Metallurgy," McGraw-Hill Book Company, Inc., New
    York, 1959.
Chalmers, B.: "Physical Metallurgy," John Wiley & Sons, Inc., New York, 1959.
Guy, A. G.: "Elements of Physical Metallurgy," 2d ed., Addison-Wesley Publishing
    Company, Reading, Mass., 1959.
"Relation of Properties to Microstructure," American Society for Metals, Metals
    Park, Ohio, 1954.

Chapter 6
DISLOCATION THEORY

6-1. Introduction

A dislocation is the linear lattice defect that is responsible for nearly all aspects of the plastic deformation of metals. This concept was introduced in Chap. 4, where the geometry of edge and screw dislocations was presented for the case of a simple cubic lattice. It was shown that the existence of a dislocationlike defect is necessary to explain the low values of yield stress observed in real crystals. A general picture has been given of the interaction of dislocations with foreign atoms, precipitate particles, and other dislocations. This has been used to give a qualitative picture of the strain hardening of single crystals and, in Chap. 5, to help explain solid-solution hardening, dispersed-phase hardening, yield-point behavior, and strain aging.

This chapter is intended to present a more complete and somewhat more rigorous treatment of dislocation theory. The rapidly improving techniques for detecting dislocations in real metals are considered, and experimental evidence to support the theory is given wherever possible in subsequent portions of the chapter. The effect on dislocation behavior of considering real fcc, bcc, or hcp crystal structures is considered. Interaction of dislocations with other dislocations, vacancies, and foreign atoms is discussed in some detail. The important problem of dislocation multiplication by means of the Frank-Read source is given particular attention.

6-2. Methods of Detecting Dislocations

The concept of the dislocation was proposed independently by Taylor, Orowan, and Polanyi[1] in 1934, but the idea lay relatively undeveloped until the end of World War II. There followed a period of approximately 10 years in which the theory of dislocation behavior was developed

---

[1] G. I. Taylor, *Proc. Roy. Soc.* (*London*), vol. 145A, p. 362, 1934; E. Orowan, *Z. Physik*, vol. 89, pp. 605, 614, 634, 1934; M. Polanyi, *Z. Physik*, vol. 89, p. 660, 1934.

extensively and applied to practically every aspect of the plastic deformation of metals. Because there were no really reliable methods for detecting dislocations in real materials, it was necessary to build much of this
theory on the basis of indirect observations of dislocation behavior.
Fortunately, since 1955 improved techniques have made it possible to
observe dislocations as they actually exist in many materials. Today,
there is no question as to the existence of lattice defects with properties
similar to those ascribed to the dislocation. Many of the theoretical
predictions have been confirmed by experiment, while others have had to
be modified and some abandoned. Undoubtedly, better experimental
techniques, applicable to a wider variety of materials, will be developed
in the future. As more information is obtained on dislocation behavior in
real materials, there certainly will be other changes in current concepts of
dislocation theory.

The resolving power of the best electron microscope would have to be
improved by a factor of 5 to 10 in order to observe directly the distortion
of the individual lattice planes around a dislocation in a metal crystal.[1]
Practically all the experimental techniques for detecting dislocations
utilize the strain field around a dislocation to increase its effective size.
These experimental techniques can be roughly classified into two categories, those involving chemical reactions with the dislocation, and those
utilizing the physical changes at the site of a dislocation.[2] Chemical
methods include etch-pit techniques and precipitation techniques. Methods based on the physical structure at a dislocation site include transmission electron microscopy of thin films and X-ray diffraction techniques.

The simplest chemical technique is the use of an etchant which forms
a pit at the point where a dislocation intersects the surface. Etch pits
are formed at dislocation sites because the strain field surrounding the
dislocation causes preferential chemical attack. A great deal of information about dislocation behavior in the ionic crystal LiF has been obtained
in this way by Gilman and Johnston.[3] Important information about

---

[1] It has been possible by means of an electron microscope to observe this lattice distortion in an organic crystal of platinum phthalocyanine, which has a very large lattice
spacing (12 A) [J. W. Menter, *Proc. Roy. Soc. (London)*, vol. 236A, p. 119, 1956]. An
indication of the lattice distortion at a dislocation in metals has been obtained by
making use of the magnification resulting from moiré patterns produced by electron
transmission through two thin overlapping crystals with slightly different orientations or lattice spacings. See G. A. Bassett, J. W. Menter, and D. W. Pashley, *Proc.
Roy. Soc. (London)*, vol. 246A, p. 345, 1958.

[2] Several excellent reviews of experimental techniques have been published. See
P. B. Hirsch, *Met. Reviews*, vol. 4, no. 14, pp. 101–140, 1959; J. Nutting, Seeing Dis-
locations, in "The Structure of Metals," Institution of Metallurgists, Interscience
Publishers, Inc., New York, 1959.

[3] J. J. Gilman and W. G. Johnston, "Dislocations and Mechanical Properties of
Crystals," John Wiley & Sons, Inc., New York, 1957.

dislocations in metals has also been obtained with etch-pit techniques. Figure 6-1 shows the excellent resolution obtainable from etch-pit studies on alpha brass.[1] Pits only 500 A apart have been resolved. In the region of heavy slip shown in this electron micrograph the dislocation density is 10^{10} cm^{-2}.

In metals, etch-pit formation at dislocations appears to be dependent on purity.[2] Because of solute segregation to the dislocation, the region

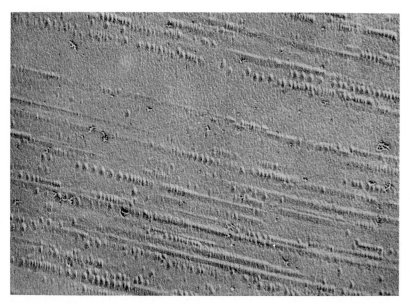

Fig. 6-1. Etch pits on slip bands in alpha brass crystals. 5,000×. (*J. D. Meakin and H. G. F. Wilsdorf, Trans. AIME, vol. 218, p. 740, 1960.*)

around the dislocation becomes anodic to the surrounding metal, and consequently preferential etching occurs at the dislocation. Figure 5-4 shows an etch-pit structure in an iron-silicon alloy which was made visible by diffusion of carbon atoms to the dislocations. Etch-pit techniques are useful because they can be used with bulk samples. However, care must be taken to ensure that pits are formed only at dislocation sites and that all dislocations intersecting the surface are revealed.

A similar method of detecting dislocations is to form a visible precipitate along the dislocation lines. Usually a small amount of impurity is added to form the precipitate after suitable heat treatment. The procedure is often called "decoration" of dislocations. This technique was first used

[1] J. D. Meakin and H. G. F. Wilsdorf, *Trans. AIME*, vol. 218, pp. 737–745, 1960.

[2] A summary of etch-pit techniques in metals is given by L. C. Lowell, F. L. Vogel, and J. H. Wernick, *Metal Prog.*, vol. 75, pp. 96–96D, 1959.

by Hedges and Mitchell[1] to decorate dislocations in AgBr with photolytic silver. It has since been used with many other ionic crystals,[2] such as AgCl, NaCl, KCl, and CaF_2. With these optically transparent crystals this technique has the advantage that it shows the internal structure of the dislocation lines. Figure 6-2 shows a hexagonal network of dislocations in a NaCl crystal which was made visible by decoration. Although dislocation decoration has not been used extensively with metals, some

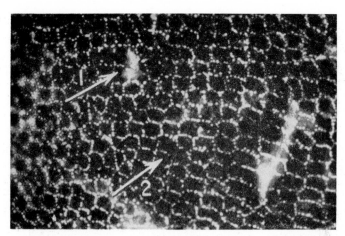

Fig 6-2. Hexagonal network of dislocations in NaCl detected by a decoration technique. (*S. Amelinckx, in "Dislocations and Mechanical Properties of Crystals," John Wiley & Sons, Inc., New York,* 1957.)

work has been done along these lines with the Al-Cu precipitation-hardening system and with silicon crystals.

The most powerful method available today for the detection of dislocations in metals is transmission electron microscopy of thin foils.[3] Thin sheet, less than 1 mm thick, is thinned after deformation by electropolishing to a thickness of about 1,000 A. At this thickness the specimen is transparent to electrons in the electron microscope. Although the crystal lattice cannot be resolved, individual dislocation lines can be observed because the intensity of the diffracted electron beam is altered by the strain field of the dislocation. By means of this technique it has been possible to observe dislocation networks (Fig. 6-3), stacking faults, dislocation pile-up at grain boundaries (Fig. 5-1), Cottrell-Lomer barriers, and many other structural features of dislocation theory. Dislocation

[1] J. M. Hedges and J. W. Mitchell, *Phil. Mag.*, vol. 44, p. 223, 1953.

[2] S. Amelinckx, "Dislocations and Mechanical Properties of Crystals," John Wiley & Sons, Inc., New York, 1957.

[3] P. B. Hirsch, R. W. Horne, and M. J. Whelan, *Phil. Mag.*, vol. 1, p. 677, 1956; W. Bollmann, *Phys. Rev.*, vol. 103, p. 1588, 1956.

movement has been observed by generating thermal stresses in the thin foil with the electron beam.   It is expected that much more information will be gained with this method as techniques for preparing and deforming thin foils are improved.

The dislocation structure of a crystal can be detected by X-ray-diffraction microradiographic techniques.[1]   The strain field at the dislocation results in a different diffracted intensity.   The method has the

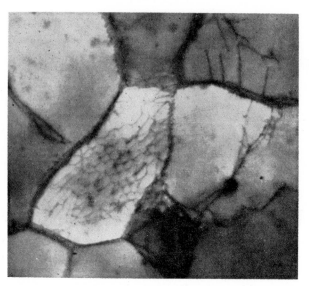

Fig. 6-3. Dislocation network in cold-worked aluminum.   32,500×.   (*P. B. Hirsch, R. W. Horne, and M. J. Whelan, Phil. Mag., ser. 8, vol. 1, p. 677, 1956.*)

advantage of being nondestructive and giving information on a bulk sample.   However, with the resolution at present available it is limited to crystals of low dislocation density (approximately $10^6 cm^{-2}$).

6-3. Burgers Vector and the Dislocation Loop

The Burgers vector **b** is the vector which defines the magnitude and direction of slip.   Therefore, it is the most characteristic feature of a dislocation.   It has already been shown that for a *pure* edge dislocation the Burgers vector is perpendicular to the dislocation line, while for a *pure* screw dislocation the Burgers vector is parallel to the dislocation line. Actually, dislocations in real crystals are rarely straight lines and rarely lie in a single plane.   In general, a dislocation will be partly edge and partly screw in character.   As shown by Figs. 6-2 and 6-3, dislocations will

[1] A. R. Lang, *J. Appl. Phys.*, vol. 30, pp. 1748–1755, 1959.

ordinarily take the form of curves or loops, which in three dimensions form an interlocking dislocation network. In considering a dislocation loop in a slip plane any small segment of the dislocation line can be resolved into edge and screw components. For example, in Fig. 6-4, the dislocation loop is pure screw at point A and pure edge at point B, while along most of its length it has mixed edge and screw components. Note, however, that the Burgers vector is the same along the entire dislocation loop. If this were not so, part of the crystal above the slipped region would have to slip by a different amount relative to another part of the crystal and this would mean that another dislocation line would run across the slipped region.

A convenient way of defining the Burgers vector of a dislocation is by means of the *Burgers circuit*. Consider Fig. 4-8, which shows the atomic arrangement around an edge dislocation. Starting at a lattice point, imagine a path traced from atom to atom, an equal distance in each direction, always in the direction of one of the vectors of the unit cell. If the region enclosed by the path does not contain a dislocation, the Burgers circuit will close. However, if the path encloses a dislocation, the Burgers circuit will not close. The closure failure of the Burgers circuit is the Burgers vector **b**. The closure failure of a Burgers circuit around several dislocations is equal to the sum of their separate Burgers vectors.

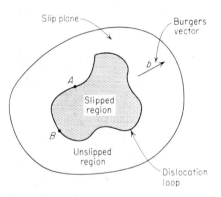

Fig. 6-4. Dislocation loop lying in a slip plane (schematic).

Because a dislocation represents the boundary between the slipped and unslipped region of a crystal, topographic considerations demand that it either must be a closed loop or else must end at the free surface of the crystal. In general, a dislocation line cannot end inside of a crystal. The exception is at a *node*, where three or four dislocation lines meet. A node can be considered as two dislocations with Burgers vectors $\mathbf{b}_1$ and $\mathbf{b}_2$ combining to produce a resultant dislocation $\mathbf{b}_3$. The vector $\mathbf{b}_3$ is given by the vector sum of $\mathbf{b}_1$ and $\mathbf{b}_2$.

Since the periodic force field of the crystal lattice requires that atoms must move from one equilibrium position to another, it follows that the Burgers vector must always connect one equilibrium lattice position with another. Therefore, the crystal structure will determine the possible Burgers vectors. A dislocation with a Burgers vector equal to one lattice spacing is said to be a *dislocation of unit strength*. Because of energy considerations dislocations with strengths larger than unity are generally unstable and dissociate into two or more dislocations of lower strength. The criterion for deciding whether or not dissociation will occur is based[1] on the fact that the strain energy of a dislocation is proportional to the square of its Burgers vector. Therefore, the dissociation reaction $\mathbf{b}_1 \rightarrow \mathbf{b}_2 + \mathbf{b}_3$ will occur when $b_1{}^2 > b_2{}^2 + b_3{}^2$, but not if $b_1{}^2 < b_2{}^2 + b_3{}^2$.

Dislocations with strengths less than unity are possible in close-packed lattices where the equilibrium positions are not the edges of the structure cell. A Burgers vector is specified by giving its components along the axes of the crystallographic structure cell. Thus, the Burgers vector for slip in a cubic lattice from a cube corner to the center of one face has the components $a_0/2$, $a_0/2$, 0. The Burgers vector is $[a_0/2, a_0/2, 0]$, or, as generally written, $\mathbf{b} = (a_0/2)[110]$. The strength of a dislocation with Burgers vector $a_0[uvw]$ is $|b| = a_0[u^2 + v^2 + w^2]^{1/2}$. For example, the magnitude of the Burgers vector given above is $|b| = a_0/\sqrt{2}$.

A dislocation of unit strength, or *unit dislocation*, has a minimum energy when its Burgers vector is parallel to a direction of closest atomic packing in the lattice. This agrees with the experimental observation that crystals almost always slip in the close-packed directions. A unit dislocation of this type is also said to be a *perfect dislocation* because translation equal to one Burgers vector produces an identity translation. For a perfect dislocation there is perfect alignment of atom planes above and below the slip plane within the dislocation loop. A unit dislocation parallel to the slip direction cannot dissociate further unless it becomes an *imperfect dislocation*, where a translation of one Burgers vector does not result in an identity translation. A stacking fault is produced by the dissociation of a unit dislocation into two imperfect dislocations. For a stacking fault to be stable, the decrease in energy due to dissociation must be greater than the increase in interfacial energy of the faulted region.

6-4. Dislocations in the Face-centered Cubic Lattice

Slip occurs in the fcc lattice on the $\{111\}$ plane in the $\langle 110 \rangle$ direction. The shortest lattice vector is $(a_0/2)$ [110], which connects an atom at a cube corner with a neighboring atom at the center of a cube face. The Burgers vector is therefore $(a_0/2)$ [110].

However, consideration of the atomic arrangement on the $\{111\}$ slip plane shows that slip will not take place so simply. Figure 6-5 represents the atomic packing on a close-packed (111) plane. It has already been shown that the $\{111\}$ planes are stacked in a sequence $ABC\ ABC\ \cdots$. The vector $\mathbf{b}_1 = (a_0/2)$ [10$\bar{1}$] defines one of the observed slip directions.

[1] F. C. Frank, *Physica*, vol. 15, p. 131, 1949.

However, if the atoms are considered as hard spheres,[1] it is easier for an atom on a type B plane to move along a zigzag path $\mathbf{b}_2 + \mathbf{b}_3$ in the valleys instead of moving over the hump that lies in the path of the vector b_1. The dislocation reaction is given by

$$\mathbf{b}_1 \rightarrow \mathbf{b}_2 + \mathbf{b}_3$$

$$\frac{a_0}{2}[10\bar{1}] \rightarrow \frac{c_0}{6}[2\bar{1}\bar{1}] + \frac{a_0}{6}[11\bar{2}]$$

To check this reaction, the summation of the x, y, z components of the right-hand side of the equation must add up to the x, y, z components of the original dislocation.

x component $\quad \tfrac{1}{2} = \tfrac{2}{6} + \tfrac{1}{6}$

y component $\quad 0 = -\tfrac{1}{6} + \tfrac{1}{6}$

z component $\quad -\tfrac{1}{2} = -\tfrac{1}{6} - \tfrac{2}{6}$

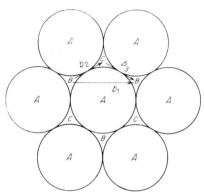

Fig. 6-5. Slip in a close-packed (111) plane in an fcc lattice. (*After A. H. Cottrell, "Dislocations and Plastic Flow in Crystals," p. 73, Oxford University Press, New York, 1953.*)

The above reaction is energetically favorable since there is a decrease in strain energy proportional to the change $a_0{}^2/2 \rightarrow a_0{}^2/3$.

Slip by this two-stage process creates a stacking fault $ABCA|CABC$ in the stacking sequence. As Fig. 6-6 shows, the dislocation with Burgers vector $\mathbf{b}_1$ has been dissociated into two *partial dislocations* $\mathbf{b}_2$ and $\mathbf{b}_3$. This dislocation reaction was suggested by Heidenreich and Shockley,[2] and therefore this dislocation arrangement is often known as *Shockley partials*, since the dislocations are imperfect ones which do not produce complete lattice translations. Figure 6-6 represents the situation looking down on (111) along [11$\bar{1}$]. AB represents the perfect dislocation line having the full slip vector $\mathbf{b}_1$. This dissociates according to the above reaction into partial dislocations with Burgers vectors $\mathbf{b}_2$ and $\mathbf{b}_3$. The combination of the two partials AC and AD is known as an *extended dislocation*. The region between them is a stacking fault representing a part of the crystal which has undergone slip intermediate between full slip and no slip. Because $\mathbf{b}_2$ and $\mathbf{b}_3$ are at a 60° angle, there will be a repulsive force between them (Sec. 6-9). However, the surface tension of the stacking fault tends to pull them together. The partial dislocations will settle at an equilibrium separation determined primarily by the stacking-fault energy. As was discussed in Sec. 4-10, the stacking-fault energy

[1] F. C. Thompson and W. E. W. Millington, *J. Iron Steel Inst.* (*London*), vol. 109, p. 67, 1924; C. H. Mathewson. *Trans. AIME*, vol. 32, p. 38, 1944.

[2] R. D. Heidenreich and W. Shockley, "Report on Strength of Solids," p. 37, Physical Society, London, 1948.

can vary considerably for different fcc metals and alloys and this in turn can have an important influence on their deformation behavior.

A characteristic of the fcc lattice is that any Burgers vector is common to two slip planes. This presents the possibility that screw dislocations, which have no fixed glide plane, may surmount obstacles by gliding onto another slip plane having a common slip direction. This is the process of *cross slip*. However, in order to do this, the extended dislocations

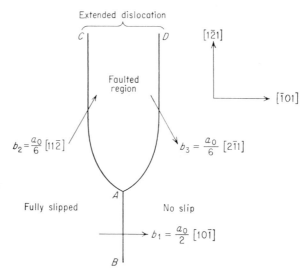

Fig. 6-6. Dissociation of a dislocation into two partial dislocations.

must first recombine into perfect dislocations since an extended disloca- tion cannot glide on any plane except the plane of the fault. Figure 4-26 shows that this requires the formation of a constriction in the stacking- fault ribbon. The greater the width of the stacking fault, or the lower the stacking fault energy, the more difficult it is to produce constrictions in the stacking faults. This may explain why cross slip is quite prevalent in aluminum, which has a very narrow stacking-fault ribbon, while it is difficult in copper, which has a wide stacking-fault ribbon.

These ideas are borne out by electron-microscope transmission studies of dislocation networks in thin foils.[1] Stacking faults can be readily detected in these thin films. The nature of the dislocation network in fcc metals changes with the stacking-fault energy. Austenitic stainless steel, with a stacking-fault energy around 13 ergs/cm^2, shows dislocation net- works only along slip planes, even for large deformations. Gold, copper, and nickel, where the energy is about 30, 40, and 80 ergs/cm^2, respectively,

[1] Hirsch, *op. cit.*

show the dislocations arranged in complex three-dimensional networks at low strains.   This changes into poorly developed subboundaries at higher deformations.   Aluminum, with a stacking-fault energy of 200 ergs/cm², shows almost perfect subboundaries.   This picture of a graded transition in the way the dislocations are arranged is in agreement with the influence of the stacking-fault energy on the ability of a metal to undergo cross slip.   Cross slip is very difficult in stainless steel, even at high strains, so that the dislocations are confined to the slip planes.   In gold, copper, and nickel, cross slip is possible, but probably only at highly stressed regions.   Therefore, cross slip of screw dislocations occurs, and at high strains they try to form low-angle boundary networks to lower

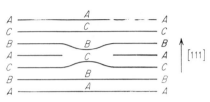

Fig. 6-7. A Frank partial dislocation or sessile dislocation.   (*After A. H. Cottrell, Dislocations and Plastic Flow in Crystals,*" *p.* 75, *Oxford University Press, New York,* 1953.)

their strain energy.   In aluminum, cross slip is very prevalent, and screw dislocations can easily arrange themselves into a network of low-angle boundaries.

Frank[1] pointed out that another type of partial dislocation can exist in the fcc lattice.   Figure 6-7 illustrates a set of (111) planes viewed from the edge.   The center part of the middle A plane is missing.   An edge dislocation is formed in this region with a Burgers vector $(a_0/3)[111]$.   This is called a *Frank partial dislocation*.   Its Burgers vector is perpendicular to the central stacking fault.   Since glide must be restricted to the plane of the stacking fault and the Burgers vector is normal to this plane, the Frank partial dislocation cannot move by glide.   For this reason it is called a *sessile dislocation*.   A sessile dislocation can move only by the diffusion of atoms or vacancies to or from the fault, i.e., by the process of climb.   Because climb is not a likely process at ordinary temperatures, sessile dislocations provide obstacles to the movement of other dislocations.   Dislocations which glide freely over the slip plane, such as perfect dislocations or Shockley partials, are called *glissile*.   A method by which a missing row of atoms can be created in the (111) plane is by the condensation of a disk of vacancies on that plane.   Evidence for the collapse of disks of vacancies in aluminum has been obtained by transmission electron microscopy.[2]

Sessile dislocations are produced in the fcc lattice by the glide of dislocations on intersecting (111) planes.   These sessile dislocations are

[1] F. C. Frank, *Proc. Phys. Soc.* (*London*), vol. 62A, p. 202, 1949.

[2] P. B. Hirsch, J. Silcox, R. E. Smallman, and K. H. Westmacott, *Phil. Mag.*, vol. 3, p. 897, 1958.

known as *Cottrell-Lomer barriers*. They are an important element in the mechanism of the strain hardening of metals. Lomer[1] pointed out that dislocations moving on intersecting slip planes will attract and combine if their Burgers vectors have suitable orientations. Figure 6-8 illustrates two dislocations moving on the slip planes of an fcc lattice. Dislocation A is moving in a (111) plane with a Burgers vector $(a_0/2)[10\bar{1}]$. Dislocation B glides in a $(11\bar{1})$ plane with a Burgers vector $(a_0/2)[011]$. These

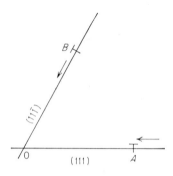

dislocations attract each other and move toward the intersection point O, which is the intersection of the two Burgers vectors along the direction $[1\bar{1}0]$. At this point the two dislocations react according to Lomer's reaction

$$\frac{a_0}{2}[10\bar{1}] + \frac{a_0}{2}[011] \rightarrow \frac{a_0}{2}[110]$$

Fig. 6-8. Dislocation reaction leading to Cottrell-Lomer barriers. (*After A. H. Cottrell, "Dislocations and Plastic Flow in Crystals," p. 171, Oxford University Press, New York, 1953.*)

to form a new dislocation of reduced energy. Since all three dislocations must be parallel to the line of intersection of the slip plane, $[1\bar{1}0]$, the edge dislocation formed by Lomer's reaction has a slip plane (001). The plane (001) contains both the Burgers vector [110] and the line $[1\bar{1}0]$. Since (001) is not a common slip plane in the fcc lattice, the dislocation formed from Lomer's reaction should not glide freely. However, it is not a true sessile dislocation, in the sense of the Frank partial, because it is not an imperfect dislocation.

Cottrell[2] showed that the product of Lomer's reaction could be made truly immobile by the following dislocation reaction:

$$\frac{a_0}{2}[110] \rightarrow \frac{a_0}{6}[11\bar{2}] + \frac{a_0}{6}[112] + \frac{a_0}{6}[110]$$

The products of this dislocation reaction are imperfect edge dislocations which form the boundaries of stacking faults. The dislocation $(a_0/6)[11\bar{2}]$ is a Shockley partial which glides in the (111) plane. It is repelled from the line O and forms a stacking fault bounded by two $[1\bar{1}0]$ lines, the line O and the line of the dislocation. In a similar way, the dislocation $(a_0/6)[112]$ glides in the $(11\bar{1})$ plane and forms a stacking fault bounded by the line O and the line of the dislocation. The third dislocation with Burgers vector $(a_0/6)[110]$ lies along the line O where the two stacking

[1] W. M. Lomer, *Phil. Mag.*, vol. 42, p. 1327, 1951.
[2] A. H. Cottrell, *Phil. Mag.*, vol. 43, p. 645, 1952.

faults join. This combination of three dislocations produced by the Cottrell-Lomer reaction forms an isosceles triangle which is locked rigidly in place and cannot glide. Therefore, Cottrell-Lomer locking provides an effective barrier to slip. Studies by transmission electron microscopy of dislocation interaction in thin foils have confirmed the existence of interaction that is in agreement with the model of Cottrell-Lomer locking.[1]

Cottrell-Lomer barriers can be overcome at high stresses and/or temperatures. A mathematical analysis of the stress required to break down a barrier either by slip on the (001) plane or by dissociation into the dislocations from which it was formed has been given by Stroh.[2] However, it has been shown[3] that for the important case of screw dislocations piled up at Cottrell-Lomer barriers the screw dislocations can generally escape the pile-up by cross slip before the stress is high enough to collapse the barrier.

6-5. Dislocations in the Hexagonal Close-packed Lattice

The basal plane of the hcp lattice is a close-packed plane with the stacking sequence $ABABAB \cdots$. Slip occurs on the basal plane (0001) in the $\langle 11\bar{2}0 \rangle$ direction (Fig. 4-3). The smallest unit vector for the hcp structure has a length a_0 and lies in the close-packed $\langle 11\bar{2}0 \rangle$ direction. Therefore, the Burgers vector is $a_0[11\bar{2}0]$. Dislocations in the basal plane can reduce their energy by dissociating into Shockley partials according to the reaction

$$a_0[11\bar{2}0] \rightarrow a_0[10\bar{1}0] + a_0[01\bar{1}0]$$

The stacking fault produced by this reaction lies in the basal plane, and the extended dislocation which forms it is confined to glide in this plane.

6-6. Dislocations in the Body-centered Cubic Lattice

Slip occurs in the $\langle 111 \rangle$ direction in the bcc lattice. The shortest lattice vector extends from an atom corner to the atom at the center of the unit cube. Therefore, the Burgers vector is $(a_0/2)[111]$. It will be recalled that slip lines in iron have been found to occur on $\{110\}$, $\{112\}$, and $\{123\}$, although in other bcc metals slip appears to occur predominantly on the $\{110\}$ planes.

[1] M. J. Whelan, *Proc. Roy. Soc. (London)*, vol. 249A, p. 114, 1958; all possible dislocation reactions in the fcc lattice have been worked out by J. P. Hirth, *J. Appl. Phys.*, vol. 32, pp. 700–706, 1961.

[2] A. N. Stroh, *Phil. Mag.*, vol. 1, ser. 8, p. 489, 1956.

[3] A. Seeger, J. Diehl, S. Mader, and R. Rebstock, *Phil. Mag.*, vol. 2, p. 323, 1957.

Dislocation reactions have not been studied so extensively in the bcc lattice as in the fcc lattice. Cottrell[1] has suggested that a perfect dislocation in a (112) plane can dissociate according to the reaction

$$\frac{a_0}{2}[111] \rightarrow \frac{a_0}{3}[112] + \frac{a_0}{6}[11\bar{1}]$$

The dislocation $(a_0/3)[112]$ is a pure edge dislocation since its Burgers vector lies perpendicular to the slip plane. It is also an imperfect sessile dislocation that forms the boundary of a stacking fault in the (112) planes. The dislocation $(a_0/6)[11\bar{1}]$ is an imperfect glissile dislocation similar to the Shockley partial of the fcc lattice. However, because $[11\bar{1}]$ is the line of intersection of three planes of the type $\{112\}$, this dislocation can glide out of the plane of the stacking fault too easily to be part of a true extended dislocation. A dislocation in the (112) plane may also lower its energy by dissociating according to the reaction

$$\frac{a_0}{2}[11\bar{1}] \rightarrow \frac{a_0}{6}[11\bar{1}] + \frac{a_0}{3}[11\bar{1}]$$

As discussed above, both the partial dislocations formed by this reaction are pure screw, and because of the geometry of the situation, they are not completely confined to the (112) slip plane. An analysis[2] of the atomic positions giving rise to stacking faults on $\{112\}$ planes shows that there are two types which may result. While the existence of stacking faults in the bcc lattice has been demonstrated by X-ray diffraction, detailed studies of the dislocation reactions discussed in this paragraph have not yet been made.

Cottrell[3] has suggested another dislocation reaction, which appears to lead to the formation of immobile dislocations in the bcc lattice. This dislocation reaction may be important to the brittle fracture of bcc metals. Consider Fig. 6-9a. Dislocation A, with Burgers vector $(a_0/2)[\bar{1}11]$, is gliding in the (101) plane. Dislocation B, with Burgers vector $(a_0/2)[111]$, is gliding in the intersecting slip plane $(10\bar{1})$. The two dislocations come together and react to lower their strain energy by the reaction

$$\frac{a_0}{2}[\bar{1}\bar{1}1] + \frac{a_0}{2}[111] \rightarrow a_0[001]$$

The product of this reaction is a pure edge dislocation which lies on the (001) plane. Since this is not a common slip plane in the bcc lattice,

[1] A. H. Cottrell, "Dislocations and Plastic Flow in Crystals," Oxford University Press, New York, 1953.

[2] J. M. Silcock, *Acta Met.*, vol. 7, p. 359, 1959.

[3] A. H. Cottrell, *Trans. Met. Soc. AIME*, vol. 212, p. 192, 1958.

the dislocation is immobile. However, the (001) plane is the cleavage plane along which brittle fracture occurs. Cottrell suggests that the formation of a dislocation on the cleavage plane by slip on intersecting {110} planes is equivalent to introducing a crack one lattice spacing thick (Fig. 6-9b). This crack can then grow by additional dislocations gliding over the {110} planes. While this particular dislocation reaction has not

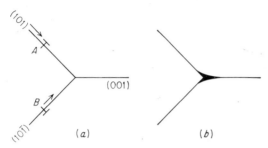

Fig. 6-9. Slip on intersecting (110) planes.   (*A. H. Cottrell, Trans. AIME, vol.* 212, *p.* 196, 1958.)

been established by experiment in bcc metals, it has been found to operate in cubic ionic crystals such as LiF and MgO.

6-7. Stress Field of a Dislocation

A dislocation is surrounded by an elastic stress field that produces forces on other dislocations and results in interaction between dislocations and solute atoms. For the case of a perfect dislocation a good approximation of the stress field can be obtained from the mathematical theory of elasticity for continuous media. However, the equations obtained are not valid close to the core of the dislocation line. The equations given below apply to straight edge and screw dislocations in an isotropic crystal.[1] The stress around a straight dislocation will be a good approximation to that around a curved dislocation at distances that are small compared with the radius of curvature. Appreciably greater complexity results from the consideration of a crystal with anisotropic elastic constants.[2]

Figure 6-10 represents the cross section of a cylindrical piece of elastic material containing an edge dislocation running through point O parallel to the z axis (normal to the plane of the figure). The original undistorted cylinder without a dislocation is shown by the dashed line. The dis-

[1] For derivations see F. R. N. Nabarro, *Advances in Phys.*, vol. 1, no. 3, pp. 271–395, 1952; W. T. Read, Jr., "Dislocations in Crystals," pp. 114–123, McGraw-Hill Book Company, Inc., New York, 1953.

[2] J. D. Eshelby, W. T. Read, and W. Shockley, *Acta Met.*, vol. 1, pp. 351–359, 1953.

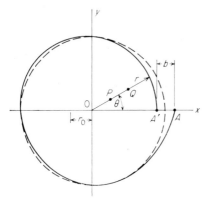

Fig. 6-10. Deformation of a circle containing an edge dislocation. The unstrained circle is shown by a dashed line. The solid line represents the circle after the dislocation has been introduced.

location was produced by making a radial cut along the plane $y = 0$ (line OA), sliding the cut surfaces along each other the distance AA', and joining them back together again. This sequence of operations[1] produces a positive edge dislocation running along the z axis with a strain field identical with that around a dislocation model such as that of Fig. 4-8. Since the dislocation line is parallel to the z axis, strains in that direction are zero and the problem can be treated as one in plane strain.

For the case of a straight edge dislocation in an elastically isotropic material the stresses, in terms of three orthogonal coordinate axes, are given by the following equations. The notation is the same as that used in Chaps. 1 and 2.

$$\sigma_x = -\tau_0 \frac{by(3x^2 + y^2)}{(x^2 + y^2)^2} \tag{6-1}$$

$$\sigma_y = \tau_0 \frac{by(x^2 - y^2)}{(x^2 + y^2)^2} \tag{6-2}$$

$$\sigma_z = \nu(\sigma_x + \sigma_y) \tag{6-3}$$

where

$$\tau_0 = \frac{G}{2\pi(1 - \nu)}$$

$$\tau_{xy} = \tau_0 \frac{bx(x^2 - y^2)}{(x^2 + y^2)^2} \tag{6-4}$$

$$\tau_{xz} = \tau_{yz} = 0 \tag{6-5}$$

For polar coordinates, the equations are

$$\sigma_r = \sigma_\theta = \frac{-\tau_0 b \sin \theta}{r} \tag{6-6}$$

$$\tau_{r\theta} = \tau_{\theta r} = \tau_0 \frac{b \cos \theta}{r} \tag{6-7}$$

σ_r acts in the radial direction, while σ_θ acts in a plane perpendicular to r. Note that the stresses vary inversely with distance from the dislocation

---

[1] It is interesting that this problem was analyzed by Volterra in 1907, long before the concept of dislocations was originated. The mathematical details may be found in A. E. H. Love, "A Treatise on the Mathematical Theory of Elasticity," pp. 221–228, Cambridge University Press, New York, 1934.

line. Since the stress becomes infinite at $r = 0$, a small cylindrical region $r = r_0$ around the dislocation line must be excluded from the analysis.

A straight screw dislocation in an isotropic medium has complete cylindrical symmetry. For a rectangular-coordinate system only two components of stress are not equal to zero.

$$\tau_{xz} = -\frac{Gb}{2\pi}\frac{y}{x^2 + y^2} \tag{6-8}$$

$$\tau_{yz} = \frac{Gb}{2\pi}\frac{x}{x^2 + y^2} \tag{6-9}$$

Since there is no extra half plane of atoms in a screw dislocation, there are no tensile or compressive normal stresses. The stress field is simply one of shear. The radial symmetry of this stress field is apparent when the shear stress is expressed in a polar-coordinate system.

$$\tau_{\theta z} = \frac{Gb}{2\pi r} \tag{6-10}$$

The strain field around an edge dislocation in a silicon crystal has been observed[1] by means of polarized infrared radiation. The variation in intensity is in agreement with what would be expected from the equations for a stress field around an edge dislocation in an isotropic medium.

The strain energy involved in the formation of an edge dislocation can be estimated from the work involved in displacing the cut OA in Fig. 6-10 a distance b along the slip plane.

$$U = \frac{1}{2}\int_{r_0}^{r_1} \tau_{r\theta}\, b\, dr = \frac{1}{2}\int_{r_0}^{r_1}\tau_0 b^2 \cos\theta\,\frac{dr}{r} \tag{6-11}$$

But $\cos\theta = 1$ along the slip plane $y = 0$, so that the strain energy is given by

$$U = \frac{Gb^2}{4\pi(1-\nu)}\ln\frac{r_1}{r_0} \tag{6-12}$$

In the same way, the strain energy of a screw dislocation is given by

$$U = \frac{1}{2}\int_{r_0}^{r_1}\tau_{\theta z} b\, dr = \frac{Gb^2}{4\pi}\ln\frac{r_1}{r_0} \tag{6-13}$$

Note that, in accordance with our assumption up to this point, the strain energy per unit length of dislocation is proportional to Gb^2. This strain energy corresponds to about 10 ev for each atom plane threaded by an edge dislocation (Prob. 6-9). The total energy of a crystal containing

[1] W. L. Bond and J. Andrus, *Phys. Rev.*, vol. 101, p. 1211, 1956.

many dislocation lines is the sum of the strain energies of the individual dislocations, plus terms expressing the interactions of the stress fields of the dislocations, plus a term describing the internal stresses developed by the external forces.

6-8. Forces on Dislocations

When an external force of sufficient magnitude is applied to a crystal, the dislocations move and produce slip. Thus, there is a force acting on a dislocation line which tends to drive it forward. Figure 6-11 shows a dislocation line moving in the direction of its Burgers vector under the influence of a uniform shear stress τ. An element of the dislocation line ds is displaced in the direction of slip normal to ds by an amount dl. The area swept out by the line element is then $ds\,dl$. This corresponds to an average displacement of the crystal above the slip plane to the crystal below the slip plane of an amount $ds\,dl\,b/A$, where A is the area of the slip plane. The work done by the shear stress acting in the slip plane is $dW = \tau A (ds\,dl\,b)/A$. This corresponds to a force dW/dl acting on the element ds in the direction of its normal. Therefore, the force per unit length acting on the dislocation line is

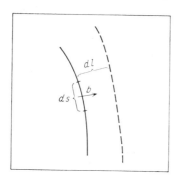

Fig. 6-11. Force acting on a dislocation line.

$$F = \tau b \qquad (6\text{-}14)$$

This force is normal to the dislocation line at every point along its length and is directed toward the unslipped part of the glide plane.

Because the strain energy of a dislocation line is proportional to its length, work must be performed to increase its length. Therefore, it is convenient to consider that a dislocation possesses a *line tension* which attempts to minimize its energy by shortening its length. The line tension has the units of energy per unit length and is analogous to the surface tension of a liquid. For a curved dislocation line, the line tension produces a restoring force which tends to straighten it out. The magnitude of this force is Γ/R, where Γ is the line tension and R is the radius of curvature of the bent dislocation line. The direction of this force is perpendicular to the dislocation line and toward the center of curvature. Because of line tension, a dislocation line can have an equilibrium curvature only if it is acted on by a shear stress. The equilibrium condition for this to occur is

$$F = \tau b = \frac{\Gamma}{R}$$

Therefore, the shear stress needed to maintain a dislocation line in a radius of curvature R is

$$\tau = \frac{\Gamma}{Rb} \qquad (6\text{-}15)$$

Orowan[1] has pointed out that the determination of this stress bears an analogy with the problem of blowing a bubble from a nozzle submerged in a liquid. The line tension will vary from point to point along a dislocation line. Stroh[2] has shown that Eq. (6-13) provides a good approximation of the line tension. An approximation often used is $\Gamma \approx 0.5Gb^2$. This is obtained from Eq. (6-13) when typical values $r_1 = 1{,}000$ A and $r_0 = 2$ A are used.

6-9. Forces between Dislocations

Dislocations of opposite sign on the same slip plane will attract each other, run together, and annihilate each other. This can be seen readily for the case of an edge dislocation (Fig. 4-8), where the superposition of a positive and negative dislocation on the same slip plane would eliminate the extra plane of atoms and therefore the dislocation would disappear. Conversely, dislocations of like sign on the same slip plane will repel each other.

The simplest situation to consider is the force between two parallel screw dislocations. Since the stress field of a screw dislocation is radially symmetrical, the force between them is a central force which depends only on the distance that they are apart.

$$F_r = \tau_{\theta z} b = \frac{Gb^2}{2\pi r} \qquad (6\text{-}16)$$

The force is attractive for dislocations of opposite sign (antiparallel screws) and repulsive for dislocations of the same sign (parallel screws).

Consider now the forces between two parallel edge dislocations with the same Burgers vectors. Referring to Fig. 6-10, the edge dislocations are at P and Q, parallel to the z axis, with their Burgers vectors along the x axis. The force between them is not a central force, and so it is necessary to consider both a radial and a tangential component. The

---

[1] E. Orowan, "Dislocations in Metals," pp. 99–102, American Institute of Mining and Metallurgical Engineers, New York, 1953.

[2] A. N. Stroh, *Proc. Phys. Soc. (London)*, vol. 67B, p. 427, 1954.

force per unit length is given by[1]

$$F_r = \frac{Gb^2}{2\pi(1 - \nu)} \frac{1}{r} \qquad F_\theta = \frac{Gb^2}{2\pi(1 - \nu)} \frac{\sin 2\theta}{r} \qquad (6\text{-}17)$$

Because edge dislocations are mainly confined to the slip plane, the force

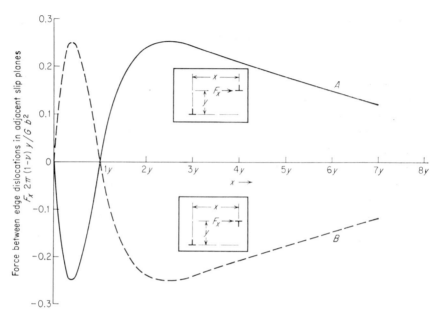

Fig. 6-12. Graphical representation of Eq. (6-18).   Solid curve A is for two edge dislocations of same sign.   Dashed curve B is for two unlike edge dislocations.   (*After A. H. Cottrell, "Dislocations and Plastic Flow in Crystals," p. 48, Oxford University Press, New York, 1953.*)

component along the x direction, which is the slip direction, is of most interest.

$$F_x = F_r \cos \theta - F_\theta \sin \theta$$
$$= \frac{Gb^2 x(x^2 - y^2)}{2\pi(1 - \nu)(x^2 + y^2)^2} \qquad (6\text{-}18)$$

Figure 6-12 is a plot of the variation of F_x with distance x, where x is expressed in units of y.   Curve A is for dislocations of the same sign; curve B is for dislocations of opposite sign.   Note that dislocations of the same sign repel each other when $x > y$ ($\theta < 45°$) and attract each other when $x < y$ ($\theta > 45°$).   The reverse is true for dislocations of

[1] A. H. Cottrell, "Dislocations and Plastic Flow in Crystals," p. 46, Oxford University Press, New York, 1953.

opposite sign. F_x is zero at $x = 0$ and $x = y$. The situation $x = 0$, where the edge dislocations lie vertically above one another, is a condition of equilibrium. Thus, theory predicts that a vertical array of edge dislocations of the same sign is in stable equilibrium. This is the arrangement of dislocations that exists in a low-angle grain boundary of the tilt variety.

The situation of two parallel dislocations with different Burgers vectors can be rationalized by considering their relative energies.[1] This represents the situation of dislocations on two intersecting slip planes. In general there will be no stable position, as for the previous case. The dislocations either will try to come together or will move far apart. Consider two parallel dislocations b_1 and b_2, which may or may not attract and combine into b_3. The two dislocations will attract if $b_3{}^2 < b_1{}^2 + b_2{}^2$ and will repel if $b_3{}^2 > b_1{}^2 + b_2{}^2$. Expressed another way, the dislocations will attract if the angle between their Burgers vectors is greater than 90°. They will repel if it is less than 90°.

A free surface exerts a force of attraction on a dislocation, since escape from the crystal at the surface would reduce its strain energy. Koehler[2] has shown that this force is approximately equal to the force which would be exerted in an infinite solid between the dislocation and one of opposite sign located at the position of its image on the other side of the surface. This *image force* is equal to

$$F = \frac{Gb^2}{4\pi(1 - \nu)} \frac{1}{r} \tag{6-19}$$

for an edge dislocation. However, it should be noted that metal surfaces are often covered with thin oxide films. A dislocation approaching a surface with a coating of an elastically harder material will encounter a repulsive rather than an attractive image force.

6-10. Dislocation Climb

An edge dislocation can glide only in the plane containing the dislocation line and its Burgers vector (the slip direction). To move an edge dislocation in a direction perpendicular to the slip plane requires the process of climb. The motion of a screw dislocation always involves glide, so that it is not involved with climb. Climb requires mass transport by diffusion, and therefore it is a thermally activated process. By convention, the positive direction of climb is the direction in which atoms are taken away from the extra half plane of atoms in an edge dislocation so that this extra half plane moves up one atomic layer. The usual way

---

[1] Read, *op. cit.*, p. 131.
[2] J. S. Koehler, *Phys. Rev.*, vol. 60, p. 397, 1941.

for this to occur is by a vacancy diffusing to the dislocation and the extra atom moving into the vacant lattice site (Fig. 6-13). It is also possible, but not energetically favorable, for the atom to break loose from the extra half plane and become an interstitial atom. To produce negative climb, atoms must be added to the extra half plane of atoms. This can occur by atoms from the surrounding lattice joining the extra half plane, which creates vacancies, or, less probably, by an interstitial atom diffusing to the dislocation.

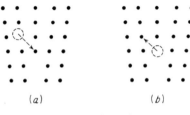

(a)   (b)

Fig. 6-13. (a) Diffusion of vacancy to edge dislocation; (b) dislocation climbs up one lattice spacing.

Dislocation climb is necessary to bring about the vertical alignment of edge dislocations on slip planes that produces low-angle grain boundaries by the process of polygonization. Etch-pit techniques on bent and annealed crystals have amply demonstrated the existence of this phenomenon. Dislocation climb is also a very important factor in the creep of metals, where the activation energy for steady-state creep is equal to the activation energy for self-diffusion in pure metals. Since self-diffusion occurs by the movement of vacancies, this implies that dislocation climb is involved in creep.

6-11. Jogs in Dislocations

There is no requirement that a dislocation must be confined to a single plane. When a dislocation moves from one slip plane to another, it creates a step, or *jog*, in the dislocation line. Jogs can be produced by the intersection of dislocations, as was shown earlier, in Fig. 4-29, or a jog can be produced during climb owing to the failure of climb to occur along the entire length of the extra half plane of atoms.

The intersection of two edge dislocations is illustrated in Fig. 6-14. An edge dislocation XY with a Burgers vector b_i is moving on plane P_{xy}. It cuts through dislocation AD, with Burgers vector b, lying on plane P_{AD}. The intersection produces a jog PP' in dislocation AD. The resulting jog is parallel to b_i, but it has a Burgers vector b since it is part of the dislocation line $APP'D$. The length of the jog will be equal to the length of the Burgers vector b_i. It can be seen that the jog resulting from the intersection of two edge dislocations has an edge orientation, and therefore it can readily glide with the rest of the dislocation. Hence, the formation of jogs in edge dislocations will not impede their motion. However, it requires energy to cut a dislocation because the formation of a jog increases its length. The energy of a jog will be about $0.5Gb^3$, since the average line tension is $0.5Gb^2$ and the jog has a length b_i.

Figure 4-29 illustrates the intersection of two screw dislocations. As is the general rule when jogs are formed by dislocation intersection, the jogs are perpendicular to the slip planes in which the dislocations are moving. It can be seen that the jogs formed by the intersection of two screw dislocations have an edge orientation because they lie perpendicular to the Burgers vector of the screw dislocations. Since an edge dislocation can move easily only in the plane containing its line and its Burgers vector, the jog can move only along the screw axis of the dislocation. Therefore, so long as the jog is present on the screw dislocation, it cannot move in a direction normal to the screw axis except by the process of climb. Hence, it is more difficult to move screw dislocations through an intersecting forest of dislocations than it is to move edge dislocations through an intersecting array. This is substantiated by the observation[1] that slip bands in aluminum advance more slowly when viewed in a direction perpendicular to the slip direction than when viewed along

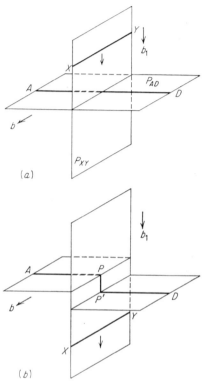

Fig. 6-14. Intersection of two edge dislocations. (*W. T. Read, Jr., "Dislocations in Crystals," McGraw-Hill Book Company, Inc., New York, 1953.*)

the slip direction. For the intersection of mixed dislocations, part edge and part screw, the jog can move sidewise by glide as the dislocation moves through the lattice.

6-12. Dislocation and Vacancy Interaction

There is a growing amount of evidence that point defects, mainly vacancies, are produced during plastic deformation. Most of the experi-

[1] N. K. Chen and R. B. Pond, *Trans. AIME*, vol. 194, pp. 1085–1092, 1952.

mental evidence[1] is based on deformation at low temperature (so as to suppress the mobility of vacancies) followed by the measurement of electrical resistivity and mechanical strength before and after annealing treatments. It is found that about half the increased resistivity due to cold work anneals out over well-defined temperature ranges and with activation energies which generally agree with the temperatures and activation energies observed for the annealing of quenched and irradiated samples. Moreover, the changes in resistivity are accomplished with little change in mechanical strength, indicating that dislocations are not responsible for the resistivity changes. The generation of point defects due to deformation has been demonstrated in ionic crystals by measurements of conductivity and density and by the observation of color centers.

Jogs in dislocation lines can act as sources and sinks for point defects. Because of the reentrant corner at a jog, it is a favorable center for the absorption and annihilation of vacancies. It is also generally considered that vacancies can be generated at jogs. The usual mechanism[2] involves the jogs formed by the intersection of screw dislocations. As was pointed out in the previous section, motion of a screw dislocation containing jogs in a direction normal to its axis can occur only by climb. As the jog climbs, it generates vacancies. However, two points of doubt have been raised about this mechanism. Friedel[3] has pointed out that there is no reason why a jog should not glide along a screw dislocation without producing vacancies so long as it can shortly attach itself to an edge component of the dislocation line. Cottrell[4] has shown that the jogs formed by intersecting screw dislocations will generally produce interstitials, not vacancies. However, annealing experiments show that vacancies rather than interstitials are the predominant point defect in cold-worked metals. Other mechanisms for the generation of vacancies by jogs on dislocations have been proposed by Friedel, Mott, and Cottrell.[5] While the exact details for the mechanism of vacancy formation during cold work have not been established, there is little question that jog formation due to the intersection of dislocations is involved.

An attractive force exists between vacancies and dislocations. There-

---

[1] For reviews of this subject see T. Broom, *Advances in Phys.*, vol. 3, pp. 26–83, 1954, and "Symposium on Vacancies and Other Point Defects in Metals and Alloys," Institute of Metals, London, 1958.

[2] F. Seitz, *Advances in Phys.*, vol. 1, p. 43, 1952.

[3] J. Friedel, *Phil. Mag.*, vol. 46, p. 1165, 1955.

[4] A. H. Cottrell, "Dislocations and Mechanical Properties of Crystals," pp. 509–512, John Wiley & Sons, Inc., New York, 1957.

[5] J. Friedel, "Les Dislocations," Gauthier-Villars & Cie, Paris, 1956; N. F. Mott, "Dislocations and Mechanical Properties of Crystals," pp. 469–471, John Wiley & Sons, Inc., New York, 1957; A. H. Cottrell, "Vacancies and Other Point Defects in Metals and Alloys," pp. 28–29, Institute of Metals, London, 1958.

fore, vacancies should be able to form atmospheres around dislocations in the same way as solute atoms. Vacancies may also interact with each other to form vacancy pairs (divacancies), and there is some evidence to support the hypothesis that they collect into larger groups or clusters.

6-13. Dislocation—Foreign-atom Interaction

The presence of a large foreign atom produces a dilation of the matrix. An oversized atom will be attracted to the tension region and repelled from the compression region of an edge dislocation. The segregation of solute atoms to dislocations lowers the strain energy of the system. For simplicity, it is assumed that the solute atom produces a symmetrical hydrostatic distortion of the matrix. If the solute atom occupies a volume ΔV greater than the volume of the matrix atom it replaces, the energy of interaction between the local stress field of the dislocation and the foreign atom will be

$$U_i = \sigma_m \, \Delta V \tag{6-20}$$

where $\sigma_m = -\tfrac{1}{3}(\sigma_x + \sigma_y + \sigma_z)$ is the hydrostatic component of the stress field. The volume change is given by

$$\Delta V = \tfrac{4}{3}\pi\epsilon a^3 \tag{6-21}$$

where a is the radius of the solvent atom and $\epsilon = (a' - a)/a$ is the strain produced by introducing a solute atom of radius a'. When the solute atom is located at a point given by the polar coordinate r, θ from an edge dislocation, the interaction energy is given by[1]

$$U_i = \frac{A \, \sin\theta}{r} = 4Gb\epsilon a^3 \frac{\sin\theta}{r} \tag{6-22}$$

The force between an edge dislocation and a solute atom is not a central force. The radial and tangential components are given by

$$F_r = -\left(\frac{\partial U_i}{\partial r}\right) \qquad F_\theta = -\left(\frac{1}{r}\right)\left(\frac{\partial U_i}{\partial \theta}\right) \tag{6-23}$$

When the solute atom produces an unequal distortion of the matrix lattice in different directions, solute atoms can interact with the shear component of the stress field as well as the hydrostatic component. Under these conditions interaction occurs between solute atoms and both screw and edge dislocations. For the case of carbon and nitrogen atoms in iron the tetragonal symmetry around the interstitial sites leads to a shear component of the stress field. In fcc alloys the dissociation of dis-

[1] B. A. Bilby, *Proc. Phys. Soc. (London)*, vol. 63A, p. 191, 1950.

locations into partial dislocations produces two elastically bound dislocations with a substantial edge component.

Cottrell and Bilby have shown that in time t the number of solute
atoms, $n(t)$, that migrate to a unit length of dislocation line from a solution containing initially n_0 solute atoms per unit volume is

$$n(t) = 3 \left(\frac{\pi}{2}\right)^{\frac{1}{3}} \left(\frac{ADt}{kT}\right)^{\frac{2}{3}} n_0 \qquad (6\text{-}24)$$

where A = interaction parameter of Eq. (6-22)

D = diffusion coefficient of solute atoms at temperature T

In the derivation of this equation the dislocation line serves as a solute-
atom sink which captures any passing atom but does not obstruct the
entry of other atoms. This concept is valid during the early stages of
strain aging, where the $t^{\frac{2}{3}}$ relationship is found to hold. However,
toward the later stages of strain aging the sites on the dislocation line
become saturated, and the assumption that it acts like a sink can no
longer be valid. Now the probability of atoms leaving the center equals
the probability of atoms flowing in, and a steady-state concentration
gradient develops. The steady-state distribution of solute atoms around
the dislocation is referred to as an atmosphere. The local concentration
c is related to the average concentration c_0 by the relationship

$$c = c_0 \exp \frac{-U_i}{kT} \qquad (6\text{-}25)$$

It has been suggested[1] that solute atoms can diffuse along dislocations
until they meet a barrier. If the interaction between the solute atoms is
strong, a fine precipitate can be formed. In this way the dislocation lines
are freed to act as sinks for a longer period of time, and the $t^{\frac{2}{3}}$ relationship will remain valid until all dislocation lines have been saturated with
solute atoms.

When the concentration of solute atoms around the dislocation becomes
high enough, the atmosphere will condense into a single line of solute
atoms parallel to the dislocation line at the position of maximum binding
about two atomic spacings below the core of a positive edge dislocation.
The breakaway stress required to pull a dislocation line away from a line
of solute atoms at 0°K is

$$\sigma \approx \frac{A}{b^2 r_0{}^2} \qquad (6\text{-}26)$$

where A is given by Eq. (6-22) and $r_0 \approx 2 \times 10^{-8}$ cm is the distance from
the dislocation core to the site of the line of solute atoms. When the

[1] B. A. Bilby and G. M. Leak, *J. Iron Steel Inst.* (*London*), vol. 184, p. 64, 1956.

dislocation line is pulled free from the field of influence of the solute atoms, slip can proceed at a stress lower than that given by Eq. (6-26). This is the origin of the upper yield point in the stress-strain curve.

When an external force tries to move a dislocation line away from its atmosphere, the atmosphere exerts a restoring force that tries to pull it back to its original position. If the speed of the dislocation line is slow, it may be able to move by dragging the atmosphere along behind it. According to Cottrell, the maximum velocity at which a dislocation line can move and still drag its atmosphere with it is

$$v = \frac{D}{kT}\frac{A}{r^2} \qquad (6\text{-}27)$$

If the dislocation line is moving faster than this velocity, it will be necessary for the restoring force to be overcome and the atmosphere is left behind. Serrations in the stress-strain curve are the result of the dislocation line pulling away from the solute atmosphere and then slowing down and allowing the atmosphere to interact once again with the dislocations.

6-14. Dislocation Sources

The low yield strength of pure crystals leads to the conclusion that dislocation sources must exist in completely annealed crystals and in crystals carefully solidified from the melt. The line energy of a dislocation is so high as to make it very unlikely that stresses of reasonable magnitude can create new dislocations in a region of a crystal where no dislocations exist, even with the assistance of thermal fluctuations. This results in an important difference between line defects and point defects. The density of dislocations in thermal equilibrium with a crystal is vanishingly small. There is no general relationship between dislocation density and temperature such as exists with vacancies. Since dislocations are not affected by thermal fluctuations at temperatures below which recrystallization occurs, a metal can have widely different dislocation densities depending upon processing conditions. Completely annealed material will contain about 10^6 to 10^8 dislocation lines per square centimeter, while heavily cold-worked metal will have a dislocation density of about 10^{12} dislocation lines per square centimeter.

It is generally believed that all metals, with the exception of tiny whiskers, initially contain an appreciable number of dislocations, produced as the result of the growth of the crystal from the melt or the vapor phase. Experimental evidence for dislocations in crystals solidified under carefully controlled conditions has been obtained by etch-pit studies and by X-ray diffraction methods. For crystals grown by vapor deposition it has been shown that nucleation of the solid phase occurs around screw dislocations emerging from the surface of the solid substrate.

Ample evidence of the existence of three-dimensional dislocation networks in annealed ionic crystals has been provided by dislocation decoration techniques. In annealed metals, dislocation loops have been observed by transmission-electron microscopy of thin films.[1] These loops are believed to originate from the collapse of disks of vacancies and correspond to *prismatic dislocations*. There is some evidence to indicate that these loops can grow and join up to form dislocation networks in annealed, unworked crystals. There is also some evidence to suggest that some of the condensed vacancies form voids, which are then responsible for the formation of dislocations. While there is little doubt that dislocations exist in annealed or carefully solidified metal, much more information is needed about the mechanism by which they are produced and the way in which they are arranged in the metal.

6-15. Multiplication of Dislocations—Frank-Read Source

One of the original stumbling blocks in the development of dislocation theory was the formulation of a reasonable mechanism by which sources originally present in the metal could produce new dislocations by the process of slip. Such a mechanism is required when it is realized that the surface displacement at a slip band is due to the movement of about 1,000 dislocations over the slip plane. Thus, the number of dislocation sources initially present in a metal could not account for the observed slip-band spacing and displacement unless there were some way in which each source could produce large amounts of slip before it became immobilized. Moreover, if there were no source generating dislocations, cold work should decrease, rather than increase, the density of dislocations in a single crystal. Thus, there must be a method of generating dislocations or of multiplying the number initially present to produce the high dislocation density found in cold-worked metal. The scheme by which dislocations could be generated from existing dislocations was proposed by Frank and Read[2] and is commonly called a *Frank-Read source*.

Consider a dislocation line DD' lying in a slip plane (Fig. 6-15a). The plane of the figure is the slip plane. The dislocation line leaves the slip plane at points D and D', so that it is immobilized at these points. This could occur if D and D' were nodes where the dislocation in the plane of the paper intersects dislocations in other slip planes, or the anchoring could be caused by impurity atoms. If a shear stress τ acts in the slip plane, the dislocation line bulges out and produces slip. For a given

---

[1] Hirsch, Silcox, Smallman, and Westmacott, *op. cit.*

[2] F. C. Frank and W. T. Read, *Phys. Rev.*, vol. 79, pp. 722–723, 1950.

stress the dislocation line will assume a certain radius of curvature given
by Eq. (6-15). The maximum value of shear stress is required when the
dislocation bulge becomes a semicircle so that R has the minimum value
$l/2$ (Fig. 6-15b). From the approximation that $\Gamma \approx 0.5Gb^2$ and Eq.

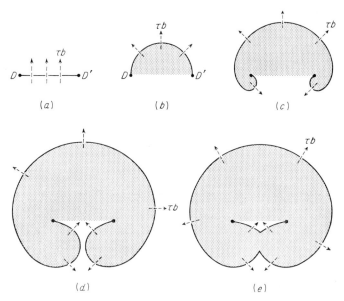

(a)   (b)   (c)

(d)   (e)

Fig. 6-15. Schematic representation of the operation of a Frank-Read source. (*W. T.
Read, Jr., "Dislocations in Crystals," McGraw-Hill Book Company, Inc., New York,
1953.*)

(6-15) it can be readily seen that the stress required to produce this
configuration is

$$\tau \approx \frac{Gb}{l} \tag{6-28}$$

where l is the distance DD' between the nodes. When the stress is raised
above this critical value, the dislocation becomes unstable and expands
indefinitely. Figure 6-15c shows the expanded loop, which has started
to double back on itself. In Fig. 6-15d the dislocation has almost doubled
back on itself, while in Fig. 6-15e the two parts of the loop have joined
together. This produces a complete loop and reintroduces the original
dislocation line DD'. The loop can continue to expand over the slip
plane with increasing stress. The section DD' will soon straighten out
under the influence of applied stress and line tension, and the Frank-
Read source will then be in a position to repeat the process. This process
can be repeated over and over again at a single source, each time pro-

ducing a dislocation loop which produces slip of one Burgers vector along the slip plane. However, once the source is initiated, it does not continue indefinitely. The back stress produced by the dislocations piling up along the slip plane opposes the applied stress. When the back stress

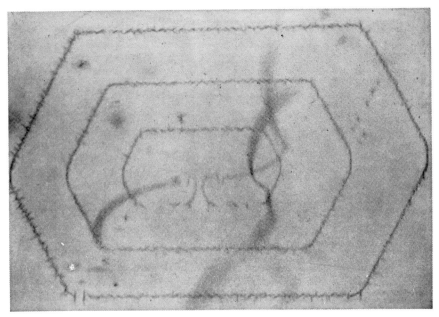

Fig. 6-16. Frank-Read source in silicon crystal. (*W. C. Dash, in "Dislocations and Mechanical Properties of Crystals," John Wiley & Sons, Inc., New York, 1957.*)

equals the critical stress given by Eq. (6-28), the source will no longer operate.

The most dramatic evidence for the existence of a Frank-Read source has been found by Dash[1] in silicon crystals decorated with copper. Figure 6-16 shows a Frank-Read source in a silicon crystal as photographed with infrared light. Evidence has also been found by precipitation techniques in aluminum alloys and in ionic crystals and by means of thin-film electron microscopy in stainless steel.

6-16. Dislocation Pile-up

Frequent reference has been made to the fact that dislocations pile up on slip planes at obstacles such as grain boundaries, second-phase particles, and sessile dislocations. The dislocations in the pile-up will be

[1] W. C. Dash, "Dislocations and Mechanical Properties of Crystals," p. 57, John Wiley & Sons, Inc., New York, 1957.

tightly packed together near the head of the array and more widely spaced toward the source (Fig. 6-17). The distribution of dislocations of like sign in a pile-up along a single slip plane has been studied by Eshelby, Frank, and Nabarro.[1] The number of dislocations that can

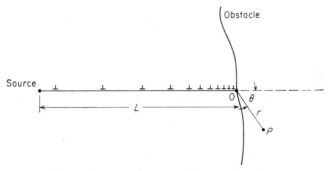

Fig. 6-17. Dislocation pile-up at an obstacle.

occupy a distance L along the slip plane between the source and the obstacle is

$$n = \frac{k\pi\tau_s L}{Gb} \qquad (6\text{-}29)$$

where τ_s is the average resolved shear stress in the slip plane and k is a factor close to unity. For an edge dislocation $k = 1 - \nu$, while for a screw dislocation $k = 1$. When the source is located at the center of a grain of diameter D, the number of dislocations in the pile-up is given by

$$n = \frac{k\pi\tau_s D}{4Gb} \qquad (6\text{-}30)$$

The factor 4 is used instead of the expected factor of 2 because the back stress on the source arises from dislocations piled up on both sides of the source.

A piled-up array of n dislocations can be considered for many purposes to be a giant dislocation with Burgers vector nb. At large distances from the array the stress due to the dislocations can be considered to be due to a dislocation of strength nb located at the center of gravity three-quarters of the distance from the source to the head of the pile-up. The total slip produced by a pile-up can be considered that due to a single dislocation nb moving a distance $3L/4$. Very high forces act on the dis-

[1] J. D. Eshelby, F. C. Frank, and F. R. N. Nabarro, *Phil. Mag.*, vol. 42, p. 351, 1951; calculations for more complicated types of pile-ups have been given by A. K. Head, *Phil. Mag.*, vol. 4, pp. 295–302, 1959; experimental confirmation of theory has been obtained by Meakin and Wilsdorf, *op. cit.*, pp. 745–752.

locations at the head of the pile-up. This force is equal to $nb\tau_s$, where τ_s is the average resolved shear stress on the slip plane. Koehler[1] has pointed out that large tensile stresses of the order of $n\tau$ will be produced at the head of a pile-up. Stroh[2] has made a somewhat more detailed analysis of the stress distribution at the head of a dislocation pile-up. Using the coordinate system given in Fig. 6-17, he showed that the tensile stress normal to a line OP is given by

$$\sigma = \frac{3}{2}\left(\frac{L}{r}\right)^{\frac{1}{2}} \tau_s \sin\theta \cos\frac{\theta}{2} \qquad (6\text{-}31)$$

The maximum value of σ occurs at $\cos\theta = \frac{1}{3}$ or $\theta = 70.5°$. For this situation

$$\sigma_{max} = \frac{2}{\sqrt{3}}\left(\frac{L}{r}\right)^{\frac{1}{2}} \tau_s \qquad (6\text{-}32)$$

The shear stress acting in the plane OP is given by

$$\tau = \beta\tau_s\left(\frac{L}{r}\right)^{\frac{1}{2}} \qquad (6\text{-}33)$$

where β is an orientation-dependent factor which is close to unity.

The number of dislocations which can be supported by an obstacle will depend on the type of barrier, the orientation relationship between the slip plane and the structural features at the barrier, the material, and the temperature. Breakdown of a barrier can occur by slip on a new plane, by climb of dislocations around the barrier, or by the generation of high enough tensile stresses to produce a crack.

Petch's equation that expresses the dependence of yield stress on grain size can be developed from the concepts discussed above. Yielding is assumed to occur when a critical shear stress τ_c is produced at the head of the pile-up. This stress is assumed independent of grain size. From Eq. (6-30) we get

$$n\tau_s = \frac{\pi(1-\nu)\tau_s{}^2 D}{4Gb} = \tau_c$$

It is assumed that the resolved shear stress is equal to the applied stress minus the average internal stress required to overcome resistances to dislocation motion. If, in addition, shear stresses are converted to uniaxial tensile stresses, for example, $\tau_c = \sigma_c/2$, the above expression becomes

$$\frac{\pi(1-\nu)(\sigma_0 - \sigma_i)^2 D}{8Gb} = \sigma_c$$

[1] J. S. Koehler, *Phys. Rev.*, vol. 85, p. 480, 1952.
[2] A. N. Stroh, *Proc. Roy. Soc. (London)*, vol. 223, pp. 404–414, 1954.

This can be rearranged to give the desired relationship between yield stress σ_0 and grain diameter D.

$$\sigma_0 = \sigma_i + \sqrt{\frac{8Gb\sigma_c}{\pi(1-\nu)}} \frac{1}{D} = \sigma_i + K_y D^{-\frac{1}{2}} \tag{6-34}$$

BIBLIOGRAPHY

Burgers, J. M., and W. G. Burgers: Dislocations in Crystal Lattices, in F. R. Eirich (ed.), "Rheology," vol. I, Academic Press Inc., New York, 1956.

Cohen, M. (ed.): "Dislocations in Metals," American Institute of Mining and Metallurgical Engineers, New York, 1953.

Cottrell, A. H.: "Dislocations and Plastic Flow in Crystals," Oxford University Press, New York, 1953.

Fisher, J. C., W. G. Johnston, R. Thomson, and T. Vreeland, Jr. (eds.): "Dislocations and Mechanical Properties of Crystals," John Wiley & Sons, Inc., New York, 1957.

Read, W. T., Jr.: "Dislocations in Crystals," McGraw-Hill Book Company, Inc., New York, 1953.

Schoek, G.: Dislocation Theory of Plasticity of Metals, in "Advances in Applied Mechanics," vol. IV, Academic Press, Inc., New York, 1956.

Van Bueren, H. G.: "Imperfections in Crystals," Interscience Publishers, Inc., New York, 1960.

Chapter 7

FRACTURE

7-1. Introduction

Fracture is the separation, or fragmentation, of a solid body into two or more parts under the action of stress. The process of fracture can be considered to be made up of two components, crack initiation and crack propagation. Fractures can be classified into two general categories, ductile fracture and brittle fracture. A ductile fracture is characterized by appreciable plastic deformation prior to and during the propagation of the crack. An appreciable amount of gross deformation is usually present at the fracture surfaces. Brittle fracture in metals is characterized by a rapid rate of crack propagation, with no gross deformation and very little microdeformation. It is akin to cleavage in ionic crystals. The tendency for brittle fracture is increased with decreasing temperature, increasing strain rate, and triaxial stress conditions (usually produced by a notch). Brittle fracture is to be avoided at all cost, because it occurs without warning and usually produces disastrous consequences.

This chapter will present a broad picture of the fundamentals of the fracture of metals. Since most of the research has been concentrated on the problem of brittle fracture, this topic will be given considerable prominence. The engineering aspects of brittle fracture will be considered in greater detail in Chap. 14. Fracture occurs in characteristic ways, depending on the state of stress, the rate of application of stress, and the temperature. Unless otherwise stated, it will be assumed in this chapter that fracture is produced by a single application of a uniaxial tensile stress. Fracture under more complex conditions will be considered in later chapters. Typical examples are fracture due to torsion (Chap. 10), fatigue (Chap. 12), and creep (Chap. 13) and low-temperature brittle fracture, temper embrittlement, or hydrogen embrittlement (Chap. 14).

7-2. Types of Fracture in Metals

Metals can exhibit many different types of fracture, depending on the material, temperature, state of stress, and rate of loading. The two

190

broad categories of ductile and brittle fracture have already been considered. Figure 7-1 schematically illustrates some of the types of tensile fractures which can occur in metals. A brittle fracture (Fig. 7-1a) is characterized by separation normal to the tensile stress. Outwardly there is no evidence of deformation, although with X-ray diffraction analysis it is possible to detect a thin layer of deformed metal at the fracture surface. Brittle fractures have been observed in bcc and hcp metals, but not in fcc metals unless there are factors contributing to grain-boundary embrittlement.

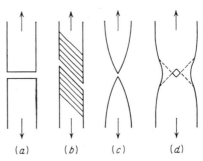

Ductile fractures can take several forms. Single crystals of hcp metals may slip on successive basal planes until finally the crystal separates by shear (Fig. 7-1b). Polycrystalline specimens of very ductile metals, like gold or lead, may actually be drawn down to a point before they rupture (Fig. 7-1c). In the tensile fracture of moderately ductile metals the

Fig. 7-1. Types of fractures observed in metals subjected to uniaxial tension. (a) Brittle fracture of single crystals and polycrystals; (b) shearing fracture in ductile single crystals; (c) completely ductile fracture in polycrystals; (d) ductile fracture in polycrystals.

plastic deformation eventually produces a necked region (Fig. 7-1d). Fracture begins at the center of the specimen and then extends by a shear separation along the dashed lines in Fig. 7-1d. This results in the familiar "cup-and-cone" fracture.

Fractures are classified with respect to several characteristics, such as strain to fracture, crystallographic mode of fracture, and the appearance of the fracture. Gensamer[1] has summarized the terms commonly used to describe fractures as follows:

Behavior described	Terms used	
Crystallographic mode...........	Shear	Cleavage
Appearance of fracture...........	Fibrous	Granular
Strain to fracture...............	Ductile	Brittle

A shear fracture occurs as the result of extensive slip on the active slip plane. This type of fracture is promoted by shear stresses. The cleavage mode of fracture is controlled by tensile stresses acting normal to a crystallographic cleavage plane. A fracture surface which is caused

[1] M. Gensamer, General Survey of the Problem of Fatigue and Fracture, in "Fatigue, and Fracture of Metals," John Wiley & Sons, Inc., New York, 1952.

by shear appears at low magnification to be gray and fibrous, while a cleavage fracture appears bright or granular, owing to reflection of light from the flat cleavage surfaces. Fracture surfaces frequently consist of a mixture of fibrous and granular fracture, and it is customary to report the percentage of the surface area represented by one of these categories. Based on metallographic examination, fractures in polycrystalline samples are classified as either *transgranular* (the crack propagates through the grains) or *intergranular* (the crack propagates along the grain boundaries). A ductile fracture is one which exhibits a considerable degree of deformation. The boundary between a ductile and brittle fracture is arbitrary and depends on the situation being considered. For example, nodular cast iron is ductile when compared with ordinary gray iron; yet it would be considered brittle when compared with mild steel. As a further example, a deeply notched tensile specimen will exhibit little gross deformation; yet the fracture could occur by a shear mode.

7-3. Theoretical Cohesive Strength of Metals

Metals are of great technological value, primarily because of their high strength combined with a certain measure of plasticity. In the most basic terms the strength is due to the cohesive forces between atoms. In general, high cohesive forces are related to large elastic constants, high melting points, and small coefficients of thermal expansion. Figure 7-2 shows the variation of the cohesive force between two atoms as a function of the separation between these atoms. This curve is the resultant of the attractive and repulsive forces between the atoms. The interatomic spacing of the atoms in the unstrained condition is indicated

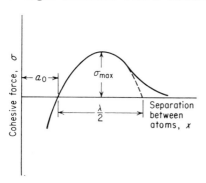

Fig. 7-2. Cohesive force as a function of the separation between atoms.

by a_0. If the crystal is subjected to a tensile load, the separation between atoms will be increased. The repulsive force decreases more rapidly with increased separation than the attractive force, so that a net force between atoms balances the tensile load. As the tensile load is increased still further, the repulsive force continues to decrease. A point is reached where the repulsive force is negligible and the attractive force is decreasing because of the increased separation of the atoms. This corresponds to the maximum in the curve, which is equal to the theoretical cohesive strength of the material.

A good approximation to the theoretical cohesive strength can be obtained if it is assumed that the cohesive force curve can be represented by a sine curve.

$$\sigma = \sigma_{max} \sin \frac{2\pi x}{\lambda} \qquad (7\text{-}1)$$

where σ_{max} is the theoretical cohesive strength. The work done during fracture, per unit area, is the area under the curve.

$$U_0 = \int_0^{\lambda/2} \sigma_{max} \sin \frac{2\pi x}{\lambda} \, dx = \frac{\lambda \sigma_{max}}{\pi} \qquad (7\text{-}2)$$

The energy per unit area required to produce a new surface is γ. If it is assumed that all the work involved in fracture goes into creating two new surfaces, Eq. (7-2) can be written

$$\frac{\lambda \sigma_{max}}{\pi} = 2\gamma$$

or

$$\sigma_{max} = \frac{2\pi\gamma}{\lambda} \qquad (7\text{-}3)$$

Since Hooke's law holds for the initial part of the curve, the stress can be written as

$$\sigma = \frac{Ex}{a_0} \qquad (7\text{-}4)$$

In order to eliminate λ from Eq. (7-3), take the first derivative of Eq. (7-1).

$$\frac{d\sigma}{dx} = \sigma_{max} \frac{2\pi}{\lambda} \cos \frac{2\pi x}{\lambda}$$

Since $\cos (2\pi x/\lambda)$ is approximately unity for the small values of x which are involved, the above expression can be written as

$$\frac{d\sigma}{dx} = \sigma_{max} \frac{2\pi}{\lambda} \qquad (7\text{-}5)$$

Also, Eq. (7-4) can be differentiated to give

$$\frac{d\sigma}{dx} = \frac{E}{a_0} \qquad (7\text{-}6)$$

Equating (7-5) and (7-6) and substituting into Eq. (7-3) produces the final expression for the theoretical cohesive strength of a crystal.

$$\sigma_{max} = \left(\frac{E\gamma}{a_0}\right)^{1/2} \qquad (7\text{-}7)$$

The substitution of reasonable values for the quantities involved in the above expression (see Prob. 7-1) results in the prediction of a cohesive strength of the order of 2×10^6 psi. This is 10 to 1,000 times greater than the observed fracture strengths of metals. Only the fracture strength of dislocation-free metal whiskers approaches the theoretical cohesive strength.

7-4. Griffith Theory of Brittle Fracture

The first explanation of the discrepancy between the observed fracture strength of crystals and the theoretical cohesive strength was proposed by Griffith.[1] Griffith's theory in its original form is applicable only to a perfectly brittle material such as glass. However, while it cannot be applied directly to metals, Griffith's ideas have had great influence on the thinking about the fracture of metals.

Griffith proposed that a brittle material contains a population of fine cracks which produce a stress concentration of sufficient magnitude so

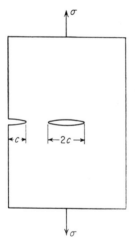

Fig. 7-3. Griffith crack model.

that the theoretical cohesive strength is reached in localized regions at a nominal stress which is well below the theoretical value. When one of the cracks spreads into a brittle fracture, it produces an increase in the surface area of the sides of the crack. This requires energy to overcome the cohesive force of the atoms, or, expressed in another way, it requires an increase in surface energy. The source of the increased surface energy is the elastic strain energy which is released as the crack spreads. Griffith established the following criterion for the propagation of a crack: *A crack will propagate when the decrease in elastic strain energy is at least equal to the energy required to create the new crack surface.* This criterion can be used to determine the magnitude of the tensile stress which will just cause a crack of a certain size to propagate as a brittle fracture.

Consider the crack model shown in Fig. 7-3. The thickness of the plate is negligible, and so the problem can be treated as one in plane stress. The cracks are assumed to have an elliptical cross section. For a crack at the interior the length is $2c$, while for an edge crack it is c. The effect of both types of crack on the fracture behavior is the same. The stress

[1] A. A. Griffith, *Phil. Trans. Roy. Soc. London,* vol. 221A, pp. 163–198 1920; *First Intn. Congr. Appl. Mech.,* Delft, 1924, p. 55.

distribution for an elliptical crack was determined by Inglis.[1]   A decrease in strain energy results from the formation of a crack.   The elastic strain energy per unit of plate thickness is equal to

$$U_E = -\frac{\pi c^2 \sigma^2}{E} \tag{7-8}$$

where σ is the tensile stress acting normal to the crack of length $2c$.   The surface energy due to the presence of the crack is

$$U_S = 4c\gamma \tag{7-9}$$

The total change in potential energy resulting from the creation of the crack is

$$\Delta U = U_S + U_E \tag{7-10}$$

According to Griffith's criterion, the crack will propagate under a constant applied stress σ if an incremental increase in crack length produces no change in the total energy of the system; i.e., the increased surface energy is compensated by a decrease in elastic strain energy.

$$\frac{d\Delta U}{dc} = 0 = \frac{d}{dc}\left(4c\gamma - \frac{\pi c^2 \sigma^2}{E}\right)$$

$$4\gamma - \frac{2\pi c\sigma^2}{E} = 0$$

$$\sigma = \left(\frac{2E\gamma}{\pi c}\right)^{\frac{1}{2}} \tag{7-11}$$

Equation (7-11) gives the stress required to propagate a crack in a brittle material as a function of the size of the microcrack.   Note that this equation indicates that the fracture stress is inversely proportional to the square root of the crack length.   Thus, increasing the crack length by a factor of 4 reduces the fracture stress by one-half.

For a plate which is thick compared with the length of the crack (plane strain) the Griffith equation is given by

$$\sigma = \left[\frac{2E\gamma}{(1-\nu)^2\pi c}\right]^{\frac{1}{2}} \tag{7-12}$$

Analysis of the three-dimensional case, where the crack is a very flat oblate spheroid,[2] results only in a modification to the constant in Griffith's equation.   Therefore, the simplification of considering only the two-dimensional case introduces no large error.

An alternative way of rationalizing the low fracture strength of solids

[1] C. E. Inglis, *Trans. Inst. Naval Architects*, vol. 55, pt. I, pp. 219–230, 1913.

[2] R. A. Sack, *Proc. Phys. Soc. (London)*, vol. 58, p. 729, 1946.

with the high theoretical cohesive strength was proposed by Orowan.[1]
Inglis showed that the stress at the end of an ellipsoidal crack of length
$2c$, with a radius of curvature ρ at the end of the crack, is given by

$$\sigma_{max} = 2\sigma \left(\frac{c}{\rho}\right)^{1/2} \tag{7-13}$$

where σ is the nominal stress when no crack is present. The sharpest
radius of curvature at the end of the crack should be of the order of the
interatomic spacing, $\rho = a_0$. Making this substitution in Eq. (7-13) and
combining it with Eq. (7-7) results in an expression for the critical stress
to cause brittle fracture which is similar to Griffith's equation.

$$\sigma = \left(\frac{E\gamma}{4c}\right)^{1/2} \tag{7-14}$$

Within the accuracy of the estimate, this equation predicts the same
stress needed to propagate a crack through a brittle solid as the Griffith
equation.

Griffith's theory satisfactorily predicts the fracture strength of a completely brittle material such as glass.[2]   In glass, reasonable values of
crack length of about 1 μ are calculated from Eq. (7-11). For zinc, the
theory predicts a crack length of several millimeters. This average
crack length could easily be greater than the thickness of the specimen,
and therefore the theory cannot apply.

Early experiments on the fracture of glass fibers showed that strengths
close to the theoretical fracture strength could be obtained with fibers
freshly drawn from the melt. The highest fracture strengths were found
with the smallest-diameter fibers, since on the average these fibers would
have the shortest microcracks. However, other factors besides diameter, such as method of preparation, temperature of the melt, and
amount and rate of drawing from the melt, can affect strength. Recent
results[3] indicate that there is no dependence of strength on diameter
when different-size glass fibers are prepared under nearly identical conditions. Experiments on metal whiskers[4] have also demonstrated fracture strengths close to the theoretical value. The strength of a metal
whisker varies inversely with its diameter. This is the type of size
dependence that would be expected if the strength were controlled by
the number of surface defects. On the other hand, if the whisker contains a certain number of dislocation sources, the length of the most

[1] E. Orowan, *Welding J.*, vol. 34, pp. 157s–160s, 1955.

[2] O. L. Anderson, The Griffith Criterion for Glass Fracture, in "Fracture," pp. 331–353, John Wiley & Sons, Inc., New York, 1959.

[3] F. Otto, *J. Am. Ceramic Soc.*, vol. 38, p. 123, 1955.

[4] S. S. Brenner, *J. Appl. Phys.*, vol. 27, p. 1484, 1956.

extended source will vary directly with the diameter and the strength will again be inversely related to the whisker diameter. Thus, it is not possible from the size dependence of strength to establish whether the high strength of whiskers is due to a freedom from surface defects or dislocations.

The strength of glass fibers is extremely sensitive to surface defects. If the surface of a freshly drawn fiber is touched with a hard object, the strength will instantly decrease to a low value. Even the strength of a fiber which has not been handled will, under the influence of atmospheric attack, decrease to a low value within a few hours of being drawn from the melt.

Joffe[1] showed that the fracture strength of NaCl crystals could be greatly increased when the test was carried out under water. This *Joffe effect* has been attributed to the healing of surface cracks by the solution of the salt crystal in the water. The fracture behavior of other ionic crystals has been shown to depend on the environment in contact with the surface. However, the Joffe effect in these crystals cannot always be explained simply by surface dissolution.

7-5. Modifications of the Griffith Theory

Metals which fracture in a brittle manner show evidence of a thin layer of plastically deformed metal when the fracture surface is examined by X-ray diffraction.[2] Other indications that brittle fracture in metals is always preceded by a small amount of plastic deformation, on a microscopic scale, are given in Sec. 7-7. Therefore, it appears that Griffith's theory, in its original form, should not be expected to apply to the brittle fracture of metals.

Orowan[3] suggested that the Griffith equation could be made more compatible with brittle fracture in metals by the inclusion of a term p expressing the plastic work required to extend the crack wall.

$$\sigma = \left[\frac{2E(\gamma + p)}{\pi c} \right]^{1/2} \sim \left(\frac{Ep}{c} \right)^{1/2} \qquad (7-15)$$

The surface-energy term can be neglected, since estimates of the plastic-work term are about 10^5 to 10^6 ergs/cm^2, compared with values of γ of

[1] A. F. Joffe, "The Physics of Crystals," McGraw-Hill Book Company, Inc., New York, 1928.

[2] E. P. Klier, *Trans. ASM*, vol. 43, pp. 935–957, 1951; L. C. Chang, *J. of Mech. and Phys. Solids*, vol. 3, pp. 212–217, 1955; D. K. Felbeck and E. Orowan, *Welding J.*, vol. 34, pp. 570s–575s, 1955.

[3] E. Orowan, in "Fatigue and Fracture of Metals," symposium at Massachusetts Institute of Technology, John Wiley & Sons, Inc., New York, 1950.

about 1,000 to 2,000 ergs/cm^2. There is some experimental evidence that p decreases with decreasing temperature.

An extension of the Griffith theory into the area of fracture mechanics has been made by Irwin.[1] The objective is to find a reliable design criterion for predicting the stress at which rapidly propagating fractures will occur. This is essentially a macroscopic theory that is concerned with cracks that are tenths of an inch in length or greater. The quantity of interest is the *crack-extension force*, also called the strain-energy release rate. The crack-extension force $\mathcal{G}$, measured in units of in.-lb/in.^{2}, is the quantity of stored elastic strain energy released from a cracking specimen as the result of the extension of an advancing crack by a unit area. When this quantity reaches a critical value $\mathcal{G}_c$, the crack will propagate rapidly. $\mathcal{G}_c$ is the *fracture toughness*. It represents the fraction of the total work expended on the system which is irreversibly absorbed in local plastic flow and cleavage to create a unit area of fracture surface. $\mathcal{G}_c$ appears to be a basic material property which is essentially independent of size effects. It does depend on composition, microstructure, temperature, and rate of loading. Values of $\mathcal{G}_c$ for steel vary from about 100 to 600 in.-lb/in.^{2}, depending on temperature and composition.

To measure $\mathcal{G}_c$, it is necessary to have a reliable mathematical expression for $\mathcal{G}$ in terms of the crack dimensions, the geometry of the specimen, the elastic constants, and the nominal applied stress.[2] The specimen is then loaded until a stress is reached at which the crack which was initially present in the specimen propagates rapidly. The calculated value of $\mathcal{G}$ for this condition is equal to $\mathcal{G}_c$. For a crack of length $2c$ in an infinitely wide plate the relationship between the stress and $\mathcal{G}$ is given by

$$\sigma = \left(\frac{E\mathcal{G}}{\pi c}\right)^{1/2} \tag{7-16}$$

Comparison of Eq. (7-16) with the modified Griffith equation (7-15) shows that $\mathcal{G}$ is analogous to Orowan's plastic-work factor p. In the original Griffith theory, a crack was assumed to propagate rapidly when $\mathcal{G} = 2\gamma$. However, in Irwin's modification of this theory $\mathcal{G}$ is taken as an experimentally determined parameter. For a finite plate of width L with a central crack of length $2c$ or two edge cracks of length c, the crack-extension force for tensile loading is given by

$$\mathcal{G} = \frac{\sigma^2 L}{E}(1 - \nu^2)\tan\left(\frac{\pi c}{L}\right) \tag{7-17}$$

---

[1] G. R. Irwin, *Naval Research Lab. Rept.* 4763, May, 1956, available from Office of Technical Services, PB 121224; G. R. Irwin, J. A. Kies, and H. L. Smith, *Proc. ASTM*, vol. 58, pp. 640–660, 1958.

[2] Detailed procedures for measuring $\mathcal{G}_c$ in tension have been presented in the *ASTM Bulletin*, January and February, 1960. Methods using a notched-bend test and a high-speed rotating disk have been given by D. H. Winne and B. M. Wundt, *Trans. ASME*, vol. 80, p. 1643, 1958.

7-6. Fracture of Single Crystals

The brittle fracture of single crystals is considered to be related to the resolved normal stress on the cleavage plane. Sohncke's law states that fracture occurs when the resolved normal stress reaches a critical value. Considering the situation used to develop the resolved shear stress for slip (Fig. 4-18), the component of the tensile force which acts normal to the cleavage plane is $P \cos \phi$, where ϕ is the angle between the tensile axis and the normal to the plane. The area of the cleavage plane is $A/(\cos \phi)$. Therefore, the critical normal stress for brittle fracture is

$$\sigma_c = \frac{P \cos \phi}{A/(\cos \phi)} = \frac{P}{A} \cos^2 \phi \tag{7-18}$$

The cleavage planes for certain metals and values of the critical normal stress are given in Table 7-1.

TABLE 7-1
CRITICAL NORMAL STRESS FOR CLEAVAGE OF SINGLE CRYSTALS†

Metal	Crystal lattice	Cleavage plane	Temper- ature, °C	Critical normal stress, kg/mm²
Iron.................	bcc	(100)	−100	26
			−185	27.5
Zinc (0.03% Cd)........	hcp	(0001)	−185	0.19
Zinc (0.13% Cd)........	hcp	(0001)	−185	0.30
Zinc (0.53% Cd)........	hcp	(0001)	−185	1.20
Magnesium.............	hcp	(0001), (10$\bar{1}$1) (10$\bar{1}$2), (10$\bar{1}$0)		
Tellurium.............	Hexagonal	(10$\bar{1}$0)	20	0.43
Bismuth...............	Rhombohedral	(111)	20	0.32
Antimony.............	Rhombohedral	(11$\bar{1}$)	20	0.66

† Data from C. S. Barrett, "Structure of Metals," 2d ed., McGraw-Hill Book Company, Inc., New York, 1952; N. J. Petch, The Fracture of Metals, in "Progress in Metal Physics," vol. 5, Pergamon Press, Ltd., London, 1954.

Although Sohncke's law has been accepted for over 25 years, it is not based on very extensive experimental evidence. Doubt was cast on its reliability by fracture studies[1] on zinc single crystals at −77 and −196°C. The resolved normal cleavage stress was found to vary by over a factor of 10 for a large difference in orientation of the crystals. This variation from the normal-stress law may be due to plastic strain prior to fracture, although it is doubtful that this could account for the observed discrepancy.

[1] A. Deruyttere and G. B. Greenough, *J. Inst. Metals*, vol. 84, pp. 337–345, 1955–56.

Several modes of ductile fracture in single crystals are shown in Fig. 7-1. Under certain conditions hcp metals tested at room temperature or above will shear only on a restricted number of basal planes. Fracture will then occur by "shearing off" (Fig. 7-1b). More usually, slip will occur on systems other than the basal plane, so that the crystal necks down and draws down almost to a point before rupture occurs. The usual mode of fracture in fcc crystals is the formation of a necked region due to multiple slip, followed by slip on one set of planes until fracture occurs. The crystal can draw down to a chisel edge or a point (if multiple slip continues to fracture). The best stress criterion for ductile fracture in fcc metals appears to be the resolved shear stress on the fracture plane (which is usually the slip plane).

The mode of fracture in bcc iron crystals is strongly dependent on temperature, purity, heat treatment, and crystal orientation.[1] Crystals located near the [001] corner of the stereographic triangle show no measurable ductility when tested in tension at $-196°C$, while crystals closer to [$\bar{1}11$] and [011] orientations may rupture by drawing down to a chisel edge when tested at the same temperature. An interesting point is that the change from brittle to ductile fracture is very sharp, occurring over a change in orientation of only about 2°.

7-7. Metallographic Aspects of Brittle Fracture

Because of the prominence of the Griffith theory, it has been natural for metallurgists to use their microscopes in a search for Griffith cracks in metals. However, based on observations up to the magnifications available with the electron microscope, there is no reliable evidence that Griffith cracks exist in metals in the unstressed condition. There is, however, a growing amount of experimental evidence to show that microcracks can be produced by plastic deformation.

Metallographic evidence of the formation of microcracks at nonmetallic inclusions in steel as a result of plastic deformation has existed for a number of years. These microcracks do not necessarily produce brittle fracture. However, they do contribute to the observed anisotropy in the ductile-fracture strength. The fact that vacuum-melted steel, which is very low in inclusions, shows a reduction in the fracture anisotropy supports the idea of microcracks being formed at second-phase particles.

An excellent correlation between plastic deformation, microcracks, and brittle fracture was made by Low.[2] He showed that for mild steel of a

[1] N. P. Allen, B. E. Hopkins, and J. E. McLennan, *Proc. Roy. Soc. (London)*, vol. 234A, p. 221, 1956.

[2] J. R. Low, I.U.T.A.M. Madrid Colloqium, "Deformation and Flow of Solids," p. 60, Springer-Verlag OHG, Berlin, 1956.

given grain size tested at −196°C brittle fracture occurs in tension at the same value of stress that is required to produce yielding in compression. Microcracks only one or two grains long were observed. More detailed studies of the conditions for microcrack formation have been made[1] with tensile tests on mild steel at carefully controlled subzero temperatures. Figure 7-4 illustrates a typical microcrack found in a specimen before it fractured.

The correlation between the temperature dependence of yield stress,

Fig. 7-4. Microcracks produced in iron by tensile deformation at −140°C. 250×. (*Courtesy G. T. Hahn.*)

fracture stress, and ductility and microcrack formation is shown in Fig. 7-5. In region A, in the neighborhood of room temperature, a tensile specimen fails with a ductile cup-and-cone fracture. The reduction of area at fracture is of the order of 50 to 60 per cent. In region B the fracture is still ductile, but the outer rim of the fracture contains cleavage facets. A transition from ductile to brittle fracture occurs at the ductility transition temperature T_d. The existence of a transition temperature is indicated by the drop in the reduction of area at the fracture to practically a zero value. Accompanying this is a large decrease in the fracture stress. The percentage of grains containing microcracks increases rapidly in region C just below T_d. However, microcracks are found above T_d. Therefore, the ductility transition occurs when the conditions are suitable for the growth of microcracks into propagating fractures. The initiation of microcracks is not a sufficient criterion for

[1] G. T. Hahn, W. S. Owen, B. L. Averbach, and M. Cohen, *Welding J.*, vol. 38, pp. 367s–376s, 1959.

brittle fracture. Microcracks occur only in regions which have undergone discontinuous yielding as a result of being loaded through the upper yield point. As the temperature drops in region C, eventually the fracture stress drops to a value equal to the lower yield stress. In region D the lower yield stress and fracture stress are practically identical. Fracture occurs at a value equal to the lower yield stress after the material

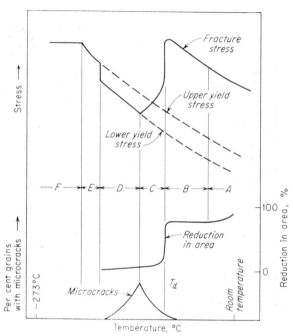

Fig. 7-5. Temperature dependence of fracture stress, yield stress, and microcrack frequency for mild steel. (*After G. T. Hahn, W. S. Owen, B. L. Averbach, and M. Cohen, Welding J., vol. 38, p. 372s, 1959.*)

has undergone some discontinuous yielding. The fracture stress increases because the yield stress is increasing with decreasing temperature. In region E cleavage fracture occurs abruptly before there is time for discontinuous yielding. Presumably fracture occurs at the first spot to undergo discontinuous yielding. Finally, at very low temperatures in region F fracture is initiated by mechanical twins. Mechanical twins are observed at temperatures as high as T_d, but it is only in region F that they appear to be the source of initiation of fracture.

Detailed experiments such as these demonstrate that the cracks responsible for brittle-cleavage-type fracture are not initially present in the material but are produced by the deformation process. The fact that at appropriate temperatures appreciable numbers of microcracks are present shows that the conditions for the initiation of a crack are not necessarily the same as conditions for the propagation of a crack. The process of cleavage fracture should be considered to be made up of three steps, (1) plastic deformation, (2) crack initiation, and (3) crack propagation.

Most brittle fractures occur in a transgranular manner. However, if the grain boundaries contain a film of brittle constituent, as in sensitized

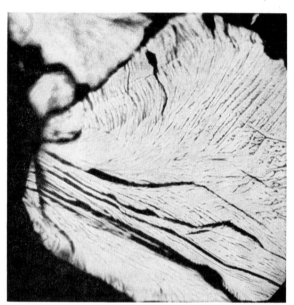

Fig. 7-6. Cleavage steps and river pattern on a cleavage surface.

austenitic stainless steel or molybdenum alloys containing oxygen, nitrogen, or carbon, the fracture will occur in an intergranular manner. Intergranular failure can also occur without the presence of a microscopically visible precipitate at the grain boundaries. Apparently, segregation at the grain boundaries can lower the surface energy sufficiently to cause intergranular failure. The embrittlement produced by the addition of antimony to copper and oxygen to iron and the temper embrittlement of alloy steels are good examples.

Sometimes a considerable amount of information can be obtained by examining the surfaces of the fracture at fairly high magnifications. This type of examination is known as *fractography*.[1] At high magnification, transgranular-cleavage surfaces usually contain a large number of cleavage steps and a "river pattern" of branching cracks (Fig. 7-6). These are indications of the absorption of energy by local deformation. The

[1] C. A. Zappfe and C. O. Worden, *Trans. ASM*, vol. 42, pp. 577–603, 1950.

surfaces of intergranular brittle fractures are much smoother, with a general absence of cleavage steps. From the appearance of the fracture surface, the energy absorbed in an intergranular fracture is much lower than for transgranular cleavage.

7-8. Dislocation Theories of Fracture

The idea that the high stresses produced at the head of a dislocation pile-up could produce fracture was first advanced by Zener.[1] The shear stress acting on the slip plane squeezes the dislocations together. At some critical value of stress the dislocations at the head of the pile-up are pushed so close together that they coalesce into an embryonic crack or cavity dislocation. After analyzing the stresses at a dislocation pile-up and making use of the Griffith criterion, Stroh[2] has proposed that a cleavage crack can form when n dislocations piled up under the action of a resolved shear stress τ_s satisfy the condition

$$nb\tau_s = 12\gamma \tag{7-19}$$

where b is the Burgers vector and γ is the surface energy. The length of the slip plane that the pile-up will occupy is given by

$$L = \frac{nbG}{\pi(1 - \nu)\tau_s} \tag{7-20}$$

Eliminating n from these equations gives

$$\tau_s{}^2 L = \frac{12\gamma G}{\pi(1 - \nu)} \tag{7-21}$$

When a specimen of grain size D is tested in tension, $\tau_s = \sigma/2$ and $L = D/2$. The fracture stress in tension can be expressed in terms of grain size by

$$\sigma_f = 4\left[\frac{6G\gamma}{\pi(1 - \nu)}\right]^{1/2} D^{-1/2} = KD^{-1/2} \tag{7-22}$$

However, Petch[3] has found that experimental data for iron and steel agree best with an equation of the type

$$\sigma_f = \sigma_i + KD^{-1/2} \tag{7-23}$$

[1] C. Zener, The Micro-mechanism of Fracture, in "Fracturing of Metals," American Society for Metals, Metals Park, Ohio, 1948.

[2] A. N. Stroh, *Proc. Roy. Soc. (London)*, vol. 223A, p. 404, 1954; *Phil. Mag.*, vol. 46, p. 968, 1955.

[3] N. J. Petch, *J. Iron Steel Inst. (London)*, vol. 174, p. 25, 1953.

This equation is very similar to the equation expressing the grain-size dependence of the yield strength.

$$\sigma_0 = \sigma_i + K_y D^{-\frac{1}{2}} \tag{7-24}$$

This similarity is to be expected in view of the fact that yielding and brittle fracture are closely related. In both equations σ_i is the frictional stress resisting the motion of an unlocked dislocation. This term increases with decreasing temperature of testing. The constant K in the fracture equation is given approximately by Eq. (7-22). The constant K_y in the yield-strength equation is a measure of the localized stress needed to unlock dislocations held up at a grain boundary so that yielding can be transmitted to the next grain by the propagation of a Lüders band. This quantity is important in current theories of fracture.

The fact that brittle fracture can occur in single crystals suggests that the role of grain boundaries as barriers for dislocation pile-up may be overemphasized in current theories. Also, it is questionable that the necessary stress concentration can be produced at the head of a pile-up before slip occurs in the neighboring grains to relieve the high localized stresses. It is possible that deformation twins may act as barriers for dislocation pile-up. For example, the strong orientation dependence of the brittle fracture of iron single crystals can be explained[1] on this basis. While there is experimental evidence to indicate that twin intersections may initiate brittle fracture,[2] there is also evidence to show that brittle fracture can be produced in the absence of mechanical twins. Another mechanism by which cracks can form is the glide of dislocations on intersecting slip planes according to the hypothesis of Cottrell[3] (see Sec. 6-6 and Fig. 6-9). This mechanism is energetically favorable for a bcc and hcp metal, but not for an fcc lattice, in agreement with the fact that fcc metals do not undergo brittle fracture.

A consideration of the known facts of fracture has led Cottrell and Petch independently to conclude that the growth of a microcrack into a self-propagating fracture is a more difficult step than the nucleation of microcracks from glide dislocations. Support for this viewpoint is found in the fact that many nonpropagating microcracks are observed. Moreover, crack nucleation by dislocation coalescence should depend only on the shear stress, not the hydrostatic component of stress. But there is ample experimental evidence that fracture is strongly influenced by the hydrostatic component of stress (see Sec. 7-16). If the propagation of microcracks, according to a Griffith-type criterion, is the controlling step in fracture, the stress normal to the crack would be an important factor.

[1] H. K. Birnbaum, *Acta Met.*, vol. 7, pp. 516–517, 1959.

[2] D. Hull, *Acta Met.*, vol. 8, pp. 11–18, 1960.

[3] A. H. Cottrell, *Trans. Met. Soc. AIME*, vol. 212, pp. 192–203, 1958.

This should lead to a strong dependence of fracture on the hydrostatic component of stress.

Utilizing the Griffith criterion, Cottrell[1] has shown that the stress required to propagate a microcrack is given by

$$\sigma \simeq \frac{2\gamma}{nb} \tag{7-25}$$

where n is the number of dislocations of Burgers vector b that coalesce into the crack and γ is the surface energy of the crack. To evaluate nb, assume that a slip plane of length L is acted on by an applied shear stress $\tau \approx \sigma/2$. The effective shear stress on the slip plane is given by $\tau - \tau_i$, where τ_i is the frictional resistance. The shear displacement at the center of the length L is given by $(\tau - \tau_i)L/G$, and this is approximately equal to nb. If L is taken as about one-half the average grain diameter D,

$$nb \simeq \frac{(\tau - \tau_i)D}{G} \tag{7-26}$$

Equation (7-24) can be written in terms of shear stress as

$$\tau_0 = \tau_i + k_y D^{-\frac{1}{2}} \tag{7-27}$$

Writing Eq. (7-25) as $nb\tau_0 = \gamma$ and substituting for nb and τ_0 from the above equations results in

$$(\tau_i D^{\frac{1}{2}} + k_y)k_y = G\gamma\beta \tag{7-28}$$

or the equivalent relationship

$$\tau_0 k_y D^{\frac{1}{2}} = G\gamma\beta \tag{7-29}$$

In the above equations β is a term which expresses the ratio of the maximum shear stress to the maximum normal stress. For torsion $\beta = 1$, for tension $\beta = \frac{1}{2}$, and for the plastically constrained region at the root of a notch $\beta \approx \frac{1}{3}$.

When the glide dislocations coalesce into a crack or a cavity dislocation, the frictional resistance to glide equals zero. Therefore, by making substitutions from the above equations into Eq. (7-25) one arrives at an expression for the stress required to propagate a microcrack of length D.

$$\sigma \simeq 2\left(\frac{G\gamma\beta}{D}\right)^{\frac{1}{2}} \tag{7-30}$$

Equations (7-28) and (7-29) express the limiting conditions for the formation of propagating crack from a pile-up of glide dislocations. If conditions are such that the left-hand side of the equation is less than the

[1] *Ibid.*

right-hand side, a crack can form but it cannot grow beyond a certain
length. This is the case of nonpropagating microcracks. When the left-
hand side of the equations is greater than the right side, a propagating
brittle fracture can be produced at a shear stress equal to the yield stress.
Therefore, these equations predict a ductile-to-brittle transition, such
as was shown in Fig. 7-5 for tension tests on mild steel at decreasing
temperature.

The equations describing the ductile-to-brittle transition are expressed
in terms of the following metallurgical or mechanical factors: grain size,
state of stress, surface energy, yield stress, friction stress, and k_y. The
parameter k_y is very important, since it determines the number of dislocations that are released into a pile-up when a source is unlocked.
Table 7-2 gives some typical values of k_y obtained from measurements of

TABLE 7-2
VALUES OF k_y/G†

Material	Temperature, °K	k_y/G, cm$^{1/2}$
Iron................	300	0.4×10^{-4}
Molybdenum.........	300	0.55×10^{-4}
Columbium..........	200	0.1×10^{-4}
Tantalum...........	200	0.1×10^{-4}

† A. H. Cottrell, *Trans. Met. Soc. AIME*, vol. 212, p. 194, 1958.

fracture stress vs. grain size. Large values of k_y indicate brittle behavior,
which agrees with the observations that pure columbium and tantalum
are less prone to brittle fracture than the other bcc metals, iron and
molybdenum. Equation (7-28) shows that at a constant temperature
there is a certain grain size above which the metal will be brittle and
below which it will be ductile. This is shown in Fig. 7-7, where above a
certain grain size there is measurable ductility at fracture. The frictional resistance τ_i increases with decreasing temperature. However,
since this term enters into Eq. (7-28) as the product of $D^{1/2}$, it can be seen
that a fine-grained metal can withstand higher values of τ_i (lower temperatures) before becoming brittle. Many of the effects of the composition
of steel on the ductile-to-brittle transition are due to changes in grain size
or in k_y or τ_i. For example, manganese decreases the grain size and
reduces k_y, while silicon produces larger grain size and increases τ_i.

The yield stress increases with decreasing temperature, and in agreement with Eq. (7-29) this increases the tendency for brittle fracture. If
conditions are such that microcracks cannot propagate at the yield point,
it is necessary to increase the stress by $\Delta\tau$ in order to produce fracture.

From Eq. (7-29), the necessary value of shear stress is

$$\tau_f = \tau_0 + \Delta\tau = \frac{G\gamma\beta}{k_y} D^{-\frac{1}{2}} \qquad (7\text{-}31)$$

This predicts that fracture stress is a linear function of $D^{-\frac{1}{2}}$, which extrapolates to zero at $D^{-\frac{1}{2}} = 0$. Figure 7-7 shows that this relationship is satisfied. In the region of grain size for which cracks propagate as completely brittle fractures, the fracture stress equals the yield stress.

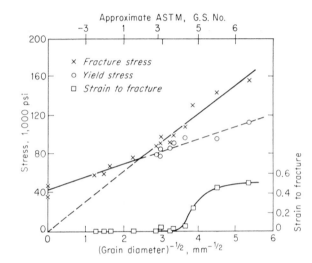

Fig. 7-7. Effect of grain size on the yield and fracture stresses for a low-carbon steel tested in tension at $-196°C$. (*J. R. Low, in "Relation of Properties to Microstructure," American Society for Metals, Metals Park, Ohio, 1954.*)

This branch of the curve extrapolates to the fracture stress for a single crystal.

High values of surface energy tend to promote ductile fracture. Unfortunately, this is not a factor which is readily increased, although various environmental and metallurgical conditions may lower the surface energy. The embrittlement of steel due to hydrogen has been attributed to this factor. Intergranular fracture due to an embrittling film may also be explained in this way.

It is well known that the presence of a notch greatly increases the tendency for brittle fracture. The complicated effects of a notch will be considered more fully in Sec. 7-12. The effect of a notch in decreasing the ratio of shear stress to tensile stress is covered in Cottrell's equations by the constant β. Strain rate or rate of loading does not enter explicitly into Cottrell's equations. However, for a notch to produce the plastic constraint that results in a value of $\beta \simeq \frac{1}{3}$, it is necessary for the material to yield locally. At high rates of strain, such as occur in a notched-impact test, yielding will have to occur more rapidly. As is indicated by Eq. (7-32) in the next section, this can occur at the same value of τ_0 if the temperature is increased. Therefore, increasing the strain rate raises the transition temperature.

7-9. Delayed Yielding

A phenomenon which is important to brittle fracture is *delayed yielding*. When certain metals, notably mild steel, are rapidly loaded to a constant

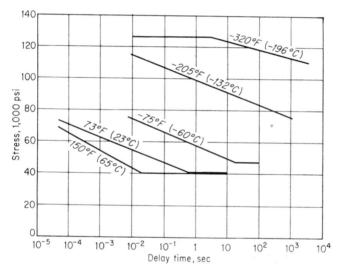

Fig. 7-8. Delay time for initiation of yielding in mild steel as a function of stress. (*D. S. Clark, Trans. ASM, vol.* 46, *p.* 49, 1954.)

stress above the yield stress, it is found that a certain *delay time* is required before plastic yielding occurs.[1] Figure 7-8 shows that the delay time increases with decreasing temperature at a constant stress. For a constant temperature, the delay time increases with decreasing stress. The lower limiting stress shown by the horizontal portion of the curves corresponds to the upper yield point for tests carried out at slow speeds.

The temperature dependence of the delay time may be expressed by an exponential relationship

$$t = t_0 \exp \frac{Q(\sigma/\sigma_0)}{kT} \tag{7-32}$$

[1] D. S. Clark, *Trans. ASM*, vol. 46, p. 34, 1954.

where t = delay time

t_0 = a constant, approximately 10^{-11} sec

k = Boltzmann's constant

$Q(\sigma/\sigma_0)$ = stress-dependent activation energy

Cottrell[1] has estimated that $Q(\sigma/\sigma_0)$, in electron volts, is given approximately by $0.9(1 - \sigma/\sigma_0)^3$, where σ is the applied stress and σ_0 is the yield stress.

The fact that brittle fracture occurs when plastic deformation fails to keep the stress below a critical value indicates that there should be a connection between delayed yielding and brittle fracture. The delay time is quite temperature-dependent, and so is brittle fracture. In the temperature region where brittle fracture is caused by an avalanche of dislocations breaking away from a barrier and running together to form a crack, delayed yielding probably plays the important role of localizing the slip by preventing nearby dislocation sources from operating. At temperatures where the metal fractures in a ductile manner the delay time is so short that slip occurs around the pile-ups and the high localized stresses are dissipated by plastic deformation. This agreement is supported by the fact that metals which have a ductile-to-brittle fracture transition also have a delayed yield phenomenon.

7-10. Velocity of Crack Propagation

Brittle fracture is not possible unless the cracks which are nucleated can propagate at a high velocity throughout the metal. Mott[2] has made an analysis of the velocity of a crack in an ideal elastic, isotropic medium. The elastic energy that is released by the movement of the crack is the driving force. This must be balanced by the surface energy of the new surface that is created and the kinetic energy associated with the rapid sidewise displacement of material on each side of the crack. The crack velocity v is given by

$$v = Bv_0 \left(1 - \frac{c_G}{c}\right) \tag{7-33}$$

where B is a constant and $v_0 = (E/\rho)^{1/2}$ is the velocity of sound in the material. The term c_G is the length of a Griffith crack, as evaluated by Eq. (7-11), and c is the actual crack length. When c is large compared with c_G, Eq. (7-33) approaches the limiting value Bv_0. The constant has been evaluated[3] for the plane-stress condition and found to be $B \simeq 0.38$.

[1] A. H. Cottrell, *Proc. Conf. on Properties Materials at High Rates of Strain*, Institution of Mechanical Engineers, London, 1957.

[2] N. F. Mott, *Engineering*, vol. 165, p. 16, 1948.

[3] D. K. Roberts and A. A. Wells, *Engineering*, vol. 178, p. 820, 1954.

Table 7-3 shows that experimental values for the crack velocity in brittle materials agree quite well with the theoretical prediction that the limiting crack velocity is given by

$$v = 0.38v_0 = 0.38 \left(\frac{E}{\rho}\right)^{\frac{1}{2}} \tag{7-34}$$

TABLE 7-3
VELOCITY OF PROPAGATION OF BRITTLE FRACTURE

Material	Observed velocity, ft/sec	v/v_0	Reference
Steel.................	6,000	0.36	†
Fused quartz..........	7,200	0.42	‡
Lithium fluoride.......	6,500	0.31	§

† T. S. Robertson, *J. Iron Steel Inst.* (*London*), vol. 175, p. 361, 1953.
‡ H. Schardin and W. Struth, *Glastech. Ber.*, vol. 16, p. 219, 1958.
§ J. J. Gilman, C. Knudsen, and W. P. Walsh, *J. Appl. Phys.*, vol. 29, p. 601, 1958.

7-11. Ductile Fracture

Ductile fracture has been studied much less extensively than brittle fracture, probably because it is a much less serious problem. Up to this point ductile fracture has been defined rather ambiguously as fracture occurring with appreciable gross plastic deformation. Another important characteristic of ductile fracture, which should be apparent from previous considerations of brittle fracture, is that it occurs by a slow tearing of the metal with the expenditure of considerable energy. Many varieties of ductile fractures can occur during the processing of metals and their use in different types of service. For simplification, the discussion in this section will be limited to ductile fracture of metals produced in uniaxial tension. Other aspects of tensile fracture are considered in Chap. 9. Ductile fracture in tension is usually preceded by a localized reduction in diameter called *necking*. Very ductile metals may actually draw down to a line or a point before separation. This kind of failure is usually called *rupture*.

The stages in the development of a ductile "cup-and-cone" fracture are illustrated in Fig. 7-9. Necking begins at the point of plastic instability where the increase in strength due to strain hardening fails to compensate for the decrease in cross-sectional area (Fig. 7-9a). This occurs at maximum load or at a true strain equal to the strain-hardening coefficient (see Sec. 9-3). The formation of a neck introduces a triaxial state of stress in the region. A hydrostatic component of tension acts

along the axis of the specimen at the center of the necked region.   Many
fine cavities form in this region (Fig. 7-9b), and under continued straining these grow and coalesce into a central crack (Fig. 7-9c).   This crack
grows in a direction perpendicular to the axis of the specimen until it

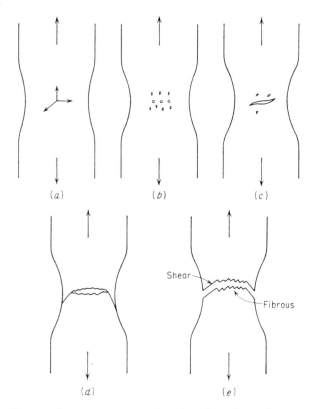

Fig. 7-9. Stages in the formation of a cup-and-cone fracture.

approaches the surface of the specimen.   It then propagates along localized shear planes at roughly 45° to the axis to form the "cone" part of
the fracture (Fig. 7-9d).
    When the central "cup" region of the fracture is viewed from above,
it has a very fibrous appearance, much as if the individual elements of
the specimen were split into longitudinal fibers and were then drawn
down to a point before rupture.   When the fracture is sectioned longi-
tudinally, the central crack has a zigzag contour, such as would be produced by tearing between a number of holes.   The outer cone of the
fracture is a region of highly localized shear.   Extensive localized deformation occurs by the sliding of grains over one another, and because the

shear fracture propagates rapidly compared with the fibrous fracture, there is appreciable localized heating.

Petch[1] has shown that the fracture stress (corrected for necking) for the ductile fracture of iron has the same dependence on grain size as is found for brittle fracture. This suggests that the voids are nucleated by dislocation pile-ups at grain boundaries. However, it is extremely unlikely that dislocation pile-ups large enough to produce cavity dislocations can be produced in ductile fcc metals like aluminum and copper. Instead, voids in these metals appear to be nucleated at foreign particles such as oxide particles, impurity phases, or second-phase particles. Under tensile strain either the metal separates from the inclusion, or the inclusion itself fractures.[2] Even in metals for which no crack-nucleating second-phase particles can be observed, it appears that fracture-nucleating elements are present before deformation. This is borne out by the fact that the fracture stress and reduction in area can be appreciably lower when tested in a direction perpendicular to the original rolling or extrusion direction than when tested in the direction of working, even though all microstructural evidence of working has been removed by heat treatment and there is no strong crystallographic texture. It must be assumed that working elongates these "sites" so that they open into voids more readily when the tensile stress is applied perpendicular to their length.

7-12. Notch Effect in Fracture

The changes produced by the introduction of a notch have important implications for the fracture of metals. The presence of a notch will very appreciably increase the temperature at which a steel changes from ductile to brittle fracture. The introduction of a notch results in a stress concentration at the root of the notch. Figure 7-10 shows the non-uniform distribution of the longitudinal tensile stress in a notched tensile bar. When yielding occurs at the root of the notch, the stress concentration is reduced. However, transverse and radial stresses are set up in the vicinity of the notch (Fig. 7-10). The radial stress σ_R is zero at the free surface at the root of the notch, but it rises to a high value in the interior of the specimen and then drops off again. The transverse stress σ_T acts in the circumferential direction of a cylindrical specimen. This stress drops from a high value at the notch root to a lower value at the specimen axis.

The occurrence of this state of stress can be explained by the constraints to plastic flow which a notch sets up. For an equilibrium of

[1] N. J. Petch, *Phil. Mag.*, ser. 8, vol. 1, p. 186, 1956.
[2] K. E. Puttick, *Phil. Mag.*, ser. 8, vol. 4, p. 964, 1959.

forces to be maintained in the notched bar, it is necessary that no stresses act normal to the free surfaces of the notch. All the tensile load must be taken by the metal in the core of the notch. Therefore, a relatively large mass of unstressed metal exists around a central core of highly stressed material. The central core tries to contract laterally because of the Poisson effect, but it is restrained by what amounts to a hoop of unstressed material around it. The resistance of the unstressed mass of material to the deformation of the central core produces radial and transverse stresses.

The existence of radial and transverse stresses (triaxial stress state) raises the value of longitudinal stress at which yielding occurs. For simplification, consider that yielding occurs at a critical shear stress τ_c. For an unnotched tension specimen this critical value is given by

$$\tau_c = \frac{\sigma_L - 0}{2}$$

For a notched tension specimen this becomes

$$\tau_c = \frac{\sigma_L - \sigma_R}{2}$$

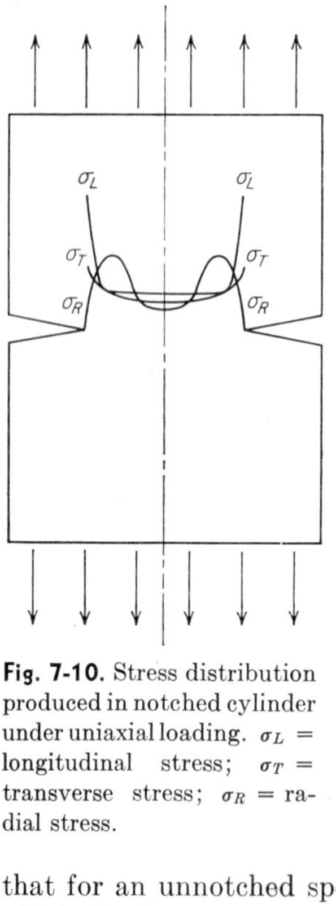

Fig. 7-10. Stress distribution produced in notched cylinder under uniaxial loading. σ_L = longitudinal stress; σ_T = transverse stress; σ_R = radial stress.

Since the critical shear stress for yielding is the same for both cases, it is apparent from these equations that the existence of transverse stresses requires a higher longitudinal stress to produce yielding. The entire flow curve of a notched specimen is raised over that for an unnotched specimen because of this effect. The amount by which the flow curve is raised because of the notch can be expressed by a *plastic-constraint factor q.*

Plastic constraint differs from elastic-stress concentration in a basic way. From elastic considerations the stress concentration at the root of a notch can be made extremely high as the radius at the root of the notch approaches zero. When plastic deformation occurs at the root of the notch, the elastic-stress concentration is reduced to a low value. However, plastic deformation produces plastic constraint at the root of the notch. In contrast to elastic-stress concentrations, no matter how sharp the notch the plastic-constraint factor[1] cannot exceed a value of about 3.

[1] E. Orowan, J. F. Nye, and W. J. Cairns, "Strength and Testing of Materials," vol. 1, H. M. Stationery Office, London, 1952.

A third important contribution of a notch is to produce an increase in the local strain rate. While the notch is still loaded in the elastic region, the stress at a point near the notch is rapidly increasing with time because of the sharp gradients. Since stress is proportional to strain, there is a high local elastic strain rate. When yielding occurs, the plastic flow tends to relieve the stresses. The stress picture changes from one of high elastic stresses to a lower plastic constraint, and in so doing a high plastic strain rate develops near the notch.

7-13. Concept of the Fracture Curve

In earlier chapters it was shown that the flow curve, or the true stress-strain curve, can be considered to represent the stress required to cause plastic flow at any particular value of plastic strain. In an analogous manner it was proposed by Ludwik[1] that a metal has a *fracture stress*

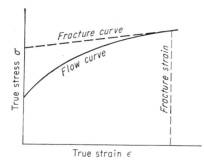

Fig. 7-11. Schematic drawing of intersection of flow curve and fracture curve according to the Ludwik theory.

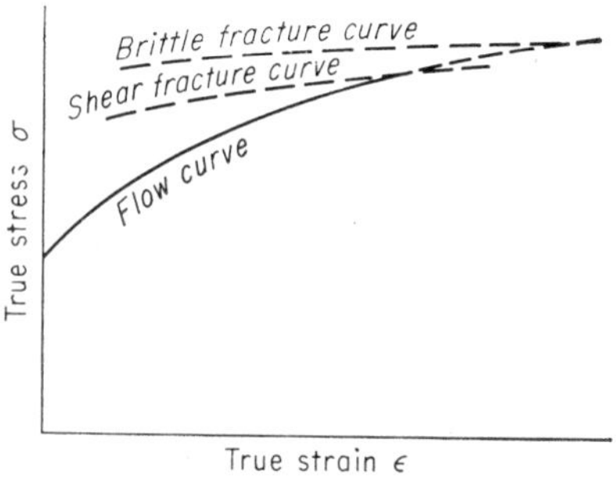

Fig. 7-12. Modification of the Ludwik theory to include shear and brittle fracture curves.

curve which indicates the stress required to cause fracture at any value of plastic strain. He further suggested that fracture would occur when the flow curve intersects the fracture curve (Fig. 7-11). This concept was widely accepted until after World War II, and several measurements of the fracture curve were attempted. However, it eventually was realized that basic factors in the fracture mechanism of metals prevent a correct determination of the fracture curve of metals. Since this realization, the idea of the fracture curve has lost much of its popularity. It is, however, still a useful concept for obtaining a qualitatively correct picture of the fracture phenomenon if the limitations which will be discussed shortly are recognized. With this in mind, and in view of the current realization that both shear and cleavage fractures are possible in metals, it is often found that a separate fracture curve for each mode of fracture is considered, as shown in Fig. 7-12. The curves in this figure

[1] P. Ludwik, *Z. Ver. deut. Ing.*, vol. 71, pp. 1532–1538, 1927.

are for the ordinary tensile fracture of a ductile metal in which a shear type of fracture takes place. The separation between the two fracture curves and their relative height will be different for other conditions of fracture.

In principle, a point on the fracture curve is obtained by plastically straining a specimen to a given point on the flow curve and then introducing embrittling parameters (low temperature or a notch) so that the specimen is stressed to failure without added strain. By repeating this process with different specimens stressed to different values of plastic strain it would be possible to construct the entire fracture curve. However, since the embrittling effect of a notch is limited to a plastic-constraint factor of about 3, it is generally more effective to attempt to resist any further deformation by carrying out the test at a very low temperature. Actually, with most metals this is not possible since a slight amount of deformation invariably results on straining at low temperature. In view of the evidence that fracture is initiated by plastic deformation, it would appear that the fracture stress measured by this technique does not measure the true resistance of the metal to fracture. Further, the fracture stress for ductile fracture is very difficult to measure accurately because the ductile fracture is initiated at the interior of the specimen, and the stress distribution is complicated by necking of the tensile specimen. Therefore, there is no reliable method for determining the fracture curve of metals. However, this does not prohibit using the concept of the fracture stress, in a qualitative sense, where it is useful for describing certain aspects of fracture.

7-14. Classical Theory of the Ductile-to-Brittle Transition

Brittle fracture is promoted by three main factors, (1) a triaxial state of stress, (2) a low temperature, and (3) a high strain rate. In the previous section it was shown that the presence of a notch provides condition 1 and contributes to condition 3. Temperature has a strong effect on the basic flow and fracture properties of the metal. For all metals the yield stress or flow stress increases with decreasing temperature. With fcc metals, where there is no ductile-to-brittle transition, the increase in yield stress on going from room temperature to liquid-nitrogen temperature ($-196°C$) is about a factor of 2. In bcc metals, which show a ductile-to-brittle transition, the yield stress increases by a factor of 3 to 8 over the same temperature range. Figure 7-5 illustrates the trends in fracture stress and yield stress with temperature. It also shows that the reduction of area at fracture in a tensile specimen drops off rapidly over a narrow temperature interval. The temperature range at which this transition occurs is called the *transition temperature.*

The so-called classical theory of the ductile-to-brittle transition was suggested by Davidenkov and Wittman.[1] According to this concept, the existence of a transition temperature is due to the difference in the way the resistances to shear and cleavage change with temperature. The relative values of these two parameters determine whether the fracture will be ductile or brittle. Above the transition temperature the flow stress is reached before the fracture stress, while below the transition temperature the fracture stress is reached first. Factors which increase the critical shear stress for slip without at the same time raising the fracture stress will favor brittle fracture. Decreasing the temperature and increasing the strain rate both have this effect. In Fig. 7-13, the curve marked σ_0 gives the temperature dependence of yield stress for simple tension. The curve $q\sigma_0$, where $q \approx 3$, is the temperature dependence of the yield stress in the presence of the plastic constraint at a notch. The curve marked σ_f is

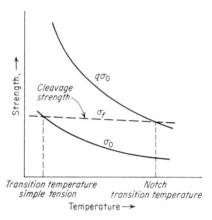

Fig. 7-13. Schematic description of transition temperature.

the fracture strength or cleavage strength as a function of temperature. In agreement with available data, it is drawn as a less sensitive function of temperature than the yield stress. A transition temperature occurs when a curve of flow stress intersects the cleavage strength. For an unnotched tension specimen this occurs at a quite low temperature, but for a notched test the transition temperature is much closer to room temperature.

While this picture of the ductile-to-brittle transition does not provide for the structural details embodied in the dislocation theory, it does give an easily grasped working model of the phenomenon. As originally proposed, this classical theory ascribes no major effect to the role of strain rate; yet recent experiments have indicated that strain rate may be more important than plastic constraint in producing brittle fracture. Using sharp cleavage cracks as notches, Felbeck and Orowan[2] were unable to produce cleavage fracture in steel plates unless the crack reached a high velocity. Extensive plastic deformation was present at the base of the crack in all cases. These experiments could be interpreted only by con-

---

[1] N. N. Davidenkov and F. Wittman, *Phys. Tech. Inst.* (U.S.S.R.), vol. 4, p. 300, 1937.

[2] Felbeck and Orowan, *op. cit.*

sidering that the yield stress is raised to the value of the fracture stress, not by plastic constraint, but by the effect of high strain rate on increasing the yield stress. It is difficult to separate these two effects, and additional experiments would be very worthwhile. However, it is interesting to note that the yield stress of mild steel is very sensitive to strain rate. Also, the large increase in transition temperature that is brought about by using a notched-impact test can be understood on this basis when it is considered that the strain rate in the impact test is about 10^7 times greater than in the ordinary tension test.

7-15. Fracture under Combined Stresses

The phenomenological approach to fracture is concerned with uncovering the general macroscopic laws which describe the fracture of metals under all possible states of stress. This same approach was discussed in Chap. 3 with regard to the prediction of yielding under complex states of stress. The problem of determining general laws for the fracture strength of metals is quite difficult because fracture is so sensitive to prior plastic straining and temperature. In principle we can conceive of a three-dimensional fracture surface in terms of the three principal stresses σ_1, σ_2, and σ_3. For any combination of principal stresses the metal will fracture when the limiting surface is reached. Enough experimentation has been done to realize that the fracture surface cannot be rigid but must be considered as a flexible membrane which changes shape with changes in stress and strain history.

Most experimentation in this field has been with biaxial states of stress where one of the principal stresses is zero. Tubular specimens in which an axial tensile or compressive load is superimposed on the circumferential stress produced by internal pressure are ordinarily used for this type of work. For accurate results bulging or necking during the later stages of the test must be avoided. This makes it difficult to obtain good data for very ductile metals.

Figure 7-14 illustrates the fracture criteria which have been most frequently proposed for fracture under a biaxial state of stress. The maximum-shear-stress criterion and the Von Mises, or distortion-energy, criterion have already been considered previously in the discussion of yielding criteria. The maximum-normal-stress criterion proposes that fracture is controlled only by the magnitude of the greatest principal stress. Available data on ductile metals such as aluminum and magnesium alloys[1] and steel[2] indicate that the maximum-shear-stress criterion

---

[1] J. E. Dorn, "Fracturing of Metals," American Society for Metals, Metals Park, Ohio, 1948.

[2] E. A. Davis, *J. Appl. Mech.*, vol. 12, pp. A13–A24, 1945.

for fracture results in the best agreement. Agreement between experiment and theory is not nearly so good as for the case of yielding criteria. The fracture criterion for a brittle cast iron[1] is shown in Fig. 7-15. Note that the normal stress criterion is followed in the tension-tension region and that the fracture strength increases significantly as one of the principal stresses becomes compressive. Two theories[2,3] which consider the

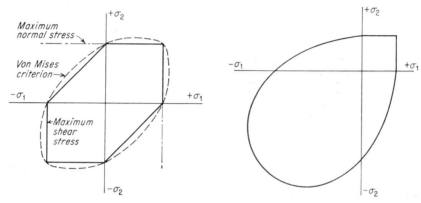

Fig. 7-14. Proposed fracture criteria for biaxial state of stress in ductile metals.   **Fig. 7-15.** Biaxial fracture criterion for brittle cast iron.

stress concentration of graphite flakes in cast iron are in good agreement with the fracture data. These data are also in substantial agreement with the fracture curve predicted from Griffith's theory of brittle fracture.

7-16. Effect of High Hydrostatic Pressure on Fracture

Bridgman's work[4] on the effect of superimposed hydrostatic pressure on the fracture characteristics of metals has produced many interesting results. His results have also shown that fracture is a complex phenomenon which in many cases cannot be described by the simple criteria of the previous section.

Bridgman tested metal specimens in such a way that hydrostatic pressures of up to 450,000 psi were superimposed on an axial tensile stress. These extreme conditions produced a very great increase in the ductility at fracture. The strain at the location of fracture was as much as 300 times greater when mild steel was fractured with superimposed hydro-

---

[1] W. R. Clough and M. E. Shank, *Trans. ASM*, vol. 49, pp. 241–262, 1957.

[2] L. F. Coffin, Jr., *J. Appl. Mech.*, vol. 17, p. 233, 1950.

[3] J. C. Fisher, *ASTM Bull.* 181, p. 74, April, 1952.

[4] P. W. Bridgman, "Studies in Large Plastic Flow and Fracture," McGraw-Hill Book Company, Inc., New York, 1952.

static pressure than when tested with simple uniaxial loading.   Materials which are completely brittle under ordinary conditions, like limestone or rock salt, actually necked down when pulled in tension with superimposed hydrostatic pressure.   It was also found that, if a tensile specimen was loaded with superimposed pressure to a point short of fracture and then tested at atmospheric pressure, it required further deformation before fracturing, even if the elongation under pressure was greater than the metal could withstand when ordinarily tested at atmospheric pressure. Further, the amount of deformation required to produce fracture after removal of the hydrostatic pressure increases with an increase in the magnitude of the pressure.   These facts indicate that, in general, fracture is not determined completely by the instantaneous state of stress or strain.   Bridgman was able to find no simple stress function which described his results.

BIBLIOGRAPHY

Averbach, B. L., D. K. Felbeck, G. T. Hahn, and D. A. Thomas (eds.): "Fracture," Technology Press and John Wiley & Sons, Inc., New York, 1959.
Barrett, C. S.: Metallurgy at Low Temperatures, Campbell Memorial Lecture, 1956, *Trans. ASM*, vol. 49, pp. 53–117, 1957.
"Fracturing of Metals," American Society for Metals, Metals Park, Ohio, 1948.
Orowan, E.: Fracture and Strength of Solids, *Repts. Progr. in Phys.*, vol. 12, pp. 185–232, 1949.
Parker, E. R.: "Brittle Behavior of Engineering Structures," John Wiley & Sons, Inc., New York, 1957.
Petch, N. J.: The Fracture of Metals, in "Progress in Metal Physics," vol. 5, Pergamon Press, Ltd., London, 1954.
Stroh, A. N.: *Advances in Phys.*, vol. 6, pp. 418–465, 1957.

Chapter 8
INTERNAL FRICTION

8-1. Introduction

The ability of a vibrating solid which is completely isolated from its surroundings to convert its mechanical energy of vibration into heat is called *internal friction*, or *damping capacity*. The former term is preferred by physicists, and the latter is generally used in engineering. If metals behaved as perfectly elastic materials at stresses below the nominal elastic limit, there would be no internal friction. However, the fact that damping effects can be observed at stress levels far below the macroscopic elastic limit indicates that metals have a very low true elastic limit, if, indeed, one exists at all. Internal-friction, or damping, effects correspond to a phase lag between the applied stress and the resulting strain. This may be due simply to plastic deformation at a high stress level, or at low stress levels it may be due to thermal, magnetic, or atomic rearrangements.

An important division of the field of nonelastic behavior is called *anelasticity*. This subject is concerned with internal-friction effects which are independent of the amplitude of vibration. Anelastic behavior can be due to thermal diffusion, atomic diffusion, stress relaxation across grain boundaries, stress-induced ordering, and magnetic interactions. Certain static effects such as the elastic-aftereffect are concerned with anelastic behavior. Internal friction resulting from cold work is strongly amplitude-dependent and, therefore, is not an anelastic phenomenon. Much of our present knowledge of the mechanisms which contribute to anelasticity is due to Zener[1] and his coworkers.

Studies of internal friction are primarily concerned with using damping as a tool for studying internal structure and atom movements in solids. The method has provided information on diffusion, ordering, and solubilities of interstitial elements and has been used for estimating the density of dislocations. The vibration amplitudes employed in this type of

[1] C. Zener, "Elasticity and Anelasticity," University of Chicago Press, Chicago, 1948.

work are usually quite small, and the stresses are very low. Another aspect of this field is the determination of engineering data on the dissipation of energy in vibrating members. This work is usually concerned with determining the damping capacity of a material at the relatively large amplitudes encountered in engineering practice.

Internal friction is measured by a number of techniques.[1] The simplest device is a torsional pendulum for use in the low-frequency region around 1 cps. For higher-frequency measurements the specimen is excited by an electromagnetic drive, a piezoelectric crystal, or ultrasonic energy.

8-2. Phenomenological Description of Internal Friction

For energy to be dissipated by internal friction, the strain must lag behind the applied stress. The phase angle, or lag angle, α can be used as a measure of internal friction.

$$\alpha \simeq \frac{\epsilon_2''}{\epsilon_1'} \tag{8-1}$$

where ϵ_2'' = nonelastic strain component 90° out of phase with stress
ϵ_1' = elastic strain in phase with stress

Internal friction is frequently measured by a system which is set into motion with a certain amplitude A_0 and then allowed to decay freely. The amplitude at any time, A_t, can be expressed by an equation

$$A_t = A_0 \exp(-\beta t) \tag{8-2}$$

where β is the attenuation coefficient. The most common way of defining internal friction or damping capacity is with the logarithmic decrement δ. The logarithmic decrement is the logarithm of the ratio of successive amplitudes.

$$\delta = \ln \frac{A_n}{A_{n+1}} \tag{8-3}$$

If the internal friction is independent of amplitude, a plot of $\ln A$ versus the number of cycles of vibration will be linear and the slope of the curve is the decrement. If the damping is amplitude-dependent, the decrement is given by the slope of the curve at a chosen amplitude. The logarithmic decrement is related to the lag angle by

$$\delta = \pi \alpha \tag{8-4}$$

For a condition of forced vibration in which the specimen is driven at

[1] C. Wert, "Modern Research Techniques in Physical Metallurgy," pp. 225–250, American Society for Metals, Metals Park, Ohio, 1953.

a constant amplitude a measure of internal friction is the fractional decrease in vibrational energy per cycle. Vibrational energy is proportional to the square of the amplitude, so that the logarithmic decrement can be expressed by

$$\delta = \frac{\Delta W}{2W} \tag{8-5}$$

where ΔW is the energy lost per cycle and W is the vibrational energy at the start of the cycle. In a forced-vibration type of experiment it is customary to determine a resonance curve such as that of Fig. 8-1. The logarithmic decrement for a resonance curve is given approximately by

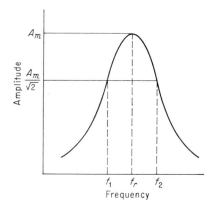

$$\delta = \frac{\pi(\text{bandwidth})}{f_r} = \frac{\pi(f_2 - f_1)}{f_r} \tag{8-6}$$

A measure of internal friction that is often used is the Q, where $Q = \pi/\delta$. Since in electrical-circuit theory the reciprocal of this value is called the Q of the circuit, the symbol Q^{-1} has been adopted as a measure of internal friction.

Fig. 8-1. Resonance curve.

$$Q^{-1} = \frac{f_2 - f_1}{f_r} \tag{8-7}$$

Under conditions of cyclic excitation the dynamic elastic modulus will be greater than the static elastic modulus because of nonelastic internal friction. The modulus under dynamic conditions is frequently termed the *unrelaxed elastic modulus* E_u, while the static modulus is called the *relaxed modulus* E_R. The unrelaxed modulus is given by

$$E_u = \frac{\sigma_1}{\epsilon_1{}^E + \epsilon_1{}^P} \tag{8-8}$$

where $\epsilon_1{}^E$ is the elastic and $\epsilon_1{}^P$ is the plastic strain component in phase with the stress. The fact that the dynamic modulus is larger than the static elastic modulus is called the ΔE *effect*.

A number of models have been proposed to describe the nonelastic behavior of materials. The models suggested by Voight[1] and Maxwell[2]

[1] W. Voight, *Ann. Physik*, vol. 47, p. 671, 1892.
[2] J. C. Maxwell, *Phil. Mag.*, vol. 35, p. 134, 1868.

are frequently mentioned.   Both models consider that the material has an elastic component coupled with a viscous component.   The behavior of a material, with the properties attributed to it by the theory, can be duplicated by a mechanical model composed of springs (elastic component) and dashpots (viscous component).   Figure 8-2 illustrates the composition of a Voight and Maxwell solid, together with the equations which the models predict.   For real metals the frequency dependence of internal friction does not agree with the equations predicted by the models.   Further, the models do not account for the dependence of dynamic modulus on internal friction, which is observed with real metals.   Various modifications of the models have been useful in studying the mechanical properties of polymers, but they are of limited usefulness in dealing with metals.

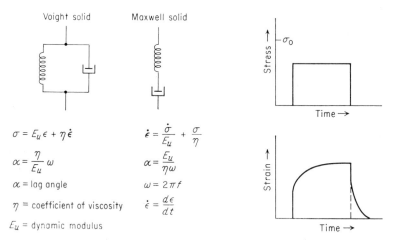

Fig. 8-2. Spring and dashpot models of   Fig. 8-3. Time dependence of stress and
Voight and Maxwell solids.   strain for anelastic material, showing
                                           elastic aftereffect.

8-3. Anelasticity

A nonelastic body is said to behave anelastically when the stress and strain are not single-valued functions of each other *and* the internal friction is independent of amplitude.   One manifestation of this is the *elastic aftereffect*.   Consider a metal which is subjected to a constant stress at a level well below the conventional elastic limit (Fig. 8-3).   The strains involved may be of the order of 10^{-5}, so that very sensitive measurements are required.   After an initial strain the metal will gradually creep until the strain reaches an essentially constant value.   This can be observed in many metals at room temperature, although the effect is greater at higher temperatures. When the stress is removed, the strain will decrease but there will be a certain amount which remains and slowly decreases with time, approaching its original value. This time dependence of strain on loading and unloading has been called the elastic aftereffect.

In considering the stress-strain relationship for an anelastic material it is apparent that a constant linear relationship between these two factors will not adequately describe the situation. A realistic relationship is obtained by equating the stress and its first derivative with respect to time to the strain and the strain rate.

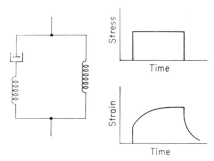

$$a_1\sigma + a_2\dot{\sigma} = b_1\epsilon + b_2\dot{\epsilon} \quad (8\text{-}9)$$

A material which obeys this type of equation is known as a *standard linear solid*. The mechanical model for this material is shown in Fig. 8-4. Note that the time dependence of strain closely duplicates the

Fig. 8-4. Mechanical model of standard linear solid and associated time dependence of stress and strain.

behavior of a material with an elastic aftereffect. The general equation for a standard linear solid can be rewritten in terms of three independent constants.

$$\sigma + \tau_\epsilon\dot{\sigma} = E_R(\epsilon + \tau_\sigma\dot{\epsilon}) \quad (8\text{-}10)$$

where τ_ϵ = time of relaxation of stress for constant strain
τ_σ = time of relaxation of strain for constant stress
E_R = relaxed elastic modulus
The relationship between the relaxation times and the relaxed and unrelaxed modulus is given by

$$\frac{E_R}{E_u} = \frac{\tau_\epsilon}{\tau_\sigma} \quad (8\text{-}11)$$

A dimensionless combination of elastic constants, called the *relaxation strength*, is a measure of the total relaxation

$$E_s = \frac{E_u - E_R}{\sqrt{E_u E_R}} \quad (8\text{-}12)$$

For a standard linear solid there is only a single relaxation time

$\tau = (\tau_\epsilon + \tau_\sigma)/2$. The lag angle, on the basis of this model, is given by the following equation:[1]

$$\alpha = E_s \frac{\omega\tau}{1 + \omega^2\tau^2} \qquad (8\text{-}13)$$

where $\omega = 2\pi f$ is the angular frequency of vibration. Equation (8-13) is symmetrical in both ω and τ and has a maximum when $\omega\tau = 1$. Therefore, for a material which behaves like an anelastic standard linear solid, an internal-friction peak will occur at an angular frequency which is the reciprocal of the relaxation time of the process causing the relaxation.

It is often difficult experimentally to vary the angular frequency by a factor much greater than 100. Therefore, it is usually easier to determine the relaxation spectrum by holding ω constant and varying the relaxation time τ. In many materials, including metals, τ varies exponentially with temperature so that

$$\tau = \tau_0 \exp \frac{\Delta H}{RT} \qquad (8\text{-}14)$$

Therefore, to determine the relaxation spectrum, all that is necessary is to measure α as a function of temperature for constant angular frequency.

Internal-friction measurements are well suited for studying the diffusion of interstitial atoms in bcc metals. Relaxation peaks arise owing to diffusion of interstitial atoms to minimum-energy positions in the stress fields of the dislocations. For a given frequency the relaxation time is expressed by $\tau = 1/\omega$, and the peak occurs at a temperature T_1. At another value of frequency the relaxation peak will occur at a temperature T_2. From the temperature dependence of relaxation time [Eq. (8-14)] the activation energy ΔH can be determined.

$$\Delta H = R \frac{\ln (f_2/f_1)}{1/T_1 - 1/T_2} \qquad (8\text{-}15)$$

For a given relaxation time the diffusion coefficient of the interstitial atoms is given by

$$D = \frac{a_0^2}{36\tau} \qquad (8\text{-}16)$$

where a_0 is the interatomic spacing. The temperature dependence of D is given by

$$D = D_0 \exp - \frac{\Delta H}{RT} \qquad (8\text{-}17)$$

[1] A. S. Nowick, Internal Friction in Metals, in "Progress in Metal Physics," vol. 4, pp. 15–16, Pergamon Press, Ltd., London, 1953.

8-4. Relaxation Spectrum

A number of relaxation processes with different relaxation times can occur in metals. Each will occur in a different frequency region, so that a number of internal-friction peaks can be found if a wide range of frequency is investigated. Provided that the peaks are sufficiently separated, the behavior of the metal in the region of the peak can be expressed by Eq. (8-10) with suitably determined constants. This variation of internal friction with frequency can be considered as a relaxation spectrum which is characteristic of a particular material.

The application of stress to a substitutional solid solution can produce ordering in an otherwise random distribution of atoms. An alternating stress can give rise to relaxation between pairs of solute atoms.

A large and broad internal-friction peak is produced in polycrystalline specimens by the relaxation of shear stress across grain boundaries. Work in this area has led to the conclusion that grain boundaries behave in some ways like a viscous material. This interesting aspect of internal friction is discussed in more detail in the next section.

The movement of low-energy twin boundaries due to stress is believed to produce relaxation effects.[1] This type of deformation is also responsible for anelastic effects found in conjunction with domain-boundary movement in ferromagnetic materials. Since twin interfaces are crystallographically coherent boundaries, the internal friction cannot be due to the viscous slip associated with incoherent boundaries.

The relaxation peak due to preferential ordering of interstitial atoms in the lattice from an applied stress is one of the best-understood relaxation processes. Studies of this relaxation process have provided data on the solubility and diffusion of interstitial atoms. This type of internal friction is considered in Sec. 8-6. Relaxation produced by thermal fluctuations will be considered in Sec. 8-7.

8-5. Grain-boundary Relaxation

An important source of internal friction in metals is stress relaxation along grain boundaries. Ke[2] first demonstrated the strong internal-friction peak due to grain-boundary relaxation by experiments on high-purity aluminum wires. At the low torsional strains used in this work the strain was completely recoverable, and all internal-friction effects were independent of amplitude. Ke found that a broad peak occurred in the region of 300°C in polycrystalline aluminum, while no internal-friction

---

[1] F. T. Worrell, *J. Appl. Phys.*, vol. 19, p. 929, 1948, vol. 22, p. 1257, 1951.

[2] T. S. Ke, *Phys. Rev.*, vol. 71, p. 533, vol. 72, p. 41, 1947.

peak was observed in aluminum single crystals (Fig. 8-5). In addition, measurements of the modulus (which is proportional to the square of frequency) at different temperatures showed a sharp drop for the polycrystalline specimen which was not found with the single-crystal specimen (Fig. 8-6). This behavior is consistent with the assumption that grain boundaries behave to a certain extent in a viscous manner at elevated temperatures.

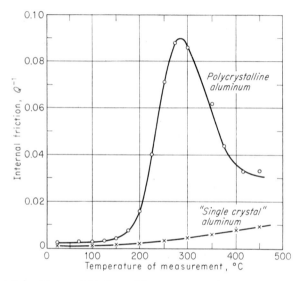

Fig. 8-5. Variation of internal friction with temperature for polycrystalline and single-crystal specimens of aluminum. (*T. S. Ke, Phys. Rev., vol.* 71, *p.* 533, 1947.)

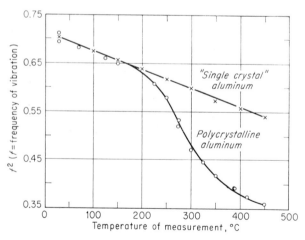

Fig. 8-6. Variation of modulus (f^2) with temperature for polycrystalline and single-crystal aluminum. (*T. S. Ke, Phys. Rev., vol.* 71, *p.* 533, 1947.)

8-6. The Snoek Effect

Internal friction resulting from preferential ordering of interstitial atoms under applied stress was first explained by Snoek[1] and is known as the *Snoek effect*. This type of relaxation has been most extensively studied in iron containing small amounts of either carbon or nitrogen in solid solution. Interstitial carbon atoms in bcc iron occupy the octahedral holes in the lattice. Even though no external forces are applied, the crystal will have tetragonal symmetry because of the distortion produced by the interstitial atoms. As long as no stress is applied, the distribution of atoms among the octahedral sites is random and the tetragonal axes of the unit cells are randomly oriented with respect to the specimen axes. However, if a stress is applied along the y axis, the interstitial atoms will migrate to octahedral positions which tend to give a preferred alignment in the y direction. When the stress is removed, the atoms will migrate toward a random distribution. Under the oscillating stresses imposed by an internal-friction apparatus the interstitial atoms will be in continuous motion, either tending toward or tending away from a preferred orientation. A strong relaxation peak results. A similar but weaker relaxation peak can be observed due to short-range order in substitutional solid solutions.

8-7. Thermoelastic Internal Friction

The thermal and the mechanical behavior of materials are interrelated. The application of a small stress to a metal will produce an instantaneous strain, and this strain will be accompanied by a small change in temperature. An extension of the specimen will result in a decrease in temperature, while a contraction produces a temperature rise. This behavior is called the thermoelastic effect. If the applied stress is not uniform throughout the specimen, a temperature gradient will be set up and additional nonelastic strain will result. If the nonuniform stress varies periodically with time, a fluctuating temperature gradient is produced. When the stress fluctuations occur at a very high frequency, so that there is not time for appreciable heat flow to take place during a stress cycle, the process is adiabatic. No energy loss or damping occurs under adiabatic conditions. On the other hand, at very low frequencies there is adequate time for heat flow, and an equilibrium temperature is maintained in the specimen. This is an isothermal process, and no energy or heat is lost. In the region of intermediate frequencies the conversion of energy into heat is not reversible, and internal-friction effects are observed.

Nonuniform stress can result in macroscopic thermal currents which

[1] J. Snoek, *Physica*, vol. 6, p. 591, 1939, vol. 8, p. 711, 1941, vol. 9, p. 862, 1942.

produce internal-friction peaks. A rectangular bar which is vibrated transversely behaves like a standard linear solid (single relaxation time). The compression side of the specimen will increase in temperature, and the tension side will undergo a decrease in temperature. Therefore, an alternating temperature gradient is produced across the thickness of the bar. A relaxation process occurs, provided that the frequency is such that there is enough time for thermal currents to flow back and forth and effect a partial neutralization of the temperature gradient. Zener[1] has shown that the relaxation time is

$$\tau = \frac{h^2}{\pi^2 D_t} \tag{8-18}$$

where h = thickness of specimen
  D_t = thermal-diffusion constant
    = thermal conductivity/(specific heat)(density)

The frequency at which this relaxation peak occurs can be determined from the relationship $\omega t = 1$. For specimens of ordinary thickness, the peak would occur in the region of 1 to 100 cps. It is theoretically possible for a specimen vibrated in a longitudinal mode to show relaxation from macroscopic thermal currents. However, the frequency region where the peak would occur would be of the order 10^{10} to 10^{11} cps, which is well beyond the range of normal observations. No relaxation from macroscopic thermal currents occurs in a specimen subjected to torsional vibration, because shearing stresses are not accompanied by a change in temperature.

A polycrystalline specimen which is subjected to completely uniform stress can show relaxation due to intergranular thermal currents arising from the fluctuations in stress from grain to grain. The localized stress differences from grain to grain are due to the elastic anisotropy of individual grains. The relaxation peak due to intergranular thermal currents will not occur at a sharp frequency and, therefore, represent a single relaxation time. The frequency at which the relaxation will occur is related to the grain size of the metal. Internal friction due to intergranular thermal currents can occur for all types of stressing. It is important that effects from this source be considered in experiments where the prime interest is in damping from other sources.

8-8. Dislocation Damping

The internal friction of metals is quite sensitive to plastic deformation. The effects are very complex and depend on variables such as the amount of plastic deformation, the method by which the deformation was intro-

[1] C. Zener, *Phys. Rev.*, vol. 52, p. 230, 1937.

duced into the metal, the purity of the metal, the frequency of vibration, and the time between the deformation and the measurement of internal friction. Read[1] demonstrated that internal friction arising from cold work is strongly amplitude-dependent, even for strain amplitudes as small as 10^{-6}.

A freshly cold-worked metal has a relatively high internal friction which anneals out very rapidly at temperatures well below those required for recrystallization. The high damping is also accompanied by a decrease in the dynamic modulus. As the internal friction anneals out, the dynamic modulus returns to its steady-state value. The decrease in modulus due to cold work which can be eliminated by annealing at relatively low temperatures is called the *modulus defect*, or the Köster effect.[2] Mott has proposed a dislocation model[3] for the modulus defect which is based on the bowing out under stress of a network of dislocation lines anchored at nodes and impurities. The theory predicts that the modulus defect is proportional to the products of the dislocation length per cubic centimeter and the square of the effective loop length of a dislocation segment.

$$\frac{\Delta E}{E} \propto NL^2 \tag{8-19}$$

In a cold-worked metal typical values of $N \simeq 10^9$ and $L \simeq 10^{-5}$ cm would lead to values of $\Delta E/E$ of 10 per cent, in agreement with observed results.

The dislocation mechanism for the internal-friction effects observed in cold-worked metals is not well established. The theory due to Koehler[4] and Granato and Lücke[5] assumes that amplitude-dependent internal friction is due to a stress-strain hysteresis arising from the irreversibility of dislocation lines breaking away from pinning impurity atoms. However, amplitude-independent internal friction is assumed to result from a viscouslike damping force acting on the bowed-out segments of the dislocation lines.

The only relaxation process which gives an internal peak that is definitely ascribable to dislocations is the Bordoni peak[6] found in fcc metals at very low temperatures in the region of 30 to 100°K. There are indications that the Bordoni peak is due to some intrinsic property of dislocations and is not involved with the interaction of dislocations with impurity atoms and other dislocations.

[1] T. A. Read, *Trans. AIME*, vol. 143, p. 30, 1941.

[2] W. Köster, *Z. Metallk.*, vol. 32, p. 282, 1940.

[3] N. F. Mott, *Phil. Mag.*, vol. 43, p. 1151, 1952.

[4] J. S. Koehler, "Imperfections in Nearly Perfect Crystals," John Wiley & Sons, Inc., New York, 1953.

[5] A. Granato and K. Lücke, *J. Appl. Phys.*, vol. 27, p. 583, 1956.

[6] P. G. Bordoni, *Nuovo cimento*, vol. 7, ser. 9, suppl. 2, p. 144, 1950

8-9. Damping Capacity

This section is concerned with the engineering aspects of internal friction. The damping capacity of structures and machine elements is concerned with the internal friction of materials at strain amplitudes and stresses which are much greater than the values usually considered in internal-friction experiments. A high damping capacity is of practical engineering importance in limiting the amplitude of vibration at resonance conditions and thereby reducing the likelihood of fatigue failure. Turbine blades, crankshafts, and aircraft propellers are typical applications where damping capacity is important.

Damping capacity can be defined as the amount of work dissipated into heat per unit volume of material per cycle of completely reversed stress. The damping properties of materials are frequently expressed in terms of the logarithmic decrement δ or the specific damping capacity ψ.

$$\psi = 2\delta = \frac{4(A_1 - A_n)}{N(A_1 + A_n)} \tag{8-20}$$

where ψ = specific damping capacity
δ = logarithmic decrement [see Eqs. (8-3) and (8-5)]
A_1 = amplitude of vibration of first cycle
A_n = amplitude of vibration of nth cycle
N = number of cycles from A_1 to A_n

Values of these damping parameters depend not only on the condition of the material but also on the shape and stress distribution of the specimens. Since these conditions are often not specified, there is considerable variation and contradiction in the published literature[1] on the damping properties of materials. The proposal has been made to express the engineering damping properties of materials by the *specific damping energy*. This quantity represents the area inside a stress-strain hysteresis loop under uniform stress conditions and is a true material property. Methods of converting logarithmic decrement and damping capacity to specific damping energy have been published.[2]

Engineering damping-capacity measurements are not very dependent upon frequency of vibration. They are, however, strongly dependent on the stress or strain amplitude. Specific damping energy is approximately a power function of stress level, with the exponent varying between 2 and

[1] L. J. Demer, Bibliography of the Material Damping Field, *WADC Tech. Rept.* 56–180, June, 1956; available from Office of Technical Services.

[2] E. R. Podnieks and B. J. Lazan, Analytical Methods for Determining Specific Damping Energy Considering Stress Distribution, *WADC Tech. Rept.* 56–44, June, 1957.

3 for most materials.   The damping behavior is a function of the number of reversed stress cycles.   Generally, the damping capacity increases with number of cycles of stress reversal, the magnitude of the effect increasing with stress level.   The damping capacity for a given metal and test condition depends on the type of stress system, i.e., whether tested in torsion or tension.   This is the result of differences in stress distribution produced by different methods.   A number of attempts have been made to relate damping behavior with other properties such as fatigue strength and notch sensitivity.   While in certain cases it appears

TABLE 8-1
DAMPING CAPACITY OF SOME ENGINEERING MATERIALS[†]

Material	Specific damping capacity at various stress levels $\Delta W/W$		
	4,500 psi	6,700 psi	11,200 psi
Carbon steel (0.1% C).....................	2.28	2.78	4.16
Ni-Cr steel—quenched and tempered..........	0.38	0.49	0.70
12% Cr stainless steel......................	8.0	8.0	8.0
18-8 stainless steel.........................	0.76	1.16	3.8
Cast iron.................................	28.0	40.0	
Yellow brass..............................	0.50	0.86	

† S. L. Hoyt, "Metal Data," rev. ed., Reinhold Publishing Corporation, New York, 1952.

that high damping capacity correlates with a low notch sensitivity, there is no general relationship between these properties.   Furthermore, there is no general relationship between damping capacity and fatigue limit.

Table 8-1 lists some values of damping capacity for a number of engineering materials at several stress levels.   Cast iron has one of the highest damping capacities of these materials.   This is attributed to energy losses in the graphite flakes.   One important contribution to damping in many alloys used for turbine-blade applications comes from the motion of ferromagnetic domain walls.   This has been demonstrated[1] by the fact that a ferromagnetic alloy which showed high damping had much decreased damping capacity when tested in a magnetic field.   The lower damping in the magnetic field can be attributed to the fact that the domains are lined up in the direction of the field and cannot move freely under stress.

[1] A. W. Cochardt, *Trans. AIME*, vol. 206, pp. 1295–1298, 1956.

BIBLIOGRAPHY

Entwistle, K. M.: The Damping Capacity of Metals, in B. Chalmers and A. G. Quarrell (eds.), "The Physical Examination of Metals," 2d ed., Edward Arnold & Co., London, 1960.

Niblett, D. H., and J. Wilks: Dislocation Damping in Metals *Advances in Phys.*, vol. 9, pp. 1–88, 1960.

Nowick, A. S.: Internal Friction in Metals, in "Progress in Metal Physics," vol. 4, Pergamon Press, Ltd., London, 1953.

Zener, C.: "Elasticity and Anelasticity of Metals," University of Chicago Press, Chicago, 1948.

Part Three
APPLICATIONS TO MATERIALS TESTING

Chapter 9
THE TENSION TEST

9-1. Engineering Stress-Strain Curve

The engineering tension test is widely used to provide basic design information on the strength of materials and as an acceptance test for the specification of materials. In the tension test[1] a specimen is subjected to a continually increasing uniaxial tensile force while simultaneous observations are made of the elongation of the specimen. An engineering stress-strain curve is constructed from the load-elongation measurements (Fig. 9-1). The significant points on the engineering stress-strain curve have already been considered in Sec. 1-5, while the appearance of a yield point in the stress-strain curve was covered in Sec. 5-5. The stress used in this stress-strain curve is the *average* longitudinal stress in the tensile

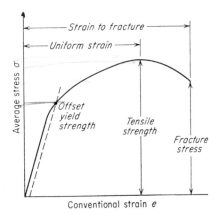

Fig. 9-1. The engineering stress-strain curve.

specimen. It is obtained by dividing the load by the *original area* of the cross section of the specimen.

$$\sigma = \frac{P}{A_0} \tag{9-1}$$

The strain used for the engineering stress-strain curve is the *average*

[1] H. E. Davis, G. E. Troxell, and C. T. Wiskocil, "The Testing and Inspection of Engineering Materials," 2d ed., chaps. 2–4, McGraw-Hill Book Company, Inc., New York 1955.

linear strain, which is obtained by dividing the elongation of the gage length of the specimen, δ, by its original length.

$$e = \frac{\delta}{L_0} = \frac{\Delta L}{L} = \frac{L - L_0}{L_0} \tag{9-2}$$

Since both the stress and the strain are obtained by dividing the load and elongation by constant factors, the load-elongation curve will have the same shape as the engineering stress-strain curve. The two curves are frequently used interchangeably.

The shape and magnitude of the stress-strain curve of a metal will depend on its composition, heat treatment, prior history of plastic deformation, and the strain rate, temperature, and state of stress imposed during the testing. The parameters which are used to describe the stress-strain curve of a metal are the *tensile strength, yield strength* or *yield point, per cent elongation*, and *reduction of area*. The first two are strength parameters; the last two indicate ductility.

Tensile Strength

The tensile strength, or ultimate tensile strength (UTS), is the maximum load divided by the original cross-sectional area of the specimen.

$$\sigma_u = \frac{P_{max}}{A_0} \tag{9-3}$$

The tensile strength is the value most often quoted from the results of a tension test; yet in reality it is a value of little fundamental significance with regard to the strength of a metal. For ductile metals the tensile strength should be regarded as a measure of the maximum load which a metal can withstand under the very restrictive conditions of uniaxial loading. It will be shown that this value bears little relation to the useful strength of the metal under the more complex conditions of stress which are usually encountered. For many years it was customary to base the strength of members on the tensile strength, suitably reduced by a factor of safety. The current trend is to the more rational approach of basing the static design of ductile metals on the yield strength. However, because of the long practice of using the tensile strength to determine the strength of materials, it has become a very familiar property, and as such it is a very useful identification of a material in the same sense that the chemical composition serves to identify a metal or alloy. Further, because the tensile strength is easy to determine and is a quite reproducible property, it is useful for the purposes of specifications and for quality control of a product. Extensive empirical correlations between tensile strength and properties such as hardness and fatigue strength are often quite useful. For brittle materials, the tensile strength is a valid criterion for design.

Yield Strength

The yield strength is the load corresponding to a small specified plastic strain divided by the original cross-sectional area of the specimen.

$$\sigma_0 = \frac{P_{e=0.002}}{A_0} \tag{9-4}$$

Because of the practical difficulties of measuring the elastic limit or proportional limit, the yield strength and yield point are the preferred engineering parameters for expressing the start of plastic deformation. When the design of a ductile metal requires that plastic deformation be prevented, the yield strength is the appropriate criterion of the strength of the metal. An important feature of the yield strength is that the value determined from the tension test can be used to predict the conditions for static yielding under other, more complex conditions of stress by means of the distortion-energy yielding criterion (Sec. 3-4). An example of this is the determination of the elastic-breakdown pressure of thick-wall tubes subjected to internal pressure from the results of a tension test.[1] The yield strength and yield point are more sensitive than the tensile strength to differences in heat treatment and method of testing.

Percentage Elongation

The percentage elongation is the ratio of the increase in the length of the gage section of the specimen to its original length, expressed in per cent.

$$\% \text{ elongation} = \frac{L_f - L_0}{L_0} = e_f \tag{9-5}$$

where L_f = gage length at fracture
L_0 = original gage length
e_f = conventional strain at fracture
The numerator in Eq. (9-5) is simply the total measured elongation of the specimen. This value is influenced by the deformation during the necking of the specimen, and hence the value of per cent elongation depends somewhat on the specimen gage length. The elongation of the specimen is uniform along the gage length up to the point of maximum load. Beyond this point necking begins, and the deformation is no longer uniform along the length of the specimen. This uniform strain is of more fundamental importance than total strain to fracture, and it is also of

[1] J. H. Faupel, *Trans. ASME*, vol. 78, pp. 1031–1064, 1956.

some practical use in predicting the formability of sheet metal. However, the uniform elongation is not usually determined in a routine tension test, so that, unless specifically stated, the percentage elongation is always based on the total elongation. It is determined by putting the broken tensile specimen together and measuring the change in gage length. The original gage length should always be given in reporting percentage elongation values.

Reduction of Area

The percentage reduction of area is the ratio of the decrease in the cross-sectional area of the tensile specimen after fracture to the original area, expressed in per cent.

$$\text{Reduction of area} = q = \frac{A_0 - A_f}{A_0} \tag{9-6}$$

The determination of the reduction of area in thin sheet specimens is difficult, and for this reason it is usually not measured in this type of specimen. For thicker, flat, rectangular tensile specimens, the area after fracture may be approximated by

$$A = \frac{h}{3}(a + 2d) \tag{9-7}$$

where h = width of specimen
a = thickness at center of specimen
d = thickness at ends of cross section of specimen

The elongation and reduction of area are usually not directly useful to the designer. There appear to be no quantitative methods for determining the minimum elongation or reduction of area which a material must have for a particular design application. However, a qualitative indication of formability of a metal can sometimes be obtained from these values. A high reduction of area indicates the ability of the metal to deform extensively without fracture (see Prob. 9.4).

The reduction of area is the most structure-sensitive parameter that is measured in the tension test. Therefore, its most important aspect is that it is used as an indication of material quality. A decrease in reduction of area from a specified level for which experience has shown that good service performance will result is a warning that quality is substandard.

Modulus of Elasticity

The slope of the initial linear portion of the stress-strain curve is the modulus of elasticity, or Young's modulus. The modulus of elasticity is a measure of the stiffness of the material. The greater the modulus, the smaller the elastic strain resulting from the application of a given stress. Since the modulus of elasticity is needed for computing deflections of beams and other members, it is an important design value.

The modulus of elasticity is determined by the binding forces between atoms. Since these forces cannot be changed without changing the basic nature of the material, it follows that the modulus of elasticity is one of the most structure-insensitive of the mechanical properties. It is only slightly affected by alloying additions, heat treatment, or cold work.[1] However, increasing the temperature decreases the modulus of elasticity. The modulus is usually measured at elevated temperatures by a dynamic method[2] which measures the mode and period of vibration of a metal specimen. Typical values of the modulus of elasticity for common engineering metals at different temperatures are given in Table 9-1.

TABLE 9-1
TYPICAL VALUES OF MODULUS OF ELASTICITY AT
DIFFERENT TEMPERATURES

Material	Modulus of elasticity, psi $\times 10^{-6}$				
	Room temp.	400°F	800°F	1000°F	1200°F
Carbon steel.................	30.0	27.0	22.5	19.5	18.0
Austenitic stainless steel.......	28.0	25.5	23.0	22.5	21.0
Titanium alloys...............	16.5	14.0	10.7	10.1	
Aluminum alloys.............	10.5	9.5	7.8		

Resilience

The ability of a material to absorb energy when deformed elastically and to return it when unloaded is called *resilience*. This is usually measured by the *modulus of resilience*, which is the strain energy per unit volume required to stress the material from zero stress to the yield stress σ_0. Referring to Eq. (2-57), the strain energy per unit volume for uniaxial tension is

$$U_0 = \tfrac{1}{2}\sigma_x e_x$$

From the above definition the modulus of resilience is

$$U_R = \tfrac{1}{2}\sigma_0 e_0 = \tfrac{1}{2}\sigma_0 \frac{\sigma_0}{E} = \frac{\sigma_0^2}{2E} \tag{9-8}$$

This equation indicates that the ideal material for resisting energy loads in applications where the material must not undergo permanent distortion, such as mechanical springs, is one having a high yield stress and a

[1] D. J. Mack, *Trans. AIME*, vol. 166, pp. 68–85, 1946.
[2] C. W. Andrews, *Metal Progr.*, vol. 58, pp. 85–89, 96, 98, 100, 1950.

low modulus of elasticity.   Table 9-2 gives some values of modulus of
resilience for different materials.

TABLE 9-2
MODULUS OF RESILIENCE FOR VARIOUS MATERIALS

Material	E, psi	σ_0, psi	Modulus of resilience U_R, in.-lb/in.^{3}
Medium-carbon steel.........	30×10^6	45,000	33.7
High-carbon spring steel......	30×10^6	140,000	320
Duraluminum...............	10.5×10^6	18,000	17
Copper....................	16×10^6	4,000	5.3
Rubber....................	150	300	300

Toughness

The toughness of a material is its ability to absorb energy in the plastic
range.   The ability to withstand occasional stresses above the yield stress
without fracturing is particularly desirable in parts such as freight-car
couplings, gears, chains, and crane hooks.   Toughness is a commonly
used concept which is difficult to pin down and define.   One way of
looking at toughness is to consider that it is the total area under the
stress-strain curve.   This area is an indication of the amount of work
per unit volume which can be done on the material without causing it to
rupture.   Figure 9-2 shows the
stress-strain curves for high- and
low-toughness materials.   The high-
carbon spring steel has a higher
yield strength and tensile strength
than the medium-carbon structural steel.   However, the structural
steel is more ductile and has a
greater total elongation.   The total
area under the stress-strain curve
is greater for the structural steel,
and therefore it is a tougher material.   This illustrates that toughness is a parameter which com-
prises *both* strength and ductility.   The crosshatched regions in Fig. 9-2
indicate the modulus of resilience for each steel.   Because of its higher
yield strength, the spring steel has the greater resilience.

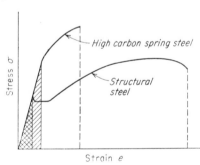

Fig. 9-2. Comparison of stress-strain
curves for high- and low-toughness materials.

Several mathematical approximations for the area under the stress-
strain curve have been suggested.   For ductile metals which have a

stress-strain curve like that of the structural steel, the area under the curve can be approximated by either of the following equations:

$$U_T \simeq \sigma_u e_f \qquad (9\text{-}9)$$

or
$$U_T \simeq \frac{\sigma_0 + \sigma_u}{2} e_f \qquad (9\text{-}10)$$

For brittle materials the stress-strain curve is sometimes assumed to be a parabola, and the area under the curve is given by

$$U_T \simeq \tfrac{2}{3}\sigma_u e_f \qquad (9\text{-}11)$$

All these relations are only approximations to the area under the stress-strain curves. Further, the curves do not represent the true behavior in the plastic range, since they are all based on the original area of the specimen.

9-2. True-stress–True-strain Curve

The engineering stress-strain curve does not give a true indication of the deformation characteristics of a metal because it is based entirely on the original dimensions of the specimen, and these dimensions change continuously during the test. Also, ductile metal which is pulled in tension becomes unstable and necks down during the course of the test. Because the cross-sectional area of the specimen is decreasing rapidly at this stage in the test, the load required to continue deformation falls off. The average stress based on original area likewise decreases, and this produces the fall-off in the stress-strain curve beyond the point of maximum load. Actually, the metal continues to strain-harden all the way up to fracture, so that the stress required to produce further deformation should also increase. If the *true stress*, based on the actual cross-sectional area of the specimen, is used, it is found that the stress-strain curve increases continuously up to fracture. If the strain measurement is also based on instantaneous measurements, the curve which is obtained is known as a *true-stress–true-strain* curve. This is also known as a *flow curve* (Sec. 3-2) since it represents the basic plastic-flow characteristics of the material. Any point on the flow curve can be considered as the yield stress for a metal strained in tension by the amount shown on the curve. Thus, if the load is removed at this point and then reapplied, the material will behave elastically throughout the entire range of reloading.

The true stress is the load at any instant divided by the cross-sectional area of the specimen at that instant.

$$\sigma = \frac{P}{A_i} \qquad (9\text{-}12)$$

True strain was defined in Sec. 3-3 as

$$\epsilon = \ln \frac{L}{L_0} = \ln \frac{A_0}{A} \tag{9-13}$$

This definition of strain was proposed by Ludwik[1] near the beginning of

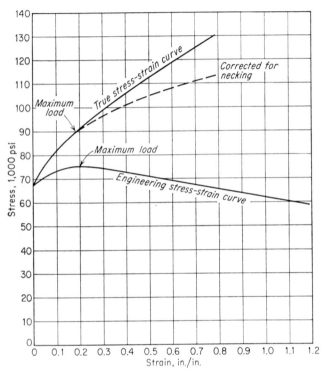

Fig. 9-3. Comparison of engineering and true stress-strain curves for nickel.

the century.   It was also shown previously (Sec. 3-3) that the relation between true strain and conventional linear strain is given by

$$\epsilon = \ln(e + 1) \tag{9-14}$$

The true stress may be determined from the average engineering stress as follows:

$$\sigma = \frac{P}{A_i} = \frac{P}{A_0} \frac{A_0}{A_i}$$

[1] P. Ludwik, "Elemente der technologischen Mechanik," Springer-Verlag OHG, Berlin, 1909.

But, by the constancy-of-volume relationship,

$$\frac{A_0}{A_i} = \frac{L}{L_0}$$

From Eq. (9-14)

$$\epsilon = \ln \frac{L}{L_0} = \ln (e + 1)$$

or

$$\frac{L}{L_0} = \frac{A_0}{A_i} = e + 1$$

$$\sigma = \frac{P}{A_0} (e + 1) \tag{9-15}$$

Figure 9-3 compares the true stress-strain curve for a nickel specimen with its engineering stress-strain curve. Note that the large scale on the strain axis, which was used to emphasize the plastic region, has compressed the elastic region into the y axis. Frequently, the true stress-strain curve is linear from the maximum load to fracture, while in other cases its slope continuously decreases up to fracture. Little significance should be attached to this linear region of the flow curve. When necking occurs, the triaxial state of stress that is created in this region increases the average longitudinal stress needed to continue plastic flow. Therefore, the shape of the flow curve from maximum load to fracture depends on the rate of development of the neck. This can be different for materials with different strain-hardening behavior, and therefore there is no assurance that the flow curve will be linear in this region.

The following parameters are usually determined from the true stress-strain curve.

True Stress at Maximum Load

The true stress at maximum load corresponds to the true tensile strength. For most materials necking begins at maximum load. As a good approximation, necking will occur at a value of strain where the true stress equals the slope of the flow curve. Let σ_m and ϵ_u denote the true stress and strain at maximum load, while A_m represents the cross-sectional area of the specimen at maximum load. Then,

$$\sigma_u = \frac{P_{max}}{A_0} \qquad \sigma_m = \frac{P_{max}}{A_m} \qquad \epsilon_u = \ln \frac{A_0}{A_m}$$

and

$$\sigma_u = \sigma_m \exp (-\epsilon_u) \tag{9-16}$$

Equation (9-16) relates the ultimate tensile strength to the true stress and strain at maximum load.

True Fracture Stress

The true fracture stress is the load at fracture divided by the cross-sectional area at fracture. This stress should be corrected for the triaxial state of stress existing in the tensile specimen at fracture. Since the data required for this correction are often not available, true-fracture-stress values are frequently in error.

True Fracture Strain

The true fracture strain ϵ_f is the true strain based on the original area A_0 and the area after fracture, A_f.

$$\epsilon_f = \ln \frac{A_0}{A_f} \qquad (9\text{-}17)$$

This parameter represents the maximum true strain that the material can withstand before fracture and is analogous to the total strain to fracture of the engineering stress-strain curve. Since Eq. (9-14) is not valid beyond the onset of necking, it is not possible to calculate ϵ_f from measured values of e_f. However, for cylindrical tensile specimens the reduction of area, q, is related to the true fracture strain by the relationship

$$q = 1 - \exp(-\epsilon_f) \qquad (9\text{-}18)$$

True Uniform Strain

The true uniform strain ϵ_u is the true strain based only on the strain up to maximum load. It may be calculated from either the specimen cross-sectional area A_u or the gage length L_u at maximum load. Equation (9-14) may be used to convert conventional uniform strain to true uniform strain. The uniform strain is often useful in estimating the formability of metals from the results of a tension test.

$$\epsilon_u = \ln \frac{A_0}{A_u} \qquad (9\text{-}19)$$

True Local Necking Strain

The local necking strain ϵ_n is the strain required to deform the specimen from maximum load to fracture.

$$\epsilon_n = \ln \frac{A_u}{A_f} \qquad (9\text{-}20)$$

The usual method of determining a true stress-strain curve is to measure the cross-sectional area of the specimen at increments of load up to fracture. Micrometers or special dial gages can be used. Care should be taken to measure the minimum diameter of the specimen. This method is applicable over the complete range of stress to fracture, including the region after necking has occurred. However, to correct precisely for the complex stresses at the neck, it is necessary to know the profile of the contour of the neck. This method of determination is limited to fairly slow rates of strain and to tests at room temperature. If the specimen has a circular cross section, the true strain may be readily calculated from the original diameter D_0 and the instantaneous diameter D_i.

$$\epsilon = \ln \frac{L}{L_0} = \ln \frac{A_0}{A} = \ln \frac{D_0{}^2}{D_i{}^2} = 2 \ln \frac{D_0}{D_i} \tag{9-21}$$

True stress and strain may also be determined from the conventional stress and strain by means of Eqs. (9-14) and (9-15). The use of these equations implies that the axial strain is uniformly distributed over the gage length of the specimen, since their derivation is based on the constancy-of-volume relationship. Stresses and strains determined from these equations are accurate up to the beginning of necking, but beyond this stage the major portion of the strain is localized at the neck and the equations do not apply.

True stress-strain curves may be obtained at high strain rates and at elevated temperatures by using the two-load method.[1] Diameters at various positions along tapered specimens are measured before and after testing. The true stress acting at each location on the specimen is the maximum load divided by the area at that point after testing. This gives the flow curve from the state of yielding to the point of maximum load. If the load at fracture is measured, the curve can be extended to the fracture stress by linear extrapolation.

It is usually desirable to be able to express the true stress-strain curve by a mathematical relationship. The simplest useful expression is the power curve described earlier in Sec. 3-2.

$$\sigma = K\epsilon^n \tag{9-22}$$

where n is the *strain-hardening coefficient* and K is the *strength coefficient*. A log-log plot of true stress and strain up to maximum load will give a straight line if this equation is satisfied by the data (Fig. 9-4). The linear slope of this line is n, and K is the true stress at $\epsilon = 1.0$. In order to make the data fall closer to a straight line, it is usually desirable

[1] C. W. MacGregor, *J. Appl. Mech.*, vol. 6, pp. A156–158, 1939.

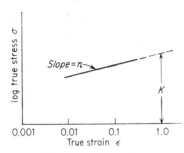

Fig. 9-4. log-log plot of true stress-strain curve.

to subtract the elastic strain from the total strain. Some typical values of n and K are listed in Table 9-3.

There is nothing basic about Eq. (9-22), so that frequent deviations from this relationship are observed. One common type of deviation is for a log-log plot of Eq. (9-22) to result in two straight lines with different slopes, while in other cases a curve with continuously changing slope is obtained. Equation (9-23) is typical of the more complicated relationships which have been suggested[1] to provide better agreement with the data.

$$\sigma = C_1 - (C_1 - C_2) \exp\left(-\frac{\epsilon}{C_3}\right)$$ (9-23)

TABLE 9-3
VALUES OF n AND K FOR METALS AT ROOM TEMPERATURE

Metal	Condition	n	K, psi	Ref.
0.05% C steel.......	Annealed	0.26	77,000	†
SAE 4340 steel......	Annealed	0.15	93,000	†
0.6% C steel........	Quenched and tempered 1000°F	0.10	228,000	‡
0.6% C steel........	Quenched and tempered 1300°F	0.19	178,000	‡
Copper.............	Annealed	0.54	46,400	‡
70/30 brass.........	Annealed	0.49	130,000	‡

† J. R. Low and F. Garofalo, *Proc. Soc. Exptl. Stress Anal.*, vol. 4, no. 2, pp. 16–25, 1947.

‡ J. R. Low, "Properties of Metals in Materials Engineering," American Society for Metals, Metals Park, Ohio, 1949.

9-3. Instability in Tension

Necking generally begins at maximum load during the tensile deformation of a ductile metal.[2]   An ideal plastic material in which no strain hardening occurs would become unstable in tension and begin to neck just as soon as yielding took place.   However, a real metal undergoes

[1] E. Voce, *Metallurgia*, vol. 51, pp. 219–226, 1955.

[2] An exception to this is the behavior of cold-rolled zirconium tested at 200 to 370°C, where necking occurred at a strain of twice the strain at maximum load. See J. H. Keeler, *Trans. ASM*, vol. 47, pp. 157–192, 1955, and discussion by A. J. Opinsky, pp. 189–190.

strain hardening, which tends to increase the load-carrying capacity of the specimen as deformation increases. This effect is opposed by the gradual decrease in the cross-sectional area of the specimen as it elongates. Necking or localized deformation begins at maximum load, where the increase in stress due to decrease in the cross-sectional area of the specimen becomes greater than the increase in the load-carrying ability

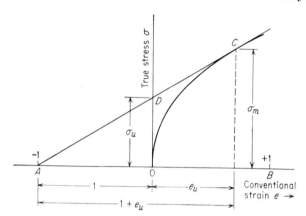

Fig. 9-5. Considère's construction for the determination of the point of maximum load.

of the metal due to strain hardening. This condition of instability leading to localized deformation is defined by the condition $dP = 0$.

$$P = \sigma A$$
$$dP = \sigma \, dA + A \, d\sigma = 0$$

From the constancy-of-volume relationship,

$$\frac{dL}{L} = -\frac{dA}{A}$$

$$-\frac{dA}{A} = \frac{dL}{L} = \frac{d\sigma}{\sigma} = d\epsilon = \frac{de}{1+e}$$

Therefore
$$\frac{d\sigma}{d\epsilon} = \sigma \tag{9-24}$$

or
$$\frac{d\sigma}{de} = \frac{\sigma}{1+e} \tag{9-25}$$

Equation (9-24) says that necking will occur in uniaxial tension at a strain at which the slope of the true stress-strain curve equals the true stress at that strain.

Equation (9-25) permits an interesting geometrical construction for the determination of the point of maximum load.[1] In Fig. 9-5 the stress-

[1] A. Considère, *Ann. ponts et chaussées*, vol. 9, ser. 6, pp. 574–775, 1885.

strain curve is plotted in terms of true stress against conventional linear strain. Let point A represent a negative strain of 1.0. A line drawn from point A which is tangent to the stress-strain curve will establish the point of maximum load, for according to Eq. (9-25) the slope at this point is $\sigma/(1 + e)$. The stress at this point is the true stress at maximum load, σ_m. If we had plotted average stress, this would have been the tensile strength σ_u. The relation between these two stresses is

$$\frac{\sigma_u}{\sigma_m} = \frac{A}{A_0} = \frac{L_0}{L}$$

From the definition of conventional linear strain,

$$\frac{L_0}{L} = \frac{1}{1 + e}$$

so that

$$\sigma_u = \sigma_m \frac{1}{1 + e_u} \qquad (9\text{-}26)$$

A study of the similar triangles in Fig. 9-5 shows that Eq. (9-26) is satisfied when OD is the tensile strength.

If the flow curve for a material is given by the power law of Eq. (9-22), it is possible readily to determine the strain at which necking occurs.

$$\sigma = K\epsilon^n$$
$$\frac{d\sigma}{d\epsilon} = \sigma = K\epsilon^n = nK\epsilon^{n-1}$$
$$\epsilon_u = n \qquad (9\text{-}27)$$

Therefore, the strain at which necking occurs is numerically equal to the strain-hardening coefficient.

Plastic instability is often important in forming operations with sheet metal since the strain at which the deformation becomes localized constitutes the forming limit of the metal. Lankford and Saibel[1] have determined the criteria for localized deformation for the case of a sheet subjected to biaxial tensile forces (stretching), a thin-wall tube subjected to internal pressure and axial loading, and a sheet subjected to a hydrostatic bulge test.

9-4. Stress Distribution at the Neck

The formation of a neck in the tensile specimen introduces a complex triaxial state of stress in that region. The necked region is in effect a mild notch. As was discussed in Sec. 7-12, a notch under tension pro-

[1] W. T. Lankford and E. Saibel, *Trans. AIME*, vol. 171, pp. 562–573, 1947.

duces radial and transverse stresses which raise the value of longitudinal stress required to cause plastic flow. Therefore, the average true stress at the neck, which is determined by dividing the axial tensile load by the minimum cross-sectional area of the specimen at the neck, is higher than the stress which would be required to cause flow if simple tension prevailed. Figure 9-6 illustrates the geometry at the necked region and the stresses developed by this localized deformation. R is the radius of curvature of the neck, which can be measured either by projecting the contour of the necked region on a screen or by using a tapered, conical radius gage.

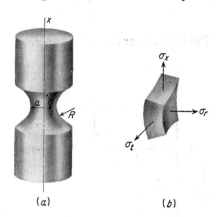

(a)　　　　　　　　(b)

Fig. 9-6. (a) Geometry of necked region; (b) stresses acting on element at point O.

Bridgman[1] made a mathematical analysis which provides a correction to the average axial stress to compensate for the introduction of transverse stresses. This analysis was based on the following assumptions:

1. The contour of the neck is approximated by the arc of a circle.
2. The cross section of the necked region remains circular throughout the test.
3. The Von Mises criterion for yielding applies.
4. The strains are constant over the cross section of the neck.

TABLE 9-4

CORRECTION FACTORS TO BE APPLIED TO AVERAGE TRUE STRESS TO
COMPENSATE FOR TRANSVERSE STRESSES AT NECK OF
TENSILE SPECIMEN

a/R	Bridgman factor	Davidenkov factor
0	1.000	1.000
$\frac{1}{3}$	0.927	0.923
$\frac{1}{2}$	0.897	0.889
1	0.823	0.800
2	0.722	0.667
3	0.656	0.571
4	0.606	0.500

[1] P. W. Bridgman, *Trans. ASM*, vol. 32, p. 553, 1944.

According to this analysis the ratio of the true axial stress σ to the average axial stress σ_{av} is

$$\frac{\sigma}{\sigma_{av}} = \frac{1}{(1 + 2R/a)[\ln{(1 + a/2R)}]} \qquad (9\text{-}28)$$

Davidenkov and Spiridonova[1] determined a correction for necking based

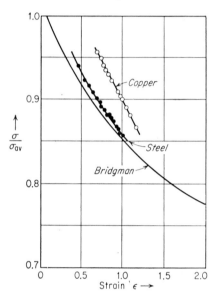

on somewhat different assumptions from those of Bridgman. Their expression is given by

$$\frac{\sigma}{\sigma_{av}} = \frac{1}{1 + a/4R} \qquad (9\text{-}29)$$

These two equations differ by less than 1 per cent for values of a/R less than 0.6. Typical values for these corrections are given in Table 9-4.

The determination of the radius of curvature of the neck during the progress of the test is certainly not a routine or easy operation. In order to help with this situation, Bridgman determined an empirical relationship between the neck contour (a/R) and the true strain, based on about 50 steel specimens. Figure 9-7 shows this relationship converted into the variation of σ/σ_{av} with true strain.

Fig. 9-7. Relationship between Bridgman correction factor σ/σ_{av} and true tensile strain. (*E. R. Marshall and M. C. Shaw, Trans. ASM, vol.* 44, *p.* 716, 1952.)

Experimental values[2] for copper and steel are also included in this figure. This investigation showed that Bridgman's equation provides better agreement with experiment than Davidenkov's. The dashed curve in Fig. 9-3 is the true stress-strain curve of nickel adjusted for necking by means of Bridgman's correction factor. The problem of the stress distribution at the neck of flat tensile specimens has been considered by Aronofsky.[3]

9-5. Strain Distribution in the Tensile Specimen

The strain distribution along the length of a tensile specimen is not uniform, particularly in metals which show pronounced necking before

[1] N. N. Davidenkov and N. I. Spiridonova, *Proc. ASTM*, vol. 46, p. 1147, 1946.

[2] E. R. Marshall and M. C. Shaw, *Trans. ASM*, vol. 44, pp. 705–725, 1952.

[3] J. Aronofsky, *J. Appl. Mech.*, vol. 18, pp. 75–84, 1951.

fracture.   Figure 9-8 shows in a schematic way the distribution of local elongation along the length of a tensile specimen.   The exact distribution of strain will depend upon the metal, the gage length, and the shape of the cross section of the test section.   In general, the softer and more ductile the metal, the greater the amount of deformation away from the necked region. Also, the shorter the gage length, the greater the influence of localized deformation at the neck on the total elongation of the gage length. Therefore, for a given material, the shorter the gage length, the greater the percentage elongation.   It is

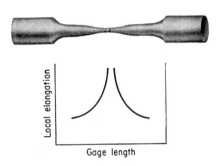

Fig. 9-8. Schematic drawing of variation of local elongation with position along gage length of tensile specimen.

for this reason that the specimen gage length should always be reported with the percentage elongation.

It is generally recognized that in order to compare elongation measurements of different-sized specimens, the specimens must be geometrically similar; i.e., the ratio of gage length to diameter must be constant.   In the United States the standard tensile specimen has a 0.505-in. diameter and a 2-in. gage length.   Thus, $L/D \simeq 4$, or $L = 4.51 \sqrt{A}$.   This is the basis for the dimensions of the ASTM tensile specimens listed in Table 9-5.   The British standards specify $L/D = 3.54$, while the German standards use $L/D = 10$.

TABLE 9-5
DIMENSIONS OF ASTM TENSILE SPECIMENS

Diam, in.	Gage length, in.	L/D
0.505	2	3.97
0.357	1.4	3.92
0.252	1	3.97
0.160	0.634	3.96

For tensile specimens cut from thin sheet the ratio of width to thickness can affect the total elongation.   With a constant gage length, an increase in either the width or the thickness of the specimen results in an increase in elongation.   However, so long as the width and thickness are varied without changing the cross-sectional area, the elongation is not affected.   Available data indicate that the percentage elongation increases in proportion to the area raised to a fractional power.

The uniform elongation is not affected by specimen geometry, since up to maximum load the specimen elongates and contracts in diameter uniformly. The specimen changes from a cylinder of a certain length and diameter to a cylinder of longer length and smaller diameter. For this reason the uniform elongation is a more fundamental measure of ductility than the conventional percentage elongation.

9-6. Effect of Strain Rate on Tensile Properties

The room-temperature stress-strain curve is not greatly influenced by changes in the rate of straining of the order obtainable in the ordinary

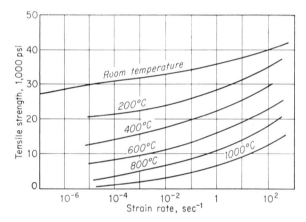

Fig. 9-9. Effect of strain rate on the tensile strength of copper for tests at various temperatures. (*A. Nadai and M. J. Manjoine, J. Appl. Mech., vol. 8, p.* A82, 1941.)

tension test. (The effect of impact and very high-speed loading will be considered in Chap. 14.) High-speed tensile tests[1-3] in which the rate of loading has been varied by a factor of about 100,000 have shown that the yield stress is more sensitive to increases in strain rate than the tensile strength. High rates of strain cause a yield point to appear in specimens of low-carbon steel which do not show a yield point under ordinary rates of loading. The effect of strain rate in raising resistance to deformation generally increases on testing at elevated temperature. Figure 9-9 shows the effect of strain rate on the tensile strength of copper at various temperatures.

The determination of a mathematical relationship between the flow

[1] J. Winlock, *Trans. AIME*, vol. 197, pp. 797–803, 1953.

[2] R. J. MacDonald, R. L. Carlson, and W. T. Lankford, *Proc. ASTM*, vol. 56, pp. 704–723, 1956.

[3] A. Nadai and M. J. Majoine, *J. Appl. Mech.*, vol. 8, pp. A77–A91, 1941.

stress and the strain rate is difficult because of the many experimental problems associated with measuring tensile properties at very rapid rates of deformation. Among the experimental problems is that an adiabatic condition is created at high strain rates, causing the temperature of the specimen to increase; there is not enough time for the heat of plastic deformation to be dissipated. Tests in which the specimen is pulled at a constant true strain rate are not readily performed on conventional testing machines. Although it is fairly easy to maintain a constant rate of crosshead movement, this does not ensure a constant rate of strain in the specimen since the rate of straining in the specimen increases with load, particularly during necking.

Nadai[1] has presented a mathematical analysis of the conditions existing during the extension of a cylindrical specimen with one end fixed and the other attached to the movable crosshead of the testing machine. The crosshead velocity is $v = dL/dt$. The strain rate expressed in terms of conventional linear strain is $\dot{e}$.

$$\dot{e} = \frac{de}{dt} = \frac{d(L - L_0)/L_0}{dt} = \frac{1}{L_0}\frac{dL}{dt} = \frac{v}{L_0} \qquad (9\text{-}30)$$

Thus, the conventional strain rate is proportional to the crosshead velocity. The equation is applicable up to the onset of necking.

The true strain rate $\dot{\epsilon}$ is given by

$$\dot{\epsilon} = \frac{d\epsilon}{dt} = \frac{d[\ln (L/L_0)]}{dt} = \frac{1}{L}\frac{dL}{dt} = \frac{v}{L} \qquad (9\text{-}31)$$

This equation indicates that for a constant crosshead speed the true strain rate will decrease as the specimen elongates. To maintain a constant true strain rate, the crosshead velocity must increase in proportion to the increase in length of the specimen. For a cylindrical specimen the true strain rate is related to the instantaneous diameter D_i by

$$\dot{\epsilon} = \frac{d\epsilon}{dt} = \frac{d[2 \ln (D_0/D_i)]}{dt} = -\frac{2}{D_i}\frac{d(D_i)}{dt} \qquad (9\text{-}32)$$

The true strain rate is related to the conventional strain rate by the following equation:

$$\dot{\epsilon} = \frac{v}{L} = \frac{L_0}{L}\frac{de}{dt} = \frac{1}{1 + e}\frac{de}{dt} = \frac{\dot{e}}{1 + e} \qquad (9\text{-}33)$$

Strain-rate experiments with mild steel have shown a semilogarithmic relationship between the lower yield point and the strain rate.

$$\sigma_0 = k_1 + k_2 \log \dot{\epsilon} \qquad (9\text{-}34)$$

[1] A. Nadai, "Theory of Flow and Fracture of Solids," vol. I, pp. 74–75, McGraw-Hill Book Company, Inc., New York, 1950.

However, a more general relationship[1] between flow stress and strain rate, at constant temperature and strain, seems to be

$$\sigma = C(\dot{\epsilon})^m \Big|_{\epsilon, T} \tag{9-35}$$

where m is a coefficient known as the *strain-rate sensitivity*. The strain-rate sensitivity m may be defined as the ratio of the incremental change in log σ to the resultant change in log $\dot{\epsilon}$, at a given strain and temperature. A value for this parameter can be obtained from a test where the strain rate is rapidly changed from one value to another.

$$m = \frac{\log (\sigma_2/\sigma_1)}{\log (\dot{\epsilon}_2/\dot{\epsilon}_1)} \tag{9-36}$$

The strain-rate sensitivity for most metals increases with temperature and with strain.

9-7. Effect of Temperature on Tensile Properties

In general, strength decreases and ductility increases as the test temperature is increased. However, structural changes such as precipitation,

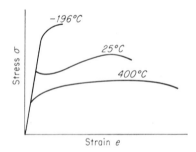

Fig. 9-10. Changes in engineering stress-strain curves of mild steel with temperature.

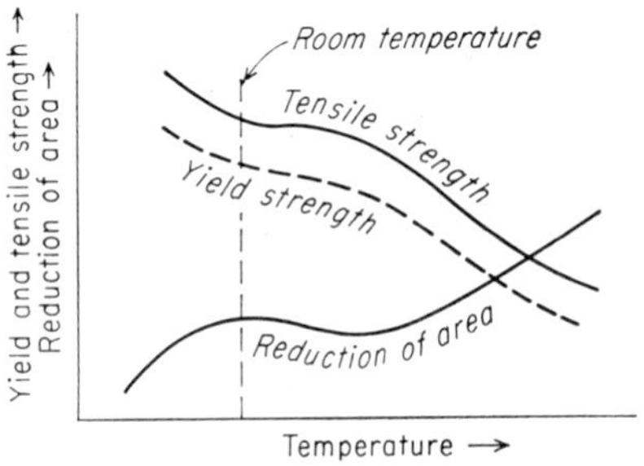

Fig. 9-11. Variation of tensile properties of steel with temperature.

strain aging, or recrystallization may occur over certain temperature ranges to alter this general behavior. Further, extended exposure at elevated temperature may cause creep.

The change with temperature in the shape of the engineering stress-strain curve in mild steel is shown schematically in Fig. 9-10. The variation of the tensile properties of steel with temperature is shown in Fig. 9-11. The strength of steel increases as the temperature is raised above room temperature. The maximum in strength is accompanied by a mini-

---

[1] C. Zener and J. H. Hollomon, *J. Appl. Phys.*, vol. 15, pp. 22–32, 1944.

mum in ductility, which occurs in the vicinity of 400°F, due to strain aging or blue brittleness. Figure 9-12 shows the variation of yield strength with temperature for body-centered cubic tantalum,[1] tungsten, molybdenum, and iron and face-centered cubic nickel. Note that the yield strength of nickel increases with decreasing temperature to a lesser extent than in the body-centered cubic metals. This difference in the

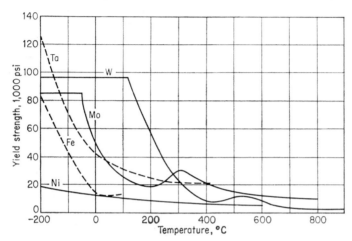

Fig. 9-12. Effect of temperature on the yield strength of body-centered cubic Ta, W, Mo, Fe and face-centered cubic Ni. (*J. H. Bechtold, Acta Met., vol. 3, p. 252, 1955.*)

temperature dependence of yield strength is believed to be of significance in explaining why face-centered cubic metals do not exhibit brittle fracture at low temperatures. The horizontal portion of the curves for W and Mo at low temperature represents the brittle-fracture strength, for these metals undergo brittle fracture without extensive yielding at these temperatures. In comparing the flow stress or yield stress of a material at two temperatures it is advisable to correct for the effect of temperature on elastic modulus by comparing ratios of σ/E rather than simple ratios of flow stress.

Figure 9-13 shows the variation of the reduction of area with temperature for these same metals. Note that tungsten is almost completely brittle at 200°C, iron at −200°C, while nickel decreases little in ductility over the entire temperature range. The lack of a brittle transition in nickel is a general characteristic of face-centered cubic metals and correlates with its small temperature dependence of yield strength. The behavior of body-centered tantalum is anomalous in this respect, for it shows no ductility transition although the yield stress increases rapidly at low temperature.

[1] J. H. Bechtold, *Acta Met.*, vol. 3, pp. 249–254, 1955.

The temperature dependence of the flow stress at constant strain and strain rate can be generally represented by

$$\sigma = C_2 \exp \frac{Q}{RT}\bigg|_{\epsilon, \dot{\epsilon}} \qquad (9\text{-}37)$$

where Q = an activation energy for plastic flow, cal/g mole
   R = universal gas constant, 1.987 cal/(deg)(mole)
   T = testing temperature, °K
If this equation represents the data, a straight line is obtained for a plot of $\ln \sigma$ versus $1/T$. The activation energy is obtained from the slope of

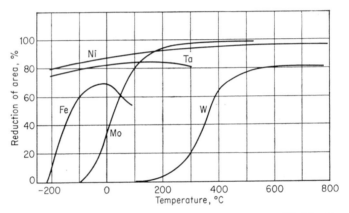

Fig. 9-13. Effect of temperature on the reduction of area of Ta, W, Mo, Fe, and Ni. (*J. H. Bechtold, Acta Met., vol. 3, p. 253, 1955.*)

the line. Equation (9-37) has been found valid for steel, molybdenum, and tungsten over a considerable temperature range. It is, however, not valid[1] at temperatures below around 100°K.

9-8. Combined Effect of Strain Rate and Temperature

Zener and Hollomon[2] suggested that the flow stress at constant strain was related to both the strain rate and the temperature in the following way:

$$\sigma = f\left(\dot{\epsilon} \exp \frac{\Delta H}{RT}\right)\bigg|_{\epsilon} \qquad (9\text{-}38)$$

ΔH is an activation energy expressed in calories per gram mole and is related to the activation energy Q in Eq. (9-37) by $Q = m\,\Delta H$, where

[1] E. T. Wessel, *Trans. ASM*, vol. 49, pp. 149–172, 1957.
[2] Zener and Hollomon, *op. cit.*

m is the strain-rate sensitivity. The quantity in parentheses in Eq. (9-38) is often called the Zener-Hollomon parameter Z.

$$Z = \dot{\epsilon} \exp \frac{\Delta H}{RT} \tag{9-39}$$

A plot of ln $\dot{\epsilon}$ versus $1/T$ should result in a straight line. Zener and Hollomon originally based this relationship on the fact that the yield strength and tensile strength of steel and copper correlated well with Z over rather wide ranges of $\dot{\epsilon}$ and T. More recently it has been found to hold for true stress data on molybdenum[1] and pure aluminum.[2] It has been shown that the same functional relationship is obtained between stress and strain for a constant value of Z, but since ΔH is not independent of stress this relationship does not uniquely describe the flow curve.

A slightly different type of approach to this problem was taken by MacGregor and Fisher.[3] They proposed that strain rate and temperature could be combined into a *velocity-modified temperature*. Then, the flow stress at a particular strain is a function of the velocity-modified temperature T_v.

$$\sigma = f(T_v)$$

where
$$T_v = T\left(1 - \text{k ln} \frac{\dot{\epsilon}}{\dot{\epsilon}_0}\right) \tag{9-40}$$

In Eq. (9-40) k and $\dot{\epsilon}_0$ are constants related to reaction-rate constants. This equation was originally verified for data on steel and aluminum over a large temperature range but only a small range of strain rates. More recently[4] it has been verified for low-carbon steel over a greater range of strain rates.

When Eq. (9-38) was first proposed, it was interpreted much more broadly than it is today. It was suggested that Eq. (9-38) represented a *mechanical equation of state,* analogous to the equations of state for a perfect gas. The concept of the mechanical equation of state[5] indicated that the flow stress of a metal was a function only of the instantaneous values of strain, strain rate, and temperature regardless of the previous temperature and rate of straining. In other words, if a metal did not undergo a phase change or gross change in metallurgical structure, it was considered that a metal would arrive at the same final conditions of flow

---

[1] J. H. Bechtold, *Trans. AIME*, vol. 197, pp. 1469–1475, 1953.

[2] T. A. Trozera, O. D. Sherby, and J. E. Dorn, *Trans. ASM*, vol. 49, pp. 173–188, 1957.

[3] C. W. MacGregor and J. C. Fisher, *J. Appl. Mech.*, vol. 13, pp. 11–16, 1946.

[4] MacDonald, Carlson, and Lankford, *op. cit.*

[5] J. H. Hollomon, *Trans. AIME*, vol. 171, p. 535, 1947.

stress and strain by different paths of strain rate and temperature provided that Eq. (9-38) was satisfied. However, extensive experiments[1,2] on aluminum, copper, stainless steel, and low-carbon steel have shown appreciable deviations from the behavior predicted by the mechanical equation of state. It is now established that the flow stress depends on the previous conditions of temperature and strain rate as well as on the instantaneous values of strain, strain rate, and temperature. The failure of the mechanical equation of state is due to the fact that the structural changes occurring during plastic deformation are dependent not solely on strain but on the strain rate and temperature as well.

9-9. Notch Tensile Test

The ordinary tension test on smooth specimens will fail to indicate notch sensitivity in metals. However, a tension test with a notched

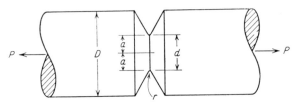

Fig. 9-14. Details of notched tensile specimen.

tensile specimen will show whether or not a material is notch-sensitive and prone to brittle fracture in the presence of a stress concentration. Notch sensitivity can also be investigated by means of the notched-impact test, as described in Chap. 14; this test has been widely used for mild steels and as a test for temper embrittlement. The impact test has the advantage of ease in preparing specimens and testing over a wide range of temperature, but it lacks the advantage of the notch tensile test of more basic interpretation of test results because of a better-defined state of stress. The notch tensile test has been used for testing high-strength steels, for studying hydrogen embrittlement in steels, and for investigating the notch sensitivity of high-temperature alloys.

Figure 9-14 shows the geometric details of a notched tensile specimen. The introduction of the notch produces a condition of biaxial stress at the root of the notch and triaxial stress at the interior of the specimen. As was shown previously in Sec. 7-12, the presence of transverse stress at the notch increases the resistance to flow and decreases the ratio of

[1] J. E. Dorn, A. Goldberg, and T. E. Tietz, *Trans. AIME*, vol. 180, p. 205, 1949.

[2] T. E. Tietz and J. E. Dorn, "Cold Working of Metals," pp. 163–179, American Society for Metals, Metals Park, Ohio, 1949.

shear stress to tensile stress. A notch is characterized by the notch sharpness a/r and the notch depth.

$$\text{Notch depth} = 1 - \frac{d^2}{D^2}$$

The notch strength is defined as the maximum load divided by the original cross-sectional area at the notch. The notch-strength ratio (NSR) is the ratio of the notch strength to the ultimate tensile strength. The NSR is a measure of notch sensitivity. If the NSR is less than unity, the material is notch-brittle. The term notch ductility is used to indicate the reduction of area at the notched region. The amount of notch ductility is often very small and therefore is difficult to determine accurately. The most commonly used notch has 50 per cent of the area removed at the notch, with a radius of 0.001 in. and a 60° notch angle.

The notch sensitivity of steel is usually evaluated by measuring the notch strength as a function of tensile strength. Figure 9-15 shows the type of curves which are obtained. The notch strength drops off sharply at about the 200,000-psi strength level, indicating that the steels are notch-brittle above this strength level.

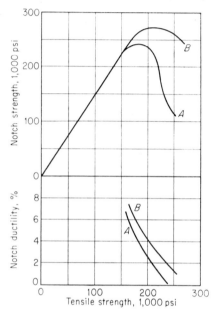

Fig. 9-15. Notch tensile properties of two steels. Steel A has higher notch sensitivity than steel B.

Below this point the NSR is about 1.5. Note that the notch ductility decreases to very low values for tensile strengths over 200,000 psi. For most heat-treated steels the NSR falls off below 1.5 when the notch ductility drops below about 6 per cent.

The notch-strength–tensile-strength curve is a function of the notch shape. Increasing the notch radius reduces the elastic-stress concentration but has little effect on the degree of triaxiality of stress. The effect of changes in notch radius on notched tensile properties depends on the strength level of the steel. At high strength levels, where ductility is low, reducing the notch sharpness increases the notch strength and the notch-strength ratio. At strength levels below about 200,000 psi there is no effect on the notch strength of increasing the radius from 0.001 to 0.050 in.

On the other hand, changing the notch depth produces large changes in triaxiality with only small changes in stress concentration. At low strength levels the notch-strength ratio is a linear function of the notch depth.

$$\text{NSR} = 1 + \frac{\text{notch depth, \%}}{100}$$

At higher strengths, where the ductility is low, the notch strength is dependent on the notch ductility. The literature on notch tensile testing has been described in a number of reviews.[1,2]

9-10. Tensile Properties of Steels

Because of the commercial importance of ferrous materials, a great deal of work has been done in correlating their tensile properties with composition and microstructure. It has been clearly demonstrated that microstructure is the chief metallurgical variable which controls the tensile properties of steels. Because of the wide variety of microstructures which are possible with changes in composition and heat treatment, this is a very interesting, yet somewhat complex, subject.

The tensile properties of annealed and normalized steels are controlled by the flow and fracture characteristics of the ferrite and by the amount, shape, and distribution of the cementite. The strength of the ferrite depends on the amount of alloying elements in solid solution (see Fig. 5-9) and the ferrite grain size. The carbon content has a very strong effect because it controls the amount of cementite present either as pearlite or as spheroidite. The strength increases and ductility decreases with increasing carbon content because of the increased amount of cementite in the microstructure. A normalized steel will have higher strength than an annealed steel because the more rapid rate of cooling used in the normalizing treatment causes the transformation to pearlite to occur at a lower temperature, and a finer pearlite spacing results. Differences in tensile properties due to the shape of the cementite particles are shown in Fig. 9-16, where the tensile properties of a spheroidized structure are compared with a pearlitic structure for a steel with the same carbon content. Empirical correlations have been worked out[3] between composition and cooling rate for predicting the tensile properties of steels with pearlitic structures.

[1] J. D. Lubahn, Notch Tensile Testing, "Fracturing of Metals," pp. 90–132, American Society for Metals, Metals Park, Ohio, 1948.

[2] J. D. Lubahn, *Trans. ASME*, vol. 79, pp. 111–115, 1957.

[3] I. R. Kramer, P. D. Gorsuch, and D. L. Newhouse, *Trans. AIME*, vol. 172, pp. 244–272, 1947.

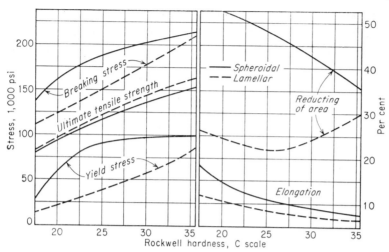

Fig. 9-16. Tensile properties of pearlite and spheroidite in a eutectoid steel. (*From E. C. Bain, "Alloying Elements in Steel," p.* 39, *American Society for Metals, Metals Park, Ohio,* 1939.)

One of the best ways to increase the strength of annealed steel is by cold working. Table 9-6 gives the tensile properties which result from the cold reduction of SAE 1016 steel bars by drawing through a die.

TABLE 9-6
EFFECT OF COLD DRAWING ON TENSILE PROPERTIES OF
SAE 1016 STEEL†

Reduction of area by drawing, %	Yield strength, psi	Tensi'e strength, psi	Elongation, in 2 in., %	Reduction of area, %
0	40,000	66,000	34	70
10	72,000	75,000	20	65
20	82,000	84,000	17	63
40	86,000	95,000	16	60
60	88,000	102,000	14	54
80	96,000	115,000	7	26

† L. J. Ebert, "A Handbook on the Properties of Cold Worked Steels," PB 121662, Office of Technical Services, U.S. Department of Commerce, 1955.

The pearlitic structure in steel can be controlled best by transforming the austenite to pearlite at a constant temperature instead of allowing it to form over a range of temperature on continuous cooling from above the critical temperature. Although isothermal transformation is not in widespread commercial use, it is a good way of isolating the effect of certain microstructures on the properties of steel.   Figure 9-17 shows the variation of tensile properties for a Ni-Cr-Mo eutectoid steel with iso-thermal-reaction temperature.[1]   This is a recent extension of Gensamer's work,[2] which showed that the tensile strength varied linearly with the logarithm of the mean free ferrite path in isothermally transformed structures.   In the region 1300 to 1000°F the transformation product is

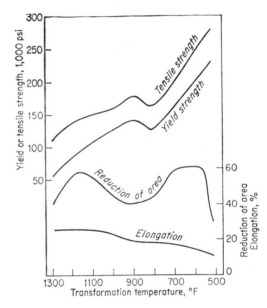

Fig. 9-17. Relationship of tensile properties of Ni-Cr-Mo steel to isothermal-transformation temperature.   (*E. S. Davenport, Trans. AIME, vol.* 209, *p.* 684, 1957.)

lamellar pearlite.   The spacing between cementite platelets decreases with transformation temperature and correspondingly the strength increases.   In the region 800 to 500°F the structure obtained on transformation is acicular bainite.   The bainitic structure becomes finer with decreasing temperature, and the strength increases almost linearly to quite high values.   Good ductility accompanies this high strength over part of the bainite temperature range.   This is the temperature region used in the commercial heat-treating process known as austempering. The temperature region 1000 to 800°F is one in which mixed lamellar and acicular structures are obtained.   There is a definite ductility minimum and a leveling off of strength for these structures.   The sensitivity

[1] E. S. Davenport, *Trans. AIME*, vol. 209, pp. 677–688, 1957.

[2] M. Gensamer, E. B. Pearsall, W. S. Pellini, and J. R. Low, *Trans. ASM*, vol. 30, pp. 983–1020, 1942.

of the reduction of area to changes in microstructure is well illustrated by these results.

The best combination of strength and ductility is obtained in steel which has been quenched to a fully martensitic structure and then tempered. The best criterion for comparing the tensile properties of quenched and tempered steels is on the basis of an as-quenched structure of 100 per cent martensite. However, the attainment of a completely martensitic structure may, in many cases, be commercially

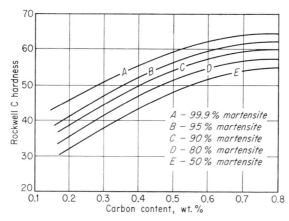

Fig. 9-18. As-quenched hardness of steel as a function of carbon content for different percentages of martensite in the microstructure. (*ASM Metals Handbook*, 1948 *ed., p.* 497.)

impractical. Because of the importance of obtaining a fully martensitic structure, it is desirable that the steel have adequate hardenability. *Hardenability*, the property of a steel which determines the depth and distribution of hardness induced by quenching, should be differentiated from *hardness*, which is the property of a material which represents its resistance to indentation or deformation. (This subject is discussed in Chap. 11.) Hardness is associated with strength, while hardenability is connected with the transformation characteristics of a steel. Hardenability may be increased by altering the transformation kinetics by the addition of alloying elements, while the hardness of a steel with given transformation kinetics is controlled primarily by the carbon content. Figure 9-18 shows the hardness of martensite as a function of carbon content for different total amounts of martensite in the microstructure. These curves can be used to determine whether or not complete hardening was obtained after quenching. Hardness is used as a convenient measure of the strength of quenched and tempered steels. The validity of this procedure is based on the excellent correlation which exists between tensile strength and hardness for heat-treated, annealed, and normalized steels (Fig. 9-19).

The mechanical properties of a quenched and tempered steel may be altered by changing the tempering temperature. Figure 9-20 shows how hardness and the tensile properties vary with tempering temperature for an SAE 4340 steel. This is the typical behavior for heat-treated steel.

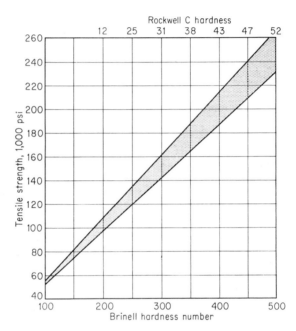

Fig. 9-19. Relationship between tensile strength and hardness for quenched and tempered, annealed, and normalized steels. (*SAE Handbook.*)

Several methods for correlating and predicting the hardness change in different steels with tempering temperature have been proposed.[1-3] In using tempering diagrams like Fig. 9-20, it is important to know whether or not the data were obtained on specimens quenched to essentially 100 per cent martensite throughout the entire cross section of the specimen. Because of the variability in hardenability from heat to heat, there is no assurance of reproducibility of data unless this condition is fulfilled.

A great many low-alloy steels have been developed and are used in the quenched and tempered condition. A study of the tensile properties of these steels could lead to considerable confusion were it not for the fact

[1] J. H. Hollomon and L. D. Jaffe, *Trans. AIME*, vol. 162, p. 223, 1945.
[2] R. A. Grange and R. W. Baughman, *Trans. ASM*, vol. 48, pp. 165–197, 1956.
[3] L. D. Jaffe and E. Gordon, *Trans. ASM*, vol. 49, pp. 359–371, 1957.

that certain generalities can be made about their properties.[1,2]   For low-alloy steels containing 0.3 to 0.5 per cent carbon which are quenched to essentially 100 per cent martensite and then tempered back to any given tensile strength in the range 100,000 to 200,000 psi, the other common tensile properties will have a relatively fixed value depending only on the tensile strength.   In other words, the mechanical properties of this

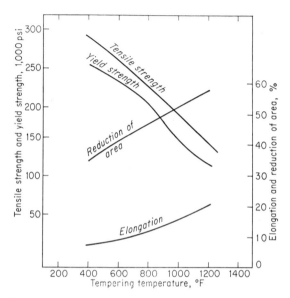

Fig. 9-20. Tensile properties of quenched and tempered SAE 4340 steel as a function of tempering temperature.   For fully hardened 1-in.-diameter bars.

important class of steels do not depend basically on alloy content, carbon content within the above limits, or tempering temperature.   It is important to note that this generalization does not say that two alloy steels given the same tempering treatment will have the same tensile properties, because different tempering temperatures would quite likely be required to bring two different alloy steels to the same tensile strength.   Figure 9-21 shows this relationship between the mechanical properties of steels with tempered martensitic structures.   The expected scatter in values is indicated by the shading.   Because of this similarity in properties, it is logical to ask why so many different alloy steels are used.   Actually, as will be seen in Chap. 14, all low-alloy steels do not have the same impact resistance or notch sensitivity, and they may differ considerably in these

[1] E. J. Janitsky and M. Baeyertz, "Metals Handbook," pp. 515–518, American Society for Metals, Metals Park, Ohio, 1939.
[2] W. G. Patton, *Metal Progr.*, vol. 43, pp. 726–733, 1943.

respects when heat-treated to tensile strengths in excess of 200,000 psi. Further, to minimize processing difficulties such as quench cracking and weld embrittlement, it is an advantage to use a steel with the lowest carbon content consistent with the required as-quenched hardness. For this reason, steels are available with closely spaced carbon contents.

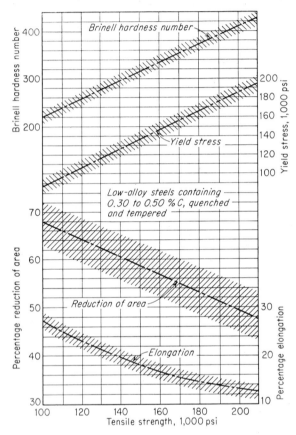

Fig. 9-21. Relationships between tensile properties of quenched and tempered low-alloy steels. (*W. G. Patton, Metal Progr., vol.* 43, *p.* 726, 1943.)

Steel sections which are too large to be quenched throughout to essentially 100 per cent martensite will contain higher-temperature transformation products such as ferrite, pearlite, and bainite interspersed with the martensite. Such a situation is known as a *slack-quenched* structure. Slack quenching results in tensile properties which are somewhat poorer than those obtained with a completely tempered martensitic structure. The yield strength and the reduction of area are generally most affected, while impact strength can be very greatly reduced. The effect of slack quenching is greatest at high hardness levels. As the tempering temperature is increased, the deviation in the properties of slack-quenched steel from those of tempered martensite becomes smaller. In steels with sufficient hardenability to form 100 per cent martensite it is frequently found that not all the austenite is transformed to martensite on quenching. Studies[1] have shown that the greatest effect of retained austenite on tensile properties is in decreasing the yield strength.

9-11. Anisotropy of Tensile Properties

It is frequently found that the tensile properties of wrought-metal products are not the same in all directions. The dependence of properties on orientation is called *anisotropy*. Two general types of anisotropy are found in metals. *Crystallographic anisotropy* results from the preferred orientation of the grains which is produced by severe deformation. Since the strength of a single crystal is highly anisotropic, a severe plastic deformation which produces a strong preferred orientation will cause a polycrystalline specimen to approach the anisotropy of a single crystal. The yield strength, and to a lesser extent the tensile strength, are the properties most affected. The yield strength in the direction perpendicular to the main (longitudinal) direction of working may be greater or less than the yield strength in the longitudinal direction, depending upon the type of preferred orientation which exists. This type of anisotropy is most frequently found in nonferrous metals, especially when they have been severely worked into sheet. Crystallographic anisotropy can be eliminated by recrystallization, although the formation of a recrystallization texture can cause the reappearance of a different type of anisotropy. A practical manifestation of crystallographic anisotropy is the formation of "ears," or nonuniform deformation in deep-drawn cups. Crystallographic anisotropy may also result in the elliptical deformation of a tensile specimen.

Mechanical fibering is due to the preferred alignment of structural discontinuities such as inclusions, voids, segregation, and second phases in the direction of working. This type of anisotropy is important in forgings and plates. The principal direction of working is defined as the *longitudinal direction.* This is the long axis of a bar or the rolling direction in a sheet or plate. Two transverse directions must be considered. The *short-transverse direction* is the minimum dimension of the product, for example, the thickness of a plate. The *long-transverse direction* is perpendicular to both the longitudinal and short-transverse directions.

[1] L. S. Castleman, B. L. Averbach, and M. Cohen, *Trans. ASM*, vol. 44, pp. 240–263, 1952.

In a round or square, both these transverse directions are equivalent, while in a sheet the properties in the short-transverse direction cannot be measured. In wrought-steel products mechanical fibering is the principal cause of directional properties. Measures of ductility like reduction of area are most affected. In general, reduction of area is lowest in the short-transverse direction, intermediate in the long-transverse direction, and highest in the longitudinal direction.

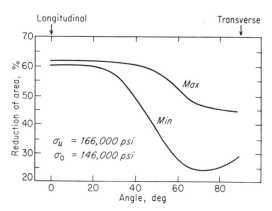

Fig. 9-22. Relationship between reduction of area and angle between the longitudinal direction in forging and the specimen axis. (*C. Wells and R. F. Mehl, Trans. ASM, vol. 41, p. 753, 1949.*)

Transverse properties are particularly important in thick-walled tubes, like guns and pressure vessels, which are subjected to high internal pressures. In these applications the greatest principal stress acts in the circumferential direction, which corresponds to the transverse direction of a cylindrical forging. While there is no direct method for incorporating the reduction of area into the design of such a member, it is known that the transverse reduction of area (RAT) is a good index of steel quality for these types of applications. For this reason the RAT may be the limiting value in the design of a part. A great deal of work[1-3] on the transverse properties of gun tubes and large forgings has provided data in this field. Figure 9-22 shows the variation of reduction of area with the angle between the axis of the tensile specimen and the longitudinal direction in a forging of SAE 4340 steel. No similar variation with orientation is found for the yield strength or the tensile strength. This figure shows both the maximum and minimum values of reduction of area obtained for different specimen orientations. Because of the large

[1] C. Wells and R. F. Mehl, *Trans. ASM*, vol. 41, pp. 715–818, 1949.

[2] A. H. Grobe, C. Wells, and R. F. Mehl, *Trans. ASM*, vol. 45, pp. 1080–1122, 1953.

[3] E. A. Loria, *Trans. ASM*, vol. 42, pp. 486–498, 1950.

scatter in measurements of RAT it is necessary to use statistical methods. The degree of anisotropy in reduction of area increases with strength level.   In the region of tensile strength between 80,000 and 180,000 psi the RAT decreases by about 1.5 per cent for each 5,000 psi increase in tensile strength.   Figure 9-23 shows the way in which the longitudinal and transverse reduction of area varies with reduction by forging.   The forging ratio is the ratio of the original to the final cross-sectional area

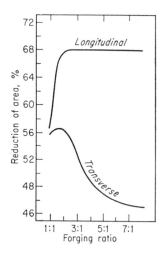

Fig. 9-23. Effect of forging reduction on longitudinal and transverse reduction of area.   Tensile strength 118,000 psi. (*C. Wells and R. F. Mehl, Trans. ASM, vol. 41, p. 755, 1949.*)

of the forging.   It is usually found that the optimum properties are obtained with a forging ratio of 2 to 3:1.   Nonmetallic inclusions are considered to be a major source of low transverse ductility.   This is based on the fact that vacuum-melted steels give higher RAT values than air-melted steel and on correlations which have been made[1] between inclusion content and RAT.   Other factors such as microsegregation and dendritic structure may also be responsible for low transverse ductility in forgings.

An interesting aspect of the anisotropic strength of metals concerns the effect of prior torsional deformation on tensile properties.   Swift[2] twisted mild-steel bars in torsion and then determined the tensile properties of the bar.   If the torsional shear strain at the surface exceeded unity, it was found that the tensile-fracture stress and reduction of area were greatly reduced.   At the same time the tensile fracture changed

---

[1] J. Welchner and W. G. Hildorf, *Trans. ASM*, vol. 42, pp. 455–485, 1950.

[2] H. W. Swift, *J. Iron Steel Inst. (London)*, vol. 140, p. 181, 1939.

from a cup-and-cone fracture to a fracture on a 45° plane.   If the specimens were twisted to this strain and then untwisted, there was little effect of the torsional deformation on the fracture stress, ductility, or type of fracture.   In interpreting these results it was suggested[1] that the twisting produced a preferred orientation of initially randomly oriented microcracks.   The cracks were presumed to become oriented along the helical surface, which is in compression during twisting (see Fig. 10-4).   Separation occurs along this 45° plane when axial tension is applied.   The cracks were assumed to become reoriented in the longitudinal direction of the bar when it was untwisted, and with this orientation they would have little effect on the tensile properties.   Although there was no real experimental evidence for the existence of microcracks, it was considered that they could be initiated at inclusions and second-phase particles. However, similar experiments[2] with OFHC copper, in which there were no second-phase particles and no preferred orientation, confirmed and extended Swift's observations.   The mechanical anisotropy which was observed was explained on the assumption that the metal contained a fibrous flaw structure, which has the characteristics of submicroscopic cracks.   There is some indication that these cracks originate during solidification of the ingot and perhaps during plastic deformation, when they are oriented in the principal working direction.

BIBLIOGRAPHY

Hollomon, J. H., and L. D. Jaffee: "Ferrous Metallurgical Design," chaps. 3 and 4, John Wiley & Sons, Inc., New York, 1947.

Lessells, John M.: "Strength and Resistance of Metals," chap. 1, John Wiley & Sons, Inc., New York, 1954.

Low, J. R., Jr.: Behavior of Metals under Direct or Non-reverse Loading, in "Properties of Metals in Materials Engineering," American Society for Metals, Metals Park, Ohio, 1949.

Marin, J.: "Engineering Materials," chaps. 1 and 11, Prentice-Hall, Inc., Englewood Cliffs, N.J., 1952.

Nadai, A.: "Theory of Flow and Fracture of Solids," vol. I, chap. 8, McGraw-Hill Book Company, Inc., New York, 1950.

Symposium on Significance of the Tension Test of Metals in Relation to Design, *Proc. ASTM*, vol. 40, pp. 501–609, 1940.

[1] C. Zener and J. H. Hollomon, *Trans. ASM*, vol. 33, p. 163, 1944.

[2] W. A. Backofen, A. J. Shaler, and B. B. Hundy, *Trans. ASM*, vol. 46, pp. 655–680, 1954.

Chapter 10
THE TORSION TEST

10-1. Introduction

The torsion test has not met with the wide acceptance and the use that have been given the tension test. However, it is useful in many engineering applications and also in theoretical studies of plastic flow. Torsion tests are made on materials to determine such properties as the modulus of elasticity in shear, the torsional yield strength, and the modulus of rupture. Torsion tests also may be carried out on full-sized parts, such as shafts, axles, and twist drills, which are subjected to torsional loading in service. It is frequently used for testing brittle materials, such as tool steels, and has been used in the form of a high-temperature twist test to evaluate the forgeability of materials. The torsion test has not been standardized to the same extent as the tension test and is rarely required in materials specifications.

Torsion-testing equipment consists of a twisting head, with a chuck for gripping the specimen and for applying the twisting moment to the specimen, and a weighing head, which grips the other end of the specimen and measures the twisting moment, or torque. The deformation of the specimen is measured by a twist-measuring device called a troptometer. Determination is made of the angular displacement of a point near one end of the test section of the specimen with respect to a point on the same longitudinal element at the opposite end. A torsion specimen generally has a circular cross section, since this represents the simplest geometry for the calculation of the stress. Since in the elastic range the shear stress varies linearly from a value of zero at the center of the bar to a maximum value at the surface, it is frequently desirable to test a thin-walled tubular specimen. This results in a nearly uniform shear stress over the cross section of the specimen.

10-2. Mechanical Properties in Torsion

Consider a cylindrical bar which is subjected to a torsional moment at one end (Fig. 10-1). The twisting moment is resisted by shear stresses set up in the cross section of the bar.   The shear stress is zero at the center of the bar and increases linearly with the radius.   Equating the

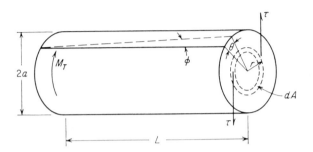

Fig. 10-1. Torsion of a solid bar.

twisting moment to the internal resisting moment,

$$M_T = \int_{r=0}^{r=a} \tau r \, dA = \frac{\tau}{r} \int_0^a r^2 \, dA \qquad (10\text{-}1)$$

But $\int r^2 \, dA$ is the polar moment of inertia of the area with respect to the axis of the shaft.   Thus,

$$M_T = \frac{\tau J}{r}$$

or
$$\tau = \frac{M_T r}{J} \qquad (10\text{-}2)$$

where τ = shear stress, psi
  M_T = torsional moment, lb-in.
  r = radial distance measured from center of shaft, in.
  J = polar moment of inertia, in.[4]
Since the shear stress is a maximum at the surface of the bar, for a solid cylindrical specimen where $J = \pi D^4/32$, the maximum shear stress is

$$\tau_{\max} = \frac{M_T D/2}{\pi D^4/32} = \frac{16 M_T}{\pi D^3} \qquad (10\text{-}3)$$

For a tubular specimen the shear stress on the outer surface is

$$\tau = \frac{16 M_T D_1}{\pi (D_1{}^4 - D_2{}^4)} \qquad (10\text{-}4)$$

where D_1 = outside diameter of tube
  D_2 = inside diameter of tube
  The troptometer is used to determine the angle of twist, θ, usually expressed in radians.   If L is the test length of the specimen, from Fig.

10-1 it will be seen that the shear strain is given by

$$\gamma = \tan \phi = \frac{r\theta}{L} \tag{10-5}$$

During a torsion test measurements are made of the twisting moment M_T and the angle of twist, θ. A torque-twist diagram is usually obtained, as shown in Fig. 10-2.

The elastic properties in torsion may be obtained by using the torque at the proportional limit or the torque at some offset angle of twist,

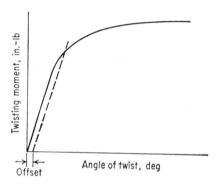

Fig. 10-2. Torque-twist diagram.

frequently 0.001 radian/in. of gage length, and calculating the shear stress corresponding to the twisting moment from the appropriate equations given above. A tubular specimen is usually required for a precision measurement of the torsional elastic limit or yield strength. Because of the stress gradient across the diameter of a solid bar the surface fibers are restrained from yielding by the less highly stressed inner fibers. Thus, the first onset of yielding is generally not readily apparent with the instruments ordinarily used for measuring the angle of twist. The use of a thin-walled tubular specimen minimizes this effect because the stress gradient is practically eliminated. Care should be taken, however, that the wall thickness is not reduced too greatly, or the specimen will fail by buckling rather than torsion. Experience has shown that for determinations of the shearing yield strength and modulus of elasticity the ratio of the length of the reduced test section to the outside diameter should be about 10 and the diameter-thickness ratio should be about 8 to 10.

Once the torsional yield strength has been exceeded the shear-stress distribution from the center to the surface of the specimen is no longer linear and Eq. (10-3) or (10-4) does not strictly apply. However, an ultimate torsional shearing strength, or *modulus of rupture*, is frequently determined by substituting the maximum measured torque into these equations. The results obtained by this procedure overestimate the ultimate shear stress. A more precise method of calculating this value will be discussed in the next section. Although the procedure just described results in considerable error, for the purpose of comparing and selecting materials it is generally sufficiently accurate. For the determination of the modulus of rupture with tubular specimens, the ratio of gage length to diameter should be about 0.5 and the diameter-thickness ratio about 10 to 12.

Within the elastic range the shear stress can be considered proportional to the shear strain. The constant of proportionality, G, is the *modulus of elasticity in shear*, or the *modulus of rigidity*.

$$\tau = G\gamma \tag{10-6}$$

Substituting Eqs. (10-2) and (10-5) into Eq. (10-6) gives an expression for the shear modulus in terms of the geometry of the specimen, the torque, and the angle of twist.

$$G = \frac{M_T L}{J\theta} \tag{10-7}$$

10-3. Torsional Stresses for Large Plastic Strains

Beyond the torsional yield strength the shear stress over a cross section of the bar is no longer a linear function of the distance from the axis, and Eqs. (10-3) and (10-4) do not apply. Nadai[1] has presented a method for calculating the shear stress in the plastic range if the torque-twist curve is known. To simplify the analysis, we shall consider the angle of twist per unit length, θ', where $\theta' = \theta/L$. Referring to Eq. (10-5), the shear strain will be

$$\gamma = r\theta' \tag{10-8}$$

Equation (10-1), for the resisting torque in a cross section of the bar, can be expressed as follows:

$$M_T = 2\pi \int_0^a \tau r^2 \, dr \tag{10-9}$$

Now the shear stress is related to the shear strain by the stress-strain curve in shear.

$$\tau = f(\gamma)$$

Introducing this equation into Eq. (10-9) and changing the variable from

[1] A. Nadai, "Theory of Flow and Fracture of Solids," 2d ed., vol. I, p. 347–349, McGraw-Hill Book Company, Inc., New York, 1950. A generalization of this analysis for strain-rate sensitive materials has been given by D. S. Fields and W. A. Backofen, *Proc. ASTM*, vol. 57, pp. 1259–1272, 1957.

r to γ by means of Eq. (10-8) gives

$$M_T = 2\pi \int_0^{\gamma_a} f(\gamma) \frac{\gamma^2}{(\theta')^2} \frac{d\gamma}{\theta'}$$

$$M_T(\theta')^3 = 2\pi \int_0^{\gamma_a} f(\gamma)\gamma^2 \, d\gamma \tag{10-10}$$

where $\gamma_a = a\theta'$. Differentiating Eq. (10-10) with respect to θ'

$$\frac{d}{d\theta'} (M_T\theta'^3) = 2\pi a f(a\theta')a^2(\theta')^2 = 2\pi a^3(\theta')^2 f(a\theta')$$

But, the maximum shear stress in the bar at the outer fiber is $\tau_a = f(a\theta')$. Therefore,

$$\frac{d(M_T\theta'^3)}{d\theta'} = 2\pi a^3(\theta')^2\tau_a$$

$$3M_T(\theta')^2 + (\theta')^3 \frac{dM_T}{d\theta'} = 2\pi a^3(\theta')^2\tau_a$$

Therefore, $$\tau_a = \frac{1}{2\pi a^3}\left(\theta' \frac{dM_T}{d\theta'} + 3M_T\right) \tag{10-11}$$

If a torque-twist curve is available, the shear stress can be calculated with the above equation. Figure 10-3 illustrates how this is done.

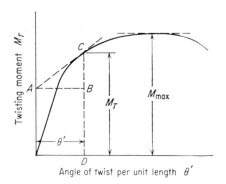

Fig. 10-3. Method of calculating shear stress from torque-twist diagram.

Examination of Eq. (10-11) shows that it can be written in terms of the geometry of Fig. 10-3 as follows:

$$\tau_a = \frac{1}{2\pi a^3}(BC + 3CD) \tag{10-12}$$

It will also be noticed from Fig. 10-3 that at the maximum value of torque $dM_T/d\theta' = 0$. Therefore, the ultimate torsional shear strength or modulus of rupture can be expressed by

$$\tau_u = \frac{3M_{max}}{2\pi a^3} \qquad (10\text{-}13)$$

10-4. Types of Torsion Failures

Figure 10-4 illustrates the state of stress at a point on the surface of a bar subjected to torsion. The maximum shear stress occurs on two mutually perpendicular planes, perpendicular to the longitudinal axis

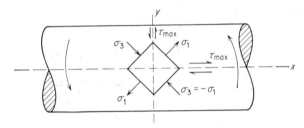

Fig. 10-4. State of stress in torsion.

(a)   (b)

Fig. 10-5. Typical torsion failures. (a) Shear (ductile) failure; (b) tensile (brittle) failure.

yy and parallel with the longitudinal axis xx. The principal stresses σ_1 and σ_3 make an angle of 45° with the longitudinal axis and are equal in magnitude to the shear stresses. σ_1 is a tensile stress, and σ_3 is an equal compressive stress. The intermediate stress σ_2 is zero.

Torsion failures are different from tensile failures in that there is little localized reduction of area or elongation. A ductile metal fails by shear along one of the planes of maximum shear stress. Generally the plane of the fracture is normal to the longitudinal axis (see Fig. 10-5a). A brittle material fails in torsion along a plane perpendicular to the direction of the maximum tensile stress. Since this plane bisects the angle between the two planes of maximum shear stress and makes an angle of 45° with the longitidunal and transverse directions, it results in a helical fracture (Fig. 10-5b). Fractures are sometimes observed in which the test section of the specimen breaks into a large number of fairly small pieces. In these cases it can usually be determined that the fracture started on a plane of maximum shear stress parallel with the axis of the specimen. A study of torsion failures in a tool steel as a function of hardness[1] showed that fracture started on planes of maximum shear stress up to a Vickers hardness of 720 and that above this hardness tensile stresses were responsible for starting fracture.

10-5. Torsion Test vs. Tension Test

A good case can be made for the position advanced by Sauveur[2] that the torsion test provides a more fundamental measure of the plasticity of a metal than the tension test. For one thing, the torsion test yields directly a shear-stress–shear-strain curve. This type of curve has more fundamental significance in characterizing plastic behavior than a stress-strain curve determined in tension. Large values of strain can be obtained in torsion without complications such as necking in tension or barreling due to frictional end effects in compression. Moreover, in torsion, tests can be made fairly easily at constant or high strain rates. On the other hand, considerable labor is involved in converting torque–angle-of-twist data into shear-stress–strain curves. Furthermore, unless a tubular specimen is used, there will be a steep stress gradient across the specimen. This will make it difficult to make accurate measurements of the yield strength.

The tension test and the torsion test are compared below in terms of the state of stress and strain developed in each test.

Tension test	*Torsion test*

$$\sigma_1 = \sigma_{max}; \sigma_2 = \sigma_3 = 0 \qquad\qquad \sigma_1 = -\sigma_3; \sigma_2 = 0$$

$$\tau_{max} = \frac{\sigma_1}{2} = \frac{\sigma_{max}}{2} \qquad\qquad \tau_{max} = \frac{2\sigma_1}{2} = \sigma_1$$

$$\epsilon_{max} = \epsilon_1; \epsilon_2 = \epsilon_3 = -\frac{\epsilon_1}{2} \qquad\qquad \epsilon_{max} = \epsilon_1 = -\epsilon_3; \epsilon_2 = 0$$

$$\gamma_{max} = \sinh\frac{3\epsilon_1}{2} \qquad\qquad \gamma_{max} = \epsilon_1 - \epsilon_3 = 2\epsilon_1$$

$$\bar{\sigma} = \frac{\sqrt{2}}{2}[(\sigma_1 - \sigma_2)^2 + (\sigma_2 - \sigma_3)^2 + (\sigma_3 - \sigma_1)^2]^{1/2}$$

$$\bar{\epsilon} = [\tfrac{2}{3}(\epsilon_1{}^2 + \epsilon_2{}^2 + \epsilon_3{}^2)]^{1/2}$$

$$\bar{\sigma} = \sigma_1 \qquad\qquad\qquad\qquad \bar{\sigma} = \sqrt{3}\sigma_1$$

$$\bar{\epsilon} = \epsilon_1 \qquad\qquad\qquad\qquad \bar{\epsilon} = \frac{2}{\sqrt{3}}\epsilon_1 = \frac{\gamma}{\sqrt{3}}$$

[1] R. D. Olleman, E. T. Wessel, and F. C. Hull, *Trans. ASM*, vol. 46, pp. 87–99, 1954.
[2] A. Sauveur, *Proc. ASTM*, vol. 38, pt. 2, pp. 3–20. 1938.

This comparison shows that τ_{max} will be twice as great in torsion as in tension for a given value of σ_{max}. Since as a first approximation it can be considered that plastic deformation occurs on reaching a critical value of τ_{max} and brittle fracture occurs on reaching a critical value of σ_{max}, the opportunity for ductile behavior is greater in torsion than in tension. This is illustrated schematically in Fig. 10-6, which can be considered representative of the condition for a brittle material such as hardened

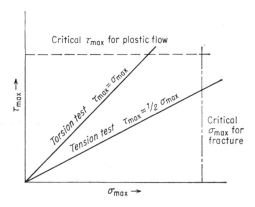

Fig. 10-6. Effect of ratio τ_{max}/σ_{max} in determining ductility. (*After Gensamer.*)

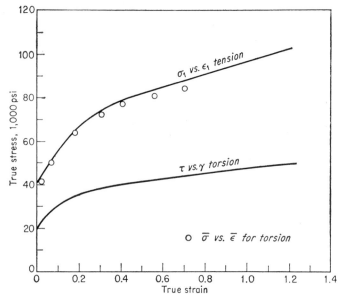

Fig. 10-7. Tension and torsion true-stress–true-strain curves for low-carbon steel.

tool steel. In the torsion test the critical shear stress for plastic flow is reached before the critical normal stress for fracture, while in tension the critical normal stress is reached before the shear stress reaches the shear stress for plastic flow. Even for a metal which is ductile in the tension test, where the critical normal stress is pushed far to the right in Fig. 10-6, the figure shows that the amount of plastic deformation is greater in torsion than in tension.

The tensile stress-strain curve can be derived from the curve for torsion when the stress-strain curve is plotted in terms of significant stress and strain or the octahedral shear stress and strain (see Prob. 10.4). Figure 10-7 shows a true-stress–true-strain curve from a tension test and the shear-stress–shear-strain curve for the same material in torsion. When both curves are plotted in terms of significant stress and significant strain (the tension curve is unchanged), the two curves superimpose within fairly close limits. A number of examples of this can be found in the literature.[1,2] Also, a straight line is obtained for torsion data when the logarithm of significant stress is plotted against the logarithm of significant strain.[3] The values of K and n obtained from these curves agree fairly well with comparable values obtained from the tension test.

BIBLIOGRAPHY

Davis, H. E., G. E. Troxell, and C. T. Wiskocil: "The Testing and Inspection of Engineering Materials," chap. 5, 2d ed., McGraw-Hill Book Company, Inc., New York, 1955.
Gensamer, M.: "Strength of Metals under Combined Stresses," American Society for Metals, Metals Park, Ohio, 1941.
Marin, J.: "Engineering Materials," chap. 2, Prentice-Hall, Inc., Englewood Cliffs, N.J., 1952.
"Metals Handbook," pp. 111–112, American Society for Metals, Metals Park, Ohio, 1948.

[1] E. A. Davis, *Trans. ASME*, vol. 62, pp. 577–586, 1940.
[2] J. H. Faupel and J. Marin, *Trans. ASM*, vol. 43, pp. 993–1012, 1951.
[3] H. Larson and E. P. Klier, *Trans. ASM*, vol. 43, pp. 1033–1051, 1951.

Chapter 11

THE HARDNESS TEST

11-1. Introduction

The hardness of a material is a poorly defined term which has many meanings depending upon the experience of the person involved. In general, hardness usually implies a resistance to deformation, and for metals the property is a measure of their resistance to permanent or plastic deformation. To a person concerned with the mechanics of materials testing, hardness is most likely to mean the resistance to indentation, and to the design engineer it often means an easily measured and specified quantity which indicates something about the strength and heat treatment of the metal. There are three general types of hardness measurements depending upon the manner in which the test is conducted. These are (1) scratch hardness, (2) indentation hardness, and (3) rebound, or dynamic, hardness. Only indentation hardness is of major engineering interest for metals.

Scratch hardness is of primary interest to mineralogists. With this measure of hardness, various minerals and other materials are rated on their ability to scratch one another. Hardness is measured according to the Mohs scale. This consists of 10 standard minerals arranged in the order of their ability to be scratched. The softest mineral in this scale is talc (scratch hardness 1), while diamond has a hardness of 10. A fingernail has a value of about 2, annealed copper has a value of 3, and martensite a hardness of 7. The Mohs scale is not well suited for metals since the intervals are not widely spaced in the high-hardness range. Most hard metals fall in the Mohs hardness range of 4 to 8. A different type of scratch-hardness test[1] measures the depth or width of a scratch made by drawing a diamond stylus across the surface under a definite load. This is a useful tool for measuring the relative hardness of microconstituents, but it does not lend itself to high reproducibility or extreme accuracy.

In dynamic-hardness measurements the indenter is usually dropped

---

[1] E. B. Bergsman, *ASTM Bull.* 176, pp. 37–43, September, 1951.

onto the metal surface, and the hardness is expressed as the energy of impact. The Shore sceleroscope, which is the commonest example of a dynamic-hardness tester, measures the hardness in terms of the height of rebound of the indenter.

11-2. Brinell Hardness

The first widely accepted and standardized indentation-hardness test was proposed by J. A. Brinell in 1900. The Brinell hardness test consists in indenting the metal surface with a 10-mm-diameter steel ball at a load of 3,000 kg. For soft metals the load is reduced to 500 kg to avoid too deep an impression, and for very hard metals a tungsten carbide ball is used to minimize distortion of the indenter. The load is applied for a standard time, usually 30 sec, and the diameter of the indentation is measured with a low-power microscope after removal of the load. The average of two readings of the diameter of the impression at right angles should be made. The surface on which the indentation is made should be relatively smooth and free from dirt or scale. The Brinell hardness number (BHN) is expressed as the load P divided by the *surface area* of the indentation. This is expressed by the formula[1]

$$\text{BHN} = \frac{P}{(\pi D/2)(D - \sqrt{D^2 - d^2})} \qquad (11\text{-}1)$$

where P = applied load, kg
   D = diameter of ball, mm
   d = diameter of indentation, mm
It will be noticed that the units of the BHN are kilograms per square millimeter. However, the BHN is not a satisfactory physical concept since Eq. (11-1) does not give the mean pressure over the surface of the indentation.

In general, the Brinell hardness number of a material is constant only for one applied load and diameter of ball. It has been shown that in order to obtain the same Brinell hardness number at a nonstandard load geometrical similitude must be maintained. This requires that the ratio of the indentation to the indenter, d/D, remains constant. To a first approximation this can be attained when P/D^2 is kept constant.

The greatest error in Brinell hardness measurements occurs in measuring the diameter of the impression. It is assumed that the diameter of the indentation is the same as the diameter when the ball was in contact with the metal. However, owing to elastic recovery, the radius of curvature of the indentation will be larger than that of the spherical

---

[1] Tables giving BHN as a function of d for standard loads may be found in most of the references in the Bibliography at the end of this chapter.

indenter, although the indentation will still be symmetrical.   The harder
the metal, the greater the elastic recovery.   Elastic recovery will affect
measurements of the depth of indentation, but it will have only a negligible effect on the chordal diameter of the impression, so that this does
not in general influence Brinell hardness.   However, two types of anomalous behavior can occur as a result of localized deformation of the metal
at the indentation.   These are shown schemat-
ically in cross section through the indentation
in Fig. 11-1.   The sketch at the top illustrates
"ridging," or "piling up," in which a lip of metal
forms around the edge of the impression.   This
behavior is most common in cold-worked metals
with little ability to strain-harden.   The measured
diameter is greater than the true diameter of the
impression, but since the ridge carries part of the
load, it is customary to base the hardness measurement on the diameter d shown in the sketch.   The
drawing on the bottom shows "sinking in," in
which there is a depression of the metal at the rim
of the indentation.   This type of behavior is common with annealed metals having a high rate of
strain hardening.   The true diameter of the impres-
sion can sometimes be obtained by coating the ball with bluing or dye
before making the indentation.   It is frequently desirable to increase
the sharpness of definition of the impression so that the diameter can be
measured more accurately.   This can sometimes be done by using a
lightly etched steel ball or by coating the surface with a dull black
pigment.

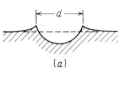

(a)

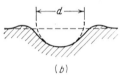

(b)

Fig. 11-1. Cross sections
through Brinell inden-
tations illustrating (a)
ridging and (b) sinking
in.

11-3. Meyer Hardness

Meyer[1] suggested that a more rational definition of hardness than that
proposed by Brinell would be one based on the *projected area* of the impression rather than the surface area.   The mean pressure between the surface of the indenter and the indentation is equal to the load divided by
the projected area of the indentation.

$$p = \frac{P}{\pi r^2}$$

Meyer proposed that this mean pressure should be taken as the measure
of hardness.   It is referred to as the *Meyer hardness*.

$$\text{Meyer hardness} = \frac{4P}{\pi d^2} \qquad (11\text{-}2)$$

[1] E. Meyer, *Z. Ver. deut. Ing*, vol. 52, pp. 645–654, 1908.

Like the Brinell hardness, Meyer hardness has units of kilograms per square millimeter. The Meyer hardness is less sensitive to the applied load than the Brinell hardness. For a cold-worked material the Meyer hardness is essentially constant and independent of load, while the Brinell hardness decreases as the load increases. For an annealed metal the Meyer hardness increases continuously with the load because of strain hardening produced by the indentation. The Brinell hardness, however, first increases with load and then decreases for still higher loads. The Meyer hardness is a more fundamental measure of indentation hardness; yet it is rarely used for practical hardness measurements.

Meyer proposed an empirical relation between the load and the size of the indentation. This relationship is usually called *Meyer's law*.

$$P = kd^{n'} \tag{11-3}$$

where P = applied load, kg

d = diameter of indentation, mm

n' = a material constant related to strain hardening of metal

k = a material constant expressing resistance of metal to penetration

The parameter n' is the slope of the straight line obtained when $\log P$ is plotted against $\log d$, and k is the value of P at $d = 1$. Fully annealed metals have a value of n' of about 2.5, while n' is approximately 2 for fully strain-hardened metals. This parameter is roughly related to the strain-hardening coefficient in the exponential equation for the true-stress–true-strain curve. The exponent in Meyer's law is approximately equal to the strain-hardening coefficient plus 2.

When indentations are made with balls of different diameters, different values of k and n' will be obtained.

$$P = k_1 D_1^{n_1'} = k_2 D_2^{n_2'} = k_3 D_3^{n_3'} \cdots$$

Meyer found that n' was almost independent of the diameter of the indenter D but that k decreased with increasing values of D. This can be expressed empirically by a relationship of the form

$$C = k_1 D_1^{n'-2} = k_2 D_2^{n'-2} = k_3 D_3^{n'-2} \cdots$$

The general expression for Meyer's law then becomes

$$P = \frac{Cd_1^{n'}}{D_1^{n'-2}} = \frac{Cd_2^{n'}}{D_2^{n'-2}} = \frac{Cd_3^{n'}}{D_3^{n'-2}} \tag{11-4}$$

Several interesting conclusions result from Eq. (11-4). First, this equation can be written

$$\frac{P}{d^2} = C \left(\frac{d}{D}\right)^{n'-2} \tag{11-5}$$

Since d/D must be constant for geometrically similar indentations, the ratio P/d^2 must also be constant. However, P/d^2 is proportional to the Meyer hardness. Therefore, geometrically similar indentations give the same Meyer hardness number. Equation (11-4) can also be rearranged to give

$$\frac{P}{D^2} = C \left(\frac{d}{D}\right)^{n'} \tag{11-6}$$

Remembering again that geometrically similar indentations are obtained when d/D is constant, we see that the above equation shows that the ratio P/D^2 must also provide the same result. Therefore, the same hardness values will be obtained when the ratio P/D^2 is kept constant.

There is a lower limit of load below which Meyer's law is not valid. If the load is too small, the deformation around the indentation is not fully plastic and Eq. (11-3) is not obeyed. This load will depend upon the hardness of the metal. For a 10-mm-diameter ball the load should exceed 50 kg for copper with a BHN of 100, and for steel with a BHN of 400 the load should exceed 1,500 kg. For balls of different diameter the critical loads will be proportional to the square of the diameter.

11-4. Analysis of Indentation by a Spherical Indenter

Tabor[1] has given a detailed discussion of the mechanics of deformation of a flat metal surface with a spherical indenter. The elements of this analysis will be described here. Figure 11-2 illustrates the process. For

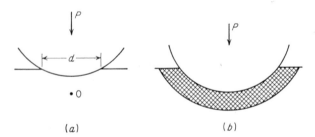

Fig. 11-2. Plastic deformation of an ideal plastic material by a spherical indenter. (a) Beginning of plastic deformation at point O; (b) full plastic flow. (*After D. Tabor, "The Hardness of Metals," p. 47, Oxford University Press, New York, 1951.*)

an ideal plastic metal with no strain hardening the highest pressure occurs immediately below the surface of contact at a depth of about $d/2$. The pressure at this point is about $0.47 p_m$, where p_m is the mean pressure over the circle of contact. Assuming that the maximum-shear-stress theory is

[1] D. Tabor, "The Hardness of Metals," Oxford University Press, New York, 1951.

the criterion for plastic flow, we can write

$$0.47p_m = 0.5\sigma_0$$

or $$p_m \approx 1.1\sigma_0 \qquad (11\text{-}7)$$

where σ_0 is the yield stress in tension or compression.

Therefore, the deformation under the indenter is elastic until the mean pressure reaches about 1.1 times the yield stress. At about this pressure plastic deformation begins in the vicinity of point O (Fig. 11-2a). As the load is further increased, the mean pressure increases and the plastically deformed region grows until it contains the entire region of contact (Fig. 11-2b). An analytical solution for the pressure between the spherical indenter and the indentation under conditions of full plasticity is very difficult. The best analysis of this problem indicates that $p_m \approx 2.66\sigma_0$. Meyer hardness tests on severely cold-worked metal indicates that full plasticity occurs when

$$p_m \approx 2.8\sigma_0 \qquad (11\text{-}8)$$

For an ideally plastic metal the pressure would remain constant at this value if the load were increased further. Since real metals strain-harden, the pressure would increase owing to an increase in σ_0 as the indentation process was continued. Most Brinell hardness tests are carried out under conditions where full plasticity is reached. This is also a necessary condition for Meyer's law to be valid.

11-5. Relationship between Hardness and the Tensile-flow Curve

Tabor[1] has suggested a method by which the plastic region of the true stress-strain curve may be determined from indentation hardness measurements. The method is based on the fact that there is a similarity in the shape of the flow curve and the curve obtained when the Meyer hardness is measured on a number of specimens subjected to increasing amounts of plastic strain. The method is basically empirical, since the complex stress distribution at the hardness indentation precludes a straightforward relationship with the stress distribution in the tension test. However, the method has been shown to give good agreement for several metals and thus should be of interest as a means of obtaining flow data in situations where it is not possible to measure tensile properties. The true stress (flow stress) is obtained from Eq. (11-8), where σ_0 is to be considered the flow stress at a given value of true strain.

$$\text{Meyer hardness} = p_m = 2.8\sigma_0$$

From a study of the deformation at indentations, Tabor concluded that

[1] Tabor, *op. cit.*, pp. 67–76; *J. Inst. Metals*, vol. 79, p. 1, 1951.

the true strain was proportional to the ratio d/D and could be expressed as

$$\epsilon = 0.2 \frac{d}{D} \qquad (11\text{-}9)$$

Thus, if the Meyer hardness is measured under conditions such that d/D varies from the smallest value for full plasticity up to large values and Eqs. (11-8) and (11-9) are used, it is possible at least to approximate the tensile-flow curve. Figure 11-3 shows the agreement which has been obtained by Tabor between the flow curve and hardness versus d/D curve for mild steel and annealed copper. Tabor's results have been verified by Lenhart[1] for duralumin and OFHC copper. However, Tabor's analysis did not predict the flow curve for magnesium, which was attributed by Lenhart to the high anisotropy of deformation in this metal. This work should not detract from the usefulness of this correlation but, rather, should serve to emphasize that its limitations should be investigated for new applications.

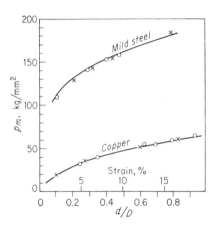

Fig. 11-3. Comparison of flow curve determined from hardness measurements (circles, crosses) with flow curve determined from compression test (solid lines). (*D. Tabor, "The Hardness of Metals," p. 74, Oxford University Press, New York, 1951.*)

There is a very useful engineering correlation between the Brinell hardness and the ultimate tensile strength of heat-treated plain-carbon and medium-alloy steels.

Ultimate tensile strength, in pounds per square inch, $= 500(\text{BHN})$. A brief consideration will show that this is in agreement with Tabor's results. If we make the simplifying assumption that this class of materials does not strain-harden, then the tensile strength is equal to the yield stress and Eq. (11-8) applies.

$$\sigma_u = \frac{1}{2.8} \, p_m = 0.36 p_m \qquad \text{kg/mm}^2$$

The Brinell hardness will be only a few per cent less than the value of Meyer hardness p_m. Upon converting to engineering units the expression becomes

$$\sigma_u = 515(\text{BHN})$$

[1] R. E. Lenhart, *WADC Tech. Rept.* 55–114, June, 1955.

It should now be apparent why the same relationship does not hold for other metals. For example, for annealed copper the assumption that strain hardening can be neglected will be grossly in error. For a metal with greater capability for strain hardening the "constant" of proportionality will be greater than that used for heat-treated steel.

11-6. Vickers Hardness

The Vickers hardness test uses a square-base diamond pyramid as the indenter. The included angle between opposite faces of the pyramid is 136°. This angle was chosen because it approximates the most desirable ratio of indentation diameter to ball diameter in the Brinell hardness test. Because of the shape of the indenter this is frequently called the diamond-pyramid hardness test. The diamond-pyramid hardness number (DPH), or Vickers hardness number (VHN, or VPH), is defined as the load divided by the surface area of the indentation. In practice, this area is calculated from microscopic measurements of the lengths of the diagonals of the impression. The DPH may be determined from the following equation,

$$\text{DPH} = \frac{2P \sin (\theta/2)}{L^2} = \frac{1.854P}{L^2} \qquad (11\text{-}10)$$

where P = applied load, kg

L = average length of diagonals, mm

θ = angle between opposite faces of diamond = 136°

The Vickers hardness test has received fairly wide acceptance for research work because it provides a continuous scale of hardness, for a given load, from very soft metals with a DPH of 5 to extremely hard materials with a DPH of 1,500. With the Rockwell hardness test, described in the next section, or the Brinell hardness test, it is usually necessary to change either the load or the indenter at some point in the hardness scale, so that measurements at one extreme of the scale cannot be strictly compared with those at the other end. Because the impressions made by the pyramid indenter are geometrically similar no matter what their size, the DPH should be independent of load. This is generally found to be the case, except at very light loads. The loads ordinarily used with this test range from 1 to 120 kg, depending on the hardness of the metal to be tested. In spite of these advantages, the Vickers hardness test has not been widely accepted for routine testing because it is slow, requires careful surface preparation of the specimen, and allows greater chance for personal error in the determination of the diagonal length.

A perfect indentation made with a perfect diamond-pyramid indenter would be a square.   However, anomalies corresponding to those described earlier for Brinell impressions are frequently observed with a pyramid indenter (Fig. 11-4).   The pincushion indentation in Fig. 11-4*b* is the

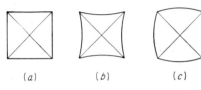

result of sinking in of the metal around the flat faces of the pyramid.   This condition is observed with annealed metals and results in an overestimate of the diagonal length.   The barrel-shaped indentation in Fig. 11-4*c* is found in cold-worked metals.   It results from ridging or piling up of the metal around the faces of the indenter.

(a)   (b)   (c)

Fig. 11-4. Types of diamond-pyramid indentations. (*a*) Perfect indentation; (*b*) pincushion indentation due to sinking in; (*c*) barreled indentation due to ridging.

The diagonal measurement in this case produces a low value of the contact area so that the hardness numbers are erroneously high.   Empirical corrections for this effect have been proposed.[1]

11-7. Rockwell Hardness Test

The most widely used hardness test in the United States is the Rockwell hardness test.   Its general acceptance is due to its speed, freedom from personal error, ability to distinguish small hardness differences in hardened steel, and the small size of the indentation, so that finished heat-treated parts can be tested without damage.   This test utilizes the depth of indentation, under constant load, as a measure of hardness.   A minor load of 10 kg is first applied to seat the specimen.   This minimizes the amount of surface preparation needed and reduces the tendency for ridging or sinking in by the indenter.   The major load is then applied, and the depth of indentation is automatically recorded on a dial gage in terms of arbitrary hardness numbers.   The dial contains 100 divisions, each division representing a penetration of 0.00008 in.   The dial is reversed so that a high hardness, which corresponds to a small penetration, results in a high hardness number.   This is in agreement with the other hardness numbers described previously, but unlike the Brinell and Vickers hardness designations, which have units of kilograms per square millimeter, the Rockwell hardness numbers are purely arbitrary.

One combination of load and indenter will not produce satisfactory results for materials with a wide range of hardness.   A 120° diamond cone with a slightly rounded point, called a *Brale indenter*, and $\frac{1}{16}$- and $\frac{1}{8}$-in.-diameter steel balls are generally used as indenters.   Major loads of 60, 100, and 150 kg are used.   Since the Rockwell hardness is dependent on the load and indenter, it is necessary to specify the combination

[1] T. B. Crowe and J. F. Hinsley, *J. Inst. Metals*, vol. 72, p. 14, 1946.

which is used. This is done by prefixing the hardness number with a letter indicating the particular combination of load and indenter for the hardness scale employed. A Rockwell hardness number without the letter prefix is meaningless. Hardened steel is tested on the C scale with the diamond indenter and a 150-kg major load. The useful range for this scale is from about R_C 20 to R_C 70. Softer materials are usually tested on the B scale with a $\frac{1}{16}$-in.-diameter steel ball and a 100-kg major load. The range of this scale is from R_B 0 to R_B 100. The A scale (diamond penetrator, 60-kg major load) provides the most extended Rockwell hardness scale, which is usable for materials from annealed brass to cemented carbides. Many other scales are available for special purposes.[1]

The Rockwell hardness test is a very useful and reproducible one provided that a number of simple precautions are observed. Most of the points listed below apply equally well to the other hardness tests:

1. The indenter and anvil should be clean and well seated.

2. The surface to be tested should be clean, dry, smooth, and free from oxide. A rough-ground surface is usually adequate for the Rockwell test.

3. The surface should be flat and perpendicular to the indenter.

4. Tests on cylindrical surfaces will give low readings, the error depending on the curvature, load, indenter, and hardness of the material. Theoretical[2] and empirical[3] corrections for this effect have been published.

5. The thickness of the specimen should be such that a mark or bulge is not produced on the reverse side of the piece. It is recommended that the thickness be at least ten times the depth of the indentation. Tests should be made on only a single thickness of material.

6. The spacing between indentations should be three to five times the diameter of the indentation.

7. The speed of application of the load should be standardized. This is done by adjusting the dashpot on the Rockwell tester. Variations in hardness can be appreciable in very soft materials unless the rate of load application is carefully controlled. For such materials the operating handle of the Rockwell tester should be brought back as soon as the major load has been fully applied.

11-8. Microhardness Tests

Many metallurgical problems require the determination of hardness over very small areas. The measurement of the hardness gradient at a carburized surface, the determination of the hardness of individual con-

---

[1] See ASTM Standard E18.

[2] W. E. Ingerson, *Proc. ASTM*, vol. 39, pp. 1281–1291, 1939.

[3] R. S. Sutton and R. H. Heyer, *ASTM Bull.* 193, pp. 40–41, October, 1953.

stituents of a microstructure, or the checking of the hardness of a delicate watch gear might be typical problems. The use of a scratch-hardness test for these purposes was mentioned earlier, but an indentation-hardness test has been found to be more useful.[1] The development of the Knoop indenter by the National Bureau of Standards and the introduction of the Tukon tester for the controlled application of loads down to 25 g have made microhardness testing a routine laboratory procedure.

The Knoop indenter is a diamond ground to a pyramidal form that produces a diamond-shaped indentation with the long and short diagonals in the approximate ratio of 7:1. The depth of indentation is about one-thirtieth of the length of the longer diagonal. The Knoop hardness number (KHN) is the applied load divided by the unrecovered projected area of the indentation.

$$\text{KHN} = \frac{P}{A_p} = \frac{P}{L^2 C} \tag{11-11}$$

where P = applied load, kg

A_p = unrecovered projected area of indentation, mm^2

L = length of long diagonal, mm

C = a constant for each indenter supplied by manufacturer

The low load used with microhardness tests requires that extreme care be taken in all stages of testing. The surface of the specimen must be carefully prepared. Metallographic polishing is usually required. Work hardening of the surface during polishing can influence the results. The long diagonal of the Knoop impression is essentially unaffected by elastic recovery for loads greater than about 300 g. However, for lighter loads the small amount of elastic recovery becomes appreciable. Further, with the very small indentations produced at light loads the error in locating the actual ends of the indentation become greater. Both these factors have the effect of giving a high hardness reading, so that it is usually observed that the Knoop hardness number increases as the load is decreased below about 300 g. Tarasov and Thibault[2] have shown that if corrections are made for elastic recovery and visual acuity the Knoop hardness number is constant with load down to 100 g.

11-9. Hardness-conversion Relationships

From a practical standpoint it is important to be able to convert the results of one type of hardness test into those of a different test. Since

[1] For a review of microhardness testing see H. Bückle, *Met. Reviews*, vol. 4, no. 3, pp. 49–100, 1959.

[2] L. P. Tarasov and N. W. Thibault, *Trans. ASM*, vol. 38, pp. 331–353, 1947.

a hardness test does not measure a well-defined property of a material and since all the tests in common use are not based on the same type of measurements, it is not surprising that no universal hardness-conversion relationships have been developed.   It is important to realize that hardness conversions are empirical relationships.   The most reliable hardness-conversion data exist for steel which is harder than 240 Brinell.   The ASTM, ASM, and SAE (Society of Automotive Engineers) have agreed on a table[1] for conversion between Rockwell, Brinell, and diamond-pyramid hardness which is applicable to heat-treated carbon and alloy steel and to almost all alloy constructional steels and tool steels in the as-forged, annealed, normalized, and quenched and tempered conditions.   However, different conversion tables are required for materials with greatly different elastic moduli, such as tungsten carbide, or with greater strain-hardening capacity.   Heyer[2] has shown that the indentation hardness of soft metals depends on the strain-hardening behavior of the material during the test, which in turn is dependent on the previous degree of strain hardening of the material before the test.   As an extreme example of the care which is required in using conversion charts for soft metals, it is possible for Armco iron and cold-rolled aluminum each to have a Brinell hardness of 66; yet the former has a Rockwell B hardness of 31 compared with a hardness of R_B 7 for the cold-worked aluminum.   On the other hand, metals such as yellow brass and low-carbon sheet steel have a well-behaved Brinell-Rockwell conversion[3] relationship for all degrees of strain hardening.   Special hardness-conversion tables for cold-worked aluminum, copper, and 18-8 stainless steel are given in the ASM Metals Handbook.

11-10. Hardness at Elevated Temperatures

Interest in measuring the hardness of metals at elevated temperatures has been accelerated by the great effort which has gone into developing alloys with improved high-temperature strength.   Hot hardness gives a good indication of the potential usefulness of an alloy for high-temperature strength applications.   Some degree of success has been obtained in correlating hot hardness with high-temperature strength properties.   This will be discussed in Chap. 13.   Hot-hardness testers using a Vickers indenter made of sapphire and with provisions for testing in either

---

[1] This table may be found in ASTM Standard E48-47, SAE Handbook, ASM Metals Handbook, and many other standard references.

[2] R. H. Heyer, *Proc. ASTM*, vol. 44, p. 1027, 1944.

[3] The Wilson Mechanical Instrument Co. Chart 38 for metals softer than BHN 240 (see ASM Handbook, 1948 ed., p. 101) is based on tests on these metals.

vacuum or an inert atmosphere have been developed,[1] and a high-temperature microhardness test has been described.[2]

In an extensive review of hardness data at different temperatures

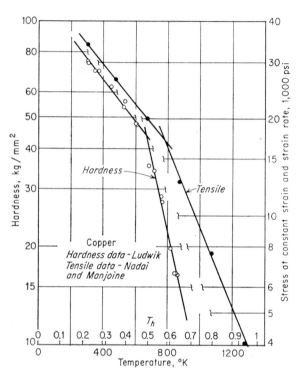

Fig. 11-5. Temperature dependence of the hardness of copper. (*J. H. Westbrook, Trans. ASM, vol. 45, p. 233, 1953.*)

Westbrook[3] showed that the temperature dependence of hardness could be expressed by

$$H = A \exp\left(-BT\right) \tag{11-12}$$

where H = hardness, kg/mm^2

T = test temperature, °K

A, B = constants

Plots of log H versus temperature for pure metals generally yield two straight lines of different slope. The change in slope occurs at a tem-

[1] F. Garofalo, P. R. Malenock, and G. V. Smith, *Trans. ASM*, vol. 45, pp. 377–396, 1953; M. Semchyshen and C. S. Torgerson, *Trans. ASM*, vol. 50, pp. 830–837, 1958.

[2] J. H. Westbrook, *Proc. ASTM*, vol. 57, pp. 873–897, 1957; *ASTM Bull.* 246, pp. 53–58, 1960.

[3] J. H. Westbrook, *Trans. ASM*, vol. 45, pp. 221–248, 1953.

perature which is about one-half the melting point of the metal being tested. Similar behavior is found in plots of the logarithm of the tensile strength against temperature. Figure 11-5 shows this behavior for copper. It is likely that this change in slope is due to a change in the deformation mechanism at higher temperature. The constant A derived from the low-temperature branch of the curve can be considered to be the intrinsic hardness of the metal, that is, H at 0°K. This value would be expected to be a measure of the inherent strength of the binding forces of the lattice. Westbrook correlated values of A for different metals with the heat content of the liquid metal at the melting point and with the melting point. This correlation was sensitive to crystal structure. The constant B, derived from the slope of the curve, is the temperature coefficient of hardness. This constant was related in a rather complex way to the rate of change of heat content with increasing temperature. With these correlations it is possible to calculate fairly well the hardness of a pure metal as a function of temperature up to about one-half its melting point.

Hardness measurements as a function of temperature will show an abrupt change at the temperature at which an allotropic transformation occurs. Hot-hardness tests on Co, Fe, Ti, U, and Zr have shown[1] that the body-centered cubic lattice is always the softer structure when it is involved in an allotropic transformation. The face-centered cubic and hexagonal close-packed lattices have approximately the same strength, while highly complex crystal structures give even higher hardness. These results are in agreement with the fact that austenitic iron-base alloys have better high-temperature strength than ferritic alloys.

BIBLIOGRAPHY

Hardness Tests, "Metals Handbook," pp. 93–105, American Society for Metals, Metals Park, Ohio, 1948.
Lysaght, V. E.: "Indentation Hardness Testing," Reinhold Publishing Corporation, New York, 1949.
Mott, B. W.: "Micro-indentation Hardness Testing," Butterworth & Co. (Publishers) Ltd., London, 1956.
Tabor, D.: "The Hardness of Metals," Oxford University Press, New York, 1951.
Symposium on the Significance of the Hardness Test of Metals in Relation to Design, *Proc. ASTM*, vol. 43, pp. 803–856, 1943.

[1] W. Chubb, *Trans. AIME*, vol. 203, pp. 189–192, 1955.

Chapter 12
FATIGUE OF METALS

12-1. Introduction

It has been recognized since 1850 that a metal subjected to a repetitive or fluctuating stress will fail at a stress much lower than that required to cause fracture on a single application of load. Failures occurring under conditions of dynamic loading are called *fatigue failures*, presumably because it is generally observed that these failures occur only after a considerable period of service. For a long time the notion persisted that fatigue was due to "crystallization" of the metal, but this view can no longer be considered in the light of concepts which hold that a metal is crystalline from the time of solidification from the melt. In fact, there is no obvious change in the structure of a metal which has failed in fatigue which can serve as a clue to our understanding of the reasons for fatigue failure. Fatigue has become progressively more prevalent as technology has developed a greater amount of equipment, such as automobiles, aircraft, compressors, pumps, turbines, etc., subject to repeated loading and vibration, until today it is often stated that fatigue accounts for at least 90 per cent of all service failures due to mechanical causes.

A fatigue failure is particularly insidious, because it occurs without any obvious warning. Fatigue results in a brittle fracture, with no gross deformation at the fracture. On a macroscopic scale the fracture surface is usually normal to the direction of the principal tensile stress. A fatigue failure can usually be recognized from the appearance of the fracture surface, which shows a smooth region, due to the rubbing action as the crack propagated through the section (top portion of Fig. 12-1), and a rough region, where the member has failed in a ductile manner when the cross section was no longer able to carry the load. Frequently the progress of the fracture is indicated by a series of rings, or "beach marks," progressing inward from the point of initiation of the failure. Figure 12-1 also illustrates another characteristic of fatigue, namely, that a failure usually occurs at a point of stress concentration such as a sharp corner or notch or at a metallurgical stress concentration like an inclusion.

Three basic factors are necessary to cause fatigue failure. These are

(1) a maximum tensile stress of sufficiently high value, (2) a large enough variation or fluctuation in the applied stress, and (3) a sufficiently large number of cycles of the applied stress.   In addition, there are a host of other variables, such as stress concentration, corrosion, temperature, overload, metallurgical structure, residual stresses, and combined stresses,

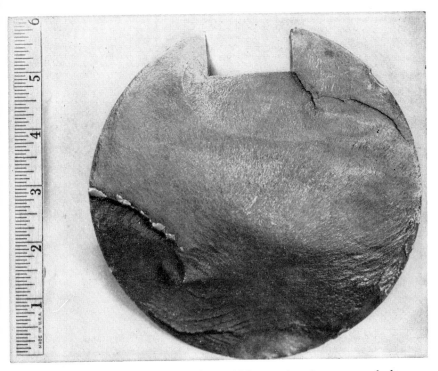

Fig. 12-1. Fracture surface of fatigue failure which started at sharp corner of a keyway in a shaft.   1×.

which tend to alter the conditions for fatigue.   Since we have not yet gained a basic understanding of what causes fatigue in metals, it will be necessary to discuss each of these factors from an essentially empirical standpoint.   Because of the mass of data of this type, it will be possible to describe only the highlights of the relationship between these factors and fatigue.   For more complete details the reader is referred to the number of excellent publications listed at the end of this chapter.

12-2. Stress Cycles

At the outset it will be advantageous to define briefly the general types of fluctuating stresses which can cause fatigue.   Figure 12-2 serves to illustrate typical fatigue stress cycles. Figure 12-2a illustrates a *completely reversed cycle of stress* of sinusoidal form. This is an idealized situation which is produced by an R. R. Moore rotating-beam fatigue machine[1] and which is approached in service by a rotating shaft operating at constant speed without overloads. For this type of stress cycle the maximum and minimum stresses are equal. In keeping with the conventions established in Chap. 2 the minimum stress is the lowest

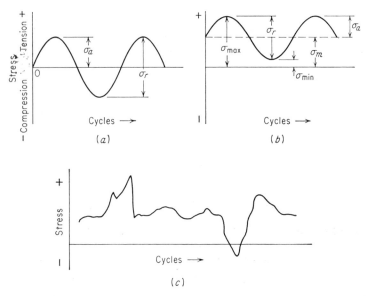

Fig. 12-2. Typical fatigue stress cycles. (*a*) Reversed stress; (*b*) repeated stress; (*c*) irregular or random stress cycle.

algebraic stress in the cycle. Tensile stress is considered positive, and compressive stress is negative. Figure 12-2b illustrates a *repeated stress cycle* in which the maximum stress σ_{max} and minimum stress σ_{min} are not equal. In this illustration they are both tension, but a repeated stress cycle could just as well contain maximum and minimum stresses of opposite signs or both in compression. Figure 12-2c illustrates a complicated stress cycle which might be encountered in a part such as an aircraft wing which is subjected to periodic unpredictable overloads due to gusts.

A fluctuating stress cycle can be considered to be made up of two components, a *mean*, or steady, stress σ_m, and an *alternating*, or variable,

---

[1] Common types of fatigue machines are described in the references listed at the end of this chapter and in the Manual on Fatigue Testing, *ASTM Spec. Tech. Publ.* 91, 1949.

stress σ_a. We must also consider the *range of stress* σ_r. As can be seen from Fig. 12-2b, the range of stress is the algebraic difference between the maximum and minimum stress in a cycle.

$$\sigma_r = \sigma_{max} - \sigma_{min} \tag{12-1}$$

The alternating stress, then, is one-half the range of stress.

$$\sigma_a = \frac{\sigma_r}{2} \tag{12-2}$$

The mean stress is the algebraic mean of the maximum and minimum stress in the cycle.

$$\sigma_m = \frac{\sigma_{max} + \sigma_{min}}{2} \tag{12-3}$$

Another quantity which is sometimes used in presenting fatigue data is the stress ratio R. Stress ratio is defined as

$$R = \frac{\sigma_{min}}{\sigma_{max}} \tag{12-4}$$

12-3. The S-N Curve

The basic method of presenting engineering fatigue data is by means of the S-N curve, which represents the dependence of the life of the specimen, in number of cycles to failure, N, on the maximum applied stress σ. Most investigations of the fatigue properties of metals have been made by means of the rotating-beam machine, where the mean stress is zero. Figure 12-3 gives typical S-N curves for this type of test. Cases

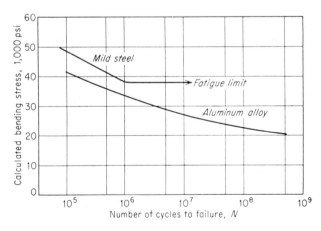

Fig. 12-3. Typical fatigue curves for ferrous and nonferrous metals.

where the mean stress is not zero are of considerable practical interest. These will be discussed later in the chapter.

As can be seen from Fig. 12-3, the number of cycles of stress which a metal can endure before failure increases with decreasing stress. Unless otherwise indicated, N is taken as the number of cycles of stress to cause complete fracture of the specimen. This is made up of the number of cycles to initiate a crack and the number of cycles to propagate the crack completely through the specimen. Usually no distinction is made between these two factors, although it can be appreciated that the number of cycles for crack propagation will vary with the dimensions of the specimen. Fatigue tests at low stresses are usually carried out for 10^7 cycles and sometimes to 5×10^8 cycles for nonferrous metals. For a few important engineering materials such as steel and titanium, the S-N curve becomes horizontal at a certain limiting stress. Below this limiting stress, which is called the *fatigue limit*, or endurance limit, the material can presumably endure an infinite number of cycles without failure. Most nonferrous metals, like aluminum, magnesium, and copper alloys, have an S-N curve which slopes gradually downward with increasing number of cycles. These materials do not have a true fatigue limit because the S-N curve never becomes horizontal. In such cases it is common practice to characterize the fatigue properties of the material by giving the fatigue strength at an arbitrary number of cycles, for example, 10^8 cycles. The reasons why certain materials have a fatigue limit are not known, although a hypothesis regarding this important question will be discussed later in the chapter.

The usual procedure for determining an S-N curve is to test the first specimen at a high stress where failure is expected in a fairly short number of cycles, e.g., at about two-thirds the static tensile strength of the material. The test stress is decreased for each succeeding specimen until one or two specimens do not fail in the specified number of cycles, which is usually at least 10^7 cycles. The highest stress at which a runout (nonfailure) is obtained is taken as the fatigue limit. For materials without a fatigue limit the test is usually terminated for practical considerations at a low stress where the life is about 10^8 or 5×10^8 cycles. The S-N curve is usually determined with about 8 to 12 specimens. It will generally be found that there is a considerable amount of scatter in the results, although a smooth curve can usually be drawn through the points without too much difficulty. However, if several specimens are tested at the same stress, there is a great amount of scatter in the observed values of number of cycles to failure, frequently as much as one log cycle between the minimum and maximum value. Further, it has been shown[1] that the fatigue limit of steel is subject to considerable variation and that a

[1] J. T. Ransom and R. F. Mehl, *Trans. AIME*, vol. 185, pp. 364–365, 1949.

fatigue limit determined in the manner just described can be considerably in error. The statistical nature of fatigue will be discussed in the next section.

An interesting test for obtaining a more rapid estimate of the fatigue limit than is possible by conventional means was proposed by Prot.[1]   In this method, each specimen is started at an initial stress below the expected value of the fatigue limit, and the stress is progressively increased at a constant rate until fracture occurs. Several specimens are tested at different values of stress increase per cycle.   Prot suggested that a linear relationship should exist between the stress at which fracture occurs and $\sqrt{\alpha}$, where α is the stress increase per cycle. The fatigue limit is obtained from this plot by extrapolation to $\sqrt{\alpha} = 0$. Prot's method has undergone considerable investigation and modification[2] and appears useful for the rapid determination of the fatigue limit of ferrous materials.

A modification of the Prot method is sometimes used when a special machine equipped to provide a continuously increasing stress is not available or when the number of specimens is not large. The initial stress level is taken at about 70 per cent of the estimated fatigue limit. The test is run for a fixed number of cycles, for example, 10^7, and if failure does not occur, the stress is raised by a certain amount. Another unit of cycles is applied at this stress, and the process is continued until failure occurs. The fatigue limit of the specimen is taken as the stress halfway between the breaking stress and the highest stress at which the specimen survived. Results obtained by this step method and the Prot method may not produce values of fatigue limit in agreement with those obtained from testing at constant stress, because of changes which can occur in the metal during testing at stresses below the fatigue limit. For example, certain metals can be strengthened by "coaxing" at stresses below the fatigue limit. This topic is discussed in greater detail in Sec. 12-13.

12-4. Statistical Nature of Fatigue

A considerable amount of interest has been shown in the statistical analysis of fatigue data and in the reasons for the variability in fatigue-test results. A more complete description of the statistical techniques will be given in Chap. 16. However, it is important here to gain an acquaintance with the concept of the statistical approach so that existing fatigue data can be properly evaluated. Since fatigue life and fatigue limit are statistical quantities, it must be realized that considerable devi-

[1] M. Prot, *Rev. mét.*, vol. 34, p. 440, 1937.

[2] H. T. Corten, T. Dimoff, and T. J. Dolan, *Proc. ASTM*, vol. 54, pp. 875–902, 1954.

ation from an average curve determined with only a few specimens is to be expected. It is necessary to think in terms of the probability of a specimen attaining a certain life at a given stress or the probability of failure at a given stress in the vicinity of the fatigue limit. To do this requires the testing of considerably more specimens than in the past so that the statistical parameters[1] for estimating these probabilities can be determined. The basic method for expressing fatigue data should then be a three-dimensional surface representing the relationship between

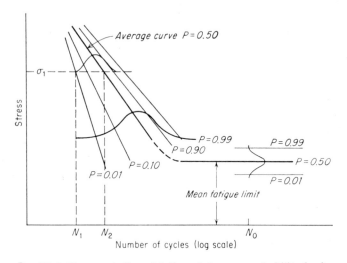

Fig. 12-4. Representation of fatigue data on a probability basis.

stress, number of cycles to failure, and probability of failure. Figure 12-4 shows how this can be presented in a two-dimensional plot.

A distribution of fatigue life at constant stress is illustrated schematically in this figure, and based on this, curves of constant probability of failure are drawn. Thus, at σ_1, 1 per cent of the specimens would be expected to fail at N_1 cycles, 50 per cent at N_2 cycles, etc. The figure indicates a decreasing scatter in fatigue life with increasing stress, which is usually found to be the case. The statistical distribution function which describes the distribution of fatigue life at constant stress is not accurately known, for this would require the testing of over 1,000 identical specimens under identical conditions at a constant stress. Muller-Stock[2] tested 200 steel specimens at a single stress and found that the

---

[1] The chief statistical parameters to be considered are the estimate of the mean (average) and standard deviation (measure of scatter) of the population.

[2] H. Muller-Stock, *Mitteilung Kohle- u. Eisenforsch. G. m. b. H.*, vol. 8, pp. 83–107, 1938.

frequency distribution of N followed the Gaussian, or normal, distribution if the fatigue life was expressed as log N. For engineering purposes it is sufficiently accurate to assume a logarithmic normal distribution of fatigue life at constant life in the region of the probability of failure of $P = 0.10$ to $P = 0.90$. However, it is frequently important to be able to predict the fatigue life corresponding to a probability of failure of 1 per cent or less. At this extreme limit of the distribution the assumption of a log-normal distribution of life is no longer justified, although it is frequently used. Alternative approaches have been the use of the extreme-value distribution[1] or Weibull's distribution.[2]

For the statistical interpretation of the fatigue limit we are concerned with the distribution of stress at a constant fatigue life. The fatigue limit of steel was formerly considered to be a sharp threshold value, below which all specimens would presumably have infinite lives. However, it is now recognized that the fatigue limit is really a statistical quantity which requires special techniques for an accurate determination. For example, in a heat-treated alloy forging steel the stress range which would include the fatigue limits of 95 per cent of the specimens could easily be from 40,000 to 52,000 psi. An example of the errors which can be introduced by ordinary testing with a few specimens is illustrated in Fig. 12-5. This figure summarizes[3] ten S-N curves determined in the conventional manner for the *same* bar of alloy steel, each curve being based on ten specimens. The specimens were as identical as it was possible to make them, and there was no excessive scatter or uncertainty as to how to draw the S-N curves. Yet, as can be seen from the figure, there is considerable difference in the measured values of the fatigue limit for the steel due to the fact that the curves were based on insufficient data.

In determining the fatigue limit of a material, it should be recognized that each specimen has its own fatigue limit, a stress above which it will fail but below which it will not fail, and that this critical stress varies from specimen to specimen for very obscure reasons. It is known that inclusions in steel have an important effect on the fatigue limit and its variability, but even vacuum-melted steel shows appreciable scatter in fatigue limit. The statistical problem of accurately determining the fatigue limit is complicated by the fact that we cannot measure the individual value of the fatigue limit for any given specimen. We can only test a specimen at a particular stress, and if the specimen fails, then the stress was somewhere above the fatigue limit of the specimen. Since the specimen cannot be retested, even if it did not fail at the test stress,

---

[1] A. M. Freudenthal and E. J. Gumbel, *J. Am. Statist. Assoc.*, vol. 49, pp. 575–597, 1954.

[2] W. Weibull, *J. Appl. Mech.*, vol. 18, no. 3, pp. 293–297, 1951.

[3] J. T. Ransom, discussion in *ASTM Spec. Tech. Publ.* 121, pp. 59–63, 1952.

we have to estimate the statistics of the fatigue limit by testing groups of specimens at several stresses to see how many fail at each stress. Thus, near the fatigue limit fatigue is a "go–no go" proposition, and all that we can do is to estimate the behavior of a universe of specimens by means of a suitable sample. The two statistical methods which are used for making a statistical estimate of the fatigue limit are called *probit analysis*

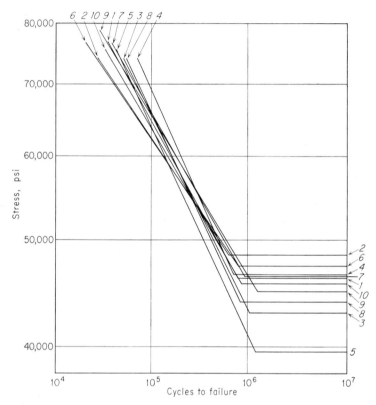

Fig. 12-5. Summary of *S-N* curves, each based on 10 specimens, drawn from the same bar of steel. (*J. T. Ransom, ASTM Spec. Tech. Publ.* 121, *p.* 61, 1952.)

and the *staircase method*. The procedures for applying these methods of analysis to the determination of the fatigue limit will be given in Chap. 16.

12-5. Structural Features of Fatigue

Only a small fraction of the effort devoted to fatigue research has been concerned with the study of the basic structural changes that occur in a metal when it is subjected to cyclic stress. Fatigue has certain things in common with plastic flow and fracture under static or unidirectional deformation. The work of Gough[1] has shown that a metal deforms under cyclic strain by slip on the same atomic planes and in the same crystallographic directions as in unidirectional strain. Whereas with unidirectional deformation slip is usually widespread throughout all the grains, in fatigue some grains will show slip lines while other grains will give no evidence of slip. Slip lines are generally formed during the first few thousand cycles of stress. Successive cycles produce additional slip bands, but the number of slip bands is not directly proportional to the number of cycles of stress. In many metals the increase in visible slip soon reaches a saturation value, which is observed as distorted regions of heavy slip. Cracks are usually found to occur in the regions of heavy deformation parallel to what was originally a slip band. Slip bands have been observed at stresses below the fatigue limit of ferrous materials. Therefore, the occurrence of slip during fatigue does not in itself mean that a crack will form.

A study of crack formation in fatigue can be facilitated by interrupting the fatigue test to remove the deformed surface by electropolishing. There will generally be several slip bands which are more persistent than the rest and which will remain visible when the other slip lines have been polished away. Such slip bands have been observed after only 5 per cent of the total life of the specimen.[2] These persistent slip bands are embryonic fatigue cracks, since they open into wide cracks on the application of small tensile strains. Once formed, fatigue cracks tend to propagate initially along slip planes, although they may later take a direction normal to the maximum applied tensile stress. Fatigue-crack propagation is ordinarily transgranular.

An important structural feature which appears to be unique to fatigue deformation is the formation on the surface of ridges and grooves called *slip-band extrusions* and *slip-band intrusions*.[3] Extremely careful metallography on tapered sections through the surface of the specimen has shown that fatigue cracks initiate at intrusions and extrusions.[4] Therefore, these structural features are the origin of the persistent slip bands, or fissures, discussed in the previous paragraph. The study of slip-band intrusions and extrusions has been undertaken too recently to uncover all the factors responsible for their formation. However, it appears that intrusions and extrusions are produced at local soft spots in the crystal, and this suggests that cross slip is needed for their formation. This

[1] H. J. Gough, *Proc. ASTM*, vol. 33, pt. 2, pp. 3–114, 1933.
[2] G. C. Smith, *Proc. Roy. Soc. (London)*, vol. 242A, pp. 189–196, 1957.
[3] P. J. E. Forsyth and C. A. Stubbington, *J. Inst. Metals*, vol. 83, p. 395, 1955–1956.
[4] W. A. Wood, Some Basic Studies of Fatigue in Metals, in "Fracture," John Wiley & Sons, Inc., New York, 1959.

hypothesis is borne out by the fact that fatigue failure is difficult to produce in certain ionic crystals which do not easily undergo cross slip and by the fact that it is not possible to produce fatigue failure in zinc crystals, which are oriented to deform only in easy glide.

In considering the structural changes produced by fatigue, it is advisable to differentiate between tests conducted at high stresses or strain amplitudes, where failure occurs in less than about 10^5 cycles of stress, and tests carried out at low stresses, where failure occurs in more than 10^6 cycles. Structural features produced in the high-stress region of the *S-N* curve bear a strong resemblance to those produced by unidirectional deformation. An annealed metal usually undergoes moderate strain hardening with increasing cycles in the high-stress region. Coarse slip bands are formed, and there is appreciable asterism in the X-ray diffraction pattern. However, in the low-stress region slip lines are very fine and are difficult to distinguish by ordinary metallographic techniques. There is essentially no strain hardening or distortion in the X-ray diffraction pattern. For copper specimens tested in the high-stress region, the stored energy is released over a fairly narrow temperature range during annealing. This represents energy release due to both recovery and recrystallization, just as would be expected for a metal plastically deformed in tension. When the copper is fatigued in the low-stress region, the stored energy is released over a wide range of temperature, as would occur if only recovery took place.[1]

A study of the dislocation structure in thin films of aluminum[2] has shown that for high fatigue stresses dislocation networks are formed similar to those formed on unidirectional loading. At low fatigue stresses the metal contains a high density of dislocation loops similar to those found in quenched specimens. This is a good indication that large numbers of point defects are produced during fatigue.

There are a number of other indications that cyclic deformation results in a higher concentration of vacancies than cold working by unidirectional deformation. The difference in the release of stored energy between fatigued and cold-worked copper is in line with what would be expected from a large concentration of point defects. The fact that initially cold-worked copper becomes softer as a result of fatigue[3] can be explained by the generation of point defects which allow the metal partly to recover by permitting dislocations to climb out of the slip plane. Age-hardening aluminum alloys in the precipitation-hardened condition can be overaged by fatigue deformation at room temperature. This sug-

[1] L. M. Clarebrough, M. E. Hargreaves, G. W. West, and A. K. Head, *Proc. Roy. Soc. (London)*, vol. 242A, pp. 160–166, 1957.

[2] R. L. Segall and P. G. Partridge, *Phil. Mag.*, vol. 4, pp. 912–919, 1959.

[3] N. H. Polakowski and A. Palchoudhuri, *Proc. ASTM*, vol. 54, p. 701, 1954.

gests that vacancies produced by fatigue are available to accomplish the diffusion required for the overaging process.[1]   Moreover, the fatigue strength increases markedly on going from 20 to −190°C, where vacancy movement is negligible.   However, the fact that fatigue fracture can be produced at 4°K indicates that a temperature-activated process such as the diffusion of vacancies is not essential for fatigue failure.[2]

The process of the formation of a fatigue crack is often divided into three stages.[3]   The primary stage occurs only in metals where the applied stress level is above the initial static yield stress.   Widespread bulk deformation occurs until the metal strain hardens to the point where it can withstand the applied stress.   Depending upon the stress, the first stage will last for 10^3 to 10^4 cycles.   The second stage comprises the major part of the fatigue life of a specimen.   It extends from the initial widespread strain hardening to the formation of a *visible* crack.   During the second stage of fatigue the crack is initiated.   The third stage of fatigue consists of the propagation of the crack to a size large enough to cause failure.

There is considerable evidence that a fatigue crack is formed before about 10 per cent of the total life of the specimen has elapsed, although the crack cannot be readily detected, except by repeated electropolishing, until many cycles later.   The principal evidence for this[4,5] is that annealing after only a small fraction of the expected total fatigue life does not significantly increase the fatigue life.   It has been concluded that the damage produced by this small number of cycles must be in the nature of a crack.

12-6. Theories of Fatigue

It is perhaps unnecessary to state that no mechanism or theory has been proposed which adequately explains the phenomenon of fatigue. For one thing, it is unlikely that our knowledge of the structural changes produced by fatigue is at all complete.   Many of the theories that exist have been qualitative and base their acceptance mainly on the fact that the analysis yields a stress–log N relationship similar to the observed *S-N* curve.   However, this may not necessarily be a satisfactory criterion, for many assumed mechanisms can lead to a prediction of the general shape of the fatigue curve.

[1] T. Broom, J. H. Molineux, and V. N. Whittaker, *J. Inst. Metals*, vol. 84, pp. 357–363, 1955–56.

[2] R. D. McCammon and H. M. Rosenberg, *Proc. Roy. Soc. (London)*, vol. 242A, p. 203, 1957.

[3] A. K. Head, *J. Mech. and Phys. Solids*, vol. 1, pp. 134–141, 1953.

[4] G. M. Sinclair and T. J. Dolan, *Proc. First Natl. Congr. Appl. Mech.*, 1951, pp. 647–651.

[5] N. Thompson, N. Wadsworth, and N. Louat, *Phil. Mag.*, vol. 1, pp. 113–126, 1956.

Orowan's Theory

Orowan's theory of fatigue[1] was one of the earliest generally accepted explanations for the fatigue process. This theory leads to the prediction of the general shape of the *S-N* curve, but it does not depend on any specific deformation mechanism other than the concept that fatigue deformation is heterogeneous. The metal is considered to contain small, weak regions, which may be areas of favorable orientation for slip or areas of high stress concentration due to metallurgical notches such as inclusions. It was assumed that these small regions could be treated as plastic regions in an elastic matrix. Orowan showed that for repeated cycles of constant stress amplitude the plastic regions will experience an increase in stress and a decrease in strain as the result of progressive localized strain hardening. He further showed that the total plastic strain (sum of positive and negative strains) converges toward a finite value as the number of cycles increases toward infinity. This limiting value of total plastic strain increases with an increase in the stress applied to the specimen. The existence of a fatigue limit hinges upon the fact that below a certain stress the total plastic strain cannot reach the critical value required for fracture. However, if the stress is such that the total plastic strain in the weak region exceeds the critical value, a crack is formed. The crack creates a stress concentration, and this forms a new localized plastic region in which the process is repeated. This process is repeated over and over until the crack becomes large enough so that fracture occurs on the application of the full tensile stress of the cycle. The essence of this theory is that localized strain hardening uses up the plasticity of the metal so that fracture takes place.

Wood's Concept of Fatigue

W. A. Wood,[2] who has made many basic contributions to the understanding of the mechanism of fatigue, has evolved a concept of fatigue failure which does not require localized strain hardening for fatigue deformation to occur. He interprets microscopic observations of slip produced by fatigue as indicating that the slip bands are the result of a systematic build-up of fine slip movements, corresponding to movements of the order of 10^{-7} cm rather than steps of 10^{-5} to 10^{-4} cm, which are observed for static slip bands. Such a mechanism is believed to allow for the accommodation of the large total strain (summation of the microstrain in each cycle) without causing appreciable strain hardening. Figure 12-6 illustrates Wood's concept of how continued deformation by fine slip might lead to a fatigue crack. The figures illustrate schematically the fine

[1] E. Orowan, *Proc. Roy. Soc. (London)*, vol. 171A, pp. 79–106, 1939.
[2] W. A. Wood, *Bull. Inst. Metals*, vol. 3, pp. 5–6, September, 1955.

structure of a slip band at magnifications obtainable with the electron microscope. Slip produced by static deformation would produce a contour at the metal surface similar to that shown in Fig. 12-6a. In contrast, the back-and-forth fine slip movements of fatigue could build up notches (Fig. 12-6b) or ridges (Fig. 12-6c) at the surface. The notch would be a stress raiser with a notch root of atomic dimensions. Such a

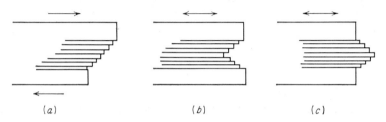

(a)   (b)   (c)

Fig. 12-6. W. A. Wood's concept of microdeformation leading to formation of fatigue crack. (a) Static deformation; (b) fatigue deformation leading to surface notch (intrusion); (c) fatigue deformation leading to slip-band extrusion.

situation might well be the start of a fatigue crack. This mechanism for the initiation of a fatigue crack is in agreement with the facts that fatigue cracks start at surfaces and that cracks have been found to initiate at slip-band intrusions and extrusions.

Dislocation Models for Fatigue

The growing awareness of the role played by subtle changes in surface topography in initiating fatigue cracks has led to several dislocation models for the generation of slip-band intrusions and extrusions. Cottrell and Hull[1] have suggested a model involving the interaction of edge dislocations on two slip systems, while Mott[2] has suggested one involving the cross slip of screw dislocations. Fatigue experiments on ionic crystals[3] tend to support the Mott mechanism and to disprove the Cottrell-Hull model.

Theory of the Fatigue Limit

One of the puzzling questions in fatigue is why certain metals exhibit an S-N curve with a well-defined fatigue limit, while other metals do not have a fatigue limit. The answer to this question appears to have been

[1] A. H. Cottrell and D. Hull, *Proc. Roy. Soc. (London)*, vol. 242A, pp. 211–213, 1957.

[2] N. F. Mott, *Acta Met.*, vol. 6, pp. 195–197, 1958; see also A. J. Kennedy, *Phil. Mag.*, ser. 8, vol. 6, pp. 49–53, 1961.

[3] A. J. McEvily, Jr., and E. S. Machlin, Critical Experiments on the Nature of Fatigue in Crystalline Materials, in "Fracture," John Wiley & Sons, Inc., New York, 1959.

given by Rally and Sinclair,[1] who noted that metals which undergo strain aging have an S-N curve with a sharp knee and a well-defined fatigue limit. Their tests with mild steel showed that as the total carbon and nitrogen content was decreased, so that the tendency for strain aging decreased, the S-N curve flattened out and the knee occurred at a larger number of cycles than if the carbon content were higher. Similar results were found by Lipsitt and Horne.[2] They proposed that the fatigue limit represents the stress at which a balance occurs between fatigue damage and localized strengthening due to strain aging. The correlation is fairly good between materials which show both strain aging and a fatigue limit. Low-carbon steel, titanium, molybdenum, and aluminum–7 per cent magnesium[3] alloy are good examples. Heat-treated steel exhibits a definite fatigue limit; yet it does not ordinarily show strain aging in the tension test. However, only very localized strain aging is required to affect fatigue properties, and it is quite likely that the fatigue test is more sensitive to strain aging than the tension test.

12-7. Effect of Stress Concentration on Fatigue

Fatigue strength is seriously reduced by the introduction of a stress raiser such as a notch or hole. Since actual machine elements invariably contain stress raisers like fillets, keyways, screw threads, press fits, and holes, it is not surprising to find that fatigue cracks in structural parts usually start at such geometrical irregularities. One of the best ways of minimizing fatigue failure is by the reduction of avoidable stress raisers through careful design[4] and the prevention of accidental stress raisers by careful machining and fabrication. While this section is concerned with stress concentrations resulting from geometrical discontinuities, stress concentration can also arise from surface roughness and metallurgical stress raisers such as porosity, inclusions, local overheating in grinding, and decarburization. These factors will be considered in other sections of this chapter.

The effect of stress raisers on fatigue is generally studied by testing specimens containing a notch, usually a V notch or a circular notch. It has been shown in Chap. 7 that the presence of a notch in a specimen

[1] F. C. Rally and G. M. Sinclair, "Influence of Strain Aging on the Shape of the S-N Diagram," Department of Theoretical and Applied Mechanics, University of Illinois, Urbana, Ill., 1955; see also J. C. Levy and S. L. Kanitkar, *J. Iron Steel Inst. (London)*, vol. 197, pp. 296–300, 1961.

[2] H. A. Lipsitt and G. T. Horne, *Proc. ASTM*, vol. 57, pp. 587–600, 1957.

[3] Broom, Molineux, and Whittaker, *op. cit.*

[4] For examples of good design practice, see J. S. Caswell, *Prod. Eng.*, January, 1947, pp. 118–119.

under uniaxial load introduces three effects: (1) there is an increase or concentration of stress at the root of the notch; (2) a stress gradient is set up from the root of the notch in toward the center of the specimen; (3) a triaxial state of stress is produced.

The ratio of the maximum stress to the nominal stress is the *theoretical stress-concentration factor* K_t. As was discussed in Sec. 2-13, values of K_t can be computed from the theory of elasticity for simple geometries and can be determined from photoelastic measurements for more complicated situations. Most of the available data on stress-concentration factors have been collected by Peterson.[1] It is often desirable to include the effect of the biaxial state of stress at the root of a notch in the value of the stress-concentration factor. The distortion-energy criterion of yielding for biaxial stress can be expressed by

$$\sigma_0 = \sigma_1(1 - C + C^2)^{1/2} \tag{12-5}$$

where $C = \sigma_3/\sigma_1$ and $\sigma_2 = 0$. If we divide both sides of Eq. (12-5) by the nominal stress, we get the expression

$$K_{t'} = K_t(1 - C + C^2)^{1/2} \tag{12-6}$$

where $K_{t'}$ is the stress concentration factor including both combined stress and stress concentration.

The effect of notches on fatigue strength is determined by comparing the S-N curves of notched and unnotched specimens. The data for notched specimens are usually plotted in terms of nominal stress based on the net section of the specimen. The effectiveness of the notch in decreasing the fatigue limit is expressed by the *fatigue-strength reduction factor*, or *fatigue-notch factor*, K_f. This factor is simply the ratio of the fatigue limit of unnotched specimens to the fatigue limit of notched specimens. For materials which do not exhibit a fatigue limit the fatigue-notch factor is based on the fatigue strength at a specified number of cycles. Values of K_f have been found to vary with (1) severity of the notch, (2) the type of notch, (3) the material, (4) the type of loading, and (5) the stress level. The values of K_f published in the literature are subject to considerable scatter and should be carefully examined for their limitations and restrictions. However, two general trends are usually observed for test conditions of completely reversed loading. First, K_f is usually less than K_t, and, second, the ratio of K_f/K_t decreases as K_t increases. Thus, very sharp notches (high K_t) have less effect on fatigue strength than would be expected from their high value of K_t. This is in agreement with observations that fatigue cracks can exist in a

[1] R. E. Peterson, "Stress-concentration Design Factors," John Wiley & Sons, Inc., New York, 1953.

specimen for millions of cycles without propagating.[1] However, this should not be interpreted as license to assume that a sharp notch or crack can be tolerated in a structure.

The notch sensitivity of a material in fatigue is usually expressed by a notch-sensitivity index q.

$$q = \frac{K_f - 1}{K_t - 1} \quad \text{or} \quad \frac{K_f - 1}{K_{t'} - 1} \tag{12-7}$$

where q = notch-sensitivity index
    K_f = notch-fatigue factor
       = fatigue limit unnotched/fatigue limit notched
    K_t = theoretical stress-concentration factor = $\sigma_{max}/\sigma_{nom}$
    $K_{t'}$ = theoretical factor which combines K_t and a biaxial stress factor

Equation (12-7) was chosen so that a material which experiences no reduction in fatigue strength due to a notch has an index of $q = 0$, while a material in which the notch has its full theoretical effect has a notch-sensitivity index of $q = 1$. However, q is not a true material constant since it varies with the severity and type of notch, the size of the specimen, and the type of loading. The notch sensitivity increases with section size and tensile strength. Thus, because of increased q it is possible under certain circumstances to decrease the fatigue performance of a member by increasing the hardness or tensile strength.

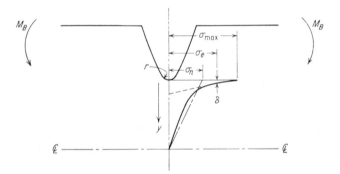

Fig. 12-7. Stress distribution at a notch in bending.

The stress gradient, or slope of the stress-distribution curve near the root of the notch, has an important influence on the notch sensitivity. Figure 12-7 illustrates the stress distribution in a notched bar in bending. The maximum stress produced by the notch is σ_{max}, and the nominal stress, neglecting the notch, is σ_n. The unnotched fatigue limit of the material is σ_e. This stress is reached at a depth δ below the root of the notch.

---

[1] N. E. Frost, *Engineer*, vol. 200, pp. 464, 501, 1955.

The stress gradient can then be written

$$\frac{d\sigma}{dy} = \frac{\sigma_{max} - \sigma_e}{\delta}$$

This expression can also be written in terms of the notch radius r.

$$\frac{d\sigma}{dy} = C_1 \frac{\sigma_{max}}{r}$$

Combining these two expressions and assuming that failure occurs when

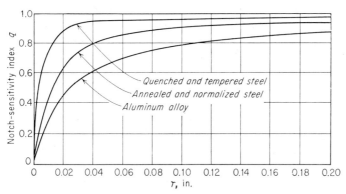

Fig. 12-8. Variation of notch-sensitivity index with notch radius for materials of different tensile strength. (*R. E. Peterson, in G. Sines and J. L. Waisman (eds.), "Metal Fatigue," p. 301, McGraw-Hill Book Company, Inc., New York, 1959.*)

the stress σ_e at the depth δ equals the fatigue strength $K_f \sigma_n$ results in

$$K_f = K_t \left(1 - \frac{C_1 \delta}{r} \right) \tag{12-8}$$

Typical values[1] of C_1 are 2.5 for bending and axial loading and 1.2 for torsion. If Eq. (12-8) is substituted into Eq. (12-7) and K_t is replaced by $K_{t'}$, we get a relationship between q and notch radius.[2]

$$q = 1 - \frac{a}{r} \tag{12-9}$$

where $a = C_1 \delta [K_{t'}/(K_{t'} - 1)]$. Figure 12-8 shows typical values of notch-sensitivity index plotted against notch radius. Note the effect of the strength of the material (see Prob. 12.1). Since the stress gradient will vary with section size in the same way as notch radius, q will also

[1] M. M. Leven, *Proc. Soc. Exptl. Stress Anal.*, vol. 13, no. 1, p. 207, 1955.

[2] R. E. Peterson, Notch-sensitivity, in G. Sines and J. L. Waisman (eds.), "Metal Fatigue," McGraw-Hill Book Company, Inc., New York, 1959.

increase with specimen diameter.   In addition, there is a measurable effect of grain size on notch-sensitivity index.   Fine grain size results in a higher q than coarse grain size.

Several hypotheses have been made to explain the variation of notch sensitivity with notch radius, section size, and grain size.   One hypothesis assumes that failure is determined by the volume of material that is stressed to within a small percentage, say, 5 per cent, of the maximum stress.   This involves a statistical argument that the probability of finding a flaw or critical crack nucleus increases with the volume of highly stressed material.   Another viewpoint is that the stress gradient across a grain is the critical factor.   For a fine grain size the stress gradient is low, and the value of q is large.   Geometrically similar notches will not produce the same stress gradient across the grains if the grain size is equal in different-diameter specimens.   The specimen with the larger diameter will have the lower stress gradient across a grain.

12-8. Size Effect

An important practical problem is the prediction of the fatigue performance of large machine members from the results of laboratory tests on small specimens.   Experience has shown that in most cases a *size effect* exists; i.e., the fatigue strength of large members is lower than that of small specimens.   A precise study of this effect is difficult for several reasons.   It is extremely difficult, if not altogether impossible, to prepare geometrically similar specimens of increasing diameter which have the same metallurgical structure and residual stress distribution throughout the cross section.   The problems in fatigue testing large-sized specimens are considerable, and there are few fatigue machines which can accommodate specimens having a wide range of cross sections.

Changing the size of a fatigue specimen usually results in a variation in two factors.   First, increasing the diameter increases the volume or surface area of the specimen.   The change in amount of surface is of significance, since fatigue failures usually start at the surface.   Second, for plain or notched specimens loaded in bending or torsion, an increase in diameter usually decreases the stress gradient across the diameter and increases the volume of material which is highly stressed.

Experimental data on the size effect in fatigue are contradictory and not very complete.   For tests in reversed bending and torsion, some investigators have found no change in fatigue limit with specimen diameter, while more commonly it is observed that the fatigue limit decreases with increasing diameter.   For mild steel the decrease in bending fatigue limit for diameters ranging from 0.1 to 2 in. does not exceed about 10 per cent. Horger's data[1] for steel shafts tested in reversed bending (Table 12-1) show that the fatigue limit can be appreciably reduced in large section sizes.

TABLE 12-1
FATIGUE LIMIT OF NORMALIZED PLAIN-CARBON STEEL
IN REVERSED BENDING

Specimen diam, in.	Fatigue limit, psi
0.30	36,000
1.50	29,000
6.00	21,000

No size effect has been found[2] for smooth plain-carbon-steel fatigue specimens with diameters ranging from 0.2 to 1.4 in. when tested in axial tension-compression loading. However, when a notch is introduced into the specimen, so that a stress gradient is produced, a definite size effect is observed. These important experiments support the idea that a size effect in fatigue is due to the existence of a stress gradient. The fact that large specimens with shallow stress gradients have lower fatigue limits is consistent with the idea that a critical value of stress must be exceeded over a certain finite depth of material for failure to occur. This appears to be a more realistic criterion of size effect than simply the ratio of the change in surface area to the change in specimen diameter. The importance of stress gradients in size effect helps explain why correlation between laboratory results and service failure is often rather poor. Actual failures in large parts are usually directly attributable to stress concentrations, either intentional or accidental, and it is usually impossible to duplicate the same stress concentration and stress gradient in a small-sized laboratory specimen.

12-9. Surface Effects and Fatigue

Practically all fatigue failures start at the surface. For many common types of loading, like bending and torsion, the maximum stress occurs at the surface so that it is logical that failure should start there. However, in axial loading the fatigue failure nearly always begins at the surface. There is ample evidence that fatigue properties are very sensitive to surface condition. The factors which affect the surface of a fatigue specimen can be divided roughly into three categories, (1) surface

[1] O. J. Horger, Fatigue Characteristics of Large Sections, in "Fatigue," American Society for Metals, Metals Park, Ohio, 1953.

[2] C. E. Phillips and R. B. Heywood, *Proc. Inst. Mech. Engrs. (London)*, vol. 165, pp. 113–124, 1951.

roughness or stress raisers at the surface, (2) changes in the fatigue strength of the surface metal, and (3) changes in the residual stress condition of the surface. In addition, the surface is subjected to oxidation and corrosion.

Surface Roughness

Since the early days of fatigue investigations, it has been recognized that different surface finishes produced by different machining procedures can appreciably affect fatigue performance. Smoothly polished specimens, in which the fine scratches (stress raisers) are oriented parallel with the direction of the principal tensile stress, give the highest values in fatigue tests. Such carefully polished specimens are usually used in

TABLE 12-2
FATIGUE LIFE OF SAE 3130 STEEL SPECIMENS TESTED UNDER
COMPLETELY REVERSED STRESS AT 95,000 PSI[†]

Type of finish	Surface roughness, μin.	Median fatigue life, cycles
Lathe-formed..............	105	24,000
Partly hand-polished........	6	91,000
Hand-polished.............	5	137,000
Ground...................	7	217,000
Ground and polished........	2	234,000
Superfinished.............	7	212,000

[†] P. G. Fluck, *Proc. ASTM*, vol. 51, pp. 584–592, 1951.

laboratory fatigue tests and are known as "par bars." Table 12-2 indicates how the fatigue life of cantilever-beam specimens varies with the type of surface preparation. Extensive data on this subject have been published by Siebel and Gaier.[1]

Changes in Surface Properties

Since fatigue failure is so dependent on the condition of the surface, anything that changes the fatigue strength of the surface material will greatly alter the fatigue properties. Decarburization of the surface of heat-treated steel is particularly detrimental to fatigue performance. Similarly, the fatigue strength of aluminum-alloy sheet is reduced when a soft aluminum coating is applied to the stronger age-hardenable aluminum-alloy sheet. Marked improvements in fatigue properties can result from the formation of harder and stronger surfaces on steel parts by

[1] E. Siebel and M. Gaier, *VDI Zt.*, vol. 98, pp. 1715–1723, 1956; abstracted in *Engineer's Digest*, vol. 18, pp. 109–112, 1957.

carburizing and nitriding.[1]   However, since favorable compressive residual stresses are produced in the surface by these processes, it cannot be
considered that the higher fatigue properties are due exclusively to the
formation of higher-strength material on the surface.   The effectiveness
of carburizing and nitriding in improving fatigue performance is greater
for cases where a high stress gradient exists, as in bending or torsion,
than in an axial fatigue test.   The greatest percentage increase in fatigue
performance is found when notched fatigue specimens are nitrided.   The
amount of strengthening depends on the diameter of the part and the
depth of surface hardening.   Improvements in fatigue properties similar
to those caused by carburizing and nitriding may also be produced by
flame hardening and induction hardening.   It is a general characteristic
of fatigue in surface-hardened parts that the failure initiates at the interface between the hard case and the softer case, rather than at the surface.

Electroplating of the surface generally decreases the fatigue limit of
steel.   Chromium plating is particularly difficult to accomplish without
impairment of fatigue properties, while a softer cadmium plating is
believed to have little effect on fatigue strength.   The particular plating
conditions used to produce an electroplated surface can have an appreciable effect on the fatigue properties, since large changes in the residual
stress, adhesion, porosity, and hardness of the plate can be produced.[2]

Surface Residual Stress

The formation of a favorable compressive residual-stress pattern at the
surface is probably the most effective method of increasing fatigue performance.   The subject of residual stress will be considered in greater
detail in Chap. 15.   However, for the present discussion, it can be considered that residual stresses are locked-in stresses which are present in
a part which is not subjected to an external force.   Only macrostresses,
which act over regions which are large compared with the grain size, are
considered here.   They can be measured by X-ray methods or by noting
the changes in dimensions when a thin layer of material is removed from
the surface.   Residual stresses arise when plastic deformation is not uniform throughout the entire cross section of the part being deformed.
Consider a metal specimen where the surface has been deformed in
tension by bending so that part of it has undergone plastic deformation.
When the external force is removed, the regions which have been plastically deformed prevent the adjacent elastic regions from undergoing complete elastic recovery to the unstrained condition.   Thus, the elastically

[1] "Fatigue Durability of Carburized Steel," American Society for Metals, Metals
Park, Ohio, 1957.
[2] A detailed review of the effect of electroplating on fatigue strength is given by
R. A. R. Hammond and C. Williams, *Met. Reviews*, vol. 5, pp. 165–223, 1960.

deformed regions are left in residual tension, and the regions which were plastically deformed must be in a state of residual compression to balance the stresses over the cross section of the specimen. In general, for a situation where part of the cross section is deformed plastically while the rest undergoes elastic deformation, the region which was plastically

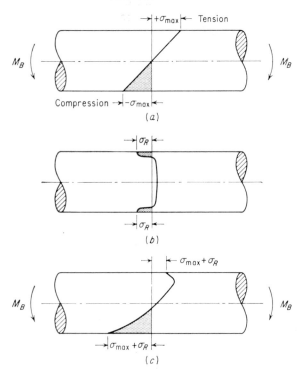

Fig. 12-9. Superposition of applied and residual stresses.

deformed in tension will have a compressive residual stress after unloading, while the region which was deformed plastically in compression will have a tensile residual stress when the external force is removed. The maximum value of residual stress which can be produced is equal to the elastic limit of the metal.

For many purposes residual stresses can be considered identical to the stresses produced by an external force. Thus, the addition of a compressive residual stress, which exists at a point on the surface, to an externally applied tensile stress on that surface decreases the likelihood of fatigue failure at that point. Figure 12-9 illustrates this effect. Figure 12-9a shows the elastic-stress distribution in a beam with no residual stress. A typical residual-stress distribution, such as would be produced by shot peening, is shown in Fig. 12-9b. Note that the high compressive residual stresses at the surface must be balanced by tensile residual stresses over the interior of the cross section. In Fig. 12-9c the stress distribution due to the algebraic summation of the external bending stresses and the residual stresses is shown. Note that the maximum tensile stress at the surface is reduced by an amount equal to the surface compressive residual stress. The peak tensile stress is displaced to a point in the interior of the specimen. The magnitude of this stress depends on the gradient of applied stress and the residual-stress distribution. Thus, subsurface initiation of failure is possible under these conditions. It should also be apparent that the improvements in fatigue performance which result from the introduction of surface compressive residual stress will be greater when the loading is one in which a stress gradient exists than when no stress gradient is present. However, some improvement in the fatigue performance of axial loaded fatigue specimens results from surface compressive residual stresses, presumably because the surface is such a potential source of weakness.

The chief commercial methods of introducing favorable compressive residual stresses in the surface are by surface rolling with contoured rollers and by shot peening. Although some changes in the strength of the metal due to strain hardening occur during these processes, it is believed that the improvement in fatigue performance is due chiefly to the formation of surface compressive residual stress. Surface rolling is particularly adapted to large parts. It is frequently used in critical regions such as the fillets of crankshafts and the bearing surface of railroad axles. Shot peening consists in projecting fine steel or cast-iron shot against the surface at high velocity. It is particularly adapted to mass-produced parts of fairly small size. The severity of the stress produced by shot peening is frequently controlled by measuring the residual deformation of shot-peened beams called Almen strips. The principal variables in this process are the shot velocity and the size, shape, and hardness of the shot. Care must be taken to ensure uniform coverage over the area to be treated. Frequently an additional improvement in fatigue properties can be obtained by carefully polishing the shot-peened surface to reduce the surface roughness. Other methods of introducing surface compressive residual stresses are by means of thermal stresses produced by quenching steel from the tempering temperature and from stresses arising from the volume changes accompanying the metallurgical changes resulting from carburizing, nitriding, and induction hardening.

It is important to recognize that improvements in fatigue properties do not automatically result from the use of shot peening or surface rolling. It is possible to damage the surface by excessive peening or rolling. Experience and testing are required to establish the proper conditions which produce the optimum residual-stress distribution.   Further, certain metallurgical processes yield surface tensile residual stresses.   Thus, surface tensile stresses are produced by quenching deep-hardening steel, and this stress pattern may persist at low tempering temperatures. Grinding of hardened steel requires particular care to prevent a large decrease in fatigue properties.   It has been shown[1] that either tensile or compressive surface residual stresses can be produced, depending upon the grinding conditions.   Further, the polishing methods ordinarily used for preparing fatigue specimens can result in appreciable surface residual stress.   It is quite likely that lack of control of this factor in specimen preparation is responsible for much of the scatter in fatigue-test results.

It is important to realize that residual-stress patterns may be modified by plastic deformation or by thermal activation.   Thus, it is possible for periods of overload or periods of increased temperature to result in some relief of residual stress.   The data on "fading" of residual stress are very meager and not too reliable.   In general, while the possibility of fading of residual stress during service should be recognized, it does not prohibit the use of compressive residual stress as the most effective method of combating fatigue failure.

12-10. Corrosion Fatigue

The simultaneous action of cyclic stress and chemical attack is known as corrosion fatigue.[2]   Corrosive attack without superimposed stress often produces pitting of metal surfaces.   The pits act as notches and produce a reduction in fatigue strength.   However, when corrosive attack occurs simultaneously with fatigue loading, a very pronounced reduction in fatigue properties results which is greater than that produced by prior corrosion of the surface.   When corrosion and fatigue occur simultaneously, the chemical attack greatly accelerates the rate at which fatigue cracks propagate.   Materials which show a definite fatigue limit when tested in air at room temperature show no indication of a fatigue limit when the test is carried out in a corrosive environment.   While ordinary fatigue tests in air are not affected by the speed of testing, over a range from about 1,000 to 12,000 cycles/min, when tests are made in a corrosive environment there is a definite dependence on testing speed.   Since corrosive attack is a time-dependent phenomenon, the higher the testing speed, the smaller the damage due to corrosion.   Corrosion-fatigue tests may be carried out in two ways.   In the usual method the specimen is

---

[1] L. P. Tarasov, W. S. Hyler, and H. R. Letner, *Proc. ASTM*, vol. 57, pp. 601–622, 1957.

[2] An extensive review of the literature on this subject has been prepared by P. T. Gilbert, *Met. Reviews*, vol. 1, pp. 379–417, 1956.

continuously subjected to the combined influences of corrosion and cyclic stress until failure occurs. In the two-stage test the corrosion fatigue test is interrupted after a certain period and the damage which was produced is evaluated by determining the remaining life in air. Tests of the last type have helped to establish the mechanism of corrosion fatigue.[1] The action of the cyclic stress causes localized disruption of the surface oxide film so that corrosion pits can be produced. Many more small pits occur in corrosion fatigue than in corrosive attack in the absence of stress. The cyclic stress will also tend to remove or dislodge any corrosion products which might otherwise stifle the corrosion. The bottoms of the pits are more anodic than the rest of the metal so that corrosion proceeds inward, aided by the disruption of the oxide film by cyclic strain. Cracking will occur when the pit becomes sharp enough to produce a high stress concentration.

There is evidence to indicate that even fatigue tests in air at room temperature are influenced by corrosion fatigue. Fatigue tests on copper showed that the fatigue strength was higher in a partial vacuum than in air.[2] Separate tests in oxygen and water vapor showed little decrease over the fatigue strength in vacuum. It was concluded that water vapor acts as a catalyst to reduce the fatigue strength in air, indicating that the relative humidity may be a variable to consider in fatigue testing. Subsequent work with copper[3] showed that the fatigue life was much longer in oxygen-free nitrogen than in air. Metallographic observation showed that the development of persistent slip bands was slowed down when tests were made in nitrogen.

A number of methods are available for minimizing corrosion-fatigue damage. In general, the choice of a material for this type of service should be based on its corrosion-resistant properties rather than the conventional fatigue properties. Thus, stainless steel, bronze, or beryllium copper would probably give better service than heat-treated steel. Protection of the metal from contact with the corrosive environment by metallic or nonmetallic coatings is successful provided that the coating does not become ruptured from the cyclic strain. Zinc and cadmium coatings on steel and aluminum coatings on Alclad aluminum alloys are successful for many corrosion-fatigue applications, even though these coatings may cause a reduction in fatigue strength when tests are conducted in air. The formation of surface compressive residual stresses tends to keep surface notches from opening up and giving ready access to the corrosive medium. Nitriding is particularly effective in combating corrosion fatigue, and shot peening has been used with success under cer-

---

[1] U. R. Evans and M. T. Simnad, *Proc. Roy. Soc. (London)*, vol. 188A, p. 372, 1947.

[2] H. J. Gough and D. G. Sopwith, *J. Inst. Metals*, vol. 72, pp. 415–421, 1946.

[3] N. Thompson, N. Wadsworth, and N. Louat, *Phil. Mag.*, vol. 1, pp. 113–126, 1956.

tain conditions.   In closed systems it is possible to reduce the corrosive attack by the addition of a corrosion inhibitor.   Finally, the elimination of stress concentrators by careful design is very important when corrosion fatigue must be considered.

Fretting

Fretting is the surface damage which results when two surfaces in contact experience slight periodic relative motion.   The phenomenon is more related to wear than to corrosion fatigue.   However, it differs from wear by the facts that the relative velocity of the two surfaces is much lower than is usually encountered in wear and that since the two surfaces are never brought out of contact there is no chance for the corrosion products to be removed.   Fretting is frequently found on the surface of a shaft with a press-fitted hub or bearing.   Surface pitting and deterioration occur, usually accompanied by an oxide debris (reddish for steel and black for aluminum).   Fatigue cracks often start in the damaged area, although they may be obscured from observation by the surface debris. Fretting is caused by a combination of mechanical and chemical effects. Metal is removed from the surface either by a grinding action or by the alternate welding and tearing away of the high spots.   The removed particles become oxidized and form an abrasive powder which continues the destructive process.   Oxidation of the metal surface occurs and the oxide film is destroyed by the relative motion of the surfaces.   Although oxidation is not essential to fretting, as is demonstrated by relative motion between two nonoxidizing gold surfaces, when conditions are such that oxidation can occur fretting damage is many times more severe.

There are no completely satisfactory methods of preventing fretting. If all relative motion is prevented, then fretting will not occur.   Increasing the force normal to the surfaces may accomplish this, but the damage increases with the normal force up to the point where relative motion is stopped.   If relative motion cannot be completely eliminated, then reduction of the coefficient of friction between the mating parts may be beneficial.   Solid lubricants such as MoS are most successful, since the chief problem is maintaining a lubricating film for a long period of time. Increasing the wear resistance of the surfaces so as to reduce surface welding is another approach.   Exclusion of the atmosphere from the two surfaces will reduce fretting, but this is frequently difficult to do with a high degree of effectiveness.   Several excellent reviews of this subject have been published.[1,2]

---

[1] R. B. Waterhouse, *Proc. Inst. Mech. Engrs.* (*London*), vol. 169, pp. 1157–1172, 1955.

[2] P. L. Teed, *Met. Reviews*, vol. 5, pp. 267–295, 1960.

12-11. Effect of Mean Stress on Fatigue

Most of the fatigue data in the literature have been determined for conditions of completely reversed cycles of stress, $\sigma_m = 0$. However, conditions are frequently met in engineering practice where the stress situation consists of an alternating stress and a superimposed mean, or steady, stress. The possibility of this stress situation has already been considered in Sec. 12-2, where various relationships between σ_m and σ_a have been given.

There are several possible methods of determining an S-N diagram for a situation where the mean stress is not equal to zero. Figure 12-10 shows the two most common methods of presenting the data. In Fig. 12-10a the maximum stress is plotted against log N for constant values of the stress ratio $R = \sigma_{min}/\sigma_{max}$. This is achieved by applying a series of stress cycles with decreasing maximum stress and adjusting the minimum stress in each case so that it is a constant fraction of the maximum stress. The case of completely reversed stress is given at $R = -1.0$. Note that as R becomes more positive, which is equivalent to increasing the mean stress, the measured fatigue limit becomes greater. Figure 12-10b shows the same data plotted in terms of the alternating stress vs. cycles to failure at constant values of mean stress. Note that as the

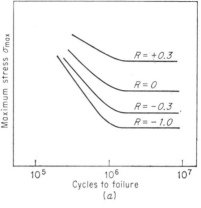

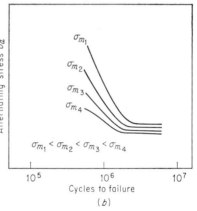

Fig. 12-10. Two methods of plotting fatigue data when the mean stress is not zero.

mean stress becomes more positive the allowable alternating stress decreases. Other ways of plotting these data are maximum stress vs. cycles to failure at constant mean stress and maximum stress vs. cycles to failure at constant minimum stress.

For each value of mean stress there is a different value of the limiting range of stress, $\sigma_{max} - \sigma_{min}$, which can be withstood without failure.

Early contributions to this problem were made by Goodman,[1] so that curves which show the dependence of limiting range of stress on mean stress are frequently called *Goodman diagrams*. Figure 12-11 shows one common type of Goodman diagram which can be constructed from fatigue data of the type illustrated in Fig. 12-10. Basically, this diagram shows the variation of the limiting range of stress, $\sigma_{max} - \sigma_{min}$ with mean stress. Note that as the mean stress becomes more tensile the allowable range of stress is reduced, until at the tensile strength σ_u the stress range is zero.

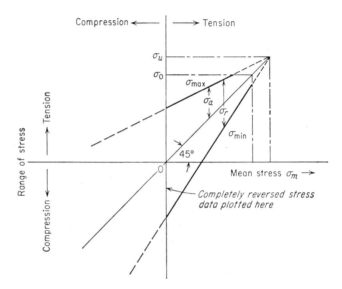

Fig. 12-11. Goodman diagram.

However, for practical purposes testing is usually stopped when the yield stress σ_0 is exceeded. The test data usually lie somewhat above and below the σ_{max} and σ_{min} lines, respectively, so that these lines shown on Fig. 12-11 may actually be curves. A conservative approximation of the Goodman diagram may be obtained, in lieu of actual test data, by drawing straight lines from the fatigue limit for completely reversed stress (which is usually available from the literature) to the tensile strength. A diagram similar to Fig. 12-11 may be constructed for the fatigue strength at any given number of cycles. Very few test data exist for conditions where the mean stress is compressive. Data[2] for SAE 4340 steel tested in axial fatigue indicate that the allowable stress range increases with increasing compressive mean stress up to the yield stress

[1] John Goodman, "Mechanics Applied to Engineering," 9th ed., Longmans, Green & Co., Inc., New York, 1930.

[2] J. T. Ransom, discussion in *Proc. ASTM*, vol. 54, pp. 847–848, 1954.

in compression. This is in agreement with the fact that compressive residual stress increases the fatigue limit.

An alternative method of presenting mean-stress data is shown in Fig. 12-12. This is sometimes known as the Haig-Soderberg diagram.[1] The alternating stress is plotted against the mean stress. A straight-line relationship follows the suggestion of Goodman, while the parabolic curve was proposed by Gerber. Test data for ductile metals generally fall closer to the parabolic curve. However, because of the scatter in the results and the fact that tests on notched specimens fall closer to the

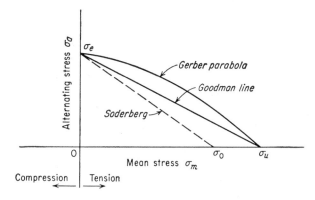

Fig. 12-12. Alternative method of plotting the Goodman diagram.

Goodman line, the linear relationship is usually preferred in engineering design. These relationships may be expressed by the following equation,

$$\sigma_a = \sigma_e \left[1 - \left(\frac{\sigma_m}{\sigma_u} \right)^x \right] \qquad (12\text{-}10)$$

where $x = 1$ for the Goodman line, $x = 2$ for the Gerber parabola, and σ_e is the fatigue limit for completely reversed loading. If the design is based on the yield strength, as indicated by the dashed Soderberg line in Fig. 12-12, then σ_0 should be substituted for σ_u in Eq. (12-10).

Figure 12-12 is obtained for alternating axial or bending stresses with static tension or compression or alternating torsion with static tension. However, for alternating torsion with static torsion or alternating bending with static torsion there is no effect of the static stress on the allowable range of alternating stress provided that the static yield strength is not exceeded. Sines[2] has shown that these results can be rationalized

[1] C. R. Soderberg, *Trans. ASME*, vol. 52, APM-52-2, 1930.

[2] G. Sines, Failure of Materials under Combined Repeated Stresses with Superimposed Static Stresses, *NACA Tech. Note* 3495, 1955.

in the following manner: The planes of maximum alternating shear stress are determined, and the static normal stresses S_1 and S_2 on these planes are established. When $S_1 + S_2$ is positive, an increase in static stress reduces the permissible value of σ_a. When $S_1 + S_2$ is negative, the permissible value of σ_a is increased. Finally, when $S_1 + S_2$ is zero, the static stress has no effect on σ_a regardless of the applied static stress.

12-12. Fatigue under Combined Stresses

Many machine parts must withstand complex loadings with both alternating and steady components of stress. Ideally, it should be possible to predict the fatigue performance of a combined stress system by substituting the fatigue strength for simple types of loading into the equation of the failure criterion, just as the yield stress in tension can be used with the distortion-energy criterion of failure to predict static yielding under a complex state of stress. Although the data on combined-stress fatigue failure are fewer and less reliable than for static yielding, certain generalizations can be made. Fatigue tests with different combinations of bending and torsion[1] show that for ductile metals the distortion-energy criterion provides the best over-all fit. For brittle materials a maximum principal stress theory provides the best criterion of failure.

Sines[2] has suggested a failure criterion that accounts for the effect of combined stresses and the influence of a static mean stress.

$$\frac{1}{\sqrt{2}}[(\sigma_1 - \sigma_2)^2 + (\sigma_2 - \sigma_3)^2 + (\sigma_3 - \sigma_1)^2]^{1/2} = \sigma_e - C_2(S_x + S_y + S_z)$$

$$(12\text{-}11)$$

where $\sigma_1, \sigma_2, \sigma_3$ = alternating principal stresses

S_x, S_y, S_z = static stresses

σ_e = fatigue strength for completely reversed stress

C_2 = a material constant giving variation of σ_a versus σ_m; i.e., it is the slope of the Goodman line in Fig. 12-12

Fatigue failure will occur if the left side of Eq. (12-11) is greater than the right side. The constants σ_e and C_2 can be evaluated at any value of cycles to failure. The effect of residual stresses can be introduced by adding these terms to the static stresses on the right side of the equation. Thus, Eq. (12-11) shows that compressive residual stress will allow a greater alternating stress for the same fatigue life.

[1] H. J. Gough, *Proc. Inst. Mech. Engrs.* (*London*), vol. 160, pp. 417–440, 1949; W. N. Findley and P. N. Mathur, *Proc. Soc. Exptl. Stress Anal.*, vol. 14, no. 1, pp. 35–46, 1956.

[2] Sines, *op. cit.*

12-13. Overstressing and Understressing

The conventional fatigue test subjects a specimen to a fixed stress amplitude until the specimen fails. Tests may be made at a number of different values of stress to determine the *S-N* curve, but each time the maximum stress is held constant until the test is completed. However, there are many practical applications where the cyclic stress does not remain constant, but instead there are periods when the stress is either above or below some average design stress level. Further, in other applications complex loading conditions, such as are illustrated in Fig. 12-2c, are encountered. For these conditions it is difficult to arrive at an average stress level, and the loading cannot be assumed to vary sinusoidally. Special fatigue tests which apply a random load have been developed for these cases.[1]

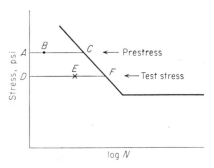

Overstressing is the process of testing a virgin specimen for some number of cycles less than that required for failure, at a stress above the fatigue limit, and then subsequently running the specimen to failure at another stress.

Fig. 12-13. Test procedure for determining fatigue damage produced by overstressing.

The initial stress to which the specimen is subjected is called the prestress, while the final stress is the test stress. The ratio of the number of cycles of overstress at the prestress to the mean virgin fatigue life at this same stress is called the *cycle ratio*. The damage produced by a given cycle ratio of overstress is frequently evaluated by the reduction in fatigue life at the test stress. Thus, referring to Fig. 12-13, for a cycle ratio at the prestress of AB/AC the damage at the test stress is EF/DF. EF represents the amount which the virgin fatigue life at the test stress has been reduced by the overstress. Extensive experience[2] with this type of test has shown that a high prestress followed by a lower test stress causes a higher percentage of damage at the test stress than the reduction in life used up by the cycle ratio. On the other hand, for a given cycle ratio at a prestress lower than the test stress, the reduction in life at the test stress will usually be a lower percentage than the cycle ratio. The higher the value of the test stress, for a constant difference between prestress and test stress, the more nearly the damage at the test stress equals the cycle ratio at the prestress.

[1] A. K. Head, *Proc. Inter. Conf. Fatigue of Metals*, London, 1956, pp. 301–303.

[2] J. B. Kommers, *Proc. ASTM*, vol. 45, pp. 532–541, 1945.

Another way of measuring the damage due to overstressing is to subject a number of specimens to a certain cycle ratio at the prestress and then determine the fatigue limit of the damaged specimens. Bennett[1] has shown that increasing the cycle ratio at the prestress produces a greater decrease in the fatigue limit of damaged specimens, while similar experiments[2] which employed a statistical determination of the fatigue limit showed a much greater reduction in the fatigue limit due to the overstressing. In line with this point, it is important to note that, because of the statistical nature of fatigue, it is very difficult to reach reliable conclusions by overstressing tests, unless statistical methods are used.

If a specimen is tested below the fatigue limit, so that it remains unbroken after a long number of cycles, and if then it is tested at a higher stress, the specimen is said to have been *understressed*. Understressing frequently results in either an increase in the fatigue limit or an increase in the number of cycles of stress to fracture over what would be expected for virgin specimens. It has frequently been considered that the improvements in fatigue properties due to understressing are due to localized strain hardening at sites of possible crack initiation. A different interpretation of the understressing effect has resulted from experiments on the statistical determination of the fatigue limit.[3] Specimens which did not fail during the determination of the fatigue limit showed greater than normal fatigue lives when retested at a higher stress. By means of statistical analysis it was possible to show that the observed lives at the higher stress were to be expected owing to the elimination of the weaker specimens during the prior testing below the fatigue limit. Thus, it was concluded that understressing was at least partly due to a statistical selectivity effect.

If a specimen is tested without failure for a large number of cycles below the fatigue limit and the stress is increased in small increments after allowing a large number of cycles to occur at each stress level, it is found that the resulting fatigue limit may be as much as 50 per cent greater than the initial fatigue limit. This procedure is known as *coaxing*. An extensive investigation of coaxing[4] showed a direct correlation between a strong coaxing effect and the ability for the material to undergo strain aging. Thus, mild steel and ingot iron show a strong coaxing effect, while brass, aluminum alloys, and heat-treated low-alloy steels show little improvement in properties from coaxing.

[1] J. A. Bennett, *Proc. ASTM*, vol. 46, pp. 693–714, 1946.
[2] G. E. Dieter, G. T. Horne, and R. F. Mehl, *NACA Tech. Note* 3211, 1954.
[3] E. Epremian and R. F. Mehl, *ASTM Spec. Tech. Publ.* 137, 1952.
[4] G. M. Sinclair, *Proc. ASTM*, vol. 52, pp. 743–758, 1952.

12-14. Effect of Metallurgical Variables on Fatigue Properties

The fatigue properties of metals appear to be quite structure-sensitive. However, at the present time there are only a limited number of ways in which the fatigue properties can be improved by metallurgical means. By far the greatest improvements in fatigue performance result from design changes which reduce stress concentrations and from the intelligent use of beneficial compressive residual stress, rather than from a change in material. Nevertheless, there are certain metallurgical factors which must be considered to ensure the best fatigue performance from a particular metal or alloy. Fatigue tests designed to measure the effect of some metallurgical variable, such as special heat treatments, on fatigue performance are usually made with smooth, polished specimens under completely reversed stress conditions. It is usually assumed that any changes in fatigue properties due to metallurgical factors will also occur to about the same extent under more complex fatigue conditions, as with notched specimens under combined stresses. That this is not always the case is shown by the notch-sensitivity results discussed previously.

Fatigue properties are frequently correlated with tensile properties. In general, the fatigue limit of cast and wrought steels is approximately 50 per cent of the ultimate tensile strength. The ratio of the fatigue limit (or the fatigue strength at 10^8 cycles) to the tensile strength is called the *fatigue ratio*. Several nonferrous metals such as nickel, copper, and magnesium have a fatigue ratio of about 0.35. While the use of correlations of this type is convenient, it should be clearly understood that these constant factors between fatigue limit and tensile strength are only approximations and hold only for the restricted condition of smooth, polished specimens which have been tested under zero mean stress at room temperature. For notched fatigue specimens the fatigue ratio for steel will be around 0.20 to 0.30.

Several parallels can be drawn between the effect of certain metallurgical variables on fatigue properties and the effect of these same variables on tensile properties. The effect of solid-solution alloying additions on the fatigue properties of iron[1] and aluminum[2] parallels nearly exactly their effect on the tensile properties. The fatigue strength of nonferrous metals[3] and annealed steel increases with decreasing grain size. Grain size does not have an important influence on the unnotched fatigue

---

[1] E. Epremian and E. F. Nippes, *Trans. ASM*, vol. 40, pp. 870–896, 1948.

[2] J. W. Riches, O. D. Sherby, and J. E. Dorn, *Trans. ASM*, vol. 44, pp. 882–895, 1952.

[3] G. M. Sinclair and W. J. Craig, *Trans. ASM*, vol. 44, pp. 929–948, 1952.

properties of heat-treated steels. Gensamer[1] showed that the fatigue
limit of a eutectoid steel increased with decreasing isothermal-reaction
temperature in the same fashion as did the yield strength and the tensile
strength. However, the greater structure sensitivity of fatigue properties, compared with tensile properties, is shown in tests comparing the
fatigue limit of a plain-carbon eutectoid steel heat-treated to coarse
pearlite and to spheroidite of the same tensile strength.[2] Even though
the steel in the two structural conditions had the same tensile strength,
the pearlitic structure resulted in a significantly lower fatigue limit due to
the higher notch effects of the carbide lamellae in pearlite.

In general, quenched and tempered microstructures result in the optimum fatigue properties in heat-treated low-alloy steels. However, at a
hardness level above about R_C 40 a bainitic structure produced by
austempering results in better fatigue properties than a quenched and
tempered structure with the same hardness.[3] Electron micrographs indicate that the poor performance of the quenched and tempered structure

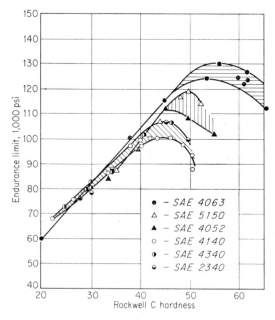

Fig. 12-14. Fatigue limit of alloy steels as a function of Rockwell hardness.   (*M. F.
Garwood, H. H. Zurburg, and M. A. Erickson, in "Interpretation of Tests and Correlation with Service," p. 12, American Society for Metals Metals Park, Ohio, 1951.*)

[1] M. Gensamer, E. B. Pearsall, W. S. Pellini, and J. R. Low, Jr., *Trans. ASM*,
vol. 30, pp. 983–1020, 1942.

[2] G. E. Dieter, R. F. Mehl, and G. T. Horne, *Trans. ASM*, vol. 47, pp. 423–439,
1955.

[3] F. Borik and R. D. Chapman, *Trans. ASM*, vol. 53, 1961.

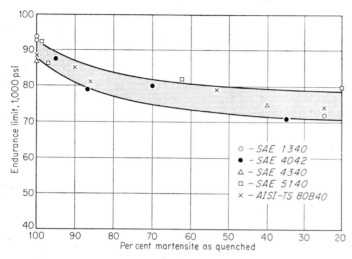

Fig. 12-15. Fatigue limit of heat-treated steel as a function of per cent martensite in as-quenched steel. (*F. Borik, R. D. Chapman, and W. E. Jominy, Trans. ASM, vol. 50, p. 250, 1958.*)

is the result of the stress-concentration effects of the thin carbide films that are formed during the tempering of martensite. For quenched and tempered steels the fatigue limit increases with decreasing tempering temperature up to a hardness of R_c 45 to R_c 55, depending on the steel.[1] Figure 12-14 shows the results obtained for completely reversed stress tests on smooth specimens. The fatigue properties at high hardness levels are extremely sensitive to surface preparation, residual stresses, and inclusions. The presence of only a trace of decarburization on the surface may drastically reduce the fatigue properties. As is shown by Fig. 12-15, only a small amount of nonmartensitic transformation products can cause an appreciable reduction in the fatigue limit.[2] The effects of slack quenching would be expected to be greater at higher hardness levels. The influence of small amounts of retained austenite on the fatigue properties of quenched and tempered steels has not been well established.

The results, which are summarized in Fig. 12-14, indicate that below a tensile strength of about 200,000 psi the fatigue limits of quenched and tempered low-alloy steels of different chemical composition are about equivalent when the steels are tempered to the same tensile strength. This generalization holds for steels made by the open-hearth or electric-furnace processes and for fatigue properties determined in the longitudinal

[1] M. F. Garwood, H. H. Zurburg, and M. A. Erickson, "Interpretation of Tests and Correlation with Service," American Society for Metals, Metals Park, Ohio, 1951.

[2] F. Borik, R. D. Chapman, and W. E. Jominy, *Trans. ASM*, vol. 50, pp. 242–257, 1958.

direction of wrought products. However, tests have shown[1] that the fatigue limit in the transverse direction of steel forgings may be only 60 to 70 per cent of the longitudinal fatigue limit. It has been established[2] that practically all the fatigue failures in transverse specimens start at nonmetallic inclusions. Nearly complete elimination of inclusions by vacuum melting produces a considerable increase in the transverse fatigue limit (Table 12-3). The low transverse fatigue limit in

TABLE 12-3
INFLUENCE OF INCLUSIONS ON FATIGUE LIMIT OF SAE 4340 STEEL†

	Electric-furnace-melted	Vacuum-melted
Longitudinal fatigue limit, psi......	116,000	139,000
Transverse fatigue limit, psi.......	79,000	120,000
Ratio transverse/longitudinal......	0.68	0.86
Hardness, R_C.................	27	29

† Determined in repeated-bending fatigue test ($R = 0$). Data from J. T. Ransom, *Trans. ASM*, vol. 46, pp. 1254–1269, 1954.

steels containing inclusions is generally attributed to stress concentration at the inclusions, which can be quite high when an elongated inclusion stringer is oriented transverse to the principal tensile stress. However, the fact that nearly complete elimination of inclusions by vacuum melting still results in appreciable anisotropy of the fatigue limit indicates that other factors may be important. Further investigations[3] of this subject have shown that appreciable changes in the transverse fatigue limit which cannot be correlated with changes in the type, number, or size of inclusions are produced by different deoxidation practices. Transverse fatigue properties appear to be one of the most structure-sensitive engineering properties.

12-15. Effect of Temperature on Fatigue

Low-temperature Fatigue

Fatigue tests on metals at temperatures below room temperature show that the fatigue strength increases with decreasing temperature. Although steels become more notch-sensitive in fatigue at low temperatures, there is no evidence to indicate any sudden change in fatigue properties at temperatures below the ductile-to-brittle transition temper-

[1] J. T. Ransom and R. F. Mehl, *Proc. ASTM*, vol. 52, pp. 779–790, 1952.
[2] J. T. Ransom, *Trans. ASM*, vol. 46, pp. 1254–1269, 1954.
[3] G. E. Dieter, D. L. Macleary, and J. T. Ransom, Factors Affecting Ductility and Fatigue in Forgings, "Metallurgical Society Conferences," vol. 3, pp. 101–142, Interscience Publishers, Inc., New York, 1959.

ature. The fact that fatigue strength exhibits a proportionately greater
increase than tensile strength with decreasing temperature has been interpreted as an indication that fatigue failure at room temperature is associated with vacancy formation and condensation.

High-temperature Fatigue

In general, the fatigue strength of metals decreases with increasing
temperature above room temperature. An exception is mild steel, which
shows a maximum in fatigue strength at 400 to 600°F. The existence of
a maximum in the tensile strength in this temperature range due to strain
aging has been discussed previously. As the temperature is increased
well above room temperature, creep will become important and at high
temperatures (roughly at temperatures greater than half the melting
point) it will be the principal cause of failure. The transition from
fatigue failure to creep failure with increasing temperature will result in
a change in the type of failure from the usual transcrystalline fatigue
failure to the intercrystalline creep failure. At any given temperature
the amount of creep will increase with increasing mean stress.

Ferrous materials, which ordinarily exhibit a sharp fatigue limit in
room-temperature tests, will no longer have a fatigue limit when tested
at temperatures above approximately 800°F. Also, fatigue tests at high
temperature will be dependent on the frequency of stress application.
It is customary to report the total time to failure as well as the number
of cycles to failure.

In general, the higher the creep strength of a material, the higher its
high-temperature fatigue strength. However, the metallurgical treatment which produces the best high-temperature fatigue properties does
not necessarily result in the best creep or stress-rupture properties. This
has been shown by Toolin and Mochel[1] in high-temperature tests of a
number of superalloys. Fine grain size results in better fatigue properties at lower temperatures. As the test temperature is increased, the
difference in fatigue properties between coarse and fine grain material
decreases until at high temperatures, where creep predominates, coarse
grain material has higher strength. In general, wrought alloys show
somewhat superior fatigue resistance, while castings are often more
resistant to creep. Procedures which are successful in reducing fatigue
failures at room temperature may not be effective in high-temperature
fatigue. For example, compressive residual stresses may be annealed out
before the operating temperature is reached.

Thermal Fatigue

The stresses which produce fatigue failure at high temperature do not
necessarily need to come from mechanical sources. Fatigue failure can

[1] P. R. Toolin and N. L. Mochel, *Proc. ASTM*, vol. 47, pp. 677–694, 1947.

be produced by fluctuating thermal stresses under conditions where no stresses are produced by mechanical causes. Thermal stresses result when the change in dimensions of a member as the result of a temperature change is prevented by some kind of constraint. For the simple case of a bar with fixed end supports, the thermal stress developed by a temperature change ΔT is

$$\sigma = \alpha E \, \Delta T \tag{12-12}$$

where α = linear thermal coefficient of expansion
E = elastic modulus
If failure occurs by one application of thermal stress, the condition is called *thermal shock*. However, if failure occurs after repeated applications of thermal stress, of a lower magnitude, it is called *thermal fatigue*.[1] Conditions for thermal-fatigue failure are frequently present in high-temperature equipment. Austenitic stainless steel is particularly sensitive to this phenomenon because of its low thermal conductivity and high thermal expansion. Extensive studies of thermal fatigue in this material have been reported.[2] The tendency for thermal-fatigue failure appears related to the parameter $\sigma_f k / E\alpha$, where σ_f is the fatigue strength at the mean temperature and k is the thermal conductivity. A high value of this parameter indicates good resistance to thermal fatigue. An excellent review of the entire subject of high-temperature fatigue has been prepared by Allen and Forrest.[3]

BIBLIOGRAPHY

Battelle Memorial Institute, "Prevention of Fatigue of Metals," John Wiley & Sons, Inc., New York, 1941. (Contains very complete bibliography up to 1941.)

Cazaud, R.: "Fatigue of Metals," translated by A. J. Fenner, Chapman & Hall, Ltd., London, 1953.

"The Fatigue of Metals," Institution of Metallurgists, London, 1955.

Freudenthal, A. M. (ed.): "Fatigue in Aircraft Structures," Academic Press, Inc., New York, 1956.

Grover, H. J., S. A. Gordon, and L. R. Jackson: "Fatigue of Metals and Structures," Government Printing Office, Washington, D.C., 1954. (Contains very complete compilation of fatigue data.)

Pope, J. A. (ed.): "Metal Fatigue," Chapman & Hall, Ltd., London, 1959.

Proceedings of the International Conference on Fatigue of Metals, London, 1956.

Sines, G., and J. L. Waisman (eds.): "Metal Fatigue," McGraw-Hill Book Company, Inc., New York, 1959.

Thompson, N., and N. J. Wadsworth: Metal Fatigue, *Advances in Phys.*, vol. 7, no. 25, pp. 72–169, January, 1958.

[1] Failure of metals like uranium which have highly anisotropic thermal-expansion coefficients under repeated heating and cooling is also called thermal fatigue.

[2] L. F. Coffin, Jr., *Trans. ASME*, vol. 76, pp. 931–950, 1954.

[3] N. P. Allen and P. G. Forrest, *Proc. Intern. Conf. Fatigue of Metals*, London, 1956, pp. 327–340.

Chapter 13

CREEP AND STRESS RUPTURE

13-1. The High-temperature Materials Problem

In several previous chapters it has been mentioned that the strength of metals decreases with increasing temperature. Since the mobility of atoms increases rapidly with temperature, it can be appreciated that diffusion-controlled processes can have a very significant effect on high-temperature mechanical properties. High temperature will also result in greater mobility of dislocations by the mechanism of climb. The equilibrium concentration of vacancies likewise increases with temperature. New deformation mechanisms may come into play at elevated temperatures. In some metals the slip system changes, or additional slip systems are introduced with increasing temperature. Deformation at grain boundaries becomes an added possibility in the high-temperature deformation of metals. Another important factor to consider is the effect of prolonged exposure at elevated temperature on the metallurgical stability of metals and alloys. For example, cold-worked metals will recrystallize and undergo grain coarsening, while age-hardening alloys may overage and lose strength as the second-phase particles coarsen. Another important consideration is the interaction of the metal with its environment at high temperature. Catastrophic oxidation and intergranular penetration of oxide must be avoided.

Thus, it should be apparent that the successful use of metals at high temperatures involves a number of problems. Greatly accelerated alloy-development programs have produced a number of materials with improved high-temperature properties, but the ever-increasing demands of modern technology require materials with even better high-temperature strength and oxidation resistance. For a long time the principal high-temperature applications were associated with steam power plants, oil refineries, and chemical plants. The operating temperature in equipment such as boilers, steam turbines, and cracking units seldom exceeded 1000°F. With the introduction of the gas-turbine engine, requirements developed for materials to operate in critically stressed parts, like turbine buckets, at temperatures around 1500°F. The design of more powerful engines has pushed this limit to around 1800°F. Rocket engines and ballistic-missile nose cones present much greater problems, which can be met only by the most ingenious use of the available high-temperature materials and the development of still better ones. There is no question that the available materials of construction limit rapid advancement in high-temperature technology.

An important characteristic of high-temperature strength is that it must always be considered with respect to some time scale. The tensile properties of most engineering metals at room temperature are independent of time, for practical purposes. It makes little difference in the results if the loading rate of a tension test is such that it requires 2 hr or 2 min to complete the test. Further, in room-temperature tests the anelastic behavior of the material is of little practical consequence. However, at elevated temperature the strength becomes very dependent on both strain rate and time of exposure. A number of metals under these conditions behave in many respects like viscoelastic materials. A metal subjected to a constant tensile load at an elevated temperature will *creep* and undergo a time-dependent increase in length.

The tests which are used to measure elevated-temperature strength must be selected on the basis of the time scale of the service which the material must withstand. Thus, an elevated-temperature tension test can provide useful information about the high-temperature performance of a short-lived item, such as a rocket engine or missile nose cone, but it will give only the most meager information about the high-temperature performance of a steam pipeline which is required to withstand 100,000 hr of elevated-temperature service. Therefore, special tests are required to evaluate the performance of materials in different kinds of high-temperature service. The *creep test* measures the dimensional changes which occur from elevated-temperature exposure, while the *stress-rupture test* measures the effect of temperature on the long-time load-bearing characteristics. Other tests may be used to measure special properties such as thermal-shock resistance and stress relaxation. These high-temperature tests will be discussed in this chapter from two points of view. The engineering significance of the information obtained from the tests will be discussed, and information which is leading to a better understanding of the mechanism of high-temperature deformation will be considered.

13-2. The Creep Curve

The progressive deformation of a material at constant stress is called *creep*. The simplest type of creep deformation is *viscous flow*. A material is said to experience pure viscous flow if the rate of shear strain is proportional to the applied shearing stress.

$$\frac{d\gamma}{dt} = f(\tau) \tag{13-1}$$

When the proportionality between these two factors can be expressed by a simple constant, the material is said to show Newtonian viscosity.

$$\tau = \eta \frac{d\gamma}{dt} \tag{13-2}$$

where η is the coefficient of viscosity. Most liquids obey Newton's law of viscosity, but it is only partially followed by metals.

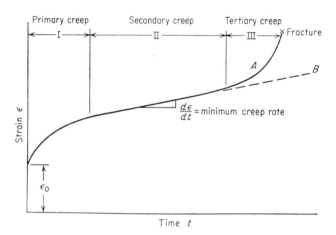

Fig. 13-1. Typical creep curve showing the three stages of creep. Curve A, constant-load test; curve B, constant-stress test.

To determine the engineering creep curve of a metal, a constant load is applied to a tensile specimen maintained at a constant temperature, and the strain (extension) of the specimen is determined as a function of time. Although the measurement of creep resistance is quite simple in principle, in practice it requires considerable laboratory equipment.[1,2] The elapsed time of such tests may extend to several months, while some tests have been run for more than 10 years. The general procedures for creep testing are covered in ASTM Specification E139-58T.

Curve A in Fig. 13-1 illustrates the idealized shape of a creep curve. The slope of this curve ($d\epsilon/dt$ or $\dot{\epsilon}$) is referred to as the *creep rate*. Follow-

---

[1] Creep and Creep Rupture Tests, ASM Metals Handbook, Supplement, August, 1955, *Metal Progr.*, vol. 68, no. 2A, pp. 175–184, Aug. 15, 1955.

[2] J. A. Fellows, E. Cook, and H. S. Avery, *Trans. AIME*, vol. 150, p. 358, 1942.

ing an initial rapid elongation of the specimen, ϵ_0, the creep rate decreases with time, then reaches essentially a steady state in which the creep rate changes little with time, and finally the creep rate increases rapidly with time until fracture occurs.   Thus, it is natural to discuss the creep curve in terms of its three stages.   It should be noted, however, that the degree to which these three stages are readily distinguishable depends strongly on the applied stress and temperature.

In making an engineering creep test, it is usual practice to maintain the load constant throughout the test.   Thus, as the specimen elongates and decreases in cross-sectional area, the axial stress increases.   The initial stress which was applied to the specimen is usually the reported value of stress.   Methods of compensating for the change in dimensions of the specimen so as to carry out the creep test under constant-stress

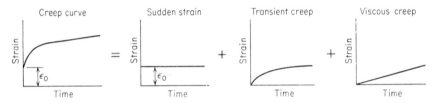

Fig. 13-2. Andrade's analysis of the competing processes which determine the creep curve.

conditions have been developed.[1,2]   When constant-stress tests are made, it is frequently found that no region of accelerated creep rate occurs (region III, Fig. 13-1) and a creep curve similar to B in Fig. 13-1 is obtained.   Accelerated creep is found, however, in constant-stress tests when metallurgical changes occur in the metal.   Curve B should be considered representative of the basic creep curve for a metal.

Andrade's pioneer work on creep[3] has had considerable influence on the thinking on this subject.   He considers that the constant-stress creep curve represents the superposition of two separate creep processes which occur after the sudden strain which results from applying the load.   The first component is a *transient creep*, which has a decreasing creep rate with time.   Added to this is a constant-rate creep process called *viscous creep*.   The superposition of these creep processes is illustrated in Fig. 13-2.   Andrade found that the creep curve could be represented by the

[1] E. N. da C. Andrade and B. Chalmers, *Proc. Roy Soc. (London)*, vol. 138A, p. 348, 1932.

[2] R. L. Fullman, R. P. Carreker, and J. C. Fisher, *Trans. AIME*, vol. 197, pp. 657–659, 1953.

[3] E. N. da C. Andrade, *Proc. Roy. Soc. (London)*, vol. 90A, pp. 329–342, 1914; "Creep and Recovery," pp. 176–198, American Society for Metals, Metals Park, Ohio, 1957.

following empirical equation,

$$L = L_0(1 + \beta t^{1/3}) \exp \kappa t \qquad (13\text{-}3)$$

where L = length of specimen at time t

L_0, β, κ = empirically determined constants

The constant L_0 approximates the length of the specimen when the sudden strain produced by the application of the load has ceased. The transient creep is represented by the constant β. Thus, when $\kappa = 0$, Eq. (13-3) yields a creep rate which vanishes at long times.

$$L = L_0(1 + \beta t^{1/3})$$

$$\dot{\epsilon} = \frac{dL}{dt} = \tfrac{1}{3}L_0\beta t^{-2/3} \qquad (13\text{-}4)$$

When $\beta = 0$,

$$\frac{L}{L_0} = \exp \kappa t$$

$$\frac{dL}{dt} = \kappa L_0 \exp \kappa t = \kappa L$$

$$\kappa = \frac{1}{L}\frac{dL}{dt} \qquad (13\text{-}5)$$

The exponent κ therefore represents an extension, per unit length, which proceeds at a constant rate. It represents the viscous component of creep. Strictly speaking, κ represents quasi-viscous flow because the rate of change of length is not proportional to stress as required by Eq. (13-2). Sometimes transient creep is referred to as β flow, and viscous (steady-state) creep is referred to as κ flow in keeping with Andrade's analysis of the creep curve. Andrade's equation has been verified for conditions extending up to several hundred hours, which result in total extensions in excess of 1 per cent. Modifications of these equations will be considered in another section of this chapter.

The various stages of the creep curve shown in Fig. 13-1 require further explanation. It is generally considered in this country that the creep curve has three stages. In British terminology the instantaneous strain designated by ϵ_0 in Fig. 13-1 is often called the first stage of creep, so that with this nomenclature the creep curve is considered to have four stages. The strain represented by ϵ_0 occurs practically instantaneously on the application of the load. Even though the applied stress is below the yield stress, not all the instantaneous strain is elastic. Most of this strain is instantly recoverable upon the release of the load (elastic), while part is recoverable with time (anelastic), and the rest is nonrecoverable (plastic). Although the instantaneous strain is not really creep, it is important because it may constitute a considerable fraction of the allowable total strain in machine parts. Sometimes the instantaneous strain is subtracted from the total strain in the creep specimen to give the strain due only to creep. This type of creep curve starts at the origin of coordinates.

The first stage of creep, known as *primary creep*, represents a region of decreasing creep rate. Primary creep is a period of predominantly transient creep in which the creep resistance of the material increases by virtue of its own deformation. For low temperatures and stresses, as in the creep of lead at room temperature, primary creep is the predominant creep process. The second stage of creep, known also as *secondary creep*, is a period of nearly constant creep rate which results from a balance between the competing processes of strain hardening and recovery. For this reason, secondary creep is usually referred to as *steady-state creep*. The average value of the creep rate during secondary creep is called the *minimum creep rate*. Third-stage or *tertiary creep* mainly occurs in constant-load creep tests at high stresses at high temperatures. The reasons for the accelerated creep rate which leads to rapid failure are not well known. It is unlikely that tertiary creep is due solely to necking of the specimen, since many materials fail in creep

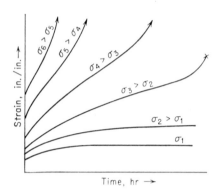

Fig. 13-3. Schematic representation of effect of stress on creep curves at constant temperature.

at strains which are too small to produce necking. Tertiary creep is more probably the result of structural changes occurring in the metal. Evidence has been found for void formation and extensive crack formation during this stage.

Figure 13-3 shows the effect of applied stress on the creep curve at constant temperature. It is apparent that a creep curve with three well-defined stages will be found for only certain combinations of stress and temperature. A similar family of curves is obtained for creep at constant stress for different temperatures. The higher the temperature, the greater the creep rate. The basic difference for this case would be that all the curves would originate from the same point on the strain axis.

The minimum creep rate is the most important design parameter derived from the creep curve. Two standards of this parameter are commonly used in this country, (1) the stress to produce a creep rate of 0.0001 per cent/hr or 1 per cent/10,000 hr, or (2) the stress for a creep rate of 0.00001 per cent/hr or 1 per cent/100,000 hr (about $11\frac{1}{2}$ years). The first criterion is more typical of the requirements for jet-engine alloys, while the last criterion is used for steam turbines and similar equipment.

A log-log plot of stress vs. minimum creep rate frequently results in a straight line. This type of plot is very useful for design purposes, and its use will be discussed more fully in a later part of this chapter.

13-3. The Stress-rupture Test

The stress-rupture test is basically similar to the creep test except that the test is always carried out to the failure of the material. Higher loads are used with the stress-rupture test than in a creep test, and therefore the creep rates are higher. Ordinarily the creep test is carried out at relatively low stresses so as to avoid tertiary creep. Emphasis in the creep test is on precision determination of strain, particularly as to the determination of the minimum creep rate. Creep tests are frequently conducted for periods of 2,000 hr and often to 10,000 hr. In the creep test the total strain is often less than 0.5 per cent, while in the stress-rupture test the total strain may be around 50 per cent. Thus, simpler strain-measuring devices, such as dial gages, can be used. Stress-rupture equipment is simpler to build, maintain, and operate than creep-testing equipment, and therefore it lends itself more readily to multiple testing units. The higher stresses and creep rates of the stress-rupture test cause structural changes to occur in metals at shorter times than would be observed ordinarily in the creep test, and therefore stress-rupture tests can usually be terminated in 1,000 hr. These factors have contributed to the increased use of the stress-rupture test. It is particularly well suited to determining the relative high-temperature strength of new alloys for jet-engine applications. Further, for applications where creep deformation can be tolerated but fracture must be prevented, it has direct application in design.

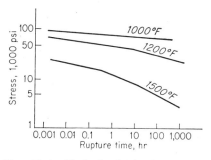

Fig. 13-4. Method of plotting stress-rupture data (schematic).

The basic information obtained from the stress-rupture test is the time to cause failure at a given nominal stress for a constant temperature. The elongation and reduction of area at fracture are also determined. If the test is of suitable duration, it is customary to make elongation measurements as a function of time and from this to determine the minimum creep rate. The stress is plotted against the rupture time on a log-log scale (Fig. 13-4). A straight line will usually be obtained for each test temperature. Changes in the slope of the stress-rupture line are due to structural changes occurring in the material, e.g., changes from transgranular to intergranular fracture, oxidation, recrystallization and grain growth, or other structural changes such as spheroidization, graphitization, or sigma-phase formation. It is important to know about the existence of such instabilities, since serious errors in extrapolation of the data to longer times can result if they are not detected.

13-4. Deformation at Elevated Temperature

The principal deformation processes at elevated temperature are slip, subgrain formation, and grain-boundary sliding. High-temperature deformation is characterized by extreme inhomogeneity. Measurements of local creep elongation[1] at various locations in a creep specimen have shown that the local strain undergoes many periodic changes with time that are not recorded in the changes in strain of the total gage length of the specimen. In large-grained specimens, local regions may undergo lattice rotations which produce areas of misorientation.

A number of secondary deformation processes have been observed in metals at elevated temperature. These include multiple slip, the formation of extremely coarse slip bands, kink bands, fold formation at grain boundaries, and grain-boundary migration. Many of the deformation studies at elevated temperature have been made with large-grain-size sheet specimens of aluminum. (Aluminum is favored for this type of study because its thin oxide skin eliminates problems from oxidation.) Studies have also been made of creep deformation in iron, magnesium, and lead. It is important to remember that all the studies of high-temperature deformation have been made under conditions which give a creep rate of several per cent in 100 or 1,000 hr, while for many engineering applications a creep rate of less than 1 per cent in 100,000 hr is required. Because the deformation processes which occur at elevated temperature depend on the rate of strain as well as the temperature, it is not always possible to extrapolate the results obtained for high strain-rate conditions to conditions of greater practical interest. Much of the work on deformation processes during creep has been reviewed by Sully[2] and Grant and Chaudhuri.[3]

Deformation by Slip

New slip systems may become operative when metals are deformed at elevated temperature. Slip occurs in aluminum[4] along the {111}, {100}, or {211} planes above 500°F. Zinc slips on the nonbasal {10$\bar{1}$0} planes

---

[1] H. C. Chang and N. J. Grant, *Trans. AIME*, vol. 197, p. 1175, 1953.

[2] A. H. Sully, "Progress in Metal Physics," vol. 6, pp. 135–180, Pergamon Press, Ltd., London, 1956.

[3] N. J. Grant and A. R. Chaudhuri, Creep and Fracture, in "Creep and Recovery," pp. 284–343, American Society for Metals, Metals Park, Ohio, 1957.

[4] I. S. Servi, J. T. Norton, and N. J. Grant, *Trans. AIME*, vol. 194, p. 965, 1952.

in the $\langle 1210 \rangle$ directions above 570°F, and there is evidence of nonbasal high-temperature slip in magnesium.[1] The slip bands produced at high temperature do not generally resemble the straight slip lines which are usually found after room-temperature deformation. Although high-temperature slip may start initially as fairly uniformly spaced slip bands, as deformation proceeds there is a tendency for further shear to be restricted to a few of the slip bands. The tendency for cross slip and the formation of deformation bands increases with temperature. Fine slip lines, which are difficult to resolve with the optical microscope, have been found between the coarse slip bands in creep specimens of aluminum.[2] These represent the traces of slip planes on which only very small amounts of shear have occurred. The significance of fine slip to creep deformation will be discussed later.

In one of the first investigations of creep-deformation processes, Hanson and Wheeler[3] established that the slip-band spacing increases with either an increase in temperature or a decrease in stress. Subsequent work on aluminum and its alloys[4,5] showed that the slip-band spacing was inversely proportional to the applied stress but independent of temperature. These observations may be interpreted in the following way: If aluminum with a certain initial grain size is tested at a certain stress, there will be a certain characteristic slip-band spacing. If the grain size is smaller than the slip-band spacing, the slip bands will not be visible in the specimen after deformation. Deformation of the grains will occur by shear along the grain boundaries and by the breakup of the grains into "cells," or subgrains.[6] Deformation at high temperatures and/or low strain rates are conditions for which it is difficult to detect slip lines but for which there is abundant evidence of grain-boundary deformation. This condition has often been called "slipless flow."

Complex deformation processes occur in the vicinity of the grain boundaries. While grain boundaries restrict deformation at high temperature to a lesser extent than at room temperature, they still exert a restraining influence on deformation.

Subgrain Formation

Creep deformation is quite inhomogeneous, so that there are many opportunities for lattice bending to occur. Kink bands, deformation bands, and local bending near grain boundaries are known to occur.

[1] A. R. Chaudhuri, H. C. Chang, and N. J. Grant, *Trans. AIME*, vol. 203, p. 682, 1955.

[2] D. McLean, *J. Inst. Metals*, vol. 81, p. 133, 1952–1953.

[3] D. Hanson and M. A. Wheeler, *J. Inst. Metals*, vol. 55, p. 229, 1931.

[4] I. S. Servi and N. J. Grant, *Trans. AIME*, vol. 191, p. 917, 1951.

[5] G. D. Gemmell and N. J. Grant, *Trans. AIME*, vol. 209, pp. 417–423, 1957.

[6] W. A. Wood, G. R. Wilms, and W. A. Rachinger, *J. Inst. Metals*, vol. 79, p. 159, 1951.

Polygonization can take place concurrently with lattice bending because dislocation climb can occur readily at high temperature (see Sec. 6-10). The formation of cells, or subgrains, as creep progresses has been observed by means of X rays and metallographic techniques. The size of the subgrains depends on the stress and the temperature. Large subgrains, or cells, are produced by high temperature and a low stress or creep rate. The decreasing creep rate found during primary creep is the result of the formation of more and more subgrains as creep continues. The increased number of low-angle boundaries provides barriers to dislocation movement and results in a decrease in creep strain.

Grain-boundary Deformation

It has already been shown in Sec. 8-5 that the grain-boundary relaxation which is measured by internal friction at elevated temperature indicates that the grain boundaries have a certain viscous behavior under these conditions. Therefore, it is not surprising that the grain boundaries behave in a manner to indicate considerable mobility when creep is produced at high temperature. The main grain-boundary processes which are observed in high-temperature creep are *grain-boundary sliding, grain-boundary migration*, and *fold formation*.

Grain-boundary sliding is a shear process which occurs in the direction of the grain boundary. It is promoted by increasing the temperature and/or decreasing the strain rate. The question whether the sliding occurs along the grain boundary[1] as a bulk movement of the two grains or in a softened area in each grain adjacent to the grain boundary[2] has not been answered. Grain-boundary shearing occurs discontinuously in time, and the amount of shear displacement is not uniform along the grain boundary. Although the exact mechanism is not known, it is clear that grain-boundary sliding is not due to simple viscous sliding of one grain past another because it is preceded by appreciable amounts of plastic flow in adjacent crystals.

Grain-boundary migration is a motion of the grain boundary in a direction which is inclined to the grain boundary. It may be considered to be stress-induced grain growth. Grain-boundary migration is a creep recovery process which is important because it allows the distorted material adjacent to the grain boundary to undergo further deformation. The wavy grain boundaries which are frequently observed during high-temperature creep are a result of inhomogeneous grain-boundary deformation and grain-boundary migration.

For grain-boundary deformation to occur without producing cracks at the grain boundaries, it is necessary to achieve continuity of strain

[1] H. C. Chang and N. J. Grant, *Trans. AIME*, vol. 206, p. 169, 1956.
[2] F. N. Rhines, W. E. Bond, and M. A. Kissel, *Trans. ASM*, vol. 48, p. 919, 1956.

along the grain boundary. A common method of accommodating grain-boundary strain at high temperature is by the formation of *folds* at the end of a grain boundary.[1] Figure 13-5 shows a sketch of a fold.

The relative importance of slip and grain-boundary displacement to the total creep deformation has been investigated by McLean[2] for aluminum at 200°C. At this relatively low temperature he has shown that only a small fraction of the total deformation is due to grain-boundary displacement, about half the total deformation is due to slip which is readily attributed to coarse slip bands, while the remainder of the total deformation cannot be attributed to any microscopic deformation mechanism. McLean attributes this "missing creep" to deformation by fine slip, which is very difficult to detect with the microscope. It is believed that deformation by fine slip can explain the observations of earlier workers that creep deformation occurs without slip (slipless flow). Greater

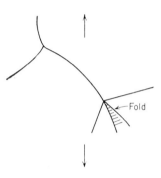

Fig. 13-5. Fold formation at a triple point (schematic).

contribution to the total deformation from grain-boundary displacement would be expected at higher temperatures and lower stresses.

13-5. Fracture at Elevated Temperature

It has been known since the early work of Rosenhain and Ewen[3] that metals undergo a transition from transgranular fracture to intergranular fracture as the temperature is increased. When transgranular fracture occurs, the slip planes are weaker than the grain boundaries, while for intergranular fracture the grain boundary is the weaker component. Jeffries[4] introduced the concept of the *equicohesive temperature* (ECT), which was defined as that temperature at which the grains and grain boundaries have equal strength (Fig. 13-6a). Like the recrystallization temperature, the ECT is not a fixed one. In addition to the effect of stress and temperature on the ECT, the strain rate has an important influence. Figure 13-6b shows that decreasing the strain rate lowers the ECT and therefore increases the tendency for intergranular fracture. The effect of strain rate on the strength-temperature relationship is believed to be much larger for the grain-boundary strength than for

[1] H. C. Chang and N. J. Grant, *Trans. AIME*, vol. 194, p. 619, 1952.
[2] D. McLean, *J. Inst. Metals*, vol. 80, p. 507, 1951–1952.
[3] W. Rosenhain and D. Ewen, *J. Inst. Metals*, vol. 10, p. 119, 1913.
[4] Z. Jeffries, *Trans. AIME*, vol. 60, pp. 474–576, 1919.

the strength of the grains. Since the amount of grain-boundary area decreases with increasing grain size, a material with a large grain size will have higher strength above the ECT than a fine grain material. Below the ECT the reverse is true. For metals and alloys of commercial purity the ECT will occur within a fairly sharp temperature interval. However, for high-purity material there is a wide range of temperature where the strengths of the grains and the grain boundaries are not

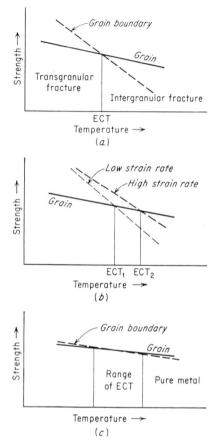

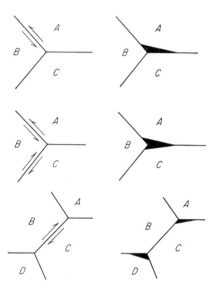

Fig. 13-6. The equicohesive temperature. (*After N. J. Grant, in "Utilization of Heat Resistant Alloys," American Society for Metals, Metals Park, Ohio, 1954.*)

Fig. 13-7. Schematic drawings of the way intergranular cracks form owing to grain-boundary sliding. (*H. C. Chang and N. J. Grant, Trans. AIME, vol. 206, p. 545, 1956.*)

very different[1] (Fig. 13-6c) so that transgranular fracture can occur up to rather high temperatures.

Under conditions where grain boundaries experience considerable mobility, we have the situation of a thin, plastically weak region embedded between two relatively strong matrix grains. This is a situation that is conducive to grain-boundary failure. While a number of

[1] Servi and Grant, *op. cit.*, p. 909.

reasonable models for grain-boundary fracture have been suggested, none are capable of predicting all the details of grain-boundary fracture.

Two types of intergranular fracture have been observed under creep conditions. Under conditions where grain-boundary sliding can occur, cracks may be initiated at triple points where three grain boundaries meet on a plane of polish. This type of grain-boundary failure is prevalent for high stresses, where the total life is fairly short. Several methods by which cracks form[1] as the result of grain-boundary sliding are shown schematically in Fig. 13-7. Zener[2] has shown that large tensile stresses should be developed at a triple point due to shear stresses acting along the grain boundaries. When grain-boundary migration and fold formation can occur, the tendency for grain-boundary fracture is diminished. Grain-boundary migration displaces the strained grain boundary to a new unstrained region of the crystal, while the formation of folds permits the relief of stress concentration at grain corners by plastic deformation within the grains.

The second type of intergranular fracture is characterized by the formation of voids at grain boundaries, particularly those which are perpendicular to the tensile stress. The voids grow and coalesce into grain-boundary cracks. This type of fracture is most prevalent when low stresses result in failure in relatively long times. At least two mechanisms have been suggested for this type of fracture. One mechanism is based on the idea that the voids are formed by the condensation of vacancies and grow by the diffusion of vacancies. Balluffi and Seigle[3] have advanced a theory for the growth of voids based on the ideas used to explain the sintering of metals. On the other hand, there are experiments[4] which show that grain-boundary voids are not formed unless there is grain-boundary sliding. It is uncertain, at present, whether voids are initiated at grain boundaries by a process of vacancy condensation or as the result of localized plastic yielding.

13-6. Theories of Low-temperature Creep

Creep is possible only because obstacles to deformation can be overcome by the combined action of thermal fluctuations and stress. Diffusion-controlled processes are important chiefly at temperatures greater than about one-half the melting point. At lower temperatures recovery proc-

[1] H. C. Chang and N. J. Grant, *Trans. AIME*, vol. 206, pp. 544–550, 1956.

[2] C. Zener, Micromechanism of Fracture, in "Fracturing of Metals," p. 3, American Society for Metals, Metals Park, Ohio, 1948.

[3] R. W. Balluffi and L. L. Seigle, *Acta Met.*, vol. 5, p. 449, 1957.

[4] C. W. Chen and E. S. Machlin, *Trans. AIME*, vol. 209, pp. 829–835, 1957; J. Intrater and E. S. Machlin, *Acta Met.*, vol. 7, p. 140, 1959.

esses which are not dependent on diffusion, such as cross slip, play important roles in the creep process. High-temperature creep is predominantly steady-state or viscous creep, while below $T_m/2$ transient, or primary, creep predominates.

Andrade's equation for describing transient and steady-state creep was discussed in Sec. 13-2. An alternative general equation for the time laws of creep was suggested by Cottrell.[1]

$$\dot{\epsilon} = At^{-n'} \tag{13-6}$$

where A and n' are empirical constants. Different types of creep behavior are described by Eq. (13-6) depending upon the value of n'. If $n' = 0$, the creep rate is constant and Eq. (13-6) represents steady-state creep. When $n' = 1$, Eq. (13-6) becomes

$$\epsilon = \alpha \ln t \tag{13-7}$$

where α is a constant. This is the logarithmic creep law found at low temperatures.[2] When $n' = \frac{2}{3}$, Eq. (13-6) becomes Andrade's equation for transient creep,

$$\epsilon = \beta t^{\frac{1}{3}} \tag{13-8}$$

Logarithmic creep occurs at low temperatures and low stresses, where recovery cannot occur. It is believed to be a true exhaustion process in which the rate-determining step is the activation energy to move a dislocation. On the initial application of stress, the dislocations with the lowest activation energy move first to produce the initial creep strain. As these easy-to-move dislocations are exhausted, creep can continue only by the movement of dislocations of higher activation energy. Therefore, the activation energy for the process continuously increases, and the creep rate decreases. Theoretical treatments of exhaustion creep that result in a logarithmic equation have been proposed by Mott and Nabarro[3] and Cottrell.[4]

Low-temperature logarithmic creep obeys a mechanical equation of state; i.e., the rate of strain at a given time depends only on the instantaneous values of stress and strain and not on the previous strain history. However, creep at higher temperatures is strongly dependent on prior strain and thermal history and hence does not follow a mechanical equation of state.

An exhaustion theory does not adequately describe the behavior during

[1] A. H. Cottrell, *J. Mech. and Phys. Solids*, vol. 1, pp. 53–63, 1952.

[2] Logarithmic creep has been observed for copper below 200°K. [O. H. Wyatt, *Proc. Phys. Soc. (London)*, vol. 66B, p. 495, 1953].

[3] N. F. Mott and F. R. N. Nabarro, "Report on Strength of Solids," p. 1, Physical Society, London, 1948.

[4] Cottrell, *op. cit.*

transient creep. The decreasing creep rate during transient creep arises from the increasing dislocation density and the formation of low-angle boundaries. The recovery mechanisms operating during transient creep are not well established. Analysis of existing data[1] indicates that the escape of screw dislocations from pile-ups by cross slip may be the chief recovery mechanism in fcc metals.

13-7. Theories of High-temperature Creep

Steady-state, or secondary, creep predominates at temperatures above about $T_m/2$. Although there is some question whether a true steady-state condition is achieved for all combinations of stress and temperature, there is ample experimental evidence to indicate that approximate steady-state conditions are achieved after a short period of testing in the high-temperature region. Steady-state creep arises because of a balance between strain hardening and recovery. The effects of strain hardening are recovered by the escape of screw dislocations from pile-ups by cross slip and the escape of edge dislocations by climb. Since dislocation climb has a higher activation energy than cross slip, it will be the rate-controlling step in steady-state creep.

Orowan[2] first suggested that steady-state creep could be treated as a balance between strain hardening and recovery. If ϕ is the slope of the stress-strain curve at the applied stress σ and $r = \partial\sigma/\partial t$ is the rate of recovery of the flow stress on annealing, then the steady-state condition requires that the flow stress must remain constant.

$$d\sigma = \frac{\partial\sigma}{\partial t} dt + \frac{\partial\sigma}{\partial\epsilon} d\epsilon = 0 \qquad (13\text{-}9)$$

$$\dot{\epsilon} = \kappa = -\frac{\partial\sigma/\partial t}{\partial\sigma/\partial\epsilon} = \frac{r}{\phi} \qquad (13\text{-}10)$$

where κ is the steady-state creep rate (κ flow) and r and ϕ are defined above. Cottrell and Aytekin[3] have shown that the thermally activated process of recovery can be expressed by

$$r = -\frac{\partial\sigma}{\partial t} = C \exp\frac{-(H - q\sigma)}{kT} \qquad (13\text{-}11)$$

where H = an activation energy
q = an activation volume related to atomic stress concentration
C = a constant
k = Boltzmann's constant

[1] G. Schoeck, Theory of Creep, in "Creep and Recovery," American Society of Metals, Metals Park, Ohio, 1957.

[2] E. Orowan, *J. West Scot. Iron Steel Inst.*, vol. 54, pp. 45–96, 1947.

[3] A. H. Cottrell and V. Aytekin, *J. Inst. Metals*, vol. 77, p. 389, 1950.

Substituting Eq. (13-11) into Eq. (13-10) gives an equation for the steady-state creep rate.

$$\dot{\epsilon} = \frac{C}{\phi} \exp \frac{-(H - q\sigma)}{kT} \qquad (13\text{-}12)$$

Theories of steady-state creep based on Eyring's chemical theory of reaction rates were at one time very prominent in the thinking on this subject.[1,2] According to this concept, creep resulted from the shear of "flow units" past each other through the periodic potential field of the crystal lattice. The metal was assumed to behave like a viscous material, and for creep to occur the flow unit had to acquire sufficient energy to surmount the potential barrier of the activated state. The theory predicted a steady-state creep rate of the form

$$\dot{\epsilon} = C \exp \frac{-\Delta F}{kT} \sinh \frac{B\sigma}{kT} \qquad (13\text{-}13)$$

where ΔF is the free energy of activation and B is a constant describing the size of the flow unit. The flow units were not defined in terms of crystal structure, so that this theory had little physical basis. However, it was an important advance in creep theory because it emphasized that creep was a thermally activated process.

A relationship very similar to Eq. (13-13) has been used by a number of investigators for describing steady-state creep data of annealed metals in terms of applied stress and temperature.[3]

$$\dot{\epsilon} = A_0 \exp \frac{-H}{kT} \sinh \frac{q\sigma}{kT} \qquad (13\text{-}14)$$

The parameters A_0, H, and q are independent of σ, and only q varies significantly with temperature. If $q\sigma/kT$ is greater than 2, the above equation simplifies to

$$\dot{\epsilon} = \tfrac{1}{2} A_0 \exp \frac{-(H - q\sigma)}{kT} \qquad (13\text{-}15)$$

Equation (13-15) implies the existence of a linear relationship between $\log \dot{\epsilon}$ and σ. A linear relationship is also often obtained when $\log \dot{\epsilon}$ is plotted against $\log \sigma$. This is a conventional method of plotting engineering creep data. The corresponding equation

$$\dot{\epsilon} = B\sigma^{n'} \qquad (13\text{-}16)$$

is often used in the engineering analysis of the creep of structures and machine elements.

[1] W. Kauzmann, *Trans. AIME*, vol. 143, pp. 57–83, 1941.

[2] S. Dushman, L. W. Dunbar, and H. Huthsteiner, *J. Appl. Phys.*, vol. 15, p. 108, 1944.

[3] P. Feltham and J. D. Meakin, *Acta Met.*, vol. 7, pp. 614–627, 1959.

Dorn[1,2] has made valuable contributions to the knowledge of high-temperature creep by putting the reaction-rate theory of creep on a better physical basis. In his creep experiments on high-purity polycrystalline aluminum, careful attention has been given to changes in lattice distortion and subgrain formation during the creep test. It has

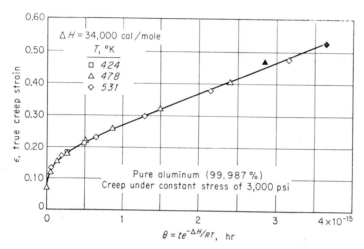

Fig. 13-8. Creep strain vs. $\theta = t \exp\left(-\Delta H/RT\right)$. (*J. E. Dorn, in "Creep and Recovery," American Society for Metals, Metals Park, Ohio, 1957.*)

been found that creep can be correlated in terms of a temperature-compensated time parameter θ.

$$\theta = t \exp \frac{-\Delta H_c}{RT} \qquad (13\text{-}17)$$

where t = time of creep exposure
ΔH_c = activation energy for creep
R = universal gas constant[3]
T = absolute temperature

For constant load or stress conditions, the total creep strain is a simple function of θ.

$$\epsilon = f(\theta, \sigma_c) \qquad \sigma_c = \text{constant} \qquad (13\text{-}18)$$

Figure 13-8 shows a typical correlation between ϵ and θ for creep data obtained at several temperatures. An important characteristic of this

[1] J. E. Dorn, The Spectrum of Activation Energies for Creep, in "Creep and Recovery," pp. 255–283, American Society for Metals, Metals Park, Ohio, 1957.

[2] J. E. Dorn, *J. Mech. and Phys. Solids*, vol. 3, p. 85, 1954.

[3] Boltzmann's constant k and the gas constant R are related through the equation $R = kN$, where N is Avogadro's number.

correlation is that equivalent structure, as determined by metallography and X rays, is obtained for the same values of ϵ and θ.

If Eq. (13-18) is differentiated with respect to time,

$$\dot{\epsilon} = \frac{d\epsilon}{dt} = \frac{\partial f}{\partial \theta} \frac{\partial \theta}{\partial t} = f'(\theta,\sigma_c) \exp \frac{-\Delta H_c}{RT} \qquad (13\text{-}19)$$

Evaluating Eq. (13-19) at the minimum creep rate $\dot{\epsilon}_m$ gives

$$\dot{\epsilon}_m = f'(\theta_m,\sigma) \exp \frac{-\Delta H_c}{RT} \qquad (13\text{-}20)$$

However, θ_m is only a function of the creep stress σ_c, so that

$$\sigma_c = F\left(\dot{\epsilon}_m \exp \frac{\Delta H}{RT}\right) = F(Z) \qquad (13\text{-}21)$$

Z is the Zener-Hollomon parameter considered previously in Sec. 9-8. Not only can this equation be used for describing the relation between temperature and strain rate for the relatively high strain rates of the tension test, but it appears to be reliable for the very low strain rates found in the creep test.

The effect of stress on time to rupture can also be correlated with the time-temperature parameter θ,

$$\theta_r = t_r \exp \frac{-\Delta H}{RT} = F(\sigma) \qquad (13\text{-}22)$$

where t_r is the time to rupture. For engineering analysis of creep, the stress dependence of the time to rupture is often expressed by the empirical equation

$$t_r = a\sigma^n \qquad (13\text{-}23)$$

An empirical relationship also exists between the rupture life and the minimum creep rate $\dot{\epsilon}_m$ such that

$$\log t_r + C \log \dot{\epsilon}_m = K \qquad (13\text{-}24)$$

where C and K are constants for a given alloy.

The activation energy for creep can be evaluated from two creep curves determined with the same applied stress at two different temperatures. Thus, for equal values of total creep strain obtained at the two temperatures, the values of θ are equal. Therefore,

$$\theta_1 = t_1 \exp \frac{-\Delta H_c}{RT_1} = \theta_2 = t_2 \exp \frac{-\Delta H_c}{RT_2}$$

$$\Delta H_c = R \frac{T_1 T_2}{T_1 - T_2} \ln \frac{t_2}{t_1} \qquad (13\text{-}25)$$

A rather extensive correlation[1] of creep and diffusion data for pure metals shows that the activation energy for high-temperature creep is approximately equal to the activation energy for self-diffusion (Fig. 13-9). At temperatures below about one-half the melting point ΔH_c is a function of temperature, and no correlation exists with the activation energy for self-diffusion. The excellent correlation between the activation energies for creep and self-diffusion indicates that dislocation climb is the rate-

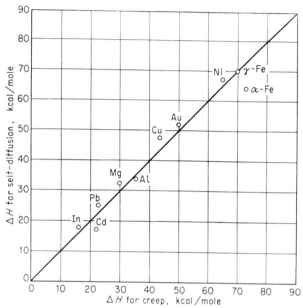

Fig. 13-9. Correlation between activation energies for high-temperature creep and self-diffusion. (*J. E. Dorn, in "Creep and Recovery," p. 274, American Society for Metals, Metals Park, Ohio, 1957.*)

determining step for high-temperature creep. The fact that a spectrum of activation energies is observed at lower temperatures indicates that the creep process is quite complex in this region.

A simple functional relationship between the steady-state creep rate and the stress does not exist because the effect of stress depends on the development of the structural changes due to creep deformation.[2] One of the most reasonable equations relating creep rate with stress and temperature is

$$\dot{\epsilon}_m = S' \exp \frac{-\Delta H}{RT} \exp B'\sigma \qquad (13\text{-}26)$$

[1] O. D. Sherby, R. L. Orr, and J. E. Dorn, *Trans. AIME*, vol. 200, pp. 71–80, 1954.
[2] A. E. Bayce, W. D. Ludemann, L. A. Shepard, and J. E. Dorn, *Trans. ASM*, vol. 52, pp. 451–468, 1960.

where S' is a structure-sensitive parameter and B' is a constant which is independent of temperature and structural changes. For low stresses (below about 5,000 psi) this equation becomes

$$\dot{\epsilon}_m = S'' \exp \frac{-\Delta H}{RT} \sigma^{n'} \tag{13-27}$$

Another equation which gives good agreement between minimum creep rate and stress has been suggested by Conrad.[1]

$$\dot{\epsilon}_m = S \exp \frac{-\Delta H}{RT} \sinh \left[\frac{\sigma}{\sigma_c(T)} \right]^{n'} \tag{13-28}$$

In Eq. (13-28) the structure term S is assumed constant at the minimum creep rate and the constant σ_c is dependent on temperature.

Weertman[2] has derived an equation for the steady-state creep rate which is similar to Eq. (13-27) by using the assumption that dislocation climb is the rate-controlling process. The obstacles to dislocation movement are considered to be immobile Cottrell-Lomer dislocations (see Sec. 6-4). In order to escape from these obstacles, the dislocations climb into adjoining slip planes, forming low-angle boundaries. The activation energy for this process is the activation energy for self-diffusion. A steady state is established between the generation of dislocations and their annihilation. An alternative dislocation model of steady-state creep proposed by Mott[3] considers that the rate-controlling process is the formation of vacancies due to the movement of jogs on screw dislocations. This dislocation model leads to an equation for the steady-state creep rate similar to Eq. (13-12) in which the stress is present as a σ/T term. The choice of the proper functional relationship between creep rate and stress is difficult to make from existing experiment and theory.

13-8. Presentation of Engineering Creep Data

It should be apparent from the previous sections that knowledge of the high-temperature strength of metals has not advanced to the point where creep and stress-rupture behavior can be reliably predicted for design purposes on a theoretical basis. There is no other recourse than to make an intelligent selection of design stresses from the existing data. Fortunately, a large number of reliable high-temperature strength data

[1] H. Conrad, *Trans. ASME*, ser. D, vol. 81, pp. 617–627, 1959.

[2] J. Weertman, *J. Appl. Phys.*, vol. 26, pp. 1213–1217, 1955.

[3] N. F. Mott, "NPL Symposium on Creep and Fracture at High Temperature," pp. 21–24, H. M. Stationery Office, London, 1955.

have been collected and published by the ASTM[1] and by the producers of high-temperature alloys.

A common method of presenting creep data is to plot the logarithm of the stress against the logarithm of the minimum creep rate (Fig. 13-10). With this type of plot straight lines will frequently be obtained for the lower temperatures, but discontinuities due to structural instabilities will often occur at higher temperatures. Values of minimum creep rate lower

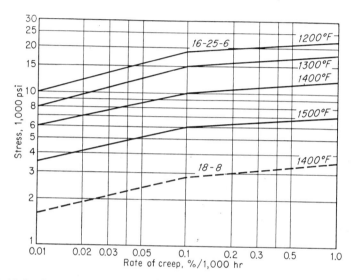

Fig. 13-10. log-log plot of stress vs. minimum creep rate. For 16-25-6 alloy. (*Courtesy C. L. Clark, Timken Roller Bearing Co.*)

than about 0.001 or 0.01 per cent/hr are generally determined by a standard creep test, while higher values of minimum creep rate are frequently determined by a stress-rupture test.

In reporting creep data it is common practice to speak of *creep strength* or *rupture strength*. Creep strength is defined as the stress at a given temperature which produces a minimum creep rate of a certain amount, usually 0.0001 per cent/hr or 0.001 per cent/hr. Rupture strength refers to the stress at a given temperature to produce a life to rupture of a certain amount, usually 100, 1,000, or 10,000 hr. A plot of creep strength or rupture strength against temperature is another common method of presenting creep data. When relatively short-time life is an important

[1] These data are published in the following *ASTM Special Technical Publications:* No. 124 (stainless steels), 1952; No. 151 (chromium-molybdenum steels), 1953; No. 160 (superalloys), 1954; No. 180 (carbon steels), 1955; No. 181 (copper and copper-base alloys), 1956; No. 199 (wrought medium-carbon alloy steels), 1957.

design criterion, it is convenient to present the data as a plot of the time to produce different amounts of total deformation at different stresses (Fig. 13-11). Each curve represents the stress and time at a fixed temperature to produce a certain per cent of total deformation (sudden strain plus creep strain). A separate set of curves is required for each temperature.

In designing missiles and high-speed aircraft data are needed at higher temperatures and stresses and shorter times than are usually determined tor creep tests. A common method of presenting these data is by the use of *isochronous stress-strain curves*. Creep tests are conducted at

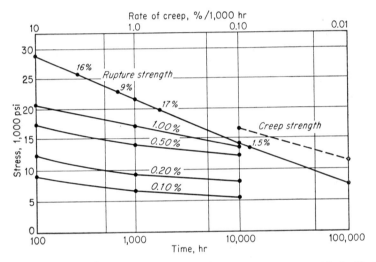

Fig. 13-11. Deformation-time curves at 1300°F for 16-25-6 alloy. (*C. L. Clark, in "Utilization of Heat Resistant Alloys," p.* 40, *American Society for Metals, Metals Park, Ohio,* 1954.)

different stresses for each temperature of interest. From the family of creep curves the isochronous stress-strain curves are then obtained by replotting with stress as the ordinate, strain as the abscissa, and time, usually ranging from about 5 to 60 min, as the parameter for each stress-strain curve.

13-9. Prediction of Long-time Properties

Frequently high-temperature strength data are needed for conditions for which there is no experimental information. This is particularly true of long-time creep and stress-rupture data, where it is quite possible to find that the creep strength to give 1 per cent deformation in 100,000 hr

(11 years) is required, although the alloy has been in existence for only 2 years. Obviously, in such situations extrapolation of the data to long times is the only alternative. Reliable extrapolation of creep and stress-rupture curves to longer times can be made only when it is certain that no structural changes occur in the region of extrapolation which would produce a change in the slope of the curve. Since structural changes generally occur at shorter times for higher temperatures, one way of checking on this point is to examine the log-stress–log-rupture life plot at a temperature several hundred degrees above the required temperature. For example, if in 1,000 hr no change in slope occurs in the curve at 200°F above the required temperature, extrapolation of the lower temperature curve as a straight line to 10,000 hr is probably safe and extrapolation even to 100,000 hr may be possible. A logical method of extrapolating stress-rupture curves which takes into consideration the changes in slope due to structural changes has been proposed by Grant and Bucklin.[1]

Several suggestions of time-temperature parameters for predicting long-time creep or rupture behavior from the results of shorter time tests at high temperature have been made. The Larson-Miller parameter[2] has the form

$$(T + 460)(C + \log t) = \text{constant} \tag{13-29}$$

where T = temperature, °F

t = time, hr

C = a constant with a value between about 10 and 30

In the original derivation of Eq. (13-29) on the basis of reaction-rate theory a value of $C = 20$ was used. While this is a good approximation when other data are lacking, for best results C should be considered a material constant which is determined experimentally. Once the proper constant has been established, then a plot of log stress vs. the Larson-Miller parameter should give a master plot which represents the high-temperature strength of the material for all combinations of temperature and time. However, since the temperature term in this parameter is given considerable weight, the Larson-Miller parameter is not very sensitive to small changes in rupture life due to structural changes in the material.

The parameter θ suggested by Dorn [see Eq. (13-17)] is another time-temperature parameter. While this parameter has been useful for correlating creep and stress-rupture data for pure metals and dilute solid-solution alloys, it has not been used to any great extent with engineering high-temperature alloys.

An extension of the Larson-Miller parameter has been suggested by

[1] N. J. Grant and A. G. Bucklin, *Trans. ASM*, vol. 42, pp. 720–761, 1950.

[2] F. R. Larson and J. Miller, *Trans. ASME*, vol. 74, pp. 765–771, 1952.

Manson and Haferd.[1] The Manson-Haferd parameter has the form

$$\frac{T - T_a}{\log t - \log t_a} = \text{constant} \tag{13-30}$$

where T = test temperature, °F
 t = time, hr
T_a, $\log t_a$ = constants derived from test data
A straight line is obtained when $\log t$ is plotted against T for data obtained

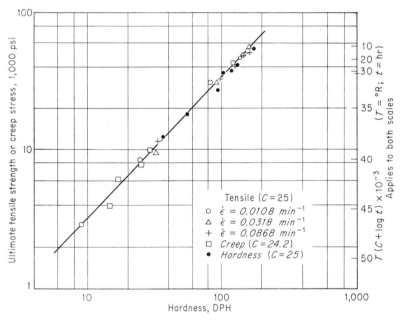

Fig. 13-12. Hot-hardness-strength correlation for iron-20 per cent chromium alloy. (*E. E. Underwood, Trans. ASM, vol.* 49, *p.* 403, 1957.)

at a constant stress. The lines obtained at different stresses converge toward a point with coordinates T_a, $\log t_a$.

A comparison of these various parameters with experimental data shows that the Manson-Haferd parameter usually results in the best over-all agreement,[2] although in certain cases[3] none of these parameters

---

[1] S. S. Manson and A. M. Haferd, *NACA Tech. Note* 2890, March, 1953; S. S. Manson, G. Succop, and W. R. Brown, Jr., *Trans. ASM*, vol. 51, pp. 911–934, 1959.

[2] R. M. Goldhoff, *Trans. ASME*, ser. D, vol. 81, pp. 629–644, 1959.

[3] F. Garofalo, G. V. Smith, and B. W. Royle, *Trans. ASME*, vol. 78, pp. 1423–1434, 1956.

has been found to provide satisfactory correlation of the data. In general, these parameters provide useful methods for presenting large numbers of data through the use of master plots of log stress vs. time-temperature parameter. Considerable use has been made of these parameters for predicting long-time data on the basis of short-time results. While there is no assurance that erroneous predictions will not result from this procedure, it is generally considered that the use of these parameters for this purpose will probably give better results than simple graphical extrapolation of log-log plots by one or two logarithmic cycles.

A short-cut approach to high-temperature properties is through the use of the hot-hardness test. There are certain parallelisms between high-temperature strength results and hot-hardness data. Just as a linear relationship exists between stress and the logarithm of the rupture time, a similar relationship holds between hot hardness and the logarithm of the indentation time. In Sec. 11-10 it was shown that a linear relation exists between hot hardness and tensile strength. Figure 13-12 illustrates a similar relation between hot hardness and high-temperature strength.[1] From the left-hand ordinate we get the relationship between tensile strength or creep strength and hot hardness. However, each point on the curve establishes a certain value of the Larson-Miller parameter along the right-hand ordinate. Thus, with a value of high-temperature stress and a value of the parameter we can establish values of temperature and rupture time. This procedure has been verified for both single-phase alloys and complex multiphase high-temperature alloys. It is a useful method for obtaining high-temperature properties of comparatively brittle materials. On the other hand, tests of this type give no indication of the ductility of the material, which in certain cases may be a more controlling factor than the strength.

13-10. High-temperature Alloys

High-temperature alloys are a particular class of complex materials developed for a very specific application. Some appreciation of the metallurgical principles behind the development of these alloys is important to an understanding of how metallurgical variables influence creep behavior. The development of high-temperature alloys has, in the main, been the result of painstaking, empirical investigation, and it is really only in retrospect that principles underlying these developments have become evident.

The nominal compositions of a number of high-temperature alloys are

[1] E. E. Underwood, *Materials & Methods*, vol. 45, pp. 127–129, 1957; *J. Inst. Metals*, vol. 88, pp. 266–271, 1959–1960.

given in Table 13-1. Only a few of the many available alloys[1] could be included in this table. The ferritic alloys were developed first to meet increased temperature requirements in steam power plants. They are essentially carbon steels, with increased chromium and molybdenum to form complex carbides, which resist softening. Molybdenum is particularly effective in increasing the creep resistance of steel. Because of

TABLE 13-1
COMPOSITIONS OF TYPICAL HIGH-TEMPERATURE ALLOYS

Alloy	C	Cr	Ni	Mo	Co	W	Cb	Ti	Al	Fe	Other
Ferritic Steels											
1.25 Cr, Mo	0.10	1.25	....	0.50	...	...	....	.....	....	Balance	
5 Cr, Mo	0.20	5.00	....	0.50	...	...	....	.....	....	Balance	
"17-22-A" S	0.30	1.25	....	0.50	...	...	....	.....	....	Balance	
410	0.10	12.0	....	.....	...	...	....	.....	....	Balance	
Austenitic Steels											
316	0.08	17.0	12.0	2.50	...	...	....	.....	....	Balance	
347	0.06	18.0	12.0	.....	...	...	0.70	.....	....	Balance	
16-25-6	0.10	16.0	25.0	6.00	...	...	....	.....	....	Balance	
A-286	0.05	15.0	26.0	1.25	...	...	....	1.95	0.20	Balance	
Nickel-base Alloys											
Inconel	0.04	15.5	76.0	.....	...	...	....	.....	....	7.0	
Inconel X	0.04	15.0	75.0	.....	...	...	....	2.5	0.6	7.0	
Nimonic 90	0.08	20.0	58.0	.....	16	...	....	2.3	1.4	0.5	
Hastelloy B	0.10	1.0	65.0	28	...	...	....	.....	....	5.0	
René 41	0.10	19.0	53.0	10	11	...	....	3.2	1.6	2.0	
Udimet 500	0.10	19.4	55.6	4	14	...	....	2.9	2.9	0.6	
Cobalt-base Alloys											
Vitallium (HS-21)	0.25	27.0	3.0	5	62	...	....	.....	....	1.0	
X-40 (HS-31)	0.40	25.0	10.0	.....	55	8	....	.....	....	1.0	
Complex Superalloys											
N-155 (Multimelt)	0.15	21.0	20.0	3	20	2.5	1.0	.....	....	Balance	0.15N
S-590	0.40	20.0	20.0	4	20	4.0	4.0	.....	....	Balance	
S-816	0.40	20.0	20.0	4	Bal.	4.0	4.0	.....	....	3.0	
K 42 B	0.05	18.0	43.0	.....	22	...	....	2.5	0.2	13	
Refractaloy 26	0.05	18.0	37.0	3	20	...	....	2.8	0.2	18	

[1] H. C. Cross and W. F. Simmons, Alloys and Their Properties for Elevated Temperature Service, "Utilization of Heat Resistant Alloys," American Society for Metals, Metals Park, Ohio, 1954.

oxidation and the instability of the carbide phase these alloys are limited in use to about 1000°F. Owing to the increased oxidation resistance of austenitic stainless steels, these alloys extend the useful stress-bearing range to about 1200°F.

The superalloys for jet-engine applications are based on either nickel or cobalt austenitic alloys or combinations of the two. In general they contain appreciable chromium for oxidation resistance. Single-phase solid-solution alloys such as Nichrome (Ni-Cr) and austenitic stainless steel become weak above about 1300°F. Superalloys, therefore, are multiphase alloys which attain their strength primarily from a dispersion of stable second-phase particles. In the cobalt-base alloys and certain complex Ni-Co-Cr-Fe alloys like N-155, S-590, and S-816 the second-phase particles are complex metal carbides. Molybdenum, tungsten, and columbium are added to these alloys to form stable complex carbides. The carbon content of these alloys is usually critical and must be controlled carefully. Increasing the carbon content up to a certain limit increases the amount of carbide particles, and hence the rupture strength is increased. However, if too much carbon is present, the carbides will no longer be present as discrete particles. Instead, massive carbide networks form and reduce the rupture strength. Certain carbide systems undergo a series of complex aging reactions which may result in additional strengthening.

Nickel-base superalloys may be strengthened by the addition of small amounts of Al and/or Ti. The intermetallic compounds Ni_3Al or Ni_3Ti are formed by these additions. Up to three out of every five atoms of Al in Ni_3Al may be replaced by Ti, to form $Ni_3(Al,Ti)$. Since this compound produces greater hardening than Ni_3Al, it is customary to add both Al and Ti to these nickel-base alloys. Nickel-base alloys containing Al and Ti are true age-hardening systems, so that their high-temperature strength depends on the ability of the system to resist overaging. The heat treatment must be carefully controlled to put these alloys in the condition of maximum particle stability. This can be destroyed if the service conditions fluctuate above the optimum aging temperature.

A new class of dispersion-strengthened high-temperature alloys are being developed in which thermally stable second-phase particles, chiefly Al_2O_3, SiO_2, and ZrO_2, are introduced into a metal matrix by artificial means.[1] The prototype for this development was the sintered aluminum-powder (SAP) alloy, in which fine Al_2O_3 particles were dispersed in an aluminum matrix owing to the breakoff of surface oxide during the extrusion of sintered aluminum powder. At present most developments are centered in the preparation of a dispersion-hardened alloy by powder-metallurgy methods. Mixtures of fine oxides and metal powders are

[1] N. J. Grant and O. Preston, *Trans. AIME*, vol. 209, pp. 349–356, 1957.

pressed, sintered, and extruded into useful shapes.   Data for copper and nickel alloys prepared in this way show that the stress-rupture curves for a dispersion-strengthened alloy drop off much less rapidly with time than for the same metal without second-phase particles.   By comparing on the basis of rupture time at a given stress, improvements of 1,000 per cent have been reported for dispersion-strengthened alloys, while increases in rupture stress at 100 hr of over 10,000 psi have been found for nickel.

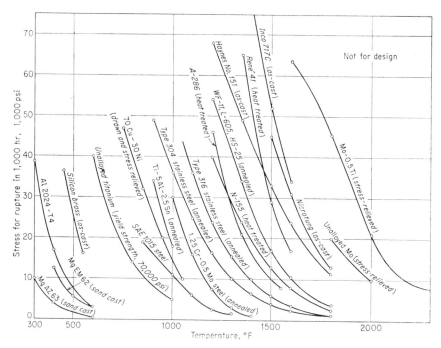

Fig. 13-13. Typical curves of stress for rupture in 1,000 hr versus temperature for selected engineering alloys.   (*D. P. Moon and W. F. Simmons, DMIC Memo 92, Battelle Memorial Institute, Mar. 23, 1961.*)

The production of artificial dispersion-strengthened alloys offers considerable promise, since in principle it permits the use of a second-phase particle with maximum resistance to growth, and at the same time the size and amount of the particles can be controlled.

An analogous approach is the development of *cermets*, in which ceramic particles such as borides, carbides, and silicides are combined with a metallic binder by powder-metallurgy methods.   Cermets have shown very high strength at 1800°F, but their use has been limited owing to poor ductility and insufficient thermal- and mechanical-shock resistance.

The high-temperature strength of metals is approximately related to their melting points. For example, aluminum has better high-temperature strength than zinc, and copper is better than aluminum. Titanium, chromium, columbium, molybdenum, tantalum, and tungsten, in order of increasing melting point, are the relatively common metals with melting points greater than iron, cobalt, and nickel, the principal constituents of present-day superalloys. Although the high-temperature strength of titanium has not proved to be so great as would be expected on the basis of its melting point, molybdenum and its alloys have the best high-temperature strength of any common metals available at the present time. Figure 13-13, which shows the stress for rupture in 1,000 hr at different temperatures for a number of engineering materials, illustrates the superiority of molybdenum. Unfortunately, the use of molybdenum is limited by the fact that it undergoes catastrophic oxidation at elevated temperature. Oxidation-resistance coatings for molybdenum are being used to a certain extent. Extensive development of ways of preparing, purifying, and fabricating the other refractory metals is under way. This work includes a search for methods of increasing their oxidation resistance and high-temperature strength by alloying.

13-11. Effect of Metallurgical Variables

The high-temperature creep and stress-rupture strengths are usually higher for coarse-grain material than for a fine-grain-size metal. This, of course, is in contrast to the behavior at lower temperature, where a decrease in grain size results in an increase in strength. The basic effect of grain size on high-temperature strength is clouded because it is practically impossible to change the grain size of complex superalloys without inadvertently changing some other factor such as the carbide spacing or the aging response. In fact, Parker[1] has proposed that the observed dependence of high-temperature strength on grain size is basically incorrect. Formerly it was suggested that the lower creep strength of fine grain material was due to greater grain-boundary area available for grain-boundary sliding. However, work which indicates that grain-boundary sliding can account for only about 10 per cent of the total creep strain has cast doubt on this explanation.

Since high-temperature creep depends on dislocation climb, which in turn depends upon the rate at which vacancies can diffuse to edge dislocations, Parker feels that the grain-size effect on creep is due to the effect of grain-boundary structure on vacancy diffusion. Vacancy diffusion is more rapid along high-energy grain boundaries than through the bulk lattice. Therefore, with fine-grain material with many high-angle grain boundaries dislocation climb will be rapid, and the creep rate is high.

[1] E. R. Parker, *Trans. ASM*, vol. 50, pp. 52–104, 1958.

However, when the same material is heated to a high temperature to coarsen the grain size, most of the high-energy grain boundaries disappear owing to grain growth. The boundaries which remain are mostly lower-energy grain boundaries, for which vacancy diffusion is relatively slow. Therefore, dislocation climb will be slower in the coarse-grain material. The fact that low-angle grain boundaries improve creep properties is shown in Fig. 13-14. Networks of low-angle boundaries were produced in nickel by straining small amounts in tension at room temperature and annealing at 800°C. Note the change in shape of the creep curves and the decreasing creep rate as more and more low-angle grain boundaries were introduced, with greater prestrain. Recent experiments by Parker

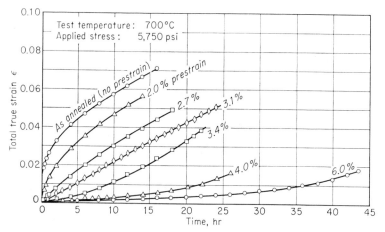

Fig. 13-14. Effect of substructure introduced by prestrain and anneal treatments on the creep curve of high-purity nickel. (*E. R. Parker, Trans. ASM, vol.* 50, *p.* 86, 1958.)

in which the grain size of copper was changed without changing the proportion of low-angle and high-angle grain boundaries have shown that the creep rate increases with increasing grain size. Thus, it appears as if the fundamental dependence of creep rate on grain size is no different from the dependence of strength on grain size at low temperature. However, secondary effects which accompany the change in grain size when it is accomplished by commercial annealing procedures are responsible for the effect which is usually observed.

Comparison of the properties of cast and forged high-temperature alloys in the same state of heat treatment shows that cast alloys generally have somewhat higher hot strength and creep resistance than forgings at temperatures above the equicohesive temperature. The reasons for this are not well established, but it appears that it is related to a strengthening from the dendritic structure of the casting. Advantages can be ascribed to both casting and forging as a method of production for high-temperature alloys. Most high-temperature alloys are hot-worked only with difficulty. There are certain alloys, particularly cobalt-base alloys, which cannot be hot-worked, and therefore they must be produced as castings. Although castings show somewhat better strength than forgings, the production conditions must be carefully controlled to provide uniform properties. Variations in grain size due to changes in section size may be a problem with castings. Because of their worked structure, forgings are more ductile than castings, and generally they show fatigue properties which are superior to those of castings.

Since high-temperature alloys are designed to resist deformation at high temperatures, it is not surprising to find that they present problems in mechanical working and fabrication. Hot working of superalloys for ingot breakdown is generally done in the range 1700 to 2200°F. It should be recognized that working highly alloyed materials like superalloys does not constitute true hot working since residual strains will be left in the lattice. For this reason the resulting properties of age-hardenable alloys are dependent on the hot-working conditions. The rupture properties of certain nonaging solid-solution alloys like 16-25-6, N-155, and S-816 are appreciably improved by controlled amounts of reduction in the range 1200 to 1700°F. This procedure is known as *hot-cold working*, or *warm working*. Deformation in this temperature region for these highly alloyed materials is about equivalent to working mild steel at room temperature. Warm working and cold working at room temperature of less highly alloyed materials produce higher creep strength because of the energy stored in the lattice as a result of the plastic deformation. For a given operating temperature there will be a critical amount of cold work beyond which the increased lattice strain causes rapid recovery and recrystallization. The critical amount of cold work decreases as the operating temperature is increased.

In general, there is little correlation between room-temperature strength and high-temperature strength. For example, the incorporation of a dispersion of fine oxide particles in the metal matrix may produce only a modest increase in room-temperature strength, but the improvement in rupture time at elevated temperature may be a thousandfold. The importance of using a thermally stable metallurgical structure for long-time high-temperature service is well illustrated by the case of low-alloy steels. Although a quenched and tempered martensitic structure of fine carbides has the best strength at room temperature and may have good strength for short times up to 1100°F, on long exposure at elevated temperature the carbides grow and coalesce and the creep properties are very poor. Much better creep properties are obtained if the steel is initially in the stable annealed condition. The problem of selecting the best heat treatment for a complex superalloy is frequently difficult. A compromise must be reached between the fineness of the dispersion of second-phase particles and their thermal stability. Assuming that the transformation characteristics for the alloy are completely known, which is usually not the case, the selection of the heat treatment would be based on the expected service temperature and the required service life. One of the difficulties which must be guarded against is the formation of grain-boundary precipitates, which lead to intergranular fracture.

High-temperature properties can show considerable scatter, and frequently measurably different results are obtained between different heats of the same material or even between different bars from the same heat. The creep properties of steels are particularly subject to variations in properties, which are related in complex ways to the composition, melting practice, type of mechanical working, and microstructure. Aluminum deoxidized steels generally have poorer creep properties than silicon deoxidized steels. Not only does aluminum refine the grain size, but it also accelerates spheroidization and graphitization. Considerable improvement in the high-temperature properties of superalloys results from vacuum melting. Fabricability is also improved, presumably because of the decrease in the number and size of inclusions. In general, life to rupture and ductility at fracture are both increased by vacuum melting. Better control of composition, and therefore more uniform response to heat treatment, is obtained with vacuum melting.

The environment surrounding the specimen can have an important influence on high-temperature strength. Creep tests on zinc single crystals showed that creep practically stopped when copper was plated on the surface of the specimens.[1] When the copper was electrolytically removed, creep began again at nearly the original rate. Stress-rupture tests on nickel and nickel-chromium alloys show a complex dependence on atmosphere.[2] At high temperatures and low strain rates these materials are stronger in air than in vacuum, while the reverse is true at low temperatures and high strain rates. This behavior is attributed to the competing effects of strengthening resulting from oxidation and weakening due to lowering of the surface energy by absorbed gases. The nature of the oxidation can have an important influence on the high-temperature properties. A thin oxide layer or a finely dispersed oxide will usually lead to strengthening, but intergranular penetration of oxide will usually lead to decreased rupture life and intergranular fracture. When mate-

[1] M. R. Pickus and E. R. Parker, *Trans. AIME*, vol. 191, pp. 792–796, 1951.
[2] P. Shahinian and M. R. Achter, *Trans. ASM*, vol. 51, pp. 244–255, 1959.

rials must operate in an atmosphere of hot combustion gases or in corrosive environments, the service life is materially reduced.

13-12. Creep under Combined Stresses

Considerable attention has been given to the problem of design for combined stress conditions during steady-state creep.[1] In the absence of metallurgical changes, the basic simplifying assumptions of plasticity theory (see Sec. 3-8) hold reasonably well for these conditions. The assumption of incompressible material leads to the familiar relationship $\dot{\epsilon}_1 + \dot{\epsilon}_2 + \dot{\epsilon}_3 = 0$. The assumption that principal shear-strain rates are proportional to principal shear stresses gives

$$\frac{\dot{\epsilon}_1 - \dot{\epsilon}_2}{\sigma_1 - \sigma_2} = \frac{\dot{\epsilon}_2 - \dot{\epsilon}_3}{\sigma_2 - \sigma_3} = \frac{\dot{\epsilon}_3 - \dot{\epsilon}_1}{\sigma_3 - \sigma_1} = C \tag{13-31}$$

Combining these equations results in

$$\dot{\epsilon}_1 = \frac{2}{3C} [\sigma_1 - \tfrac{1}{2}(\sigma_2 + \sigma_3)] \tag{13-32}$$

Similar expressions are obtained for $\dot{\epsilon}_2$ and $\dot{\epsilon}_3$.

For engineering purposes the stress dependence of the creep rate can be expressed by Eq. (13-16). For combined stress conditions $\dot{\epsilon}$ and σ must be replaced by the effective strain rate $\dot{\epsilon}$ and the effective stress $\bar{\sigma}$ [see Eqs. (3-35) and (3-36)]. Thus, we can write

$$\dot{\bar{\epsilon}} = B\bar{\sigma}^{n'} \tag{13-33}$$

Combining Eqs. (13-32) and (13-33) results in

$$\dot{\epsilon}_1 = B\bar{\sigma}^{n'-1}[\sigma_1 - \tfrac{1}{2}(\sigma_2 + \sigma_3)] \tag{13-34}$$

The effective stress and the effective strain rate are useful parameters for correlating steady-state creep data. When plotted on log-log coordinates, they give a straight-line relationship. Correlation has been obtained between uniaxial creep tests, creep of thick-walled tubes under internal pressure, and tubes stressed in biaxial tension.[2]

13-13. Stress Relaxation

Stress relaxation under creep conditions refers to the decrease in stress at constant deformation. When stress relaxation occurs, the stress

[1] The original analysis of this problem was given by C. R. Soderberg, *Trans. ASME*, vol. 58, p. 733, 1936. Subsequent analysis has been made by I. Finnie, *Trans. ASME*, ser. D, vol. 82, pp. 462–464, 1960. For a critical review see A. E. Johnson, *Met. Reviews*, vol. 5, pp. 447–506, 1960.

[2] E. A. Davis, *Trans. ASME*, ser. D, vol. 82, pp. 453–461, 1960.

needed to maintain a constant total deformation decreases as a function of time. Consider a tension specimen which is under a total strain ϵ at an elevated temperature where creep can occur.

$$\epsilon = \epsilon_e + \epsilon_p = \frac{\sigma}{E} + \epsilon_p \qquad (13\text{-}35)$$

where ϵ = total strain
ϵ_e = elastic strain
ϵ_p = plastic (creep) strain

For the total strain to remain constant as the material creeps, it is necessary for the elastic strain to decrease. This means that the stress required to maintain the total strain decreases with time as creep increases.

The relaxation of stress in bolted joints and shrink or press-fit assemblies may lead to loose joints and leakage. Therefore, stress-relaxation

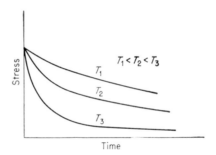

Fig. 13-15. Stress-relaxation curves.

tests are commonly made on bolting materials for high-temperature service.[1] Figure 13-15 shows the type of curves which are obtained. The initial rate of decrease of stress is high, but it levels off because the stress level is decreased and the transient creep rate decreases with time. These type of curves also can be used to estimate the time required to relieve residual stress by thermal treatments. If Eq. (13-16) can be used to express the stress dependence of creep, then the time required to relax the stress from the initial stress σ_i to σ is given by[2]

$$t = \frac{1}{BE(n' - 1)\sigma^{n'-1}} \left[1 - \left(\frac{\sigma}{\sigma_i} \right)^{n'-1} \right] \qquad (13\text{-}36)$$

BIBLIOGRAPHY

"Creep and Fracture of Metals at High Temperatures," H. M. Stationery Office, London, 1956.

[1] Relaxation properties of steels and superalloys are given in *ASTM Spec. Tech. Publ.* 187, 1956.

[2] E. L. Robinson, *Proc. ASTM*, vol. 48, p. 214, 1948.

"Creep and Recovery," American Society for Metals, Metals Park, Ohio, 1957.

Finnie, I., and W. R. Heller: "Creep of Engineering Materials," McGraw-Hill Book Company, Inc., New York, 1959.

Hehemann, R. F., and G. M. Ault (eds.): "High Temperature Materials," John Wiley & Sons, Inc., New York, 1959.

"High Temperature Properties of Metals," American Society for Metals, Metals Park, Ohio, 1951.

Smith, G. V.: "Properties of Metals at Elevated Temperatures," McGraw-Hill Book Company, Inc., New York, 1950.

Sully, A. H.: Recent Advances in Knowledge Concerning the Process of Creep in Metals, "Progress in Metal Physics," vol. 6, Pergamon Press, Ltd., London, 1956.

"Utilization of Heat Resistant Alloys," American Society for Metals, Metals Park, Ohio, 1954.

Chapter 14
BRITTLE FAILURE
AND IMPACT TESTING

14-1. The Brittle-failure Problem

During World War II a great deal of attention was directed to the brittle failure of welded Liberty ships and T-2 tankers.[1] Some of these ships broke completely in two, while, in other instances, the fracture did not completely disable the ship. Most of the failures occurred during the winter months. Failures occurred both when the ships were in heavy seas and when they were anchored at dock. These calamities focused attention on the fact that normally ductile mild steel can become brittle under certain conditions. A broad research program was undertaken to find the causes of these failures and to prescribe the remedies for their future prevention. In addition to research designed to find answers to a pressing problem, other research was aimed at gaining a better understanding of the mechanism of brittle fracture and fracture in general. Many of the results of this basic work are described in Chap. 7, which should be reviewed before proceeding further with this chapter. While the brittle failure of ships concentrated great attention on brittle failure in mild steel, it is important to understand that this is not the only application where brittle fracture is a problem. Brittle failures in tanks, pressure vessels, pipelines, and bridges have been documented[2] as far back as the year 1886.

Three basic factors contribute to a brittle-cleavage type of fracture. They are (1) a triaxial state of stress, (2) a low temperature, and (3) a high strain rate or rapid rate of loading. All three of these factors do not have to be present at the same time to produce brittle fracture. A

[1] M. L. Williams, Analysis of Brittle Behavior in Ship Plates, Symposium on Effect of Temperature on the Brittle Behavior of Metals with Particular Reference to Low Temperatures, *ASTM Spec. Tech. Publ.* 158, pp. 11–44, 1954.

[2] M. E. Shank, A Critical Survey of Brittle Failure in Carbon Plate Steel Structures Other than Ships, *ASTM Spec. Tech. Publ.* 158, pp. 45–110, 1954.

triaxial state of stress, such as exists at a notch, and low temperature are responsible for most service failures of the brittle type. However, since these effects are accentuated at a high rate of loading, many types of impact tests have been used to determine the susceptibility of materials to brittle fracture. Steels which have identical properties when tested in tension or torsion at slow strain rates can show pronounced differences in their tendency for brittle fracture when tested in a notched-impact test. However, there are certain disadvantages to this type of test, so that much work has been devoted to the development of additional tests for defining the tendency for brittle fracture, and much effort has been expended in correlating the results of different brittle-fracture tests.

Since the ship failures occurred primarily in structures of welded construction, it was considered for a time that this method of fabrication was not suitable for service where brittle fracture might be encountered. A great deal of research has since demonstrated that welding, per se, is not inferior in this respect to other types of construction. However, strict quality control is needed to prevent weld defects which can act as stress raisers or notches. New electrodes have been developed that make it possible to make a weld with better properties than the mild-steel plate. The design of a welded structure is more critical than the design of an equivalent riveted structure, and much effort has gone into the development of safe designs for welded structures. It is important to eliminate all stress raisers and to avoid making the structure too rigid. To this end, riveted sections, known as crack arresters, were incorporated in some of the wartime ships so that, if a brittle failure did occur, it would not propagate completely through the structure.

14-2. Notched-bar Impact Tests

Various types of notched-bar impact tests are used to determine the tendency of a material to behave in a brittle manner. This type of test will detect differences between materials which are not observable in a tension test. The results obtained from notched-bar tests are not readily expressed in terms of design requirements, since it is not possible to measure the components of the triaxial stress condition at the notch. Furthermore, there is no general agreement on the interpretation or significance of results obtained with this type of test.

A large number of notched-bar test specimens of different design have been used by investigators of the brittle fracture of metals. Two classes of specimens have been standardized[1] for notched-impact testing. Charpy bar specimens are used most commonly in the United States, while the Izod specimen is favored in Great Britain. The Charpy speci-

[1] ASTM Standards, pt. 3, 1958, Designation E23-56T.

men has a square cross section and contains a notch at the center of its length. Either a V notch or a keyhole notch is used. The Charpy specimen is supported as a beam in a horizontal position. The load is applied by the impact of a heavy swinging pendulum (approximately 16 ft/sec impact velocity) applied at the midspan of the beam on the side opposite from the notch. The specimen is forced to bend and fracture at a strain rate on the order of 10^3 in./(in.)(sec). The Izod specimen is either circular or square in cross section and contains a V notch near one end. The specimen is clamped vertically at one end like a cantilever beam and is struck with the pendulum at the opposite end. Figure 14-1 illustrates the type of loading used with these tests. Note that the notch is subjected to a tensile stress as the specimen is bent by the moving pendulum. Plastic constraint at the notch produces a triaxial state of stress similar to that shown in Fig. 7-10. The relative values of the three

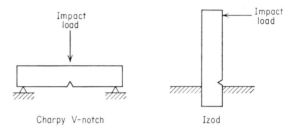

Fig. 14-1. Sketch showing method of loading in Charpy and Izod impact tests.

principal stresses depend strongly on the dimensions of the bar and the details of the notch. For this reason it is important to use standard specimens. The value of the transverse stress at the base of the notch depends chiefly on the relationship between the width of the bar and the notch radius. The wider the bar in relation to the radius of the notch, the greater the transverse stress.

The response of a specimen to the impact test is usually measured by the energy absorbed in fracturing the specimen. For metals this is usually expressed in foot-pounds and is read directly from a calibrated dial on the impact tester. In Europe impact results are frequently expressed in energy absorbed per unit cross-sectional area of the specimen. Very often a measure of ductility, such as the per cent contraction at the notch, is used to supplement this information. It is also important to examine the fracture surface to determine whether it is fibrous (shear failure) or granular (cleavage fracture). Figure 14-2 illustrates the appearance of these two types of fractures.

The notched-bar impact test is most meaningful when conducted over a range of temperature so that the temperature at which the ductile-to-

Fig. 14-2. Fracture surfaces of Charpy specimens tested at different temperatures. Left, 40°F; center, 100°F; right, 212°F. Note gradual decrease in the granular region and increase in lateral contraction at the notch with increasing temperature.

brittle transition takes place can be determined. Figure 14-3 illustrates the type of curves which are obtained. Note that the energy absorbed decreases with decreasing temperature but that for most cases the decrease does not occur sharply at a certain temperature. This makes it difficult to determine accurately the transition temperature. In selecting a material from the standpoint of notch toughness or tendency for brittle failure the important factor is the transition temperature. Figure 14-3 illustrates how reliance on impact resistance at only one temperature can be misleading. Steel A shows higher notch toughness at room temperature; yet its transition temperature is higher than that of

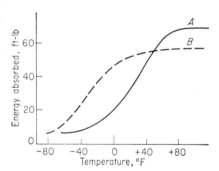

Fig. 14-3. Transition-temperature curves for two steels, showing fallacy of depending on room-temperature results.

steel B. The material with the lowest transition temperature is to be preferred.

Notched-bar impact tests are subject to considerable scatter,[1] particularly in the region of the transition temperature. Most of this scatter is

---

[1] R. H. Frazier, J. W. Spretnak, and F. W. Boulger, Symposium on Effect of Temperature on the Brittle Behavior of Metals, *ASTM Spec. Tech. Publ.* 158, pp. 286–307, 1954.

due to local variations in the properties of the steel, while some is due to difficulties in preparing perfectly reproducible notches.   Both notch shape and depth are critical variables, as is the proper placement of the specimen in the impact machine.

The shape of the transition curve depends on the type of test and also on the material.   For example, keyhole Charpy specimens usually give

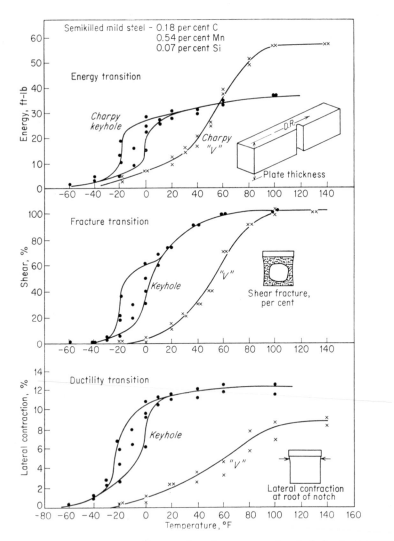

Fig. 14-4. Transition-temperature curves based on energy absorbed, fracture appearance, and notch ductility.   (*W. S. Pellini, ASTM Spec. Tech. Publ. 158, p. 222, 1954.*)

a sharper breaking curve than V-notch Charpy specimens. For a tough steel V-notch Charpy specimens generally give somewhat higher values than keyhole specimens. The transition temperature for a given steel will be different for different-shaped specimens and for different types of loading with different states of stress. The correlation of transition temperatures measured in different ways will be discussed in a later section.

Because the transition temperature is not sharply defined, it is important to understand the criteria which have been adopted for its definition. The most suitable criterion for selecting the transition temperature is whether or not it correlates with service performance. In general, criteria for determining the transition temperature are based on a transition in energy absorbed, change in the appearance of the fracture, or a transition in the ductility, as measured by the contraction at the root of the notch.[1] Figure 14-4 shows that the same type of curve is obtained for each criterion. This figure also illustrates the relative shapes of the curves obtained with keyhole and V-notch Charpy specimens. The energy transition temperature for V-notch Charpy specimens is frequently set at a level of 10 or 15 ft-lb. Where the fracture appearance changes gradually from shear through mixtures of shear and cleavage to complete cleavage, with decreasing temperature, the transition temperature is frequently selected to correspond to a temperature where 50 per cent fibrous (shear) fracture is obtained. The ductility transition temperature is sometimes arbitrarily set at 1 per cent lateral contraction at the notch. One characteristic of these criteria is that a transition temperature based on fracture appearance always occurs at a higher temperature than if based on a ductility or energy criterion.

14-3. Slow-bend Tests

The slow bending of flat-beam specimens in a testing machine is sometimes used as a method of determining the transition temperature. A biaxial state of stress is produced during the bending of an unnotched beam when the width is much greater than the thickness. When the ratio of width to thickness is close to unity, the stress is essentially uniaxial, but as the width increases, the ratio of the transverse to longitudinal stress approaches a value of $\frac{1}{2}$, the condition for a state of plane stress.[2] The unnotched-bend test represents a condition of severity inter-

---

[1] W. S. Pellini, Evaluation of the Significance of Charpy Tests, Symposium on Effect of Temperature on the Brittle Behavior of Metals with Particular Reference to Low Temperatures, *ASTM Spec. Tech. Publ.* 158, pp. 216–261, 1954.

[2] G. S. Sangdahl, E. L. Aul, and G. Sachs, *Proc. Soc. Exptl. Stress Anal.*, vol. 6, no. 1, pp. 1–18, 1948.

mediate between that of the tensile test and a notched-impact test. Usually a notch is used to introduce triaxial stress, in which case the transition temperature is raised.

The effect of adding the variable of high strain rate is complex. In a comparison of the transition temperature measured with a slow-bend test and a Charpy impact test with identically notched specimens it was found that the ductility transition was raised by impact but that the fracture transition was lower for the impact test. From this and other work, it appears as if the fracture transition temperature is not sensitive to strain rate.

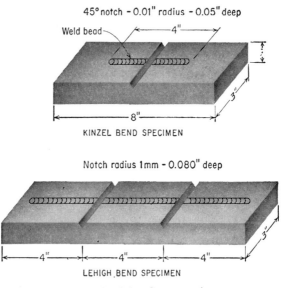

45° notch - 0.01" radius - 0.05" deep

Weld bead

4"

8"

KINZEL BEND SPECIMEN

Notch radius 1mm - 0.080" deep

4"   4"   4"

LEHIGH BEND SPECIMEN

Fig. 14-5. Notch-bend test specimens.

The Kinzel and Lehigh (Fig. 14-5) notch-bend specimens are frequently used for studying the effect of welding and metallurgical variables on notch toughness. Both specimens incorporate a longitudinal weld bead which is notched so that the weld metal, the heat-affected zone, and the unaffected base metal are exposed to the stress at the root of the notch. Both specimens are bent with the load applied opposite to the notch. The Lehigh specimen provides duplicate tests. Load-deflection curves are obtained and the data plotted in terms of energy absorbed to maximum load, energy absorbed after maximum load to fracture, or total energy absorbed. Lateral contraction at the notch and bend angle are also measured.

14-4. Specialized Tests for Transition Temperature

A number of new tests for determining the transition temperature of steel have been developed as a result of the research on the brittle failure of ships. Space will permit only a brief description of several of the most interesting of these tests, which give indication of attaining more general acceptance.

A number of tests subject the notch to simultaneous tension and bending. This can be done by eccentrically loading a notched tensile

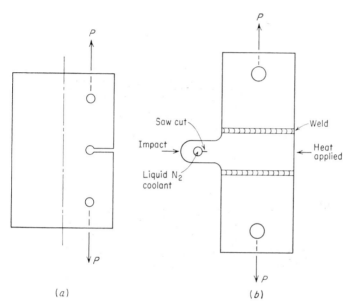

Fig. 14-6. (a) Specimen used in Navy tear test; (b) specimen used in Robertson test.

specimen or by using a specimen such as shown in Fig. 14-6a. This specimen is used in the Navy tear test.[1] It employs the full thickness of the steel plate. The advantage of a combined tension plus bending load over one of bending alone is that by suitably increasing the tensile load the compression region developed by the bending load can be eliminated. Since a high-compression region will retard crack propagation, a test which combines both bending and tension aids in crack propagation.

Robertson[2] devised an interesting test for determining the temperature at which a rapidly moving crack comes to rest. A uniform tensile stress

---

[1] N. A. Kahn and E. A. Imbemo, *Welding J.*, vol. 29, pp. 153s–165s, 1949.

[2] T. S. Robertson, *Engineering*, vol. 172, pp. 445–448, 1951; *J. Iron Steel Inst.* (*London*), vol. 175, p. 361, 1953.

is applied to a specimen of the type shown in Fig. 14-6b. A starter crack is cut with a jeweler's saw at one side of the specimen. This side is cooled with liquid nitrogen, and the other side is kept at a higher temperature. Thus, a temperature gradient is maintained across the width of the specimen. A crack is started at the cold end by an impact gun. The energy available from the impact is not sufficient to make the crack grow very large, but the applied tensile stress tends to keep it growing. The crack travels across the width of the specimen until it reaches a point where the temperature is high enough to permit enough yielding to stop the crack. This occurs when the plastic deformation required for further spread of the crack cannot be supplied by the stored elastic energy. For each applied tensile stress there is a temperature above which the crack will not propagate. Robertson's data showed that this arrest temperature decreases sharply for most mild-steel plates when the applied tensile stress is lowered to about 10,000 psi. For these steels the crack will not be arrested if the stress exceeds this value and the temperature is below room temperature. This test has been modified for use without a temperature gradient.[1]

The drop-weight test was developed by the Naval Research Laboratory[2] to measure susceptibility to the initiation of brittle fracture in the presence of a cracklike notch. The specimen is a flat plate with a 3-in.-long bead of hard-facing metal applied at the center and notched to half depth. The welded side of the specimen is placed face down over end supports, and the center of the specimen is struck with a 60-lb falling weight. The bead of hard-facing metal cracks in a brittle manner, producing a sharp, cracklike notch. Since the purpose of the drop-weight test is to see whether or not fracture will occur at a sharp notch when the amount of yielding that can occur is restricted, the bending fixture is designed so as to limit the deflection of the specimen to 5°. Only 3° of bend is needed to produce a crack in the brittle weld bead. The additional 2° of bend provides a test of whether or not the steel can deform in the presence of the cracklike notch. This is a "go–no go" type of test in that at a given temperature the specimen either fractures completely or remains intact. The highest temperature of fracture is termed the nil-ductility transition temperature. This test provides a sharp transition temperature and is quite reproducible.

The explosion-bulge test was developed by the Naval Research Laboratory[3] to measure susceptibility to propagation of brittle fracture. A crack-starter weld is applied to the center of a 14-in.-square plate. The

[1] F. J. Feely, D. Hrtko, S. R. Kleppe, and M. S. Northrup, *Welding J.*, vol. 33, pp. 99s–111s, 1954.

[2] Pellini, *op. cit.*, pp. 233–235.

[3] *Ibid.*, pp. 228–231.

specimen is placed over a circular die and subjected to the force of a controlled explosion. The explosion produces a compressive shock wave which is reflected from the bottom of the plate as a tensile wave. This test is interpreted in terms of the appearance of the fracture in the plate. At a higher temperature the plate bulges, but the cracks still run to the edges of the plate. At still higher temperatures the plate bulges considerably more, and the crack becomes a shear crack which is confined to the center of the specimen. The fracture-appearance transition temperature is selected as the temperature at which cracking is confined to the bulged region of the plate. For most steels this transition temperature will fall 40 to 60°F above the nil-ductility transition of the drop-weight test. The two tests supplement each other. The drop-weight test establishes a temperature below which the material is very susceptible to fracture initiation, while the explosion-bulge test establishes a temperature above which the material is immune to brittle-fracture propagation.

14-5. Significance of the Transition Temperature

The notch toughness of a material should really be considered in terms of two distinct transition temperatures. Figure 14-7 shows the transition-temperature curves for such an ideal material. The *ductility transition temperature* is related to the fracture-initiation tendencies of the material. Completely brittle cleavage fracture occurs readily below the ductility transition temperature. The *fracture-appearance transition temperature* is related to the crack-propagation characteristics of the material. Above the fracture transition temperature cracks do not propagate catastrophically, because fracture occurs by the shear mode with appreciable absorption of energy. In the region between these two transition temperatures fractures are difficult to initiate, but once initiated they propagate rapidly with little energy absorption.

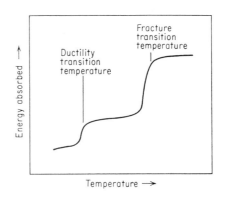

Fig. 14-7. Concept of two transition temperatures.

Actual materials do not have two distinct transition temperatures such as were shown in Fig. 14-7. Instead, Fig. 14-8 is more characteristic of the type of curves that are obtained with Charpy V-notch tests on mild steel. The ductility transition temperature usually occurs at an energy level of 5 to 20 ft-lb. Frequently a value of 15 ft-lb is used to establish this transition temperature. The ductility transition temperature may also be determined from measurements of the contraction at the root of the notch. The fracture-appearance transition temperature is measured by the per cent shear in the fracture surface. Usually it is taken at the temperature at which 50 per cent fibrous fracture is obtained. The fracture transition temperature always occurs at a higher temperature than the ductility transition temperature. For a given material the fracture-appearance transition temperature is fairly constant regardless of specimen geometry, notch sharpness, and rate of loading. On the other hand, the ductility transition temperature depends very strongly on the testing conditions. The ductility transition temperature is usu-

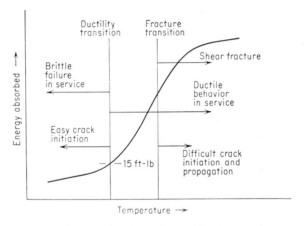

Fig. 14-8. Significance of regions of transition-temperature curve.

ally more pertinent to service performance, because if it is difficult to initiate a crack, then it is not necessary to worry about its propagation.

There is no general correlation between any of the brittle-fracture tests and service performance. The greatest number of data exist for failed hull plates in welded ships. Tests on these steels showed that they all had Charpy V-notch values of 11.4 ft-lb or less when tested at the temperature at which failure occurred. Experience with rimmed and semikilled mild-steel plates in thicknesses up to 1 in. indicates that a minimum Charpy V-notch value of 15 ft-lb at the lowest operating temperature should prevent brittle fracture if the nominal stresses are of the order of one-half the yield point. For higher alloy steels a higher value of minimum impact resistance may be required.

Part of the difficulty in correlating notch-impact data has been caused by failure to recognize and distinguish between the two general types of transition-temperature criteria. Comparisons should not be made between test results where the two criteria have been mixed. For example, no correlation is found between the keyhole and V-notch Charpy tests when the transition temperature is measured at a level corresponding to 50 per cent of the maximum energy. This is because the 50 per cent energy level is close to the ductility transition for the keyhole specimen but near the fracture transition for the V-notch specimen. Good correlation is found between the two specimens when they are both evaluated with common ductility criteria. Further, good correlation has been obtained[1] between the nil-ductility transition measured by the drop-weight test and the Charpy V-notch test. Good correlation has been shown between the drop-weight-test nil-ductility transition and service fractures. The correlation problem is well illustrated by the work of the Ship Structure Committee.[2]

14-6. Metallurgical Factors Affecting Transition Temperature

Changes in transition temperature of over 100°F can be produced by changes in the chemical composition or microstructure of mild steel. The largest changes in transition temperature result from changes in the amount of carbon and manganese.[3] The 15-ft-lb transition temperature for V-notch Charpy specimens (ductility transition) is raised about 25°F for each increase of 0.1 per cent carbon. This transition temperature is lowered about 10°F for each increase of 0.1 per cent manganese. Increasing the carbon content also has a pronounced effect on the maximum energy and the shape of the energy transition-temperature curves (Fig. 14-9). The Mn:C ratio should be at least 3:1 for satisfactory notch toughness. A maximum decrease of about 100°F in transition temperature appears possible by going to higher Mn:C ratios. The practical limitations to extending this beyond 7:1 are that manganese contents above about 1.4 per cent lead to trouble with retained austenite, while about 0.2 per cent carbon is needed to maintain the required tensile properties.

Phosphorus also has a strong effect in raising the transition temperature. The 15-ft-lb V-notch Charpy transition temperature is raised about 13°F for each 0.01 per cent phosphorus. Since it is necessary to control phosphorus, it is not generally advisable to use steel made by the Bessemer process for low-temperature applications. The role of nitrogen is difficult to assess because of its interaction with other elements. It is,

---

[1] H. Greenberg, *Metal Progr.*, vol. 71, pp. 75–81, June, 1957.

[2] E. R. Parker, "Brittle Behavior of Engineering Structures," chap. 6, John Wiley & Sons, Inc., New York, 1957.

[3] J. A. Rinebolt and W. J. Harris, Jr., *Trans. ASM*, vol. 43, pp. 1175–1214, 1951.

however, generally considered to be detrimental to notch toughness. Nickel is generally accepted to be beneficial to notch toughness in amounts up to 2 per cent and seems to be particularly effective in lowering the ductility transition temperature. Silicon, in amounts over 0.25 per cent, appears to raise the transition temperature. Molybdenum raises the transition almost as rapidly as carbon, while chromium has little effect.

Notch toughness is particularly influenced by oxygen. For high-purity iron[1] it was found that oxygen contents above 0.003 per cent produced intergranular fracture and corresponding low energy absorption. When the oxygen content was raised from 0.001 per cent to the high value of

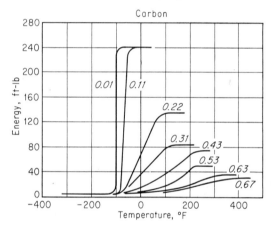

Fig. 14-9. Effect of carbon content on the energy-transition-temperature curves for steel. (*J. A. Rinebolt and W. J. Harris, Jr., Trans. ASM, vol. 43, p. 1197, 1951.*)

0.057 per cent, the transition temperature was raised from 5 to 650°F. In view of these results, it is not surprising that deoxidation practice has an important effect on the transition temperature. Rimmed steel, with its high iron oxide content, generally shows a transition temperature above room temperature. Semikilled steels, which are deoxidized with silicon, have a lower transition temperature, while for steels which are fully killed with silicon plus aluminum the 15 ft-lb transition temperature will be around −75°F. Aluminum also has the beneficial effect of combining with nitrogen to form insoluble aluminum nitride. The use of a fully killed deoxidation practice is not a completely practical answer to the problem of making steel plate with high notch toughness because there is only limited capacity for this type of production.

Grain size has a strong effect on transition temperature. An increase

[1] W. P. Rees, B. E. Hopkins, and H. R. Tipler, *J. Iron Steel Inst.* (*London*), vol. 172 pp. 403–409, 1952.

of one ASTM number in the ferrite grain size (actually a decrease in grain diameter) can result in a decrease in transition temperature of 30°F for mild steel. Decreasing the grain diameter from ASTM grain size 5 to ASTM grain size 10 can change the 10-ft-lb Charpy V-notch transition temperature[1] from about 70 to −60°F. A similar effect of decreasing transition temperature with decreasing austenite grain size is observed with higher alloyed heat-treated steels. Many of the variables concerned with processing mild steel affect the ferrite grain size and therefore affect the transition temperature. Since normalizing after hot rolling results in a grain refinement, if not carried out at too high a temperature, this treatment results in reduced transition temperature. The cooling rate from the normalizing treatment and the deoxidation practice are variables which also must be considered. Air cooling and aluminum deoxidation result in a lower transition temperature. Using the lowest possible finishing temperature for hot rolling of plate is also beneficial.

For a given chemical composition and deoxidation practice, the transition temperature will be appreciably higher in thick hot-rolled plates than in thin plates. This is due to the difficulty of obtaining uniformly fine pearlite and grain size in a thick section. Generally speaking, allowance for this effect must be made in plates greater than $\frac{1}{2}$ in. in thickness.

The notch toughness of steel is greatly influenced by microstructure. The best notch toughness is obtained with a microstructure which is completely tempered martensite. A completely pearlitic structure has poor notch toughness, and a structure which is predominately bainite is intermediate between these two. As an example of the effect of microstructure on transition temperature, in an SAE 4340 steel for which a tempered martensitic structure and pearlitic structure were compared at the same hardness, it was found that the Charpy-keyhole transition temperature at 25 ft-lb was 350°F lower for the tempered martensitic structure. Further discussion of the notch toughness of heat-treated steels will be found in Sec. 14-8.

Low-carbon steels can exhibit two types of aging phenomena which produce an increase in transition temperature. *Quench aging* is caused by carbide precipitation in a low-carbon steel which has been quenched from around 1300°F. *Strain aging* occurs in low-carbon steel which has been cold-worked. Cold working by itself will increase the transition temperature, but strain aging results in a greater increase, usually around 40 to 60°F. Quench aging results in less loss of impact properties than strain aging. The phenomenon of *blue brittleness*, in which a decrease in impact resistance occurs on heating to around 400°F, is due to strain aging.

---

[1] W. S. Owen, D. H. Whitmore, M. Cohen, and B. L. Averbach, *Welding J.*, vol. 36, pp. 503s–511s, 1957.

The notched-impact properties of rolled or forged products vary with orientation in the plate or bar. Figure 14-10 shows the typical form of the energy-temperature curves for specimens cut in the longitudinal and transverse direction of a rolled plate. Specimens A and B are oriented in the longitudinal direction of the plate. In specimen A the notch is perpendicular to the plate, while in B the notch lies parallel to the plate surface. The orientation of the notch in specimen A is generally preferred. In specimen C this notch orientation is used, but the specimen is oriented transverse to the rolling direction. Transverse specimens are used in cases where the stress distribution is such that the crack would propagate parallel to the rolling direction. Reference to

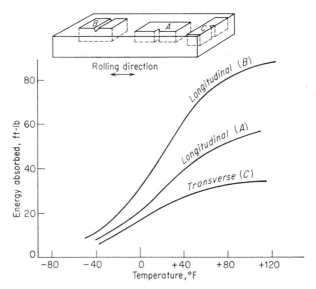

Fig. 14-10. Effect of specimen orientation on Charpy transition-temperature curves.

Fig. 14-10 shows that quite large differences can be expected for different specimen orientations at high energy levels, but the differences become much less at energy levels below 20 ft-lb. Since ductility transition temperatures are evaluated in this region of energy, it seems that specimen and notch orientation are not a very important variable for this criterion. If, however, materials are compared on the basis of room-temperature impact properties, orientation can greatly affect the results.

14-7. Effect of Section Size

Difficulty with brittle fracture usually increases as the size of the structure increases. This is due to both metallurgical and geometrical factors.

In the previous section it was shown that the transition temperature of a given steel usually decreases with increasing plate thickness because of the increased grain size produced in hot-rolling thick plates. However, Charpy tests on specimens of varying size but identical metallurgical structure and geometrically similar notches show that there is a size effect. At some temperature the largest specimens will be completely brittle, while the small specimens will be completely ductile. The fractures for in-between specimens will vary from almost fully ductile to almost fully brittle.

A dramatic demonstration of size effect was obtained in tests of ship hatch corners carried out at the University of California. Full scale, one-half scale, and one-quarter scale models were tested. These models were similar in all details and were made from the same material by the same welding procedures. When fracture strength was measured in terms of pounds per square inch of the net cross-sectional area, the full-sized specimen had only about one-half the strength of the quarter-scale model.

The higher transition temperature or lower fracture stress of large structures is due to two factors. The larger structure can contain a more unfavorable state of stress due to stress raisers, and it also provides a large reservoir for stored elastic energy. Since the Griffith criterion requires that the elastic strain energy must provide the surface energy for the formation of the fracture surface, the greater the available stored energy, the easier it is for the attainment of an uncontrollable, rapidly spreading crack.

14-8. Notch Toughness of Heat-treated Steels

It has been demonstrated many times that a tempered martensitic structure produces the best combination of strength and impact resistance of any microstructure that can be produced in steel. In Chap. 9 it was shown that the tensile properties of tempered martensites of the same hardness and carbon content are alike, irrespective of the amount of other alloy additions. This generalization holds approximately for the room-temperature impact resistance of heat-treated steels, but it is not valid for the variation of impact resistance with temperature. Figure 14-11 shows the temperature dependence of impact resistance for a number of different alloy steels, all having about 0.4 per cent carbon and all with a tempered martensite structure produced by quenching and tempering to a hardness of R_C 35. Note that a maximum variation of about 200°F in the transition temperature at the 20-ft-lb level is possible. Even greater spread in transition temperature would be obtained if the tempering temperature were adjusted to give a higher hardness.[1] Slack

[1] H. J. French, *Trans. AIME*, vol. 206, pp. 770–782, 1956.

quenching so that the microstructure consists of a mixture of tempered martensite, bainite, and pearlite results in even greater differences between alloy steels and in a general increase in the transition temperature.

The energy absorbed in the impact test of an alloy steel at a given test temperature generally increases with increasing tempering temperature. However, there is a minimum in the curve in the general region

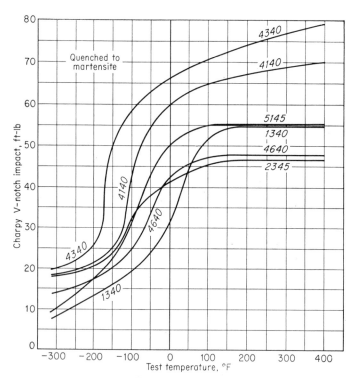

Fig. 14-11. Temperature dependence of impact resistance for different alloy steels of same carbon content, quenched and tempered to Rc 35. (*H. J. French, Trans. AIME, vol.* 206, *p.* 770, 1956.)

of 400 to 600°F (Fig. 14-12). This has been called 500°F *embrittlement*, but because the temperature at which it occurs depends on both the composition of the steel and the tempering time, a more appropriate name is *tempered-martensite embrittlement*. Embrittlement of steel in this tempering region is one of the chief deterrents to using steels at strength levels much above 200,000 psi. Studies of this embrittlement phenomenon have shown[1] that it is due to the precipitation of platelets of cementite

[1] L. J. Klingler, W. J. Barnett, R. P. Frohmberg, and A. R. Troiano, *Trans. ASM*, vol. 46, pp. 1557–1598, 1954.

from ε-carbide during the second stage of tempering. These platelets have no effect on the reduction of area of a tensile specimen, but they severely reduce the impact resistance. They can be formed at temperatures as low as 212°F and as high as 800°F, depending on the time allowed for the reaction. Silicon additions of around 2.25 per cent are

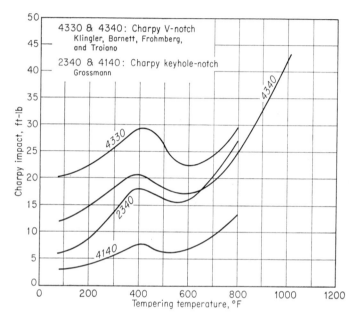

Fig. 14-12. Effect of tempering temperature on impact resistance at room temperature for four alloy steels quenched to martensite. (*H. J. French, Trans. AIME, vol.* 206, *p.* 770, 1956.)

effective in increasing the temperature at which the platelets precipitate, and this permits tempering in the region 500 to 600°F, without severe embrittlement.

14-9. Temper Embrittlement

Temper embrittlement[1] refers to a loss in notch toughness of plain-carbon and alloy steels when exposed at temperatures above about 700°F but below the temperature for the formation of austenite. Alloy steels are particularly susceptible to embrittlement when they are tempered in the region 800 to 1100°F or slow-cooled through this temperature range.

[1] The extensive literature in this field has been reviewed by B. C. Woodfine, *J. Iron Steel Inst. (London),* vol. 173, pp. 229–240, 1953, and L. D. Jaffe, *Welding J.,* vol. 34, pp. 1412–1502, 1955.

This can become a particularly important problem with heavy sections that cannot be cooled through this region rapidly enough to suppress embrittlement. Temper embrittlement also can be produced by isothermal treatments in this temperature region. The kinetics of the process produces a C-shaped curve when some parameter of embrittlement is plotted on temperature-time coordinates. More rapid embrittlement results from slow cooling through the critical temperature region than from isothermal treatment. Temper embrittlement can be completely eliminated from an embrittled steel by heating into the austenite region and cooling rapidly through the embrittling temperature region.

The presence of temper embrittlement is usually determined by measuring the transition temperature by means of a notched-bar impact test. The hardness and tensile properties are not sensitive to the embrittlement, except for very extreme cases, but the transition temperature can be increased around 200°F by ordinary embrittling heat treatments. The fracture of a temper-embrittled steel is intergranular, while the brittle fracture of a nonembrittled steel is transgranular. This suggests that temper brittleness is due to a grain-boundary weakness. However, no evidence for a grain-boundary film or precipitate has been uncovered from studies by means of the electron microscope of the microstructure of temper-embrittled steel. Therefore it is generally hypothesized that temper embrittlement is due to the segregation of impurities to the grain boundaries without the formation of an observable precipitate phase. The effect of various alloying elements on this embrittlement can then be explained on the basis of their rates of diffusion and relative solubilities at the grain boundaries and within the grains. Much more information is needed before a detailed mechanism of temper embrittlement can be determined.

Molybdenum is the only alloying element which decreases the susceptibility to temper embrittlement. The best solution to the problem is to avoid tempering in the region of greatest susceptibility to embrittlement. Tempering at a higher temperature for a short time may be better than a long tempering treatment at a lower temperature. A water quench from the tempering temperature will serve to minimize embrittlement on cooling.

14-10. Hydrogen Embrittlement

Severe embrittlement can be produced in many metals by very small amounts of hydrogen. Body-centered cubic and hexagonal close-packed metals are most susceptible to hydrogen embrittlement. As little as 0.0001 weight per cent of hydrogen can cause cracking in steel. Face-centered cubic metals are not generally susceptible to hydrogen embrittlement.[1] Hydrogen may be introduced during melting and entrapped during solidification, or it may be picked up during heat treatment, electroplating, acid pickling, or welding.

The chief characteristics of hydrogen embrittlement are its strain-rate sensitivity, its temperature dependence, and its susceptibility to delayed fracture. Unlike most embrittling phenomena, hydrogen embrittlement is enhanced by slow strain rates. At low temperatures and high temperatures hydrogen embrittlement is negligible, but it is most severe in some intermediate temperature region. For steel the region of greatest susceptibility to hydrogen embrittlement is in the vicinity of room temperature. Slow bend tests and notched and unnotched tension tests will detect hydrogen embrittlement by a drastic decrease in ductility, but notched-impact tests are of no use for detecting the phenomenon.

A common method of studying hydrogen embrittlement is to charge notched tensile specimens with known amounts of hydrogen, load them to different stresses in a dead-weight machine, and observe the time to failure. A typical delayed-fracture curve is shown in Fig. 14-13. Note that the notched tensile strength of a charged specimen may be much lower than the strength of a hydrogen-free specimen. There is a region in which the time to fracture depends only slightly on the applied stress. There is also a minimum critical value below which delayed fracture will not occur. The similarity of the delayed fracture curve to the fatigue S-N curve has led to the use of the term "static fatigue" for the delayed-fracture phenomenon. The minimum critical stress,

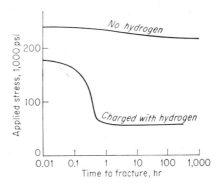

Fig. 14-13. Delayed-fracture curve.

or "static fatigue limit," increases with a decrease in hydrogen content or a decrease in the severity of the notch. The hydrogen content of steel may be reduced by "baking," or heating at around 300 to 500°F.

Hydrogen is present in solution as monatomic hydrogen. Because it is a small interstitial atom, it diffuses very rapidly at temperatures above room temperature. A commonly held concept of hydrogen embrittlement is that monatomic hydrogen precipitates at internal voids as molecular hydrogen. These voids might be true voids, microcracks, or perhaps simply regions of high dislocation density. As hydrogen diffuses

[1] The familiar example of the embrittlement of copper by hydrogen at elevated temperature is due to the reaction of hydrogen with oxygen to form internal pockets of steam.

into the voids, the pressure builds up and produces fracture. While this concept explains the general idea of hydrogen embrittlement, it is not in agreement with all the experimental facts. Further insight into the mechanism has resulted from the work of Troiano and coworkers.[1] By determining the rate of crack propagation by means of resistivity measurements they were able to show that the crack propagates discontinuously. This indicates that the rate of crack propagation is controlled by the diffusion of hydrogen to the region of high triaxial stress just ahead of the crack tip. When a critical hydrogen concentration is obtained, a small crack forms and grows, to link up with the previous main crack. The fact that the time for the initiation of the first crack has been found to be insensitive to applied stress supports the idea that the process depends on the attainment of a critical hydrogen concentration. The main effect of stress is to assist in the accumulation of this concentration. The minimum critical stress in Fig. 14-13 can be interpreted as the stress needed to cause a critical accumulation of hydrogen. The higher the average hydrogen content, the lower the necessary critical stress.

The formation of hairline cracks, or flakes, in large ingots and forgings during cooling or room-temperature aging has long been attributed to the presence of hydrogen. Studies[2] of flake formation have shown that in addition to containing hydrogen the steel must be subjected to transformation stresses for flaking to occur. The hydrogen content necessary for flaking varies widely with composition, size, and segregation. Flakes have been observed in steel with as low as 3 ppm of hydrogen. On the other hand, very high amounts of hydrogen can be tolerated without causing flakes if the transformation stresses are minimized by decomposing the austenite above the M_s temperature before cooling to room temperature.

14-11. Flow and Fracture under Very Rapid Rates of Loading

The mechanical properties of metals can be appreciably changed when they are subjected to very rapidly applied loads. Shock loading can be produced by high-velocity impact machines[3] or by shock waves from the detonation of explosives.[4] In considering dynamic loading of this type it is important to consider effects due to stress-wave propagation within

[1] A. R. Troiano, *Trans. ASM*, vol. 52, pp. 54–80, 1960.

[2] A. W. Dana, F. J. Shortsleeve, and A. R. Troiano, *Trans. AIME*, vol. 203, pp. 895–905, 1955.

[3] P. E. Duwez and D. S. Clark, *Proc. ASTM*, vol. 47, pp. 502–532, 1947.

[4] J. S. Rinehart and J. Pearson, "Behavior of Metals under Impulsive Loads," American Society for Metals, Metals Park, Ohio, 1954.

the metal.[1] This is because a rapidly applied load is not instantaneously transmitted to all parts of the loaded body. Rather, at a brief instant after the load has been applied the remote portions of the body remain undisturbed. The deformation and stress produced by the load move through the body in the form of a wave that travels with a velocity of the order of several thousand feet per second. Compression waves are generated in a metal when it is subjected to an explosive blast (impulsive loading), while tensile waves can be produced by a tension-impact machine. The propagation velocity of a compressive or tensile stress wave is given by

$$c_0 = \left(\frac{d\sigma/d\epsilon}{\rho}\right)^{1/2} \tag{14-1}$$

where c_0 = velocity of wave propagation
$d\sigma/d\epsilon$ = slope of stress-strain curve
ρ = density of metal
If the wave amplitude is low, so that the elastic limit is not exceeded, Eq. (14-1) can be written

$$c_0 = \left(\frac{E}{\rho}\right)^{1/2} \tag{14-2}$$

Corresponding to the *wave velocity* c_0, a certain *particle velocity* v_p is produced in the metal. The wave velocity and particle velocity are in the same direction for a compressive wave, but they are in opposite directions for a tensile wave. The particle velocity v_p is related to the wave velocity c_0 by the following equations:

$$v_p = \int_0^\epsilon c_0 \, d\epsilon = \frac{1}{\rho} \int_0^\sigma \frac{d\sigma}{c_0} \tag{14-3}$$

These equations can be used to determine the stress or strain in a dynamically loaded metal provided that the wave and particle velocities can be determined. When a bar is subjected to tension impact, it is found that there is a critical velocity which produces rupture at the impacted end at the instant of impact. By combining Eqs. (14-1) and (14-3) the equation for the critical velocity is obtained.

$$v_u = \int_0^{\epsilon_u} \left(\frac{d\sigma/d\epsilon}{\rho}\right)^{1/2} d\epsilon \tag{14-4}$$

where ϵ_u is the strain corresponding to the tensile strength of the metal. For shock loads below v_u the bar would undergo deformation but would not fracture. The value of critical impact velocity for most metals lies in the range of 200 to 500 ft/sec.

[1] H. Kolsky, "Stress Waves in Solids," Oxford University Press, New York, 1953.

Measurement of the dynamic stress-strain curve is difficult because of the short time during which events occur and because care must be taken to consider all wave-propagation phenomena. The information which is available indicates that for shock loading the stress-strain curve is raised about 10 to 20 per cent compared with the static curve. There is generally an increase in the energy to fracture with increasing impact velocity up to the point where the critical velocity is reached.

Marked differences occur between fracture under impulsive loads and under static loads. With impulsive loads there is not time for the stress to be disturbed throughout the entire body, so that fracture can occur in one part of the body independently of what happens in another part. The velocity of propagation of stress waves in solids lies in the range 3,000 to 20,000 ft/sec, while the velocity of crack propagation is about 6,000 ft/sec. Therefore, with impulsive loads it may be found that cracks have formed but did not have time to propagate before the stress state changed. Reflections of stress waves occur at free surfaces and fixed ends, at changes in cross section, and at discontinuities within the metal. A compression wave is reflected from a surface as a tension wave, and it is this reflected tension wave which in most cases causes fracture under impulsive loading. When a thick plate is subjected to explosive loading against one surface, the interference from the incident and reflected wave from the opposite surface will cause a tensile stress to be built up a short distance from the opposite surface. The tensile stress may be high enough to cause fracture, and the plate is said to have scabbed. From studying[1] the thickness of the scabs it is possible to arrive at values for a critical normal fracture stress.

BIBLIOGRAPHY

Parker, E. R.: "Brittle Behavior of Engineering Structures," John Wiley & Sons Inc., New York, 1957.
Queneau, B. R.: "The Embrittlement of Metals," American Society for Metals, Metals Park, Ohio, 1956.
Shank, M. E.: "Control of Steel Construction to Avoid Brittle Failure," Welding Research Council, New York, 1957.
Symposium on Effect of Temperature on the Brittle Behavior of Metals with Particular Reference to Low Temperatures, *ASTM Spec. Tech. Publ.* 158, 1954.
Tipper, C. F.: The Brittle Fracture of Metals at Atmospheric and Sub-zero Temperatures, *Met. Reviews*, vol. 2, no. 7, pp. 195–261, 1957.

[1] J. S. Rinehart, *J. Appl. Phys.*, vol. 22, p. 555, 1951; On Fractures Caused by Explosions and Impacts, *Quart. Colo. School Mines*, vol. 55, no. 4, October, 1960.

Chapter 15

RESIDUAL STRESSES

15-1. Origin of Residual Stresses

Residual stresses are the system of stresses which can exist in a body when it is free from external forces. They are sometimes referred to as *internal stresses*, or *locked-in stresses*. Residual stresses are produced whenever a body undergoes nonuniform plastic deformation. For example, consider a metal sheet which is being rolled under conditions such that plastic flow occurs only near the surfaces of the sheet (Fig. 15-1a).

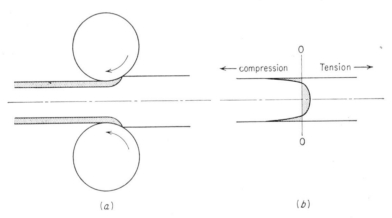

Fig. 15-1. (a) Inhomogeneous deformation in rolling of sheet; (b) resulting distribution of longitudinal residual stress over thickness of sheet (schematic).

The surface fibers of the sheet are cold-worked and tend to elongate, while the center of the sheet is unchanged. Since the sheet must remain a continuous whole, the surface and center of the sheet must undergo a strain accommodation. The center fibers tend to restrain the surface fibers from elongating, while the surface fibers seek to stretch the central fibers of the sheet. The result is a residual-stress pattern in the sheet

393

which consists of a high compressive stress at the surface and a tensile residual stress at the center of the sheet (Fig. 15-1b). In general, the sign of the residual stress which is produced by inhomogeneous deformation will be opposite to the sign of the plastic strain which produced the residual stress. Thus, for the case of the rolled sheet, the surface fibers which were elongated in the longitudinal direction by rolling are left in a state of compressive residual stress when the external load is removed.

The residual-stress system existing in a body must be in static equilibrium. Thus, the total force acting on any plane through the body and the total moment of forces on any plane must be zero. For the longitudinal stress pattern in Fig. 15-1b this means that the area under the curve subjected to compressive residual stresses must balance the area subjected to tensile residual stresses. The situation is not quite so simple as is pictured in Fig. 15-1. Actually, for a complete analysis, the residual stresses acting across the width and thickness of the sheet should be considered, and the state of residual stress at any point is a combined stress derived from the residual stresses in the three principal directions. Frequently, because of symmetry, only the residual stress in one direction need be considered. A complete determination of the state of residual stress in three dimensions is a very considerable undertaking.

Residual stresses are to be considered as only elastic stresses. The maximum value which the residual stress can reach is the elastic limit of the material. A stress in excess of this value, with no external force to oppose it, will relieve itself by plastic deformation until it reaches the value of the yield stress.

It is important to distinguish between *macro residual stresses* and *microstresses*. Macro residual stresses, with which this chapter is primarily concerned, vary continuously through the volume of the body and act over regions which are large compared with atomic dimensions. *Microstresses*, or *textural stresses*, act over dimensions as small as several unit cells, although their effects may extend throughout most of a grain. Because of the anisotropy of the elastic properties of crystals, microstresses will vary greatly from grain to grain. The back stress developed by a pile-up of dislocations is an example of this type of residual stress. Another example is the precipitation of second-phase particles from solid solution. If the precipitate particles occupy a larger volume than the components from which they formed, i.e., if the second-phase particles have a lower density than the matrix, then each particle in trying to occupy a larger volume is compressed by the matrix. This, in turn, develops tensile stresses in the matrix in directions radial and tangential to the second-phase particles. The experimental determination of these localized stresses in two-phase systems is very difficult, although measurements of their average value have been made with X rays.[1,2] Calculations of the microstresses existing in two-phase systems have been made by Lazlo,[3] who uses the terminology "tessellated stresses" for this type of residual stress. The determination of the microstresses which exist in plastically deformed single-phase metals is necessary for an understanding of the mechanism of strain hardening. Estimates of these microstresses can be made from detailed analysis of the broadening of X-ray diffraction lines. Further improvements on the techniques are needed before these measurements can be used without ambiguity.

Residual stresses arise from nonuniform plastic deformation of a body. The principal methods by which this can occur are by inhomogeneous changes in volume and in shape. A third source of residual stress may exist in built-up assemblies, such as welded structures. Even though the structure is not subjected to external loads, different members of the structure may be under stress due to various interactions between the members of the assembly. This type of residual stress is called *reaction stress*. Because it falls in the area of structural engineering, it will not be considered further in this chapter.

The precipitation of second-phase particles in a metal matrix is an example of a nonuniform volume change which produces very localized micro residual stresses. However, if the reaction does not proceed uniformly over the cross section of the body because of differences in either chemical composition or rate of heat transfer, there will be a variation in the distribution of microstresses which will produce macro residual stresses. Nitriding and carburizing are processes in which a microstress distribution is produced around each nitride or carbide particle, but because these diffusion-controlled reactions occur only on the surface, there is a nonuniform volume increase in this region. Thus, a macro compressive residual stress is produced on the surface, and this is balanced by tensile residual stresses in the interior. The phase transformation from austenite to martensite which occurs during the quenching of steel is an outstanding example of a nonuniform volume change leading to high residual stresses. Because of the technological importance of this situation, it will be considered in a separate section of this chapter.

Volume changes need not necessarily involve rapid quenching or phase changes to produce residual stresses. In the cooling of a large, hot ingot of a metal which shows no phase change, the temperature differences which are present between the surface and the center may be enough to

[1] J. Gurland, *Trans. ASM*, vol. 50, pp. 1063–1071, 1958.

[2] C. J. Newton and H. C. Vacher, *J. Research Natl. Bur. Standards*, vol. 59, pp. 239–243, 1957.

[3] For a review of Lazlo's extensive and detailed work, see F. R. N. Nabarro, "Symposium on Internal Stresses," p. 61, Institute of Metals, London, 1948.

develop residual stresses.[1] The edges of a hot slab cool faster than the center. The thermal contraction of the cooler edges produces a strain mismatch between the edges and center of the ingot which results in the distribution of longitudinal stresses shown in Fig. 15-2b. Since the hot center has a lower yield stress, it cannot support the compressive stress imposed on that region and because of plastic deformation the center of the ingot shrinks to relieve some of the stress (Fig. 15-2c). When the center of the slab finally cools, the total contraction will be greater for the center than the edges because the center contracts owing to both cooling and plastic deformation (Fig. 15-2d). The center will then be stressed in residual tension, and the edges will be in compression.

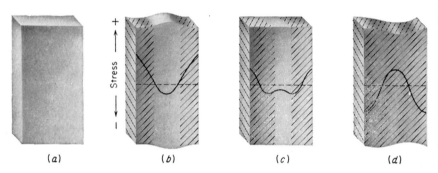

Fig. 15-2. Development of residual stresses during cooling of a hot ingot. Cool portions shown shaded. (*After W. M. Baldwin, Jr., Proc. ASTM, vol. 49, p. 541, 1949.*)

The forming operations required to convert metals to finished and semifinished shapes rarely produce homogeneous deformation of the metal. Each particular plastic forming process has a residual-stress distribution which is characteristic of the process and is influenced to a certain extent by the way in which the process has been carried out. Earlier in this section we have seen how the residual stress in the rolling direction of a sheet results from inhomogeneous deformation through the thickness of the sheet.

Other metalworking operations which are not generally classed as metal-forming processes can produce residual stresses because they involve inhomogeneous deformation. Spot welding and butt welding both produce high tensile stresses at the center of the area of application of heat. Shot peening, surface hammering, and surface rolling produce shallow biaxial compressive stresses on a surface which are balanced by biaxial tension stresses in the interior. As was noted in Chap. 12, shot peening is an effective method of reducing fatigue failures. Residual

[1] W. M. Baldwin, Jr., *Proc. ASTM*, vol. 49, pp. 539–583, 1949.

stresses are developed in electroplated coatings. Soft coatings such as lead, cadmium, and zinc creep sufficiently at room temperature to relieve most of these plating stresses. Hard coatings like chromium and nickel can have either high tensile or compressive residual stresses, depending upon the conditions of the plating process.

The superposition of several deformation operations does not produce a final residual-stress distribution which is the algebraic sum of the stress distributions produced by the preceding operations. In general, the final deformation process determines the resulting residual-stress pattern. However, superposition of stress distributions is a valid procedure when one is considering the effect of residual stress on the response of a body to an external stress system. For all practical purposes residual stresses can be considered the same as ordinary applied stresses. Thus, a compressive residual stress will reduce the effectiveness of an applied tensile stress in producing fatigue failure, and residual tensile stresses will increase the ease with which failure occurs.

15-2. Effects of Residual Stresses

The presence of residual stresses can influence the reaction of a material to externally applied stresses. In the tension test, that region of a specimen containing high residual tensile stresses will yield plastically at a lower value of applied stress than a specimen without residual stresses. Conversely, compressive residual stresses will increase the yield stress. This fact is used to strengthen gun tubes and pressure vessels by the process known as *autofrettage*. In autofrettage thick-walled cylinders are purposely strained beyond the elastic limit of the material at the bore of the cylinder so that this region will contain compressive residual stresses when the cylinder is unloaded. In a relatively brittle material like high-strength steel the presence of tensile residual stresses can cause a decrease in the fracture strength. The possibility of unknown residual stresses existing at the root of machined notches is a problem in notch tensile testing. The effect of residual stresses on fatigue performance is a well-recognized phenomenon and was considered in Sec. 12-9.

Residual stresses are responsible for warping and dimensional instability. If part of a body containing residual stresses is machined away, as in machining a long keyway in a cold-drawn bar, the residual stresses in the material removed are also eliminated. This upsets the static equilibrium of internal forces and moments, and the body distorts to establish a new equilibrium condition. Warping due to redistribution of residual stresses when surface layers are removed can be exceedingly troublesome, particularly with precision parts like tools and dies. However, there is a useful aspect to this, for as will be seen in the next section, the measurement of dimensional changes when material is removed from a body is one of the established methods for measuring residual stresses. Dimensional instability refers to changes in dimensions which occur without any removal of material. These changes result from the deformation required to maintain equilibrium when the residual-stress distribution changes from stress relaxation on long-time room-temperature aging. The residual-stress pattern in steels may also be altered by the transformation of retained austenite to martensite on aging.

Stress corrosion cracking[1] is a type of failure which occurs when certain metals are subjected to stress in specific chemical enviroments. Residual stress is just as effective as stress due to an externally applied load in producing stress corrosion cracking. Examples of combinations which produce stress corrosion cracking are mercury or ammonia compounds with brass (season cracking) and chlorides with austenitic stainless steels and certain age-hardenable aluminum alloys. Extreme care should be taken to minimize residual stress when these situations are likely to be encountered. In fact, accelerated stress corrosion cracking may be used as a qualitative test to indicate the presence of residual stresses. Typical solutions which are used for this purpose are listed below:

1. Brass–mercurous nitrate in water; standardized for detection of residual stress in brass cartridge cases (ASTM B154)
2. Austenitic stainless steel–boiling solution of 10 per cent H_2SO_4 and 10 per cent $CuSO_4$, or boiling $MgCl_2$
3. Mild steel–boiling NaOH
4. Aluminum–NaCl solution
5. Magnesium–potassium chromate solution

15-3. Mechanical Methods for Residual-stress Measurement

Residual stresses cannot be determined directly from strain-gage measurements, as is the case for stresses due to externally applied loads. Rather, residual stresses are calculated from the measurements of strain that are obtained when the body is sectioned and the locked-in residual stresses are released.

The method developed by Bauer and Heyn[2] for measuring the longitudinal residual stresses in a cylinder is a good illustration of the techniques involved. The residual stresses in the cylinder can be likened to a system of springs (Fig. 15-3). In this example the cylindrical bar is assumed to contain tensile residual stresses around the periphery and

---

[1] A review of this important subject is given by W. D. Robertson (ed.), "Stress Corrosion Cracking and Embrittlement," John Wiley & Sons, Inc., New York, 1956.

[2] E. Heyn and O. Bauer, *Intern. Z. Metallog.*, vol. 1, pp. 16–50, 1911.

compressive stresses at the center. By the spring analogy, the center springs would be compressed and the outer springs elongated (Fig. 15-3a). Now, if the static equilibrium of forces is upset by removing the outer springs, the compressed springs will elongate (Fig. 15-3b). The amount of elongation experienced by the center springs is directly proportional to the force exerted on them by the outer springs.

The strain experienced by the core is $de_1 = dL_1/L$, where L_1 is the expanded length of the element. The stress relieved by this expansion, σ_c, is related to the strain through Hooke's law.

$$\sigma_c = E\,de_1$$

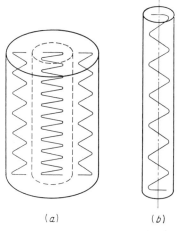

Since the cylinder was initially in equilibrium before the skin was removed, the force in the center core must balance the force in the removed material.

$$P_{\text{core}} = A_1 E\,de_1 = P_{\text{skin}}$$

If A_0 is the original area of the cylindrical bar, then the area of the skin is $dA_1 = A_0 - A_1$.

Fig. 15-3. (a) Heyn's spring model for longitudinal residual stresses in a cylinder; (b) elongation of center portion, due to removal of restraint of outer springs.

The average stress existing in the skin is $\bar{\sigma}_s$, so that the force in the skin may be written

$$P_{\text{skin}} = \bar{\sigma}_s\,dA_1$$

Equating the force in the core and the skin results in an equation for the average stress in the skin.

$$\bar{\sigma}_s = \frac{A_1 E\,de_1}{dA_1} \tag{15-1}$$

The above equation expresses the residual stress when it has the very arbitrary distribution shown in Fig. 15-4a. Actually, the distribution of longitudinal residual stress is more likely to vary in the continuous manner shown in Fig. 15-4b.

The residual-stress distribution shown in Fig. 15-4b can be determined by the Bauer and Heyn method if the stresses are determined by removing thin layers and measuring the deformation in the remaining portion. If sufficiently thin layers are removed and the process is repeated enough times, the measured stress distribution will approach the distribution shown in Fig. 15-4b. When the stress distribution is measured by the successive removal of thin layers, Eq. (15-1) gives the residual stress in the first layer removed. However, this equation will not give a true indication of the actual stress which originally existed in the second radial layer of the bar, because the removal of the first layer from the bar has caused a redistribution of stress in the remainder of the bar. The actual stress in the second layer as it existed in the original bar is given by

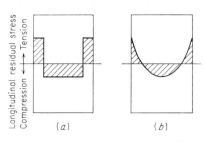

Fig. 15-4. Variation of longitudinal residual stress over the diameter of a bar. (a) Arbitrary case with constant residual stress; (b) realistic case with continuously varying stress from surface to center.

$$\sigma_2 = \frac{A_2 E \, de_2}{dA_2} - E \, de_1 \quad (15\text{-}2)$$

where A_2 is the area of the cylinder remaining after layer dA_1 has been removed. In determining the stress in succeeding layers a correction must be made for the stress relief due to all previous layer removals.

$$\sigma_n = \frac{A_n E \, de_n}{dA_n} - E(de_1 + de_2 + de_3 + \cdots + de_{n-1}) \quad (15\text{-}3)$$

If layers of differential thickness are removed, Eq. (15-3) may be written

$$\sigma = E\left(A \frac{de}{dA} - \int de\right) = E\left(A \frac{de}{dA} - e\right) \quad (15\text{-}4)$$

Equation (15-4) may be used to determine the longitudinal residual stress at any radial position in the bar. The best procedure is to plot the axial strain e after each layer removal against the area of the remaining bar, A. Connecting the points for successive layers will give a smooth curve. For any radial position, given by A, this curve will give the value of e, and the slope of the curve at the point e, A, will be de/dA.

The Bauer and Heyn method has been considered in considerable detail because it is a simple illustration of the methods used to convert measurements of strain into residual stresses. However, this technique can give values which are considerably in error because it does not consider tangential or radial residual stresses. In general, a bar will contain residual stresses in all three principal directions. The presence of transverse or radial stresses can result in up to 30 per cent error in the determination of the longitudinal residual stresses.

Sachs Boring-out Method

An exact method of determining the longitudinal, tangential, and radial residual stresses in bars or tubes was proposed by Mesnager[1] and modified

[1] M. Mesnager, *Compt. rend.*, vol. 169, pp. 1391–1393, 1919.

by Sachs.[1]   This method is commonly known as the Sachs boring-out technique.   The method is limited to cylindrical bodies in which the residual stresses vary in the radial direction but are constant in the longitudinal and circumferential directions.   This is not a particularly restrictive condition since bars and tubes made by most forming operations have the required symmetrical residual-stress pattern.

In using this technique with a solid bar the first step is to drill an axial hole.   Then a boring bar is used to remove layers from the inside diameter of the hollow cylinder, extreme care being taken to prevent overheating.   About 5 per cent of cross-sectional area should be removed between each measurement of strain.   To eliminate end effects, the specimen length should be at least three times the diameter.   After each layer is removed from the bore, measurements are made of longitudinal strain e_L and tangential strain e_t.

$$e_L = \frac{L_1 - L_0}{L_0}$$

$$e_t = \frac{D_1 - D_0}{D_0}$$

The changes in length L and diameter D may be measured with micrometers, but better accuracy can be obtained by mounting SR-4 strain gages[2,3] in the longitudinal and circumferential directions of the bar.

In accordance with the Sachs analysis, the longitudinal and tangential strains are combined in two parameters.

$$\Lambda = e_L + \nu e_t$$

$$\Theta = e_t + \nu e_L$$

The longitudinal, tangential, and radial stresses can then be expressed by the following equations,

$$\sigma_L = E' \left[(A_0 - A) \frac{d\Lambda}{dA} - \Lambda \right]$$

$$\sigma_t = E' \left[(A_0 - A) \frac{d\Theta}{dA} - \frac{A_0 + A}{2A} \Theta \right] \tag{15-5}$$

$$\sigma_r = E' \left(\frac{A_0 - A}{2A} \Theta \right)$$

[1] G. Sachs, Z. Metallk., vol. 19, pp. 352–357, 1927.

[2] J. J. Lynch, "Residual Stress Measurements," pp. 51–52, American Society for Metals, Metals Park, Ohio, 1952.

[3] A critical evaluation of experimental procedures has been presented by R. A. Dodd, Metallurgia, vol. 45, pp. 109–114, 1952.

where $E' = E/(1 - \nu^2)$

   $A_0 =$ original area of cylinder
   $A =$ area of bored-out portion of cylinder
   $\nu =$ Poisson's ratio

In using the above equations it is convenient to plot the strain parameters Θ and Λ as functions of the bored-out area A. The slopes of these curves are then used in the above equations. To estimate the stress along the axis of the bar or at the bore of a tube, it is necessary to extrapolate the Λ versus A and Θ versus A curves to $A = 0$. Similarly, to determine the stresses on the outer surface of the bar, these curves should be extrapolated to $A = A_0$. There is a limit to how closely the bored-out diameter can approach the outside diameter of the bar without buckling. Since the residual stress near the outer surface may be rapidly changing with radial distance an extrapolation in this region may be in error. One way to get a better estimate of the stresses near the outside surface of the bar is to measure the changes in diameter of the axial hole while metal is removed from the outer surface of the bar. The Sachs equations for this case are given below,

$$\sigma_L = E' \left[(A - A_h) \frac{d\Lambda}{dA} - \Lambda \right]$$

$$\sigma_t = E' \left[(A - A_h) \frac{d\Theta}{dA} - \frac{A + A_h}{2A} \Theta \right] \qquad (15\text{-}6)$$

$$\sigma_r = -E' \left(\frac{A - A_h}{2A} \Theta \right)$$

where $A_h =$ area of bored-out hole
   $A =$ area of cylinder after each layer removal

A method for accurately determining both the longitudinal and tangential (circumferential) residual stresses in thin-walled tubing has been described by Sachs and Espey.[1]

Treuting-Read Method

Treuting and Read[2] developed a method for determining the biaxial residual-stress state on the surface of a thin sheet. The method assumes that the metal behaves in an elastically homogeneous manner and that the stress varies, not in the plane of the sheet, but only through the thickness. To apply the method, the sheet specimen is cemented to a flat parallel surface, and the thickness is reduced a certain amount by careful polishing and etching. The sheet specimen is then released from

---

[1] G. Sachs and G. Espey, *Trans. AIME*, vol. 147, pp. 74–88, 1942; see also Lynch, *op. cit.*, pp. 87–92.

[2] R. G. Treuting and W. T. Read, *J. Appl. Phys.*, vol. 22, pp. 130–134, 1951.

the surface, and measurements are made of the longitudinal radius of curvature R_x, the transverse radius of curvature R_y and the thickness t. Figure 15-5 illustrates the orientation of the principal stresses and the curvature of the sheet.

The measured values of radius of curvature are expressed in terms of two parameters P_x and P_y.

$$P_x = \frac{1}{R_x} + \frac{\nu}{R_y} \qquad P_y = \frac{1}{R_y} + \frac{\nu}{R_x}$$

Measurements of R_x and R_y are made for different amounts of metal removal, and P_x and P_y are plotted against the sheet thickness t. The

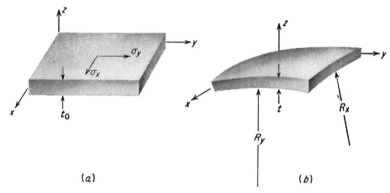

(a)   (b)

Fig. 15-5. (a) Coordinate system for measuring biaxial stress in thin sheet; (b) curvature produced by removing material from top surface.

residual stresses in the x and y directions of the sheet are determined for any value of t by the following equations:

$$\sigma_x = -\frac{E}{6(1 - \nu^2)}\left[(t_0 + t)^2\frac{dP_x}{dt} + 4(t_0 + t)P_x + 2\int_{t_0}^{t}P_x\,dt\right]$$
$$\sigma_y = -\frac{E}{6(1 - \nu^2)}\left[(t_0 + t)^2\frac{dP_y}{dt} + 4(t_0 + t)P_y + 2\int_{t_0}^{t}P_y\,dt\right] \tag{15-7}$$

Values of dP/dt are obtained from the slope of the curves of P versus t, and the integrals are evaluated by determining the area under the P versus t curve over the appropriate limits.

15-4. Deflection Methods

Complete analysis of the residual stresses in the principal directions and their variation with depth in the body by the methods described in the previous section is a laborous procedure. It is not uncommon to find that nearly 40 hr is required for the complete analysis of a single specimen. Therefore, approximate methods which are more rapid but less accurate have been developed. Since the techniques involve a mechanical slitting of the specimen and measurement of the deflection of the slit element, they are usually called *deflection methods*. Deflection methods can be applied when it is reasonable to assume that the stress varies *linearly* through the thickness of a plate or tube but is constant along the length, width, or circumference. Actually, the stress distri-

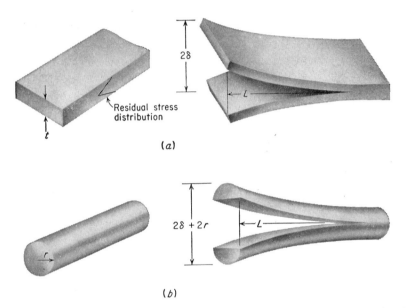

(a)

(b)

Fig. 15-6. Determination of longitudinal residual stress by deflection method. (a) Rolled sheet; (b) drawn rod.

bution through the thickness is rarely linear. The formulas that are presented below give the residual stress only at the surface of the body and consider the stress only in one particular direction. Although this is usually the direction of the maximum stress, it should be realized that the presence of stresses in the other principal directions can affect its value.

Rolled Sheet

The longitudinal residual stress at the surface of a rolled sheet can be determined by splitting the sheet down its central plane to release the bending moment which existed in the body[1] (Fig. 15-6a). The bending

[1] Lynch, *op. cit.*, pp. 81–82.

moment in this sheet may be expressed as follows,

$$M = \frac{E'I}{R} \tag{15-8}$$

where $E' = E/(1 - \nu^2)$
$\quad I$ = moment of inertia of split section
$\quad R$ = radius of curvature

Although the residual-stress distribution which went to make up this bending moment is unknown, it is assumed for the analysis that it varies linearly over the thickness t. Based on this linear relationship, the maximum longitudinal stress at the surface is given by the familiar equation from strength of materials,

$$\sigma_L = \frac{Mc}{I} \tag{15-9}$$

where c is the distance from the neutral axis to the outer fiber, in this case $t/4$. Substituting Eq. (15-8) into (15-9) and introducing the value for c results in

$$\sigma_L = \frac{E't}{4R} \tag{15-10}$$

The radius of curvature may be expressed in terms of the deflection δ and the length of the curved beam L by Eq. (15-11) if the deflection is small compared with the radius of curvature.

$$R = \frac{L^2}{2\delta} \tag{15-11}$$

Thus, the longitudinal residual stress at the surface is given by

$$\sigma_L = \frac{E't\delta}{2L^2} \tag{15-12}$$

Round Bar

The same procedure can be used to estimate the surface longitudinal stress in a round bar[1] (Fig. 15-6b). With the notation given in Fig. 15-6b the procedure outlined above results in the following equation:

$$\sigma_L = \frac{1.65E'\delta r}{L^2} \tag{15-13}$$

Thin-wall Tubing

The longitudinal stress at the surface of a tube may be determined[2] by splitting a longitudinal tongue from the wall of the tube (Fig. 15-7a).

[1] *Ibid.*, p. 82.
[2] R. J. Anderson and E. G. Fahlman, *J. Inst. Metals*, vol. 32, pp. 367–383, 1924.

With the notation given in Fig. 15-7a, the longitudinal stress is given by the following equation,

$$\sigma_L = \frac{E' t \delta}{L^2} \tag{15-14}$$

where

$$E' = \frac{E}{1 - \nu^2}$$

Equation (15-14) is the same as Eq. (15-12) for a rolled sheet, except that $t/2$ is used in the latter case because only half the sheet thickness deflects.

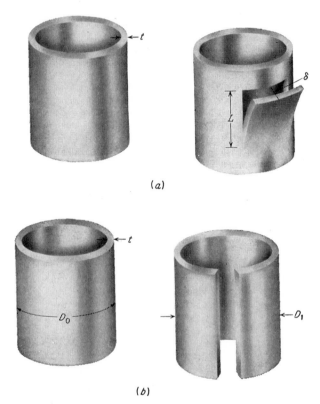

(a)

(b)

Fig. 15-7. Determination of residual stresses in thin-wall tube by deflection method. (*a*) Longitudinal stress; (*b*) circumferential stress.

Experience with the slitting of tubes has shown that the observed deflection is a function of the width of the tongue. The maximum deflection is obtained when the tongue width is 0.1 to 0.2 times the diameter of the tube.

To determine the circumferential residual stresses in a tube, a longitudinal slit is made the entire length of the tube, and the change in diameter is measured[1] (Fig. 15-7b). With the notation in the figure, the circumferential residual stress at the surface is given by

$$\sigma_c = E't\left(\frac{1}{D_0} - \frac{1}{D_1}\right) \tag{15-15}$$

15-5. X-ray Determination of Residual Stress

The measurement of residual stress with X rays utilizes the interatomic spacing of certain lattice planes as the gage length for measuring strain. In essence, the interatomic spacing for a given lattice plane is determined for the stress-free condition and for the same material containing residual stress. The change in lattice spacing can be related to residual stress. Because X rays penetrate less than 0.001 in. into the surface of a metal, X-ray methods measure only surface strains and therefore only surface residual stresses can be determined. Since no stress exists normal to a free surface, this method is limited to uniaxial and biaxial states of stress. For many applications, particularly where fatigue failure is involved, this is not a serious disadvantage.

X-ray methods have the important advantage that they are non-destructive and involve no cutting or slitting of the object to measure the stresses. Further, it is not always necessary to make measurements on the specimen in the unstressed condition. This is often an advantage in making post-mortem examinations of parts which failed in service. The X-ray method measures the residual stress in a very localized area,[2] since the X-ray beam covers an area approximately $\frac{1}{8}$ in. in diameter. This makes the X-ray technique useful for measurements of sharply changing stress gradients, but it may be a disadvantage where the objective is to characterize the over-all residual-stress condition in a surface. Since the X-ray method is based essentially on an accurate measurement of the shift in position of the X-ray reflection from a given set of lattice planes due to the presence of elastic strain, it is necessary that the diffraction lines be accurately located. Using film techniques to record the X-ray reflections requires that the specimen yield sharp diffraction lines if the lattice strain is to be measured with precision. Since severely cold-worked material and quenched and tempered steel give broad diffraction lines, the residual stresses in these important classes of specimens cannot be accurately determined by X-ray film techniques. However, the introduction of Geiger-counter X-ray spectrogoniometer equipment

[1] D. K. Crampton, *Trans. AIME*, vol. 89, pp. 233–255, 1930.

[2] Mechanical methods of measuring localized residual stresses around a small drilled hole have been developed. See J. Mathar, *Trans. ASME*, vol. 86, pp. 249–254, 1934.

has permitted a more accurate measurement of the X-ray diffraction-line profile than is possible with film techniques. Methods have been developed of measuring with considerable precision residual stresses in heat-treated steel by means of X rays.[1]

Bragg's law expresses the relationship between the distance between a given set of lattice planes, d, and the wavelength of X-ray radiation, λ, the order of the diffraction n, and the measured diffraction angle θ.

$$n\lambda = 2d \sin \theta \qquad (15\text{-}16)$$

The simplest condition to consider will give values for a uniaxial surface stress or the sum of the principal stresses $\sigma_1 + \sigma_2$. In the Sachs-Weerts[2] method two X-ray determinations are made of the lattice spacing d for the X-ray beam oriented normal to the specimen surface. One shot gives the value d_1 for the stressed surface, while the other shot gives d_0 for the stress-free surface. The lattice constant in the stress-free condition is obtained either by removing a small plug of metal from the specimen or by thermally stress-relieving the sample. The strain normal to the surface which is measured by the X rays is e_3.

$$e_3 = \frac{d_1 - d_0}{d_0} \qquad (15\text{-}17)$$

From the theory of elasticity (Chap. 2), the strain in the direction normal to the free surface can be expressed as

$$e_3 = -\frac{(\sigma_1 + \sigma_2)\nu}{E} \qquad (15\text{-}18)$$

Therefore, the sum of the principal stresses lying in the specimen surface is given by

$$\sigma_1 + \sigma_2 = -\frac{E}{\nu}\frac{d_1 - d_0}{d_0} \qquad (15\text{-}19)$$

A much more general equation for determining the principal stresses in a surface by X rays can be obtained by considering the general case for principal stress (Sec. 2-5). The situation is discussed in detail by Barrett.[3] The generalized state of principal stress acting on the surface can be represented in three dimensions by an ellipsoid (Fig. 15-8). The normal stress given by the coordinates ψ and ϕ can be expressed in terms of the three principal stresses and their direction cosines l, m, and n as

[1] A. L. Christenson and E. S. Rowland, *Trans. ASM*, vol. 45, pp. 638–676, 1953; D. P. Koistinen and R. E. Marburger, *Trans. ASM*, vol. 51, pp. 537–555, 1959.

[2] G. Sachs and J. Weerts, *Z. Physik*, vol. 64, pp. 344–358, 1930.

[3] C. S. Barrett, "Structure of Metals," 2d ed., chap. 14, McGraw-Hill Book Company, Inc., New York, 1952.

follows,

$$\sigma = l^2\sigma_1 + m^2\sigma_2 + n^2\sigma_3 \tag{15-20}$$

where $l = \sin\psi\cos\phi$, $m = \sin\psi\sin\phi$, and $n = \cos\psi$. Since the X-ray determination of residual stress considers only the stresses in the surface,

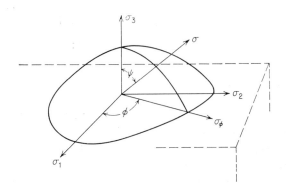

Fig. 15-8. Representation of principal stresses σ_1, σ_2, σ_3 by ellipsoid of stress.

$\sigma_3 = 0$. Referring to Fig. 15-8, this requires that $\psi = 90°$. Therefore, Eq. (15-20) can be simplified as follows to give the component of stress in the direction ϕ:

$$\sigma_\phi = \sigma_1\cos^2\phi + \sigma_2\sin^2\phi \tag{15-21}$$

An equation exactly analogous to Eq. (15-20) can be written for the principal strains.

$$e = l^2e_1 + m^2e_2 + n^2e_3 \tag{15-22}$$

If the values of the direction cosines, together with the values of e_1 and e_2 in terms of principal stresses are substituted into Eq. (15-22), we get

$$e - e_3 = \frac{1+\nu}{E}\sin^2\psi\,(\sigma_1\cos^2\phi + \sigma_2\sin^2\phi) \tag{15-23}$$

Substitution of Eq. (15-21) into Eq. (15-23) leads to the relation

$$\sigma_\phi = \frac{e - e_3}{\sin^2\psi}\frac{E}{1+\nu} \tag{15-24}$$

However,

$$e - e_3 = \frac{d_\psi - d_0}{d_0} - \frac{d_1 - d_0}{d_0} = \frac{d_\psi - d_1}{d_0} \tag{15-25}$$

where d_0 = atomic spacing in unstressed condition

d_1 = atomic spacing in stressed metal perpendicular to specimen surface

d_ψ = atomic spacing in direction defined by angles ψ and ϕ

Since the accuracy of Eq. (15-25) is chiefly determined by the precision with which the numerator is known, it is permissible to substitute d_1 for d_0 in the denominator without greatly affecting the results. This substitution is an important simplification of the experimental procedure because it eliminates the necessity for making measurements on stress-free samples. Therefore, the stress in the surface of the specimen for any orientation of the azimuth angle ϕ is related to X-ray measurements of atomic lattice spacing by the following equation:

$$\sigma_\phi = \frac{d_\psi - d_1}{d_1} \frac{E}{1 + \nu} \frac{1}{\sin^2 \psi} \qquad (15\text{-}26)$$

The number of X-ray exposures that is required depends on the information that is available. For any azimuth angle ϕ it is customary to make two exposures to determine the stress in the ϕ direction. One exposure is made normal to the surface ($\psi = 0$) to give d_1, and another exposure is made for the same value of ϕ, but with the X-ray beam inclined at an angle ψ from the normal. Generally $\psi = 45°$ is used for this second exposure to give the value of d_ψ. If the directions of two principal stresses σ_1 and σ_2 in the specimen surface are known, as is often the case for residual stresses produced by quenching or plastic-forming operations, all that is necessary is to make three exposures to determine the complete biaxial-stress state at the point on the surface. One perpendicular exposure determines d_1, one exposure at $\psi = 45°$ in the direction ϕ_1 determines σ_1 from Eq. (15-26), while a third exposure at $\psi = 45°$ in the direction of the other principal stress ϕ_2 determines σ_2 from Eq. (15-26). σ_3 is zero because the measurements are made on a free surface.

If it is necessary to determine both the magnitude and direction of σ_1 and σ_2, it is necessary to make four X-ray exposures. Three arbitrary stress components in three known ϕ directions on the surface must be determined in addition to a normal exposure to determine d_1. It is customary to make these exposures at ϕ, $\phi + 60°$, and $\phi - 60°$, with $\psi = 45°$ for each value of ϕ. The stresses in the three arbitrary ϕ directions are calculated from Eq. (15-26) and are then converted into principal stresses by the methods given in Chap. 2 or by the equations given by Barrett[1] for the specific conditions established above.

In addition to the difficulties of accurately measuring the values of interatomic spacing in highly strained metals which have already been discussed, there is some uncertainty as to the values of elastic modulus E and Poisson's ratio ν which should be used in Eq. (15-26) to calculate values of residual stress. It is known that for most metals these elastic

[1] *Ibid.*, pp. 326–327.

constants vary considerably with crystallographic direction. Since the residual stresses calculated from Eq. (15-26) are based on X-ray measurements of lattice strain in certain fixed directions in the crystal lattice, it is questionable that average values of E and ν determined from the tension test should apply. Experimental data on this point are somewhat contradictory. Most investigators who have used X-ray methods for residual-stress determination have considered that the use of the average value of E and ν introduce no serious errors beyond that due to uncontrollable factors. For greatest accuracy, these constants should be determined for each material and experimental setup by making X-ray measurements on stress-relieved specimens which are subjected to known loads.

15-6. Quenching Stresses

In the introductory discussion of residual stresses in Sec. 15-1 it was shown that cooling an ingot of a metal which does not experience a phase change can produce residual stresses because of the strain mismatch produced by the differential contraction between the cooler and hotter parts of the body. The development of the longitudinal residual-stress pattern was shown in Fig. 15-2. Quenching a body from a high temperature to a lower temperature accentuates the development of residual stresses because the greater temperature differential which is produced between the surface and the center due to the rapid rate of cooling produces a greater mismatch of strain. The situation of greatest practical interest involves the residual stresses developed during the quenching of steel for hardening. However, for this case the residual-stress pattern is due to thermal volume changes plus volume changes resulting from the transformation of austenite to martensite. The simpler situation, where the stresses are due only to thermal volume changes, will be considered first. This is the situation encountered in the quenching of a metal which does not undergo a phase change on cooling. It is also the situation encountered when steel is quenched from a tempering temperature below the A_1 critical temperature.

The distribution of residual stress over the diameter of a quenched bar in the longitudinal, tangential, and radial directions is shown in Fig. 15-9a for the usual case of a metal which contracts on cooling. Figure 15-9c shows that the opposite residual-stress distribution is obtained if the metal expands on cooling. The development of the stress pattern shown in Fig. 15-9a can be visualized as follows: The relatively cool surface of the bar tends to contract into a ring that is both shorter and smaller in diameter than the original diameter. This tends to extrude the hotter, more plastic center into a cylinder that is longer and thinner than its original dimensions. If the inner core were free to change shape independently of the outer ring, it would change dimensions to a shorter and thinner cylinder on cooling. However, continuity must be maintained throughout the bar so that the outer ring is drawn in (compressed) in the longitudinal, tangential, and radial directions at the same time as the inner core is extended in the same directions. The stress pattern given in Fig. 15-9a results.

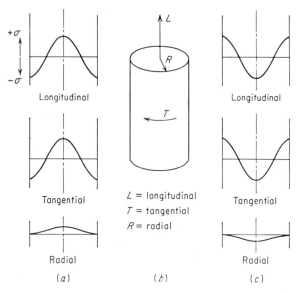

Fig. 15-9. Residual-stress patterns found in quenched bars, due to thermal strains (schematic). (*a*) For metal which contracts on cooling; (*b*) orientation of directions; (*c*) for metal which expands on cooling.

The magnitude of the residual stresses produced by quenching depends on the stress-strain relationships for the metal and the degree of strain mismatch produced by the quenching operation. For a given strain mismatch, the higher the modulus elasticity of the metal, the higher the residual stress. Further, since the residual stress cannot exceed the yield stress, the higher the yield stress, the higher the possible residual stress. The yield-stress–temperature curve for the metal is also important. If the yield stress decreases rapidly with increasing temperature, then the strain mismatch will be small at high temperature because the metal can accommodate to thermally produced volume changes by plastic flow. On the other hand, metals which have a high yield strength at elevated temperatures, like superalloys, will develop large residual stresses from quenching.

The following combination of physical properties will lead to high mismatch strains on quenching:

1. A low thermal conductivity k
2. A high specific heat c
3. A high coefficient of thermal expansion, α
4. A high density ρ

These factors can be combined into the thermal diffusivity, $D_t = k/\rho c$. Low values of thermal diffusivity lead to high strain mismatch. Other factors which produce an increase in the temperature difference between the surface and center of the bar promote high quenching stresses. These factors are (1) a large diameter of the cylinder, (2) a large temperature difference between the initial temperature and the temperature of the quenching bath, and (3) a high severity of quench.

In the quenching of steels, austenite begins to transform to martensite whenever the local temperature of the bar reaches the M_s temperature. Since an increase in volume accompanies this transformation, the metal expands as the martensite reaction proceeds on cooling from the M_s to M_f temperature. This produces a residual stress distribution of the type shown in Fig. 15-9c. The residual-stress distribution in a quenched steel bar is the resultant of the competing processes of thermal contraction and volume expansion due to martensite formation. Transformation of austenite to bainite or pearlite also produces a volume expansion, but of lesser magnitude. The resulting stress pattern depends upon the transformation characteristics of the steel, as determined chiefly by its composition and hardenability, and the heat-transfer characteristics of the system, as determined primarily by the bar diameter, the austenitizing temperature, and the severity of the quench.

Figure 15-10 illustrates some of the possible residual-stress patterns which can be produced by quenching steel bars. The left side of this figure illustrates a typical isothermal transformation diagram for the decomposition of austenite. The cooling rates of the outside, midradius, and center of the bar are indicated on this diagram by the curves marked o, m, and c. In Fig. 15-10a the quenching rate was rapid enough to convert the entire bar to martensite. By the time the center of the bar reached the M_s temperature, the transformation had been essentially completed at the surface. The surface layers tried to contract against the expanding central core, and the result is tensile residual stresses at the surface and compressive stresses at the center of the bar (Fig. 15-10b). However, if the bar diameter is rather small and it has been drastically quenched in brine so that the surface and center transform at about the same time, the surface will arrive at room temperature with compressive residual stresses.   If the bar is slack-quenched so that the outside transforms to martensite while the middle and center transform to pearlite (Fig. 15-10c), there is little restraint offered by the hot, soft core during the time when martensite is forming on the surface, and the core readily accommodates to the expansion of the outer layers.   The middle and

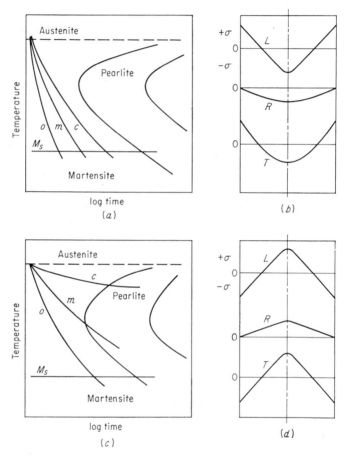

Fig. 15-10. Transformation characteristics of a steel (a and c), and resulting residual-stress distributions (b and d).

center pearlite regions then contract on cooling in the usual manner and produce a residual-stress pattern consisting of compression on the surface and tension at the center (Fig. 15-10d).   Other types of stress distributions are possible, depending upon the cooling rate and the transformation characteristics of the steel.   For example, it is possible to produce a stress pattern with tensile stresses at the surface and center of the bar and compressive stresses at midradius.

In relatively brittle materials like tool steels, the yield stress is not far below the fracture stress. Surface tensile stresses equal to the yield stress may be produced by quenching. If stress raisers are present, the residual tensile stress may exceed the fracture stress. Cracks produced by tensile quenching stresses are called *quench cracks*. In order to minimize quench cracking in brittle steels, an interrupted quench, or *martempering*, procedure is sometimes used. The steel is quenched from the austenitizing temperature into a holding bath which is maintained at a temperature above the M_s temperature of the steel. The steel is kept at the temperature long enough for it to come to thermal equilibrium, and then it is quenched to a lower temperature to form martensite.

The reasons for tempering hardened steel are to relieve the high microstresses in the martensite and to reduce the level of macro residual stress. Although tempering generally lowers the level of residual stress, there are exceptions to this behavior.[1] For steel bars which have been hardened through, the level of residual stress will decrease uniformly with increasing tempering temperature. For a bar with surface compressive stresses due to incomplete hardening an increase in tempering temperature will progressively reduce the residual stress. If a bar is almost completely hardened through, greater contraction due to tempering of the martensite will occur at the surface than at the center. This will cause the surface tensile stress to increase as tempering progresses.

15-7. Surface Residual Stresses

There are a number of important technological processes which produce high surface residual stresses which have their maximum value either at the surface or just below the surface and which fall off rapidly with distance in from the surface. The steep stress gradient produced by these processes is in contrast with the more uniform residual-stress gradient produced by quenching and most mechanical forming operations. Normally, these processes produce high surface compressive residual stresses which aid in preventing fatigue failure. Figure 15-11 is typical of the kind of residual-stress distribution which is considered in this section.

The process of *induction hardening* consists in inductively heating a thin surface layer of a steel part above the transformation temperature and then flash-quenching this region to martensite with a spray of water. The localized expansion of the martensitic case produces a residual-stress pattern of compression stresses at the surface and tension in the interior.

[1] A. L. Boegehold, *Metal Progr.*, vol. 57, pp. 183–188, 1950.

Flame hardening produces the same metallurgical changes and residual-stress pattern as induction hardening, but the local heating is produced by a gas flame. Both processes not only produce a favorable residual-stress pattern but also leave a hardened surface which improves the resistance to wear.

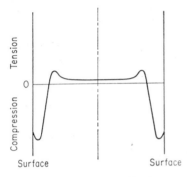

Carburizing consists in changing the carbon content of the surface layers of a steel part by the diffusion of carbon atoms into the surface. The process differs from induction hardening in that the entire part is heated into the austenite region during the diffusion process and when the part is quenched volume changes may occur through most of the cross section. In general, the carburized surface contains compressive residual stresses, but considerable variation in residual-stress distribution can be produced by changes in processing.[1] Ordinarily, the maximum compressive residual stress occurs at a depth in from the surface which is just short of the boundary between the carburized case and the lower-carbon-content core. *Nitriding* consists in the diffusion of nitrogen into a steel surface at a temperature below the A_1 transformation temperature. The only volume expansion arises from the formation of nitrides at the surface. The residual-stress pattern consists of compression at the surface and tension at the interior. Because there is no volume expansion occurring in the core, as is possible for carburizing, the residual-stress distribution produced by nitriding is easier to control.

Fig. 15-11. Typical residual-stress distribution produced by surface treatment like induction hardening, carburizing, or shot peening.

Shot peening consists in subjecting a metal surface to the impact of a stream of fine metallic particles (shot). The impact of the shot on the surface causes plastic stretching of the surface fibers at a multitude of localized regions. When this localized plastic flow is relieved, it leaves the surface in a state of compressive residual stress. In the shot peening of heat-treated steel the maximum compressive residual stress which is produced is about 60 per cent of the yield strength of the steel. The maximum residual stress occurs below the surface at a depth of about 0.002 to 0.010 in. Higher values of compressive residual stresses can be obtained by *strain peening*. For example, if a flat leaf spring is preloaded in bending, the resulting compressive residual stress on the surface which was prestressed in tension will be greater than if the steel was shot-peened in an initially stress-free condition. The variables of the shot-peening

[1] R. L. Mattson, *Proc. Intern. Conf. Fatigue of Metals*, London, 1956, pp. 593–603.

process[1,2] which influence the magnitude and distribution of the residual stresses are (1) the shot size, (2) the shot hardness, (3) the shot velocity, and (4) the exposure time (coverage).

High surface compressive residual stress can also be developed by surface rolling, as was shown in Fig. 15-1. An estimate of the loads required for rolling to a given depth may be made by the use of Hertz's theory of contact stresses.[3]

Surface rolling is well adapted to the beneficial protection of critical areas like fillets and screw threads of large parts, while shot peening lends itself to high-production volume parts where broad or irregular surfaces are to be treated. Numerous instances have been reported in the literature where the introduction of beneficial compressive residual stresses by flame hardening,[4] carburizing,[5] nitriding,[6] shot peening,[7] and surface rolling[8] has resulted in improved fatigue performance. Surface working operations such as shot peening and rolling have also been successfully used to mitigate the effects of stress corrosion cracking.

15-8. Stress Relief

The removal or reduction in the intensity of residual stress is known as *stress relief*. Stress relief may be accomplished either by heating or by mechanical working operations. Although residual stresses will slowly disappear at room temperature, the process is very greatly accelerated by heating to an elevated temperature. The stress relief which comes from a stress-relief anneal is due to two effects. First, since the residual stress cannot exceed the yield stress, plastic flow will reduce the residual stress to the value of the yield stress at the stress-relief temperature. Only the residual stress in excess of the yield stress at the stress-relief temperature can be eliminated by immediate plastic flow. Generally, most of the residual stress will be relieved by time-dependent stress relaxation. Relaxation curves such as those of Fig. 13-15 are useful for estimating stress-relief treatments. Since this process is extremely temper-

---

[1] *Ibid.*; R. L. Mattson and W. S. Coleman, *Trans. SAE*, vol. 62, pp. 546–556, 1954.

[2] J. M. Lessells and R. F. Brodrick, *Proc. Intern. Conf. Fatigue of Metals*, London, 1956, pp. 617–627.

[3] J. M. Lessells, "Strength and Resistance of Metals," pp. 256–259, John Wiley & Sons, Inc., New York, 1954.

[4] O. J. Horger and T. V. Buckwalter, *Proc. ASTM*, vol. 41, pp. 682–695, 1941.

[5] "Fatigue Durability of Carburized Steel," American Society for Metals, Metals Park, Ohio, 1957.

[6] H. Sutton, *Metal Treatment*, vol. 2, pp. 89–92, 1936.

[7] O. J. Horger and H. R. Neifert, *Proc. Soc. Exptl. Stress Analysis*, vol. 2, no. 1, pp. 178–189, 1944.

[8] O. J. Horger, *J. Appl. Mech.*, vol. 2, pp. A128–136, 1935.

ature-dependent, the time for nearly complete elimination of stress can be greatly reduced by increasing the temperature.[1] Often a compromise must be made between the use of a temperature high enough for the relief of stress in a reasonable length of time and the annealing of the effects of cold work.

The differential strains that produce high residual stresses also can be eliminated by plastic deformation at room temperature. For example, products such as sheet, plate, and extrusions are often stretched several per cent beyond the yield stress to relieve differential strains by yielding. In other cases the residual-stress distribution which is characteristic of a particular working operation may be superimposed on the residual-stress pattern initially present in the material. A surface which contains tensile residual stresses may have the stress distribution converted into beneficial compressive stresses with a surface working process like rolling or shot peening. However, it is important in using this method of stress relief to select surface working conditions which will completely cancel the initial stress distribution. For example, it is conceivable that, if only very light surface rolling were used on a surface which initially contained tensile stresses, only the tensile stresses at the surface would be reduced. Dangerously high tensile stresses could still exist below the surface.

An interesting concept is the use of thermal stresses to reduce quenching stresses. Since residual stresses result from thermal gradients produced when a part is being quenched, it is possible to introduce residual stresses of opposite sign by subjecting a cold piece to very rapid heating. This concept of an "uphill quench" has been used[2] in aluminum alloys to reduce quenching stresses by as much as 80 per cent at temperatures low enough to prevent softening.

BIBLIOGRAPHY

Baldwin, W. M.: Residual Stresses in Metals, Twenty-third Edgar Marburg Lecture, *Proc. ASTM*, vol. 49, pp. 539–583, 1949.
Heindlhofer, K.: "Evaluation of Residual Stress," McGraw-Hill Book Company, Inc., New York, 1948.
Horger, O. J.: Residual Stresses, "Handbook of Experimental Stress Analysis," pp. 459–469, John Wiley & Sons, Inc., New York, 1950.
Huang, T. C.: Bibliography on Residual Stress, *SAE Spec. Publ.* SP-125, 1954; suppl. 1, SP-167, February, 1959.
Residual Stresses, *Metal Progr.*, vol. 68, no. 2A, pp. 89–96, Aug. 15, 1955.
"Residual Stress Measurements," American Society for Metals, Metals Park, Ohio, 1952.
Symposium on Internal Stresses in Metals and Alloys, *Inst. Metals Mon. Rept. Ser.* 5, 1948.

[1] Typical stress-relief temperatures and times for many metals will be found in *Metal Prog.*, vol. 68, no. 2A, p. 95, Aug. 15, 1955.
[2] H. N. Hill, R. S. Barker, and L. A. Willey, *Trans. ASM*, vol. 52, pp. 657–674, 1960.

Chapter 16

STATISTICS APPLIED TO
MATERIALS TESTING

16-1. Why Statistics?

There are at least three reasons why a working knowledge of statistics is needed in mechanical metallurgy. First, mechanical properties, being structure-sensitive properties, frequently exhibit considerable variability, or scatter. Therefore, statistical techniques are useful, and often even necessary, for determining the precision of the measurements and for drawing valid conclusions from the data. The statistical methods which apply in mechanical metallurgy are in general no different from the techniques which are used for analysis of data in other areas of engineering and science. Mechanical metallurgy is one of the few areas of metallurgy where large numbers of data are likely to be encountered, and therefore it is a logical place in which to introduce the elements of statistical analysis of data to metallurgists who may have had no other training in the subject. A second reason for considering statistics in conjunction with mechanical metallurgy is that statistical methods can assist in designing experiments to give the maximum amount of information with the minimum of experimental investigation. Finally, statistical methods based on probability theory have been developed to explain certain problems in mechanical metallurgy. The explanation of the size effect in brittle fracture and fatigue is a good example of the use of statistical theory in mechanical metallurgy.

It is recognized that the material which can be included in a single chapter can hardly consist of more than an introduction to this subject. In order to cover the greatest amount of ground, no attempt has been made to include the mathematical niceties which are usually a part of a course in statistics. Instead, emphasis has been placed on showing how statistics can be put to work. Numerous references are included to sources of more complete discussions and to techniques and applications which could not be included because of space limitations. It is hoped that this chapter contributes to a better appreciation of the usefulness of statistics in metallurgical research by providing the background necessary to see a problem from a statistical viewpoint and enough of the standard tools of statistics to allow a valid analysis in straightforward applications. It is important to emphasize that many practical problems are just too complicated to treat by means of the simpler statistical techniques. In these cases it is important to acquire the services of a trained statistician for the planning of the experiment and the analysis of the data.

16-2. Errors and Samples

The act of making any type of experimental observation involves two types of errors, systematic errors (which exert a nonrandom bias), and experimental, or random, errors. Systematic errors arise because of faulty control of the experiment. Experimental, or random, errors are due to limitations of the measuring equipment or to inherent variability in the material being tested. As an example, in the measurement of the reduction of area of a fractured tensile specimen, a systematic error could be introduced if an improperly zeroed micrometer were used for measuring the diameter, while random errors would result from slight differences in fitting together the two halves of the tensile specimen and from the inherent variability of reduction-of-area measurements on metals. By averaging a number of observations the random error will tend to cancel out. The systematic error, however, will not cancel upon averaging. One of the major objectives of statistical analysis is to deal quantitatively with random error.

When a tensile specimen is cut from a steel forging and the reduction of area is determined for this specimen, the observation represents a sample of the *population* from which it was drawn. The population, in this case, is the collection of all possible tensile specimens which could be cut from this forging or from all other forgings which are exactly identical. As more and more tensile specimens are cut from the forging and reduction-of-area values measured, the sample estimate of the population values becomes better and better. However, it is obviously impractical to sample and test the entire forging. Therefore, one of the main purposes of statistical techniques is to determine the best *estimate* of the population parameters from a randomly selected sample. The approach which is taken is to postulate that for each sample the population has fixed and invariant parameters. However, the corresponding parameters calculated from samples contain random errors, and therefore the sample provides only an estimate of the population parameters. It is for this reason that statistical methods lead to conclusions having a given *proba-bility* of being correct.

16-3. Frequency Distribution

When a large number of observations are made from a random sample, a method is needed to characterize the data. The most common method is to arrange the observations into a number of equal-valued *class intervals* and determine the frequency of the observations falling within each class interval. In Table 16-1, out of a total sample of 449 measurements of

TABLE 16-1
FREQUENCY TABULATION OF YIELD STRENGTH OF STEEL†

Yield strength, 1,000 psi, class interval	Class midpoint X_i	Frequency f_i	f_iX_i	Frequency, % of total	Cumulative frequency	Cumulative frequency, %
(1)	(2)	(3)	(4)	(5)	(6)	(7)
114–115.9	115	4	460	0.9	4	0.9
116–117.9	117	6	702	1.3	10	2.2
118–119.9	119	8	952	1.6	18	3.8
120–121.9	121	26	3,146	5.8	44	9.6
122–123.9	123	29	3,657	6.5	73	16.1
124–125.9	125	44	5,500	9.8	117	25.9
126–127.9	127	47	5,969	10.5	164	36.4
128–129.9	129	59	7,611	13.1	223	49.5
130–131.9	131	67	8,777	15.0	290	64.5
132–133.9	133	45	5,985	10.0	335	74.5
134–135.9	135	49	6,615	10.9	384	85.4
136–137.9	137	29	3,973	6.5	413	91.9
138–139.9	139	17	2,363	3.8	430	95.7
140–141.9	141	9	1,269	2.0	439	97.7
142–143.9	143	6	858	1.3	445	99.0
144–145.9	145	4	580	0.9	449	99.9

$$\Sigma f_i = 449 \qquad \Sigma f_iX_i = 58,417$$
$$\bar{X} = 58,417/449 = 130,300 \text{ psi}$$

† Data from F. B. Stulen, W. C. Schulte, and H. N. Cummings, in D. E. Hardenbergh (ed.), "Statistical Methods in Materials Research," Pennsylvania State University, University Park, Pa., 1956.

yield strength, 4 observations fell between 114,000 and 115,900 psi, 26 fell between 120,000 and 121,900 psi, etc. An estimate of the frequency distribution of the observations can be obtained by plotting the frequency of observations against the class intervals of the yield-strength

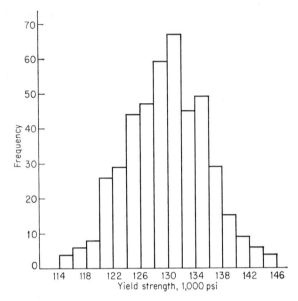

Fig. 16-1. Frequency histogram of data in Table 16-1.

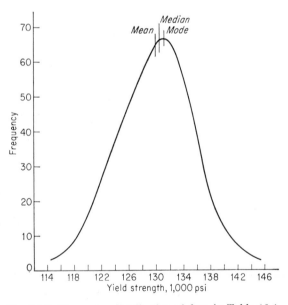

Fig. 16-2. Frequency distribution of data in Table 16-1.

measurements (Fig. 16-1). This type of bar diagram is known as a *histogram*. As the number of observations increases, the size of the class interval can be reduced until we obtain the limiting curve which represents the *frequency distribution* of the sample (Fig. 16-2). Note that most of the values of yield strength fall within the interval from 126,000 to 134,000 psi.

If the frequency of observations in each class interval is expressed as a percentage of the total number of observations, the area under a frequency-distribution curve which is plotted on this basis is equal to unity (Fig. 16-3). The probability that a single random measurement of yield strength will be between the value X_1 and a slightly higher value $X_1 + \Delta X$ is given by the area under the frequency-distribution curve bounded by these two limits. Similarly, the probability that a single observation

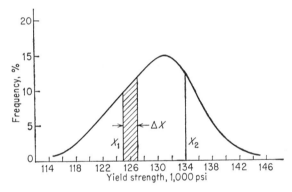

Fig. 16-3. Frequency distribution based on relative frequency.

will be greater than some value X_2 is given by the area under the curve to the right of X_2, while the probability that the single observation will be less than X_2 is given by the area to the left of X_2.

Another way of presenting these data is to arrange the frequency in a cumulative manner. In Table 16-1, column 6, the frequency for each class interval is accumulated with the values of frequency for the class intervals below it to indicate the total number of observations with a value of reduction of area less than or equal to the value of the upper limit of the class interval. As an example, for the sample described in Table 16-1, 164 out of 449 observations of yield strength have a value of 127,900 psi or less. If the cumulative frequency is expressed as the percentage of the total (Table 16-1, column 7), the values represent the probability that the yield strength will be less than or equal to the value of the observation. Figure 16-4 shows the cumulative frequency distribution plotted on this basis. The presentation of data as a cumulative

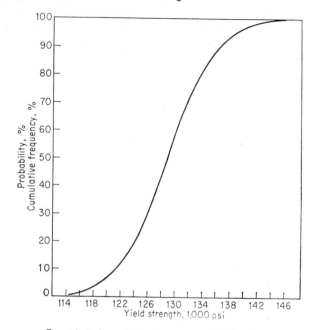

Fig. 16-4. Cumulative frequency distribution.

distribution is sometimes preferred to a frequency distribution because it is much less sensitive than the frequency distribution to the choice of class intervals.

16-4. Measures of Central Tendency and Dispersion

A frequency distribution such as that of Fig. 16-2 can be described with numbers which indicate the central location of the distribution and how the observations are spread out from the central region (dispersion). The most common and important measure of the central value of an array of data is the *arithmetic mean*, or *average*. The mean of X_1, X_2, . . . , X_n observations is denoted by $\bar{X}$ and is given by

$$\bar{X} = \frac{\sum_{i=1}^{n} X_i}{n} \tag{16-1}$$

The arithmetic mean is equal to the summation of the individual observations divided by the total number of observations, n. If the data are arranged in a frequency table, as in Table 16-1, the mean can be most conveniently determined from

$$\bar{X} = \frac{\sum\limits_{i=1}^{k} f_i X_i}{\Sigma f_i} \tag{16-2}$$

where f_i is the frequency of observations in a particular class interval with midpoint X_i. The summation is taken over all class intervals (see Table 16-1, column 4). Equation (16-2) is an approximation to Eq. (16-1).

Two other common measures of central tendency are the *mode* and the *median*. The mode is the value of the observations which occurs most frequently. The median is the middle value of a group of observations. For a set of discrete data the median can be obtained by arranging the observations in numerical sequence and determining which value falls in the middle. For a frequency distribution the median is the value which divides the area under the curve into two equal parts. The mean and the median are frequently close together; but if there are extreme values in the observations (either high or low), the mean will be more influenced by these values than the median. As an extreme example, the situation sometimes arises in fatigue testing that out of a group of specimens tested at a certain stress a few do not fail in the time allotted for the test and therefore they presumably have infinite lives. These extreme values could not be grouped with the failed specimens to calculate a mean fatigue life; yet they could be considered in determining the median. The positions of the mean, median, and mode are indicated in Fig. 16-2.

The most important measure of the dispersion of a sample is given by the *variance* s^2.

$$s^2 = \frac{\sum\limits_{i=1}^{n} (X_i - \bar{X})^2}{n - 1} \tag{16-3}$$

The term $X_i - \bar{X}$ is the deviation of each observation X_i from the arithmetic mean $\bar{X}$ of the n observations. The quantity $n - 1$ in the denominator is called the number of *degrees of freedom* and is equal to the number of observations minus the number of linear relations between the observations. Since the mean represents one such relation, the number of degrees of freedom for the variance about the mean is $n - 1$. For computational purposes it is often convenient to calculate the variance from the following relation:

$$s^2 = \frac{n \sum\limits_{i=1}^{n} X_i{}^2 - \left(\sum\limits_{i=1}^{n} X_i\right)^2}{n(n - 1)} \tag{16-4}$$

When the data are arranged in a frequency table, the variance can be most readily computed from the following equation:

$$s^2 = \frac{\sum_{i=1}^{k} f_i X_i^2 - \frac{\left(\sum_{i=1}^{k} f_i X_i\right)^2}{n}}{n - 1} \tag{16-5}$$

In dealing with the dispersion of data it is usual practice to work with the *standard deviation* s, which is defined as the positive square root of the variance.

$$s = \left[\frac{\sum_{i=1}^{n} (X_i - \bar{X})^2}{n - 1}\right]^{\frac{1}{2}} \tag{16-6}$$

Sometimes it is desirable to describe the variability relative to the average. The *coefficient of variation* v is used for this purpose.

$$v = \frac{s}{\bar{X}} \tag{16-7}$$

A measure of dispersion which is sometimes used because of its extreme simplicity is the *range*. The range is simply the difference between the largest and smallest observation. The range does not provide as precise estimates as does the standard deviation.

16-5. The Normal Distribution

Many physical measurements follow the symmetrical, bell-shaped curve of the normal, or Gaussian, frequency distribution. Repeated measurements of the length or diameter of a bar would closely approximate this frequency distribution. The distributions of yield strength, tensile strength, and reduction of area from the tension test have been found to follow the normal curve to a suitable degree of approximation. The equation of the normal curve is

$$p(X) = \frac{1}{\sigma \sqrt{2\pi}} \exp\left[-\frac{1}{2}\left(\frac{X - \mu}{\sigma}\right)^2\right] \tag{16-8}$$

where $p(X)$ is the height of the frequency curve corresponding to an assigned value X, μ is the mean of the population, and σ is the standard deviation of the population.[1]

The normal frequency distribution described by Eq. (16-8) extends from $X = -\infty$ to $X = +\infty$ and is symmetrical about μ. The constant

---

[1] It should be noted that σ is used for normal stress in the other chapters of this book.

$1/\sigma \sqrt{2\pi}$ is used to make the area under the curve equal unity. Figure 16-5 shows the standardized normal curve when $\mu = 0$ and $\sigma = 1$. The parameter z, defined by Eq. (16-9), is called the *standard normal deviate*.

$$z = \frac{X - \mu}{\sigma} \qquad (16\text{-}9)$$

For this case, the equation of the normal curve becomes

$$p(z) = \frac{1}{\sqrt{2\pi}} \exp\left(-\tfrac{1}{2}z^2\right) \qquad (16\text{-}10)$$

The total area under the curve in Fig. 16-5 is equal to unity. The relative frequency of a value of z falling between $-\infty$ and a specified value

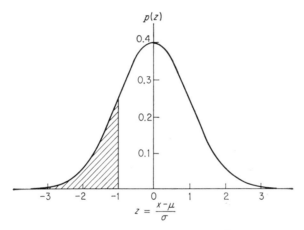

Fig. 16-5. Standardized normal frequency distribution.

is given by the area under the curve between these limits. Table 16-2 lists some typical values.[1] As an example, the area shown shaded in Fig. 16-5 is 0.16 the total area under the curve. Further, if $\mu = 20$ and $\sigma = 5$, what proportion of the sample observations would fall between $X = 20$ and $X = 10$? The respective values of z are 0 and -2, so that the area under the normal curve between these limits is

$$0.50 - 0.02 = 0.48$$

Reference to Table 16-2 will also show that approximately 68 per cent of the area lies in the limits $\mu \pm \sigma$, 95 per cent of the area is within the limits $\mu \pm 2\sigma$, while 99.7 per cent of the area is covered by the limits $\mu \pm 3\sigma$.

[1] For complete tables see W. J. Dixon and F. J. Massey, Jr., "Introduction to Statistical Analysis," 1st ed., p. 306, McGraw-Hill Book Company, Inc., New York, 1951.

TABLE 16-2
AREAS UNDER STANDARDIZED NORMAL FREQUENCY CURVE

$z = X - \mu/\sigma$	Area
-3.0	0.0013
-2.0	0.0228
-1.0	0.1587
-0.5	0.3085
0.0	0.5000
$+0.5$	0.6915
$+1.0$	0.8413
$+2.0$	0.9772
$+3.0$	0.9987

A quick method for determining whether a sample frequency distribution is a normal distribution is to plot the observed cumulative frequency distribution on normal-probability paper.[1] If the data plot is
an approximate straight line, then the distribution can be considered to
be a normal frequency distribution. Figure 16-6 shows the data from
Table 16-1 plotted on probability paper. The mean and standard deviation can be readily determined from this type of plot. The mean is the
value of the abscissa corresponding to a cumulative frequency of 50 per
cent. Since 68 per cent of the area under the standardized normal curve
is included within plus or minus one standard deviation of the mean,
it follows that the standard deviation can be obtained from Fig. 16-6
by taking half the intercept of the abscissa between 84 and 16 per cent.
This method of determining the mean and standard deviation is often
accurate enough for engineering purposes. However, it can be used only
when the data plot as a fairly good line on probability paper. The statistical advantages of the normal distribution are quite considerable, so
that in cases where the data do not fit the normal curve it is often worthwhile to search for a simple transformation which will normalize the data.
The most common transformations are $X = \log X$ and $X = X^{\frac{1}{2}}$. As
an example, the distribution of fatigue life at constant stress is skewed
with respect to the variable of number of cycles to failure, but it is
approximately normal with respect to the *logarithm* of the number of
cycles to failure. This is called a log-normal distribution.[2]

The mean of a sample provides an unbiased estimate of the mean of
the population, or universe, from which it was drawn. If repeated sam-

[1] An analytical method for determining how well a sample frequency distribution
compares with the normal distribution is the chi-square test for goodness of fit. This
technique is discussed in any standard statistics text. For example, see *ibid.*, pp.
190–191.
[2] A complete description of the log-normal distribution is given by A. Hald, "Statistical Theory with Engineering Applications," pp. 160–174, John Wiley & Sons,
Inc., New York, 1952.

ples are taken from the population, they will each in general yield a different value of mean $\bar{X}$ and standard deviation s. The sample values of the mean will, however, be normally distributed about the population mean μ. The central-limit theorem of statistics provides a method for estimating the population mean μ and standard deviation σ. According to this theorem, if $\bar{X}$ is the mean value of a random sample of n observations $\bar{X}$ is normally distributed about the population mean with a standard deviation $\sigma/\sqrt{n}$. With this as a basis, it is possible to determine the *confidence limits* within which the sample mean approaches the population mean to a certain level of certainty.

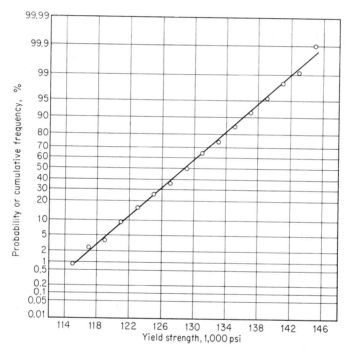

Fig. 16-6. Normal-probability plot of data in Table 16-1.

For samples with many observations ($n > 30$) or where the population variance is known (which is rarely the case), the determination of the confidence limits of the mean is based on the standard normal deviate z. For example, suppose that we want to know the interval about a measured sample mean which will include the population mean 95 per cent of the time, i.e., the 95 per cent confidence level. Reference to an enlarged version of Table 16-2 would show that 95 per cent of the area under the normal curve would be included within the interval $\mu \pm 1.96\sigma$. Now, since the central-limit theorem states that the observations of $\bar{X}$

are normally distributed about μ with a standard deviation $\sigma/\sqrt{n}$, we can conclude that 95 per cent of the time the mean of the population will be within the interval $\bar{X} \pm 1.96\sigma/\sqrt{n}$. Since the sample estimate of the variance s^2 cannot be substituted for the population variance σ^2 when the sample size is small, it is necessary to base the calculation[1] on the sampling distribution of the statistic known as t. From the standpoint of calculation, this means only that the constant changes with sample size. For a given confidence level the true mean of the population lies within the interval $\bar{X} \pm ts/\sqrt{n}$, where values of t are obtained from Table 16-3.

TABLE 16-3
VALUES OF t FOR DETERMINING THE CONFIDENCE LIMITS OF $\bar{X}$ AND s

Confidence level, %	Sample size n							
	3	5	7	10	12	15	20	∞
90	2.35	2.01	1.89	1.81	1.78	1.75	1.72	1.64
95	3.18	2.57	2.36	2.23	2.18	2.13	2.09	1.96
99	5.84	4.03	3.50	3.17	3.05	2.95	2.85	2.58

The confidence limits for the standard deviation are best obtained from a table of the chi-square (χ^2) distribution. The limits within which the population variance σ^2 will lie, based on the sample variance s^2, are given by

$$\frac{ns^2}{\chi_2^2} < \sigma^2 < \frac{ns^2}{\chi_1^2} \tag{16-11}$$

Values of χ^2 are taken from tables of the distribution for the degrees of freedom equal to $n - 1$. For example, if the limits within which s^2 approaches σ^2 are required to a 95 per cent level of confidence, then χ_1^2 is taken from the table at a probability of 0.975, while χ_2^2 is taken at the 0.025 probability level. An approximation which is good for large sample sizes is that the true standard deviation lies within the interval $s \pm ts/\sqrt{2n}$, where the same values of t listed in Table 16-3 apply.

16-6. Extreme-value Distributions

The argument is sometimes raised that the normal frequency distribution is unsuited for describing mechanical property data because the long tails on each side of the mean are unrealistic and do not represent the observed facts. However, for many practical problems involving statistics these tails can be ignored without affecting the results. Moreover, it is possible to set arbitrary lower and/or upper limits to the normal

[1] For a discussion of this point see Dixon and Massey, *op. cit.*, pp. 97–101.

distribution[1] without destroying its statistical usefulness. The central-limit theorem shows that a normal frequency distribution is to be expected when the effect being observed results from averaging the effects of a whole series of variables. However, if the effect being observed is due to the smallest or largest of a number of variables, an *extreme-value distribution* is to be expected. If failure is due to one weakest link or to a number of more or less equally weak links, the extreme-value distribution would apply.

The application of the extreme-value distribution to engineering problems has been largely the result of the work of E. J. Gumbel.[2] This theory has been used to predict the maximum wind velocity or the crest of floods (largest values) and the fatigue life for a 0.1 per cent probability of failure (smallest value). While the mathematical details of the extreme-value theory are outside the scope of this chapter, an idea of the concept can be obtained from an example. Consider a group of fatigue specimens tested to failure at a constant stress. The distribution of fatigue life obtained from this sample can be considered to be an extreme-value distribution if it is assumed that each specimen which failed represents the weakest out of a large number of specimens tested to the same particular number of cycles of stress reversal. Methods of using the extreme-value distribution with fatigue data have been developed,[3] and extreme-value probability paper is available for plotting the results.

A special type of extreme-value distribution is the Weibull distribution.[4] For this frequency distribution, the cumulative-distribution function is given by

$$P(X) = 1 - \exp - \left(\frac{X - X_u}{X_0} \right)^m \qquad (16\text{-}12)$$

where $P(X)$ is the probability that a value less than X will be obtained, X_u is the value of X for which $P(X) = 0$, and X_0 and m are empirically determined constants. This equation gives a cumulative-distribution curve which resembles that for a normal distribution except that Weibull's distribution has a finite lower limit X_u. Weibull's distribution has been used to describe the yield-strength distribution of steel and the fatigue

[1] For a discussion of the truncated normal distribution, see Hald, *op. cit.*, pp. 144–151; A. C. Cohen, *J. Am. Statist. Assoc.*, vol. 44, pp. 518–525, 1949.

[2] E. J. Gumbel, Statistical Theory of Extreme Values and Some Practical Applications, *Natl. Bur. Standards Appl. Math. Ser.* 33, Feb. 12, 1954; Probability Tables for the Analysis of Extreme-value Data, *Natl. Bur. Standards Appl. Math. Ser.* 22, July 6, 1953; see also J. Lieblein, *NACA Tech. Note* 3053, January, 1954.

[3] A. M. Freudenthal and E. J. Gumbel, *Proc. Intern. Conf. Fatigue of Metals*, London, 1956, pp. 262–271.

[4] W. Weibull, *J. Appl. Mech.*, vol. 18, pp. 293–297, 1951, vol. 19, pp. 109–113, 1952.

life at constant stress. It appears to be particularly well suited to describing the distribution of fatigue life of bearings.[1]

When a mass of mechanical test data is analyzed to select reliable design values, the design engineer is usually interested in establishing the smallest values of the property being tested, so that the design can be based on conservative yet realistic strength values. For example, the designer might be interested in knowing the value of yield strength which would be exceeded by 99.9 per cent of the specimens, while the metallurgist who is trying to improve the yield strength by heat treatment would be mainly interested in knowing the mean and standard deviation of his test values. Of course, the value of yield strength which would be exceeded by 99.9 per cent of the specimens can be calculated from the sample observations *provided* that the frequency distribution of the observations is known and the observations faithfully follow this distribution. Unfortunately, although most mechanical property data fit a normal or log-normal frequency distribution over the central region of probability, at the tails or extremes of the distribution appreciable deviations usually occur. A mean and standard deviation can be determined from any set of observations by the methods described previously, regardless of the nature of the frequency distribution, and even if the observations deviate considerably from a normal distribution, the powerful statistical tests described in the next section can still be used with relatively little error. On the other hand, estimates of the probability of failure are not valid outside the regions in which the data are known to fit the frequency distribution. The prediction of values at low probabilities of failure, e.g., the 0.1 per cent level, on the basis of the assumption that the data follow the normal distribution in this region can lead to considerable error. Further, because of the large number of tests required to make an experimental determination of the stress which gives a 1 or 0.1 per cent probability of failure, there are few experimental observations in the extreme regions which can be used for guidance. While extreme-value statistics have not yet met with universal acceptance, this approach is the most reasonable in dealing with small probabilities of failure.

16-7. Tests of Significance

An important feature of statistical analysis is the ability, through tests of significance, to make comparisons and draw conclusions with a greater assurance of being correct than if the conclusions had been based only on intuitive interpretation of the data. Most of the common statistical tests of significance are based on the use of the normal distribution, so that it

---

[1] J. Lieblein and M. Zelen, *J. Research Natl. Bur. Standards,* vol. 57, pp. 273–316, 1956.

is a distinct advantage if the test data conform to this frequency distribution. A common problem which is readily treated by means of tests of significance is to determine whether the means and/or standard deviations of two samples drawn from essentially the same population really differ significantly or whether the observed differences are due to random chance. In statistics the term *significant difference* is used much more precisely than in everyday usage. In determining whether or not two statistics are significantly different it is always necessary to specify the probability of the test predicting an erroneous conclusion. This is known as the *level of significance.* For example, if the test of significance is made at the 5 per cent level of significance there is 1 chance in 20 that an erroneous conclusion would be reached by the test.

Difference between Two Sample Standard Deviations

It is often of interest to know whether or not the variability of one set of measurements differs significantly from that of another set of data. For example, it may be important to know whether or not a certain metallurgical condition shows more scatter in fatigue life than another treatment or whether or not the scatter is significantly different at high stresses and at low stresses. The test of significance which is used for this situation is the F *test.*

Let s_1 be the standard deviation for a sample size n_1 from the first population, and let s_2 and n_2 be the same terms for the second population. The following ratio is determined, where $s_1{}^2 > s_2{}^2$:

$$F = \frac{s_1{}^2}{s_2{}^2} \tag{16-13}$$

The F ratio obtained from Eq. (16-13) is compared with tables of the F distribution.[1] The table corresponding to the selected level of significance is used. This table is based on the number of degrees of freedom, which for this case is one less than the sample size. The table is entered across the top for the degrees of freedom for the numerator in the F ratio and along the left-hand edge for the degrees of freedom for the denominator. Where this column and row intersect, we get the value of the F ratio. If the ratio calculated in Eq. (16-13) is greater than the F ratio obtained from the table, the two sets of standard deviations are significantly different at the chosen level of significance. Note that, as the level of significance is raised (less risk of making an erroneous decision), the greater must be the F ratio determined from Eq. (16-13). For example, for $n_1 = n_2 = 21$, the F tables give 2.12 at the 5 per cent level and 2.94 at the 1 per cent level of significance.

[1] M. Merrington and C. M. Thompson, *Biometrika*, vol. 33, p. 73, 1943; see also Dixon and Massey, *op. cit.*, pp. 310–313.

Difference between Two Means

Sample Standard Deviations Not Significantly Different. If the F test shows that the standard deviations of the two samples are not significantly different, the following procedure can be used to determine whether or not there is a significant difference between the means of the two samples $\bar{X}_1$ and $\bar{X}_2$: First, the variance of the two samples in common should be determined.

$$s^2 = \frac{(n_1 - 1)s_1^2 + (n_2 - 1)s_2^2}{n_1 + n_2 - 2} \tag{16-14}$$

Then a value for the t statistic can be determined.

$$t = \frac{\bar{X}_1 - \bar{X}_2}{s(1/n_1 + 1/n_2)^{1/2}} \tag{16-15}$$

If the value of t determined from Eq. (16-15) is greater than the value obtained from tables of the t distribution[1] at the specified level of significance and with the degrees of freedom equal to $n_1 + n_2 - 2$, there is a significant difference between the means.

Sample Standard Deviations Significantly Different. If the F test shows that the standard deviations of the two samples are significantly different, it is not correct to determine a common variance. The value of t is determined from Eq. (16-16), and a value of c is calculated from Eq. (16-17) to use in determining the number of degrees of freedom (d.f.) which is used with the t tables.

$$t = \frac{\bar{X}_1 - \bar{X}_2}{(s_1^2/n_1 + s_2^2/n_2)^{1/2}} \tag{16-16}$$

$$c = \frac{s_1^2/n_1}{s_1^2/n_1 + s_2^2/n_2} \tag{16-17}$$

$$\text{d.f.} = \left[\frac{c^2}{n_1 - 1} + \frac{(1 - c)^2}{n_2 - 1} \right]^{-1} \tag{16-18}$$

Nonparametric Tests of Significance

The F test and the t test depend on the requirement that the populations are a good approximation to the normal distribution. Techniques which do not depend on the mathematical form of the frequency distribution are available. These *nonparametric methods* may be useful in cases where the data are too meager to allow an estimate of the frequency distribution to be made. However, because they do not depend on any sampling distribution, they are less powerful than the methods which have been described above. Only a brief description of some of the non-

---

[1] *Ibid.*, p. 307.

parametric techniques can be given here. For details, reference should be made to the original sources.

The *rank test*[1] arranges the two samples in numerical order and assigns rank numbers. The totals of the rank for each sample are compared with tables to determine whether or not a significant difference exists.

The *run test*[2] arranges all values from both samples in ascending order. The number of "runs" from each sample are determined, and by comparing with tables, it can be found whether or not the observations of both samples have been drawn from the same population. To illustrate the meaning of the term run, if two samples *A* and *B* are arranged in order to give the series *A B A A B B A A A B B*, there are six runs *A-B-A A-B B-A A A-B B* in this series.

The confidence interval for the median of a population can be obtained very readily without any consideration of the distribution function of the population. If the observations are listed in ascending order, we know with great certainty that the median of the population lies between the smallest and largest observation. As we approach the central value of the sample, our degree of certainty decreases. Tables are available[3] for predicting at various levels of confidence and for different sample sizes what values in the array the population median would be expected to lie between. For example, if $n = 15$, the fourth and twelfth observations are confidence limits of more than 95 per cent for the population median, while if $n = 50$, the population median will lie between the eighteenth and thirty-third observation.

16-8. Analysis of Variance

The statistical tests of significance discussed in the previous section deal only with the analysis of a single factor at two different levels. For example, by using the methods of the previous section, one could determine whether the transverse reduction of area is significantly different for different forging reductions or for different heat treatments. However, to determine the interaction between the two requires the analysis of variance. One method[4] of analysis of variance will be described below by means of a simplified illustrative example.

Table 16-4 gives the values of RAT for a hypothetical situation where tensile tests were determined from forgings with 10:1 and 30:1 forging

[1] F. Wilcoxon, "Some Rapid Approximate Statistical Procedures," American Cyanamid Co., New York, 1949.

[2] Dixon and Massey, *op. cit.*, pp. 254–255.

[3] *Ibid.*, table 25, p. 360.

[4] Based on a procedure given by C. R. Smith, *Metal Progr.*, vol. 69, pp. 81–86, February, 1956.

reductions, with and without a homogenization heat treatment.   We are interested in answering the following questions.

1. Is there a significant difference in RAT for a 10:1 and 30:1 forging reduction?

2. Is there a significant difference in RAT between a forging which was given no homogenization treatment and one given the homogenization treatment?

3. Is there a significant interaction between forging reduction and homogenization which affects the level of RAT?

TABLE 16-4

EFFECT OF FORGING REDUCTION AND HOMOGENIZATION TREATMENT ON TRANSVERSE REDUCTION OF AREA (RAT)

Homogenization	Forging reduction			
	10:1	30:1		
None	25.8	22.8		
	30.4	19.5		
	28.6	30.6		
	35.6	28.5		
	20.3	25.5		
	$T_{ij.}$ 140.7	$T_{ij.}$ 126.9	$T_{.j.}$	267.6
2400°F, 50 hr	26.4	30.6		
	35.6	35.3		
	30.2	27.9		
	21.4	28.2		
	27.2	31.5		
	$T_{ij.}$ 140.8	$T_{ij.}$ 153.5	$T_{.j.}$	294.3
	$T_{i..}$ 281.5	$T_{i..}$ 280.4	$T_{...}$	561.9

For the arrangement of the data shown in Table 16-4 vertical listings are called *columns* and horizontal listings are called *rows*.   The experimental values for each condition constitute a *cell*.   The total of all the values in each cell is indicated by $(T_{ij.})$.   The total for each forging reduction irrespective of homogenization is called $(T_{i..})$.   The total for each homogenization condition regardless of forging reduction is $(T_{.j.})$. $(T_{...})$ is the total of all values in the table.   Further definitions are as follows:

$$k = \text{number of columns in table} = 2$$
$$l = \text{number of rows in table} = 2$$
$$m = \text{number of readings in each cell} = 5$$

The following computations are made from Table 16-4:

1. Total sum of squares (TSS)

$$\text{TSS} = \sum X_{ij}^2 - \frac{T_{\ldots}^2}{klm} \tag{16-19}$$

where ΣX_{ij}^2 is the summation of the square of all readings, or

$$\text{TSS} = 16{,}208.67 - \frac{(561.9)^2}{2 \times 2 \times 5} = 422.09$$

2. Subtotal sum of squares (SSS)

$$\text{SSS} = \sum \frac{T_{ij.}^2}{m} - \frac{T_{\ldots}^2}{klm} \tag{16-20}$$

$$\text{SSS} = \frac{(140.7)^2 + (126.9)^2 + (140.8)^2 + (153.5)^2}{5} - \frac{(561.9)^2}{20} = 70.82$$

3. Within-cells sum of squares (WSS)

$$\text{WSS} = \text{TSS} - \text{SSS} \tag{16-21}$$
$$\text{WSS} = 422.09 - 70.82 = 351.27$$

4. Between-columns sum of squares (BCSS)

$$\text{BCSS} = \frac{\Sigma T_{i..}^2}{lm} - \frac{T_{\ldots}^2}{klm} \tag{16-22}$$

$$\text{BCSS} = \frac{(281.5)^2 + (280.4)^2}{2 \times 5} - \frac{(561.9)^2}{20} = 0.06$$

5. Between-rows sum of squares (BRSS)

$$\text{BRSS} = \frac{\Sigma T_{.j.}^2}{km} - \frac{T_{\ldots}^2}{klm} \tag{16-23}$$

$$\text{BRSS} = \frac{(267.6)^2 + (294.3)^2}{2 \times 5} - \frac{(561.9)^2}{20} = 35.65$$

6. Interaction sum of squares (ISS)

$$\text{ISS} = \text{SSS} - \text{BCSS} - \text{BRSS} \tag{16-24}$$
$$\text{ISS} = 70.82 - 0.06 - 35.65 = 35.11$$

Once the computations are made, the results can be entered in an analysis-of-variance table such as Table 16-5. Values of mean square are obtained by dividing the values of sum of the squares by their respective degrees of freedom. To determine whether or not there are significant differences between the columns and rows and interactions between the two, the respective mean squares are used in the F test. For example, to determine whether or not there is a significant interaction between forging reduction and homogenization treatment, the following F ratio is determined:

$$F = \frac{\text{interaction mean square}}{\text{within-cells mean square}}$$

$$F = \frac{35.11}{21.92} = 1.61$$

A check of tables of the F distribution at the 5 per cent level of significance shows that the F ratio must exceed 4.49 for the variability to be significant. Therefore, there is no significant interaction between these two variables.

TABLE 16-5
ANALYSIS OF VARIANCE

Source of variability	Degrees of freedom	Sum of squares	Mean square
Between columns (forging reduction)...........	1	0.06	0.06
Between rows (homogenization)...............	1	35.65	35.65
Interaction between columns and rows..........	1	35.11	35.11
Within cells.................................	16	351.276	21.92
Total.......................................	19		

To determine whether or not there is a significant effect of homogenization on the level of RAT, the following F ratio is determined:

$$F = \frac{\text{between-rows mean square}}{\text{interaction mean square}}$$

$$F = \frac{35.65}{35.11} = 1.016 \qquad F(0.05) = 161.00$$

Since the calculated F ratio is far less than the value of F at the 5 per cent level of significance, it must be concluded that the data show no significant effect of homogenization on RAT. In the same way it can be shown that there is no significant difference between the two forging reductions.

16-9. Statistical Design of Experiments

The greatest benefit can be gained from statistical analysis when the experiments are planned in advance so that data are taken in a way which will provide the most unbiased and precise results commensurate with the desired expenditure of time and money. This can best be done through the combined efforts of a statistician and the engineer during the planning stage of the research project. Only a brief introduction to commonly used statistical designs of experiments can be given in this section. For details the reader is referred to several excellent texts on this subject.[1]

In any experimental program involving a large number of tests, it is important to randomize the order in which the specimens are selected for testing. By randomization we permit any one of the many specimens involved in the experiment to have an equal chance of being selected for a given test. In this way, bias due to uncontrolled second-order variables is minimized. For example, in any extended testing program errors can arise over a period of time owing to subtle changes in the characteristics of the testing equipment or in the proficiency of the operator of the test. In taking metal specimens from large forgings or ingots the possibility of the variation of properties with position in the forging must be considered. If the objective of the test is to measure the average properties of the entire forging, randomization of the test specimens will minimize variability due to position in the forging.

One way of randomizing a batch of specimens is to assign a number to each specimen, put a set of numbered tags corresponding to the specimen numbers in a jar, mix them thoroughly, and then withdraw numbers from the jar. Each tag should be placed back in the jar after it is withdrawn to allow an equal probability of selecting that number. The considerable labor which is involved in this procedure can be minimized by using a table of *random numbers*. The first number is selected by placing your finger on a number with your eyes closed. For two digit numbers, the next number in the table will be found on the page corresponding to the first digit of the number in the column given by the second digit. This procedure is repeated over and over until all the specimens are selected.

In the early stages of a research project it is frequently important to determine what are the important factors in the problem under study and what is the relative importance of each of these factors. The use of a *factorial design* in place of the conventional approach of changing each factor one at a time will provide a more efficient answer. Assume that the problem is to determine the effect of boron and nickel content on the yield strength of a high-strength steel. In the first trial each factor will be investigated at two levels. Table 16-6 indicates that three runs would

[1] K. A. Brownlee, "Industrial Experimentation," 4th ed., Chemical Publishing Company, Inc., New York, 1952; O. L. Davies, "The Design and Analysis of Industrial Experiments," Oliver & Boyd, Ltd., Edinburgh and London, 1954; W. G. Cochran and G. M. Cox, "Experimental Designs," John Wiley & Sons, Inc., New York, 1950.

be required by the conventional approach of varying each factor one at a time. By comparing run 1 with run 2, we can find the effect of varying the boron content at constant nickel content. Comparing run 1 with run 3 gives the effect of varying the nickel content for a constant boron content. For this design, one control experiment, run 1, is used to judge

TABLE 16-6
DESIGN OF EXPERIMENT BASED ON CONVENTIONAL ONE-AT-A-TIME VARIATION
OF EACH FACTOR

Factor	B, %	Ni, %
Run 1........	0.002	1.0
Run 2........	0.020	1.0
Run 3........	0.002	3.0

the effect produced by varying the levels of boron and nickel content. No information is provided on the effect of boron and nickel when they are both at their upper level. Furthermore, it is quite possible that the effect of changing the boron content from the low to the high level would not be the same at both the low and the high level of nickel content. In other words, there may be an *interaction* between the effect of boron and nickel. A simple design of experiment such as is given in Table 16-6 cannot determine the existence of interaction.

The factorial design of the experiment for two variables at two levels is given in Table 16-7. This design has several advantages over that

TABLE 16-7
FACTORIAL DESIGN OF THE EXPERIMENT

Factor	B, %	Ni, %
Run 1........	0.002	1.0
Run 2........	0.002	3.0
Run 3........	0.020	1.0
Run 4........	0.020	3.0

given in Table 16-6. First, more precise statements can be made about the effect of varying boron and nickel content. All four runs are used in measuring this main effect by comparing the two runs made at the low level with the two runs made at the upper level. Second, the interaction between boron and nickel is determined from a comparison of the difference in results of runs 1 and 4 with the difference in results of runs 2 and 3. An analysis of variance is used to make these comparisons.

The illustration given above represents the simplest case of a factorial design. The number of runs required in a factorial design is equal to the number of levels raised to the power of the number of factors being investigated. Thus, if we were interested in four variables at four levels, 256 runs would be required. The very rapid rate at which the number of runs required by a factorial design increases with small increases in the number of either variables or levels is the chief disadvantage of this type of experimental design. However, the disadvantages of simple factorial design are overcome to a great extent by a modification known as *fractional replication*.[1] The number of runs required is substantially reduced without greatly affecting the power of the method. The main sacrifice is in runs which, if included, would provide information on higher-order interactions between the variables. The construction of fractional replicate designs is covered in the foregoing reference and in a number of others.[2]

16-10. Linear Regression

The term *regression* is used in statistics to refer to the determination of a functional relationship between one or more independent variables X_i and a dependent variable Y_i. Regression techniques are ordinarily used where it is assumed that a fixed but unknown relationship exists between the X and Y populations but the random errors in the measurements prevent a reliable determination of the relationship by inspection. An example might be the determination of the relationship between tensile strength (Y) and Brinell hardness (X). In this section only the simplest case of linear regression will be considered. This is also called the *method of least squares* because the line which results from the analysis has the property that the sum of the squares of vertical deviations of observations from this line is smaller than the corresponding sum of the squares of deviations from any other line. Multiple regression, where there are two or more independent variables in the regression equation, is an extension of this analysis, and curvilinear regression, where a curved line is fitted to the data, is a further refinement.

Frequently, the term *correlation* is used in conjunction with regression. A clear distinction should be made between regression and correlation. Regression deals with the situation where there is a clear distinction between the dependent and independent variables, while correlation deals with the relationship between two or more sets of data which vary jointly.

[1] D. J. Finney, *Ann. Eugenics*, vol. 12, pp. 291–301, 1945.
[2] K. A. Brownlee, B. K. Kelly, and P. K. Loraine, *Biometrika*, vol. 35, pts. III, IV, pp. 268–276, 1948; A. L. Davies and W. A. Hay, *Biometrics*, vol. 6, no. 3, pp. 233–249, 1950.

A linear-regression equation between the dependent variable Y and the independent variable X is given by

$$Y = a + b(X - \bar{X}) \tag{16-25}$$

where

$$a = \frac{\sum\limits_{i=1}^{i=n} Y_i}{n} = \bar{Y} \tag{16-26}$$

$$b = \frac{n \sum\limits_{i=1}^{n} X_i Y_i - \left(\sum\limits_{i=1}^{n} X_i\right)\left(\sum\limits_{i=1}^{n} Y_i\right)}{n \sum\limits_{i=1}^{n} X_i^2 - \left(\sum\limits_{i=1}^{n} X_i\right)^2} \tag{16-27}$$

The measure of the variation of the observed value of Y from the value calculated from the regression equation is called the standard error of estimate s_{yx}. It plays the role of the standard deviation in regression analysis.

$$s_{yx} = \frac{n-1}{n-2}(s_y^2 - b^2 s_x^2) \tag{16-28}$$

The quantity which determines how well the regression equation fits the experimental data is the *correlation coefficient r*. A value of r close to zero indicates that the regression line is incapable of predicting values of Y, while a value close to unity indicates nearly perfect prediction.

$$r = \frac{n \sum\limits_{i=1}^{n} X_i Y_i - \sum\limits_{i=1}^{n} X_i \sum\limits_{i=1}^{n} Y_i}{n^2 s_x s_y} \tag{16-29}$$

16-11. Control Charts

A statistical technique which has proved very useful for routine analysis of data is the *control chart*. The use of this technique is based on the viewpoint that every manufacturing process is subject to two sources of variation, chance variation and variation due to assignable causes. The control chart is a graphical method of detecting the presence of variation which is greater than that expected as a result of chance. The control chart is one important method which is used in the branch of applied statistics known as *quality control*.[1]

The use of the control chart can best be described by means of an

[1] E. L. Grant, "Statistical Quality Control," 2d ed., McGraw-Hill Book Company, Inc., New York, 1952.

illustration.   Consider a commercial heat-treating operation where bearing races are being quenched and tempered in a conveyor-type furnace on a continuous 24-hr basis.   Every 2 hr the Rockwell hardness is measured on 10 bearing races to determine whether or not the product conforms to the specifications.   The mean of each sample $\bar{X}$ is computed and the dispersion is determined by computing the *range R*.   A separate control chart is kept for the mean and the range (Fig. 16-7).   The average of the sample means, μ, and the mean of the sample values of the

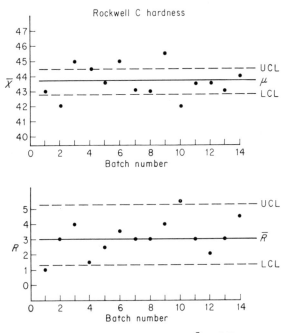

Fig. 16-7. Control charts for $\bar{X}$ and R.

range, $\bar{R}$, are first determined.   Next, the control limits are determined. Points which fall outside the control limits indicate that the variation is greater than would be expected solely from chance and that corrective action should be taken to bring the process into control.

The determination of the upper control limit (UCL) and the lower control limit (LCL) for the mean and the range is greatly simplified by the use of tables developed by Shewart.[1]   The control limits for the range and the means for a 1 per cent chance of the sample value exceeding the control limits due to random chance can be determined from Table 16-8.

[1] W. A. Shewart, "Economic Control of Quality of Manufactured Product," D. Van Nostrand Company, Inc., Princeton, N.J., 1931.

For the range

$$UCL = D_U \bar{R}$$
$$LCL = D_L \bar{R}$$

(16-30)

For the means

$$UCL = \mu + A_2 \bar{R}$$
$$LCL = \mu - A_2 \bar{R}$$

(16-31)

TABLE 16-8
MULTIPLIERS FOR USE IN DETERMINING CONTROL LIMITS
OF CONTROL CHARTS†

Sample size	D_L	D_U	A_2
2	0.009	3.52	1.88
4	0.185	2.26	0.73
6	0.308	1.97	0.48
8	0.386	1.84	0.37
10	0.441	1.76	0.31
12	0.482	1.70	0.27
15	0.524	1.64	0.22

† W. J. Dixon and F. J. Massey, Jr., "Introduction to Statistical Analysis," 1st ed., p. 113, McGraw-Hill Book Company, Inc., New York, 1951.

16-12. Statistical Aspects of Size Effects in Brittle Fracture

Mechanical-strength measurements of brittle materials, like glass and ceramics, and of metals, under conditions where they behave in a brittle manner, show a dependence of strength on the size of the test specimen. As the size of the specimen decreases, the fracture stress in tension, bending, torsion, or impact increases. This is known as a *size effect*. The existence of a size effect in fatigue has already been considered in Chap. 12.

An explanation for the size effect can be provided by statistical reasoning. If it is assumed that brittle fracture is controlled by a distribution of imperfections or cracks, the fracture stress is given by the Griffith criterion.

$$\sigma_c = \left(\frac{2E\gamma}{\pi c} \right)^{\frac{1}{2}}$$

(16-32)

For every size of crack c there will be a certain fracture stress σ_c given by Eq. (16-32). It is assumed that the specimen is made up of many volume elements which each contains a single crack. Since it is assumed that there is no interaction between the cracks in the different volume elements, the strength of the specimen is determined by the element with the longest crack, for this results in the lowest value of fracture stress.

Therefore, the brittle-fracture strength is determined, not by an average value of the distribution of imperfections, but by the one, most dangerous imperfection. This concept of brittle fracture is called the *weakest-link concept* in direct analogy with the fact that the strength of a chain is determined by the strength of its weakest link. The existence of a size effect arises quite naturally from this concept. If the crack density of the material is assumed constant, as the volume of the specimen increases the total number of cracks also increases and therefore the probability of encountering a severe crack is increased. If the stress distribution imposed by the test method is nonuniform, as in bending or torsion, the analysis must be based on the surface area.

The problem of relating the crack distribution to the fracture strength is one of finding the distribution function of the smallest value of strength as a function of the number of cracks N for a given distribution function of crack sizes. Frequently, the distribution of crack size is assumed to be Gaussian. This implies that the probability of having a small defect is the same as the probability of occurrence of a large defect. The mathematics for this crack distribution has been worked out by Frenkel and Kontorova.[1] For a Gaussian distribution of the strength of the weakest element the strength should decrease linearly with increasing $(\log V)^{1/2}$, where V is the volume of the specimen. Weibull's distribution function (see Sec. 16-6) has also been used to describe the distribution of crack sizes.[2] This predicts that the strength should decrease with increasing volume according to $V^{-1/m}$, where m is the experimentally determined factor in Weibull's distribution function. Experiments on the size effect in tension and bending of steel at low temperature show good agreement with Weibull's prediction.[3] It is also argued that a more reasonable distribution of defects decreases in proportion with the size of the defect. The Laplacian distribution adequately expresses this requirement.

$$p(c) = \exp\left(-\frac{c}{a}\right) \tag{16-33}$$

where $p(c)$ = probability of occurrence of a crack of length c
       a = a constant
The Laplacian distribution predicts that the strength decreases linearly with an increase in $\log V$. Figure 16-8 shows the calculated frequency distribution of fracture stresses as a function of the number of cracks N

[1] J. I. Frenkel and T. A. Kontorova, *J. Physics (U.S.S.R.)*, vol. 7, pp. 108–114, 1943.
[2] W. Weibull, A Statistical Theory of the Strength of Materials, *Roy. Swed. Inst. Eng. Research*, no. 151, 1939.
[3] N. Davidenkov, E. Shevandin, and F. Wittman, *J. Appl. Mech.*, vol. 14, pp. 63–67, 1946.

on the basis of a Laplacian distribution of cracks.[1] Note that the larger
the total number of cracks the smaller the scatter in fracture stress
because of the higher probability of finding a critical defect. Also, as
the number of defects increases, the mean value of the fracture stress
decreases, but as the number of defects reaches large values, there is less
relative decrease in the mean value. Existing data are not numerous
enough to determine which of these distribution functions for crack size
is most generally applicable.

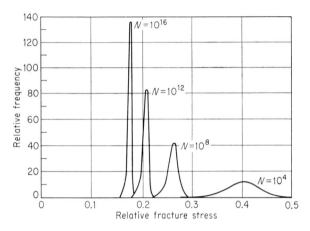

Fig. 16-8. Calculated frequency distribution of fracture stress as a function of number
of cracks, N. (*J. C. Fisher and J. H. Hollomon, Trans. AIME, vol.* 171, *p.* 555, 1947.)

Ductile metals do not exhibit so large a size effect as brittle materials.
The weakest-link concept is not well suited to this situation. The difficulty with using the weakest-link concept with ductile metals is that
plastic deformation alters both the size and the orientation of the defects,
and the individual volume elements can no longer be assumed to be
independent.

16-13. Statistical Treatment of the Fatigue Limit

The statistical nature of the fatigue properties of metals has been
discussed in Chap. 12. In analyzing the results of a number of fatigue
specimens tested to failure at a constant stress, it is usual procedure to
assume that the logarithm of the number of cycles to failure is normally
distributed. The standard procedures for determining the mean and
standard deviation and the F test and t test for significant differences
can be used provided that all computations are based on log N instead of
N. However, there are reasons to believe that the logarithmic-normal

---

[1] J. C. Fisher and J. H. Hollomon, *Trans. AIME*, vol. 171, pp. 546–561, 1947.

distribution does not accurately describe the distribution of fatigue life at the upper and lower extremes of the distribution. Since fatigue life depends on the weakest section rather than on average behavior, it is to be expected that the extreme-value distribution function would provide better agreement in these regions.

The statistical analysis of the fatigue data in the region of the fatigue limit requires special techniques which have not yet been discussed in this chapter. In making tests to measure the fatigue limit, we can test a given specimen only at a particular stress, and if the specimen fails before the cutoff limit of 10^7 cycles then we know that the fatigue limit of the specimen is somewhere below the stress level which we used. Consequently, if the specimen does not fail (a run-out) in the prescribed number of cycles, we know that its fatigue limit lies somewhere above the test stress. Because a given specimen cannot be tested more than once, even if it "ran out," it is necessary to estimate the statistics of the fatigue limit by testing a large number of presumably identical specimens at different stress levels. Experiments of this type are known as *sensitivity experiments*. Two particular types of statistical analysis of sensitivity experiments have been applied to the statistical determination of the fatigue limit. The procedures used will be briefly described below. Step-by-step procedures for the analysis will be found in the ASTM Manual on statistical analysis of fatigue data.[1]

The first of the methods for the statistical determination of the fatigue limit is known as *probit analysis*. A number of specimens are tested at each of four to six stress levels in the vicinity of the estimated fatigue limit. When the percentage of the specimens which survived at each stress is plotted on normal-probability paper against the stress level, a straight line is obtained. One way of performing the experiment is to test 20 specimens at each stress level. The analysis follows the procedures given by Finney in his book on probit analysis.[2] The percentage of survivors are converted to probit values[3] and a regression line is determined according to Finney's procedure for weighting the values at different percentages of survival. However, the same type of analysis can be made without resorting to any special techniques.

The number of specimens tested at each stress should be apportioned with regard to the expected percentage of survival. Not fewer than 5 specimens should be tested at a stress level, and at least a total of 50 specimens should be used in the determination of the median value

---

[1] "A Tentative Guide for Fatigue Testing and the Statistical Analysis of Fatigue Data," *ASTM Spec. Tech. Publ.* 91A, 1958.

[2] D. J. Finney, "Probit Analysis," Cambridge University Press, New York, 1952.

[3] The term probit is an abbreviation of probability unit. Transformation to probits is a method of eliminating negative values from the standard normal deviate z.

of fatigue limit.   If 10 specimens are tested at stress levels which give between 25 and 75 per cent survival, 15 specimens should be tested at stresses which give 15 to 20 and 80 to 85 per cent survival and 20 specimens are required at stresses which result in 10 and 90 per cent survival. With this relative distribution of specimens the test values are adequately weighted at the extreme values, and it is possible to use a standard linear-regression analysis.   In the standard linear-regression equation X is the stress level, and Y is the percentage of survivors converted to values of the standard normal deviate z.   The values of z corresponding to a given percentage of survivors p are obtained by entering an expanded version of Table 16-2 under the column headed Area with $1 - p/100$.   The

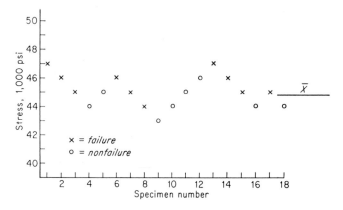

Fig. 16-9. Staircase testing sequence for determination of mean fatigue limit.

median value of the fatigue limit (often loosely called the mean fatigue limit) is given by the stress which intercepts the regression line at 50 per cent survival.   Its standard deviation is given by the stress range between 50 and 84 per cent survival.

The second method of analyzing fatigue data at the fatigue limit is the *staircase*, or *up-and-down*, method.[1]   This method provides a good measure of the mean fatigue limit with fewer specimens than are required with the probit method, but it has the disadvantage that tests must be run in sequence.   The testing procedure is illustrated in Fig. 16-9.   The first specimen is tested at the estimated value of the fatigue limit.   If this specimen fails, the stress for the next specimen is decreased by a fixed increment.   This procedure is continued for each succeeding specimen until a runout is obtained.   The stress applied to the next specimen is then increased by the increment.   The procedure is further continued,

[1] W. J. Dixon and A. M. Mood, *J. Am. Statist. Assoc.*, vol. 43, p. 109, 1948.

the stress being increased when a specimen runs out and decreased when it fails. Fifteen to twenty-five specimens must be tested.

TABLE 16-9
METHOD OF ANALYZING STAIRCASE DATA

Stress, psi	i	n_i nonfailures	in_i	i^2n_i
46,000	3	1	3	9
45,000	2	2	4	8
44,000	1	4	4	4
43,000	0	1	0	0
		$N = 8$	$A = 11$	$B = 21$

d = stress increment = 1,000 psi
X_0 = first stress level = 43,000 psi
$\bar{X}$ = 43,000 + 1,000($1\frac{1}{8}$ + $\frac{1}{2}$) = 44,870 psi

$$s = 1.620(1,000) \left[\frac{8 \times 21 - (11)^2}{8^2} + 0.029 \right] = 1,240 \text{ psi}$$

To determine the mean fatigue limit, the data are arranged in a tabular form as in Table 16-9. A study of Fig. 16-9 shows that there are 10 failures and 8 nonfailures out of the 18 specimens which were tested. Since the analysis is based on the least frequent event (failures or nonfailures), only the nonfailures are considered in Table 16-9. The lowest stress level at which a nonfailure is obtained is denoted $i = 0$, the next $i = 1$, etc. The mean fatigue limit $\bar{X}$ and its standard deviation s are determined from Eqs. (16-34) and (16-35). The constants in these equations are explained in Table 16-9. The positive sign is used in Eq. (16-34) when the analysis is based on nonfailures, while the negative sign is used when it is based on failures.

$$\bar{X} = X_0 + d\left(\frac{A}{N} \pm \frac{1}{2}\right) \tag{16-34}$$

$$s = 1.620d\left(\frac{NB - A^2}{N^2} + 0.029\right) \qquad \frac{NB - A^2}{N^2} > 0.3 \tag{16-35}$$

The staircase method provides a better estimate of the mean fatigue limit than the probit method, and with a fewer number of specimens. However, the latter method gives a better estimate of the standard deviation, and it provides over-all a greater amount of information because the probit curve is actually a response curve between percentage survival and stress.

BIBLIOGRAPHY

Dixon, W. J., and F. J. Massey, Jr.: "Introduction to Statistical Analysis," 1st ed., McGraw-Hill Book Company, Inc., New York, 1951.

Fisher, R. S.: "Statistical Methods for Research Workers," 12th ed., Hafner Publishing Company, New York, 1954.

Goulden, C. H.: "Methods of Statistical Analysis," 2d ed., John Wiley & Sons, Inc., New York, 1952.

Hald, A.: "Statistical Theory with Engineering Applications," John Wiley & Sons, Inc., New York, 1952.

Olds, E. G., and Cyril Wells: Statistical Methods for Evaluating the Quality of Certain Wrought Steel Products, *Trans. ASM*, vol. 42, pp. 845–899, 1950.

Part Four

PLASTIC FORMING OF METALS

Chapter 17

GENERAL FUNDAMENTALS
OF METALWORKING

17-1. Classification of Forming Processes

The importance of metals in modern technology is due, in large part, to the ease with which they may be formed into useful shapes. Hundreds of processes have been developed for specific metalworking applications. However, these processes may be classified into only a few categories on the basis of the type of forces applied to the work piece as it is formed into shape. These categories are:

1. Direct-compression-type processes
2. Indirect-compression processes
3. Tension-type processes
4. Bending processes
5. Shearing processes

In direct-compression processes the force is applied to the surface of the workpiece, and the metal flows at right angles to the direction of the compression. The chief examples of this type of process are forging and rolling (Fig. 17-1). Indirect-compression processes include wire and tube drawing, extrusion, and the deep drawing of a cup. The primary applied forces are frequently tensile, but the indirect compressive forces developed by the reaction of the workpiece with the die reach high values. Therefore, the metal flows under the action of a combined stress state which includes high compressive forces in at least one of the principal directions. The best example of a tension-type forming process is stretch forming, where a metal sheet is wrapped to the contour of a die under the application of tensile forces. Bending involves the application of bending moments to the sheet, while shearing involves the application of shearing forces of sufficient magnitude to rupture the metal in the plane of shear. Figure 17-1 illustrates these processes in a very simplified way.

Plastic forming operations are performed for at least two reasons. One objective is to produce a desired shape. The second objective is to improve the properties of the material through the alteration of the distribution of microconstituents, the refinement of grain size, and the introduction of strain hardening.

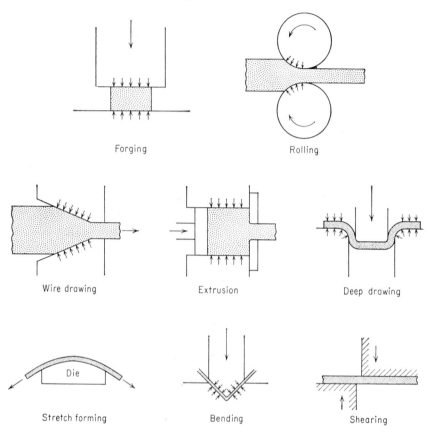

Fig. 17-1. Typical forming operations.

Plastic working processes which are designed to reduce an ingot or billet to a standard mill product of simple shape, such as sheet, plate, and bar, are called *primary mechanical working processes*. Forming methods which produce a part to a final finished shape are called *secondary mechanical working processes*. Most sheet-metal forming operations, wire drawing, and tube drawing are secondary processes. The terminology in this area is not very precise. Frequently the first category is referred to as *processing operations*, and the second is called *fabrication*.

An important purpose of plastic working operations is to break down and refine the columnar or dendritic structure present in cast metals and alloys. Frequently the low strength and ductility of castings are due to the presence of a brittle constituent at the grain boundaries and dendritic boundaries. By compressive deformation it is often possible to fragment a brittle microconstituent in such a way that the ductile matrix flows into the spaces between fragments and welds together to leave a perfectly sound structure. Once the brittle constituent is broken up, its effect on the mechanical properties is minor and ductility and strength are increased. Forging and rolling are the processes ordinarily used for breaking down a cast structure. However, extrusion is the best method because the billet is subjected to compressive forces only.

17-2. Effect of Temperature on Forming Processes

Forming processes are commonly classified into *hot-working* and *cold-working* operations. Hot working is defined as deformation under conditions of temperature and strain rate such that recovery processes take place simultaneously with the deformation. On the other hand, cold working is deformation carried out under conditions where recovery processes are not effective. In hot working the strain hardening and distorted grain structure produced by deformation are very rapidly eliminated by the formation of new strain-free grains as the result of recrystallization. Very large deformations are possible in hot working because the recovery processes keep pace with the deformation. Hot working occurs at an essentially constant flow stress, and because the flow stress decreases with increasing temperature, the energy required for deformation is generally much less for hot working than for cold working. Since strain hardening is not relieved in cold working, the flow stress increases with deformation. Therefore, the total deformation that is possible without causing fracture is less for cold working than for hot working, unless the effects of cold work are relieved by annealing.

It is important to realize that the distinction between cold working and hot working does not depend upon any arbitrary temperature of deformation. For most commercial alloys a hot-working operation must be carried out at a relatively high temperature in order that a rapid rate of recrystallization be obtained. However, lead and tin recrystallize rapidly at room temperature after large deformations, so that the working of these metals at room temperature constitutes hot working. Similarly, working tungsten at 2,000°F, in the hot-working range for steel, constitutes cold working because this high-melting metal has a recrystallization temperature above this working temperature.

Hot Working

Hot working is the initial step in the mechanical working of most metals and alloys. Not only does hot working result in a decrease in the energy required to deform the metal and an increased ability to flow without cracking, but the rapid diffusion at hot-working temperatures aids in decreasing the chemical inhomogeneities of the cast-ingot structure. Blowholes and porosity are eliminated by the welding together of these cavities, and the coarse columnar grains of the casting are broken down and refined into smaller equiaxed recrystallized grains. These changes in structure from hot working result in an increase in ductility and toughness over the cast state.

However, there are certain disadvantages to hot working. Because high temperatures are usually involved, surface reactions between the metal and the furnace atmosphere become a problem. Ordinarily hot working is done in air, oxidation results, and a considerable amount of metal may thus be lost. Reactive metals like molybdenum are severely embrittled by oxygen, and therefore they must be hot-worked in an inert atmosphere or protected from the air by a suitable container. Surface decarburization of hot-worked steel can be a serious problem, and frequently extensive surface finishing is required to remove the decarburized layer. Rolled-in oxide makes it difficult to produce good surface finishes on hot-rolled products, and because allowance must be made for expansion and contraction, the dimensional tolerances for hot-worked mill products are greater than for cold-worked products. Further, the structure and properties of hot-worked metals are generally not so uniform over the cross section as in metals which have been cold-worked and annealed. Since the deformation is always greater in the surface layers, the metal will have a finer recrystallized grain size in this region. Because the interior will be at higher temperatures for longer times during cooling than will be the external surfaces, grain growth can occur in the interior of large pieces, which cool slowly from the working temperature.

The lower temperature limit for the hot working of a metal is the lowest temperature at which the rate of recrystallization is rapid enough to eliminate strain hardening in the time when the metal is at temperature. For a given metal or alloy the lower hot-working temperature will depend upon such factors as the amount of deformation and the time when the metal is at temperature. Since the greater the amount of deformation the lower the recrystallization temperature, the lower temperature limit for hot working is decreased for large deformations. Metal which is rapidly deformed and cooled rapidly from temperature will require a higher hot-working temperature for the same degree of deformation than will metal slowly deformed and slowly cooled.

The upper limit for hot working is determined by the temperature at which either melting or excessive oxidation occurs. Generally the maximum working temperature is limited to 100°F below the melting point. This is to allow for the possibility of segregated regions of lower-melting-point material. Only a very small amount of a grain-boundary film of a lower-melting constituent is needed to make a material crumble into pieces when it is deformed. Such a condition is known as *hot shortness*, or *burning*.

Most hot-working operations are carried out in a number of multiple passes, or steps. Generally the working temperature for the intermediate passes is kept well above the minimum working temperature in order to take advantage of the economies offered by the lower flow stress. It is likely that some grain growth will occur subsequent to the recrystallization at these temperatures. Since a fine-grain-sized product is usually desired, common practice is to lower the working temperature for the last pass to the point where grain growth during cooling from the working temperature will be negligible. This *finishing temperature* is usually just above the minimum recrystallization temperature. In order to ensure a fine recrystallized grain size, the amount of deformation in the last pass should be relatively large.

Cold Working

As was shown in Sec. 5-9, cold working of a metal results in an increase in strength or hardness and a decrease in ductility. When cold working is excessive, the metal will fracture before reaching the desired size and shape. Therefore, in order to avoid such difficulties, cold-working operations are usually carried out in several steps, with intermediate annealing operations introduced to soften the cold-worked metal and restore the ductility. This sequence of repeated cold working and annealing is frequently called the *cold-work–anneal cycle*. Figure 17-2 schematically illustrates the property changes involved in this cycle.

Although the need for annealing operations increases the cost of forming by cold working, particularly for reactive metals which must be annealed in vacuum or inert atmospheres, it provides a degree of versatility which is not possible in hot-working operations. By suitably

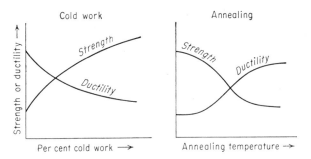

Fig. 17-2. Typical variation of strength and ductility in the cold-work–anneal cycle.

adjusting the cold-work–anneal cycle the part can be produced with any desired degree of strain hardening.   If the finished product must be stronger than the fully annealed material, then the final operation must be a cold-working step with the proper degree of deformation to produce the desired strength.   This would probably be followed by a stress relief to remove residual stresses.   Such a procedure to develop a certain combination of strength and ductility in the final product is more successful than trying to achieve the same combinations of properties by partially softening a fully cold-worked material, because the recrystallization process proceeds relatively rapidly and is quite sensitive to small temperature fluctuations in the furnace.   If it is desired to have the final part in the fully softened condition, then an anneal follows the last cold-working step.

It is customary to produce cold-worked products like strip and wire in different *tempers,* depending upon the degree of cold reduction following the last anneal.   The cold-worked condition is described as the annealed (soft) temper, quarter-hard, half-hard, three-quarter-hard, full-hard, and spring temper.   Each temper condition indicates a different percentage of cold reduction following the annealing treatment.

17-3. Effect of Speed of Deformation on Forming Processes

The response of a metal to forming operations can be influenced by the speed with which it is deformed.   The existence of a transition from a ductile to brittle condition for most body-centered cubic metals over a certain temperature range has already been discussed in earlier chapters. This transition-temperature phenomenon is more pronounced for rapid rates of deformation.   Thus, for certain metals there may be a temperature region below which the metal will shatter when subjected to a high-speed or impact load.   For example, iron and steel will crack if hammered at temperatures well below room temperature, whereas a limited amount of slow-speed deformation can be accomplished in the same temperature range.

Table 17-1 lists typical values of velocities for different types of testing and forming operations.   It is important to note that the forming velocity of most commercial equipment is appreciably faster than the cross-head velocity used in the standard tension test.   Therefore, values of flow stress measured in the tension test are not directly applicable for the computation of forming loads.   For cold working a change in the forming speed of several orders of magnitude results in only about a 20 per cent increase in the flow curve, so that for practical purposes the speed of deformation can be considered to have little effect.   Exceptions to this statement are the possibility of brittle behavior in a certain temperature region at high forming speeds and the fact that high-speed deformation accentuates the yield-point phenomenon in mild steel. High-speed deformation may produce regions of nonuniform deformation (stretcher strains) in a steel sheet which shows no stretcher strains on slow-speed deformation.

TABLE 17-1
TYPICAL VALUES OF VELOCITY ENCOUNTERED IN
DIFFERENT TESTING AND FORMING OPERATIONS

Operation	Velocity, ft/sec
Tension test	2×10^{-6} to 2×10^{-2}
Hydraulic extrusion press	0.01 to 10
Mechanical press	0.5 to 5
Charpy impact test	10 to 20
Forging hammer	10 to 30
Explosive forming	100 to 400

The flow stress for hot working is quite markedly affected by the speed of deformation. There are no routine methods for measuring the flow stress during hot working. However, a high-speed compression testing machine, called the cam plastometer, is one device which has given good results. Data obtained[1] for copper, aluminum, and mild steel at a series of constant temperatures indicate that the dependence of flow stress on strain rate over a range of $\dot{\epsilon}$ from 1 to 40 sec^{-1} can be expressed by Eq. (9-35). Because the time at temperature is shorter for high forming speeds, the minimum recrystallization temperature is raised and the minimum hot-working temperature will be higher. On the other hand, because the metal retains the heat developed by deformation to a greater extent at high forming speeds, there is a greater danger of hot shortness. For metals which have a rather narrow hot-working range these opposing effects serve to close the gap still further and make it impractical to carry out hot working at very high forming speeds.

A recent development has been the ultrahigh-velocity forming of metals at velocities of 100 to 400 ft/sec by using the energy generated by the detonation of explosives.[2] Among the advantages offered are the fact that high-strength materials can be formed without large springback, that metals flow readily into the recesses of the die, and that certain shapes can be produced which cannot be made by any other technique.

17-4. Effect of Metallurgical Structure on Forming Processes

The forces required to carry out a forming operation are directly related to the flow stress of the metal being worked. This, in turn, depends on

---

[1] J. F. Alder and V. A. Phillips, *J. Inst. Metals*, vol. 81, pp. 80–86, 1954–55; J. E. Hockett, *Proc. ASTM*, vol. 59, pp. 1309–1319, 1959.

[2] T. C. DuMond, *Metal Prog.*, vol. 74, pp. 68–76, 1958.

the metallurgical structure and composition of the alloy. For pure metals the ease of mechanical working will, in general, decrease with increasing melting point of the metal. Since the minimum recrystallization temperature is approximately proportional to the melting point, the lower temperature limit for hot work will also increase with melting point. (As a rough approximation, this temperature is about one-half the melting point.) The addition of alloying elements to form a solid-solution alloy generally raises the flow curve, and the forming loads increase proportionately. Since the melting point is often decreased by solid-solution alloying additions, the upper hot-working temperature must usually be reduced in order to prevent hot shortness.

The plastic working characteristics of two-phase (heterogeneous) alloys depend on the microscopic distribution of the second-phase particles. The presence of a large volume fraction of hard uniformly dispersed particles, such as are found in the SAP class of high-temperature alloys, greatly increases the flow stress and makes working quite difficult. If the second-phase particles are soft, they have only a small effect on the working characteristics. If these particles have a lower melting point than the matrix, then difficulties with hot shortness will be encountered. The presence of a massive, uniformly distributed microconstituent, such as pearlite in mild steel, results in less increase in flow stress than for very finely divided second-phase particles. The shape of the carbide particles can be important in cold-working processes. For annealed steel, a spheroidization heat treatment, which converts the cementite platelets to spheroidal cementite particles, is often used to increase the formability at room temperature. An important exception to the general rule that the presence of a hard second phase increases the difficulty of forming is brass alloys containing 35 to 45 per cent zinc (Muntz metal). These alloys, which consist of a relatively hard beta phase in an alpha-brass matrix, actually have lower flow stresses in the hot-working region than the single-phase alpha-brass alloys. In the cold-working region the flow stress of alpha-beta brass is appreciably higher than that of alpha brass. Alloys which contain a hard second phase located primarily at the grain boundaries present considerable forming problems because of the tendency for fracture to occur along the grain boundaries.

As the result of a mechanical working operation second-phase particles will tend to assume a shape and distribution which roughly correspond to the deformation of the body as a whole. Second-phase particles or inclusions which are originally spheroidal will be distorted in the principal working direction into an ellipsoidal shape if they are softer and more ductile than the matrix. If the inclusions or particles are brittle, they will be broken into fragments which will be oriented parallel to the working direction, while if the particles are harder and stronger than the matrix, they will be essentially undeformed.[1]   The orientation of second-phase particles during hot or cold working and the preferred fragmentation of the grains during cold working are responsible for the fibrous structure which is typical of wrought products.   The fiber structure can be observed after macroetching (Fig. 17-3).   Microscopic examination of wrought products frequently shows the results of this *mechanical fibering* (Fig. 17-4).   An important consequence of mechanical fibering is that the mechanical properties may be different for different orientations of the test specimen with respect to the fiber (working) direction.   In

Fig. 17-3. Fiber structure in wrought product revealed by macroetching.   5×.

general, the tensile ductility, fatigue properties, and impact properties will be lower in the transverse direction (normal to the fiber) than in the longitudinal direction.

The forming characteristics of an alloy can be affected if it undergoes a strain-induced precipitation or strain-induced phase transformation. If a *precipitation reaction* occurs in a metal while it is being formed, it will produce an increase in the flow stress but, more important, there will be an appreciable decrease in ductility, which can result in cracking.   When brittleness is caused by precipitation, it usually results when the working is carried out at a temperature just below the solvus line[2] or from cold

---

[1] H. Unkel, *J. Inst. Metals*, vol. 61, pp. 171–196, 1937; F. B. Pickering, *J. Iron Steel Inst. (London)*, vol. 189, pp. 148–159, 1958.

[2] The boundary on the phase diagram of the limit of solid solubility of a solid solution.

working after the alloy had been heated to the same temperature region. Since precipitation is a diffusion-controlled process, difficulty from this factor is more likely when forming is carried out at a slow speed at an elevated temperature. To facilitate the forming of age-hardenable aluminum alloys, they are frequently refrigerated just before forming in order to suppress the precipitation reaction.

A most outstanding practical example of a *strain-induced phase transformation* occurs in certain austenitic stainless steels where the Cr:Ni ratio results in an unstable austenite phase. When these alloys are cold-worked, the austenite transforms to ferrite along the slip lines and pro-

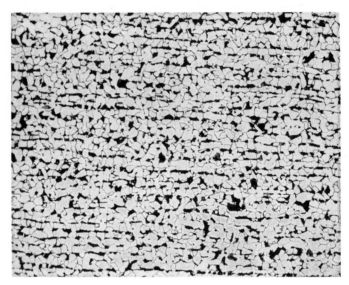

Fig. 17-4. Fibered and banded structure in logitudinal direction of a hot-rolled mild-steel plate. 100×.

duces an abnormal increase in the flow stress for the amount of deformation received. While this phase transformation is often used to increase the yield strength by cold rolling, it can also result in cracking during forming if the transformation occurs in an extreme amount in regions of highly localized strain.

17-5. Mechanics of Metal Forming

One of the prime objectives of research in metal forming is to express the forces and deformations involved in forming processes in the mathematical language of applied mechanics so that predictions can be made about the forces required to produce the desired shape. Since the forces and deformations are generally quite complex, it is usually necessary to use simplifying assumptions to obtain a tractable solution. This branch of mechanics is an outgrowth of the theory of plasticity discussed in Chap. 3, which should be reviewed before completing this chapter and the remaining chapters of this book.

Plasticity theory has made important advances since World War II, and numerous efforts have been made to utilize the new knowledge to improve the accuracy of prediction of the metal-forming equations. Most of this work involves the use of the slip-field theory discussed briefly in Sec. 3-12. While in many instances the use of these more advanced methods provides a deeper insight into the forming process, usually this additional information cannot be obtained without considerable increase in mathematical complexity. Because an analysis based on slip-field theory cannot be made with the background provided in Chap. 3, in discussing the mathematical aspects of specific forming processes in succeeding chapters only the simpler equations will be derived. References to more advanced treatments will be given wherever this is applicable.

The mathematical descriptions of technologically important forming processes which were developed by Siebel[1] and other German workers were based on the assumption that the maximum-shear-stress law was the proper criterion for describing the stress condition for producing plastic flow.[2]

$$\sigma_1 - \sigma_3 = \sigma_0 \qquad (17\text{-}1)$$

Subsequent work showed that the distortion-energy, or Von Mises, flow criterion [Eq. (17-2)] provided better agreement with experimental data.

$$(\sigma_1 - \sigma_2)^2 + (\sigma_2 - \sigma_3)^2 + (\sigma_3 - \sigma_1)^2 = 2\sigma_0^2 \qquad (17\text{-}2)$$

Therefore, the distortion-energy criterion for yielding is to be preferred and will be used in most of the analyses of forming processes presented in subsequent chapters. However, as was seen in Sec. 3-4, the distortion-energy and maximum-shear-stress criteria differ at most by only 15 per cent, and in view of the uncertainties present in the analysis of some of the complex forming operations the two yield criteria can be considered nearly equivalent. Therefore, the maximum-shear-stress law will be used in certain cases where it provides appreciable simplification to the analysis.

An important feature of plasticity theory is the assumption that the

---

[1] An excellent review of E. Siebel's work is available in an English translation by J. H. Hitchcock; it appeared weekly in the magazine *Steel*, from Oct. 16, 1933, to May 7, 1934.

[2] In much of the literature in this field the flow stress σ_0 is denoted by the symbol k. In this text k is taken to indicate the yield stress in shear.

introduction or removal of a hydrostatic or mean stress has no effect on the flow stress or the state of strain. It is considered that only the stress deviator (see Sec. 2-14) is of importance in producing plastic flow, and it is this stress term which appears in the plasticity equations [see Eq. (3-42)]. This assumption is borne out by the experimental fact that the yield stress for the beginning of flow is independent of the mean stress. However, at large plastic strains the hydrostatic stress does have an effect on the flow stress. For increasing hydrostatic stress, the flow curve at large strains is raised. Moreover, as was shown in Sec. 7-16, the ductility of metals in tension is appreciably increased when a high hydrostatic pressure is present. This explains why nominally brittle materials may often be extruded successfully, since a high hydrostatic compression is developed owing to the reaction of the workpiece with the extrusion container.

Because large deformations occur in metal forming, it is important to express stress and strain as true stress and true, or natural, strain. To a very good approximation it is permissible to assume that the volume remains constant during deformation. This leads to the convenient relationships

$$\epsilon_1 + \epsilon_2 + \epsilon_3 = 0$$

or $$d\epsilon_1 + d\epsilon_2 + d\epsilon_3 = 0 \tag{17-3}$$

Frequently it can be assumed that the strain increment is proportional to the total strain. This is called *proportional straining* and leads to the following equation, which is often useful for integrating equations containing the strain differential.

$$\frac{d\epsilon_1}{\epsilon_1} = \frac{d\epsilon_2}{\epsilon_2} = \frac{d\epsilon_3}{\epsilon_3} \tag{17-4}$$

A basic premise of plasticity theory is that equivalent strain hardening is obtained for an equivalent tensile or compressive deformation. For a tensile strain ϵ_1 equal to a compressive strain ϵ_3, we can write

$$\epsilon_1 = -\epsilon_3 = \ln\frac{L_1}{L_0} = -\ln\frac{h_1}{h_0} = \ln\frac{h_0}{h_1}$$

$$\frac{L_0}{L_1} = \frac{h_1}{h_0}$$

$$\frac{h_1}{h_0} = 1 + \frac{h_1 - h_0}{h_0}$$

From constancy of volume

$$\frac{L_0}{L_1} = \frac{A_1}{A_0} = 1 - \frac{A_0 - A_1}{A_0}$$

Therefore $$\frac{h_0 - h_1}{h_0} = \frac{A_0 - A_1}{A_0} \tag{17-5}$$

Equation (17-5) expresses the fact that for equal true strains the reduction of area is equal to the reduction in height or thickness. It is frequently useful to employ these parameters as a substitute for strain in metal-forming experiments.

The flow curve (true stress-strain curve) determined for either tension or compression is the basic relationship for the strain-hardening behavior of the material. It is used to determine the value of the flow stress σ_0 for calculating forming loads. The value of the flow stress will of course depend on the temperature, the speed of deformation, and possibly the existence of a strain-induced transformation, as described in earlier sections of this chapter. For most commercial forming operations the

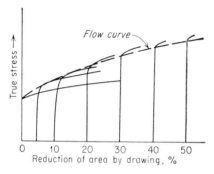

Fig. 17-5. Flow curve constructed from stress-strain curves after different amounts of reduction.

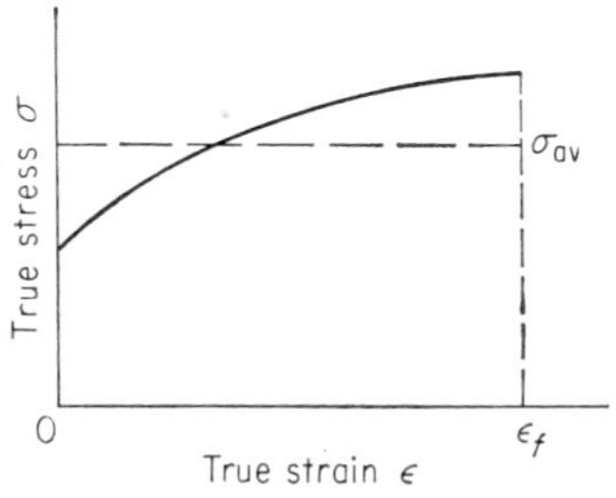

Fig. 17-6. Method of using average flow stress to compensate for strain hardening.

degree of strain hardening which occurs for a given reduction is higher than would be determined from a tensile-flow curve. This is due to the fact that the metal undergoes nonuniform flow during deformation because it is not allowed to flow freely. The lightly deformed regions provide a constraint to plastic flow, just as in the case of a notch in a tension specimen (Sec. 7-12), and the flow stress is raised. One way of determining the flow curve in cases where deformation is nonuniform is to determine the yield stress after different amounts of reduction in the forming operation (Fig. 17-5). A method for measuring the flow stress for cold-worked metals, which is used frequently in England,[1] is to measure the pressure required to produce plastic flow when a sheet is compressed between two rigid anvils. In this test the metal is subjected to plane compression, since there is no deformation in the width direction.

[1] A. B. Watts and H. Ford, *Proc. Inst. Mech. Engrs.* (*London*), vol. 1B, pp. 448–453, 1952–53.

Flow curves for a number of steels and nonferrous metals have been obtained[1] by this method.

In many plastic forming operations, such as extrusion, the strains are much greater than can be obtained in a tension or compression test. It is possible to get good estimates of the flow stress for reductions greater than 70 to 80 per cent by linear extrapolation when σ_0 is plotted against the logarithm of the strain or the reduction in area.[2]

For hot working the metal approaches an ideal plastic material, and the flow stress is constant and independent of the amount of deformation at a given temperature and speed of deformation. To allow for strain hardening in cold working, it is customary to use a constant value of flow stress which is an average over the total strain, as in Fig. 17-6. An alternative, which adds to the mathematical complexity, is to include a mathematical expression for the flow curve in the analysis. Usually this is limited to a simple power function like Eq. (3-1).

To describe the plastic flow of a metal, it is just as important to describe the geometry of flow in relation to the stress system as it is to be able to predict the stress conditions to produce plastic flow. A basic assumption of plasticity theory which allows this is that at any stage in the deformation process the geometry of strain rates is the same as the geometry of stress, i.e., that stress and strain are coaxial. This is a good assumption up to moderate strains, but at large strains, where preferred orientations may have been developed, the stress and strain systems usually are not identical. If Lode's stress and strain parameters are equal (see Sec. 3-5), then the plastic stress and strain can be considered coaxial.

Since metal-forming problems are concerned with large strains of the order of unity, elastic strains of the order of 0.001 are negligible by comparison and the metal can be treated as a rigid plastic material. Regions of the metal which have been strained only elastically and regions between the elastic-plastic boundary in which the yield stress has been exceeded but flow is constrained by the elastic region are considered to be rigid. Only flow in the completely plastic region of the body is considered in the relatively simple analyses of plastic forming given in succeeding chapters. By using the more advanced slip-field theory, it is possible to consider the stress and strain in both the elastic and plastic regions, and also along the elastic-plastic boundary.

17-6. Work of Plastic Deformation

The total work required to produce a shape by plastic deformation can be broken down into a number of components. The *work of defor-*

[1] R. B. Sims, *J. Iron Steel Inst.* (*London*), vol. 177, pp. 393–399, 1954.

[2] R. J. Wilcox and P. W. Whitton, *J. Inst. Metals*, vol. 88, pp. 145–149, 1959–1960.

mation W_d is the work required for homogeneous reduction of the volume from the initial to final cross section by uniform deformation. Often part of the total work is expended in *redundant work* W_r. The redundant, or internal-deformation, work is the energy expended in deforming the body which is not involved in a pure change in shape. Finally, part of the total work must be used to overcome the frictional resistances at the interface between the deforming metal and the tools. Therefore, the total work can be written as the summation of three components.

$$W_T = W_d + W_r + W_f \qquad (17\text{-}6)$$

From the above definitions, it can be seen that the work of deformation represents the *minimum* energy which must be expended to carry out a particular forming process. This is equal to the area under the effective stress-strain curve multiplied by the total volume.

$$W_d = V \int \bar{\sigma}\, d\bar{\epsilon} \qquad (17\text{-}7)$$

The efficiency of a forming process is the work of deformation divided by the total work of deformation.

$$\text{Efficiency} = \eta = \frac{W_d}{W_T} \qquad (17\text{-}8)$$

The total work is usually measured with a wattmeter attached to the electrical drive of the forming equipment. Typical efficiencies for forming processes[1] are extrusion 30 to 60 per cent, wire drawing 50 to 75 per cent, and sheet rolling 75 to 95 per cent.

The following analysis[2] for the work of plastic deformation assumes that the metal is an ideal plastic material which obeys the distortion-energy criterion of yielding and the Levy–Von Mises theory of plastic flow (Sec. 3-9). dW_d is the increment of *work per unit volume* dissipated during the infinitesimal straining of increments $d\epsilon_1$, $d\epsilon_2$, and $d\epsilon_3$.

$$dW_d = \sigma_1\, d\epsilon_1 + \sigma_2\, d\epsilon_2 + \sigma_3\, d\epsilon_3 \qquad (17\text{-}9)$$

Since constancy of volume exists, $d\epsilon_3 = -d\epsilon_1 - d\epsilon_2$.

$$dW_d = (\sigma_1 - \sigma_3)\, d\epsilon_1 + (\sigma_2 - \sigma_3)\, d\epsilon_2 \qquad (17\text{-}10)$$

From Eq. (3-48) it follows that

$$d\epsilon_2 = d\epsilon_1 \left(\frac{2\sigma_2 - \sigma_3 - \sigma_1}{2\sigma_1 - \sigma_2 - \sigma_3} \right) \qquad (17\text{-}11)$$

[1] J. G. Wistreich, *J. Iron Steel Inst. (London)*, vol. 180, p. 54, 1955.
[2] O. Hoffman and G. Sachs, "Introduction to the Theory of Plasticity for Engineers," pp. 52–54, McGraw-Hill Book Company, Inc., New York, 1953.

Introducing Eq. (17-11) into Eq. (17-10) and simplifying,

$$dW_d = d\epsilon_1 \frac{(\sigma_1 - \sigma_2)^2 + (\sigma_2 - \sigma_3)^2 + (\sigma_3 - \sigma_1)^2}{2\sigma_1 - \sigma_2 - \sigma_3} \qquad (17\text{-}12)$$

Upon referring to Eqs. (3-12) and (3-47) it is possible to simplify the above equation to

$$dW_d = \frac{\sigma_0^2}{3\lambda} dt \qquad (17\text{-}13)$$

To integrate this equation, the variable λ must be known as a function of strain. λ is given in terms of effective stress and strain by

$$\lambda = \frac{\bar{\sigma}}{3} \frac{dt}{d\bar{\epsilon}}$$

and since the effective stress $\bar{\sigma}$ is equal to the uniaxial yield stress in the distortion-energy yield criterion, σ_0, we can write

$$\lambda = \frac{\sigma_0}{3} \frac{dt}{d\bar{\epsilon}} \qquad (17\text{-}14)$$

Substituting into Eq. (17-13),

$$dW_d = \frac{2\sigma_0^2}{3} \frac{3 d\bar{\epsilon}}{2\sigma_0} \frac{dt}{dt} = \sigma_0 \, d\bar{\epsilon} \qquad (17\text{-}15)$$

From the definition of effective strain

$$d\bar{\epsilon} = \frac{\sqrt{2}}{3} [(d\epsilon_1 - d\epsilon_2)^2 + (d\epsilon_2 - d\epsilon_3)^2 + (d\epsilon_3 - d\epsilon_1)^2]^{\frac{1}{2}} \qquad (17\text{-}16)$$

and from the constancy-of-volume relationship

$$d\epsilon_3 = -d\epsilon_1 - d\epsilon_2$$

Simplifying Eq. (17-16),

$$d\bar{\epsilon} = \frac{2}{\sqrt{3}} (d\epsilon_1^2 + d\epsilon_1 \, d\epsilon_2 + d\epsilon_2^2)^{\frac{1}{2}} \qquad (17\text{-}17)$$

For the case of proportional straining, Eq. (17-15) can be integrated to obtain the total ideal work per unit volume.

$$W_d = \int dW_d = \frac{2}{\sqrt{3}} \sigma_0(\epsilon_1^2 + \epsilon_1\epsilon_2 + \epsilon_2^2)^{\frac{1}{2}} \qquad (17\text{-}18)$$

17-7. Formability Tests and Criteria

The success of a forming operation depends on the application of high enough forces to overcome the resistance to deformation without exhausting the ductility of the metal. It is only natural that attempts have been made to predict the success of forming operations on the basis of simple laboratory tests. Reliable information on the flow stress required to produce deformation can be obtained with the tension or compression test for slow rates of deformation, but there is no convenient test for exactly determining these data at high rates of deformation.

Because of the difficulty of obtaining reliable data on the deformation resistance of metals during hot working at high deformation rates a number of empirical tests have been developed to evaluate the hot formability of materials. The single-blow impact test[1] has been used for many years to evaluate whether or not a material can be hot-worked without cracking. Good correlation with hot-working operations, such as forging and piercing of solid rounds to make seamless tubes, has been obtained with the hot twist test.[2,3] In this test the metal is stressed in torsion at a high rate. The torque required to twist the specimen is a measure of the flow stress, and the number of twists before fracture is a criterion of the ductility.

The standard measures of ductility which are obtained from the tension test, elongation and reduction of area, give only a very crude indication of the ease with which the metal may be formed without cracking. However, at least a qualitative indication of the forming limits for sheet-metal forming can be obtained from a more detailed analysis of the tensile stress-strain curve. In forming operations where the sheet is restricted from deforming in one area while it is stretched into shape in another region the metal must be able to deform to a large extent without localized deformation. A measure of its ability to do this is the uniform elongation ϵ_u. Further, since $\epsilon_u = n$, a metal with a high strain-hardening coefficient should perform well in this type of forming operation. For sheet-metal forming operations like bending, roll forming, and dimpling, the forming limit is the ability of the metal to deform without fracture. The reduction of area is a qualitative indication of this forming limit. A common qualitative test for the evaluation of the formability of sheet metals is the bend test. Samples of sheet are bent around successively smaller radii until cracking occurs on the tensile (outside) surface of the bend. The minimum bend radius is taken as the smallest radius which can be used without cracking. The minimum bend radius is usually expressed in multiples of the sheet thickness, e.g., a $2T$ bend radius indicates a more ductile sheet than a $4T$ bend radius.

[1] O. W. Ellis, "Working of Metals," American Society for Metals, Metals Park, Ohio, 1937, pp. 943–966.

[2] H. K. Ihrig, *Trans. AIME*, vol. 167, pp. 749–790, 1946.

[3] C. L. Clark and J. Russ, *Trans. AIME*, vol. 167, pp. 736–748, 1946.

17-8. Friction in Forming Operations

An important consideration in the forming of metals is the friction forces developed between the workpiece and the forming tools. Friction forces can materially increase the deformation resistance. They are difficult to measure,[1] and therefore they represent one of the major uncertainties in the analysis of forming operations. Various methods of lubrication are used to minimize friction forces. In fact, the ability to find a suitable lubricant often determines whether or not a forming operation will be successful. For example, the hot extrusion of steel was not commercially possible until molten glass was used as a lubricant in the Ugine-Sejournet process, and the cold extrusion of steel is not possible without a phosphate coating for a lubricant.

The friction between the work and the tools gives rise to shearing stresses along the contact surfaces. The relationship between the shearing stress τ, the normal stress on the interface between the work and the tools, σ, and the coefficient of friction f is generally expressed by Coulomb's law of sliding friction

$$\frac{\tau}{\sigma} = f \tag{17-19}$$

The value of the coefficient of friction will depend upon the material being worked, the material used for the tools or dies, the surface roughness of the work and the tools, the efficiency of the lubricant, the speed of deformation, and the temperature. Friction increases with an increase in the relative motion between the work and the tools, but at high speeds it decreases appreciably. The lowest coefficients of friction are of the order of 0.01 to 0.05. These values occur under conditions of slow speed and excellent lubrication where the tool surfaces are highly polished. Some typical values[2] are $f = 0.05$ for the cold rolling of mild steel with flood lubrication and $f = 0.05$ to 0.15 for cold drawing and deep drawing of steel, copper, and brass using hardened polished dies and efficient lubricants. A value of $f = 0.10$ is typical for the cold rolling of most metals with polished rolls, but if the roll surface is only a ground finish, a value of $f = 0.15$ is more typical. The coefficients of friction are usually higher for hot working because oxidation roughens the work and the tools. A value of $f = 0.4$ is found for rolling steel at a temperature between 700 and 1650°F, but on rolling above 2000°F the coefficient of

---

[1] A sensitive measurement of friction can be made with a pressure-sensitive pin inserted at an angle to the interface; see G. T. van Rooyen and W. A. Backofen, *J. Iron Steel Inst.* (*London*), vol. 186, p. 235, 1957.

[2] Hoffman and Sachs, *op. cit.*, p. 65.

friction drops to 0.2 because of a change in the frictional characteristics of the oxide film.

17-9. Experimental Techniques for Forming Analysis

Experimental investigations of forming operations require techniques for measuring the forming loads and the deformations. Measurement of the forces presents no fundamental problems, although considerable ingenuity is required to instrument most pieces of forming equipment. SR-4 strain gages and load cells, capacitance strain gages, and piezo-electric gages are ordinarily used for this purpose. The gross deformation of the workpiece can be determined by means of conventional measuring instruments. However, the information that is really needed is the strain distribution throughout the workpiece. Most theories of forming assume that the metal is deformed homogeneously; yet there are many indications that inhomogeneous deformation is the general situation in commercial forming processes. Theories of plastic forming which are based on the theory of slip-line fields attempt to take the inhomogeneity of deformation into consideration. However, greater experimental information on the nature of the deformation in forming processes is needed to allow for the formulation of more realistic slip-line fields.

Most studies[1] of the deformation in forming operations have employed grid networks. A number of identical specimens are deformed by different amounts, and the progress of the deformation is determined from the distortion of the network. Either rectangular or polar-coordinate grids are used, depending upon the application. The grid network may be applied either by scribing or by photographic methods. However, only a limited amount of information can be obtained from grids placed on the surface of the workpiece. The flow in the interior of the workpiece can be studied by cutting the billet in half, affixing a grid network to the two faces, fastening them back together, and then machining to a symmetrical shape. Under certain circumstances the interior deformation can be determined by embedding a lead grid in the casting. The distortion of the lead grid is obtained by radiographing the deformed billet. Sometimes plugs are inserted in the workpiece, and their distortion is measured by sectioning and examining under the microscope.

Metallographic techniques are useful for determining regions of heavy deformation. The direction of flow can be determined from the grain distortion and the preferred alignment of second-phase particles and inclusions. An initially banded structure provides a unidirectional internal grid system. Etches are available for most metals which selectively

[1] H. P. Tardiff, *Steel Processing and Conversion*, vol. 43, pp. 626–632, 643–644, 650, 1957.

attack the plastically deformed regions. Since recrystallization will begin first in the most heavily deformed grains, the examination of the microstructure of a deformed metal after annealing will indicate the presence of nonuniform deformation.

Use is sometimes made of plasticine models[1] for studying inhomogeneous deformation in forming operations. Deformation in plasticine is similar to deformation in an ideal plastic material; therefore plasticine is useful for checking theoretical analyses of plastic forming. Grid networks can be readily placed in the interior of plasticine models, and only very light equipment is needed to deform the material. Similar studies using paraffin wax[2] have also been made.

BIBLIOGRAPHY

Burton, M. S.: "Applied Metallurgy for Engineers," McGraw-Hill Book Company, Inc., New York, 1956.

Sachs, G.: "Fundamentals of the Working of Metals," Interscience Publishers, Inc., New York, 1954.

——— and K. R. Van Horn: "Practical Metallurgy," American Society for Metals, Metals Park, Ohio, 1940.

  [1] A. P. Green, *Phil. Mag.*, vol. 42, pp. 365–373, 1951.

  [2] J. W. Barton, C. Bodsworth, and J. Halling, *J. Iron Steel Inst. (London)*, vol. 188, pp. 321–331, 1958.

Chapter 18

FORGING

18-1. Classification of Forging Processes

Forging is the working of metal into a useful shape by hammering or pressing. It is the oldest of the metalworking arts, having its origin with the primitive blacksmith of Biblical times. The development of machinery to replace the arm of the smith occurred early during the Industrial Revolution. Today there is a wide variety of forging machinery which is capable of making parts ranging in size from a bolt to a turbine rotor or an entire airplane wing.

Most forging operations are carried out hot, although certain metals may be cold-forged. Two major classes of equipment are used for forging operations. The forging hammer, or drop hammer, delivers rapid impact blows to the surface of the metal, while the forging press subjects the metal to a slow-speed compressive force. With impact forging the pressure is at maximum intensity when the hammer touches the metal, and it decreases rapidly in intensity as the energy of the blow is absorbed in deforming the metal. Therefore, impact forging produces deformation primarily in the surface layers. In press forging the pressure increases as the metal is being deformed, and its maximum value is obtained just before the pressure is released. Therefore, press forging results in deeper penetration of the deformed zone.

In many forging processes open dies of simple geometrical shape are used. This is true for very large objects or where the number of items produced is small. The simplest forging operation is the *upsetting* of a cylinder between two flat dies (Fig. 18-1). The compressive forces cause the metal to flow out equally in all directions, so that ideally the final shape would be a cylinder of increased diameter and decreased height (Fig. 18-1b). However, because there is always friction between the dies and the metal, the cylinder flows to a lesser extent at these interfaces than it does at the center. The resulting shape is therefore a cylinder which is barreled at the center (Fig. 18-1c). This illustrates the general rule that a metal will flow most easily toward the nearest free surface, which is the point of least resistance.   If the workpiece has a noncylindri-cal shape (Fig. 18-1d), the greatest flow will occur along the narrowest sides (Fig. 18-1e).

The effect of friction in restraining metal flow is used to produce shapes with simple dies.   *Edging* dies are used to shape the ends of bars and to gather metal.   As is shown in Fig. 18-2a and b, the metal is confined by the die from flowing in the horizontal direction but it is free to flow laterally to fill the die.   *Fullering* is used to reduce the cross-sectional area of a portion of the stock.   The metal flow is outward and away

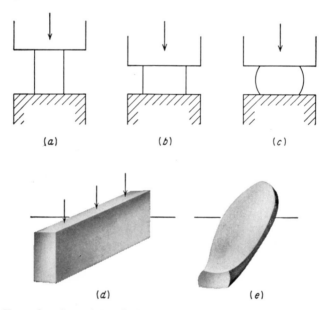

(a)   (b)   (c)

(d)   (e)

Fig. 18-1. Examples of metal flow during upset forging.   (a) Cylinder ready to upset; (b) ideal flow in upsetting; (c) barreling due to friction between dies and work; (d) thin rectangular section before upsetting; (e) rectangular section after upsetting.

from the center of the fullering die (Fig. 18-2c).   An example of the use of this type of operation would be in the forging of a connecting rod for an internal-combustion engine.   The reduction in cross section of the work with concurrent increase in length is called *drawing down*, or draw-ing out (Fig. 18-2d).   If the drawing-down operation is carried out with concave dies (Fig. 18-2e) so as to produce a bar of smaller diameter, it is called *swaging*.   Other operations which can be achieved by forging are bending, twisting, extrusion, piercing (Fig. 18-2f), punching (Fig. 18-2g), and indenting.

Closed-die forging uses carefully machined matching die blocks to pro-duce forgings to close dimensional tolerances.   Large production runs

are generally required to justify the expensive dies.   In closed-die forging the forging billet is usually first fullered and edged to place the metal
in the correct places for subsequent forging.   The preshaped billet is
then placed in the cavity of the *blocking die* and rough-forged to close
to the final shape.   The greatest change in the shape of the metal usually occurs in this step.   It is then transferred to the *finishing die*, where

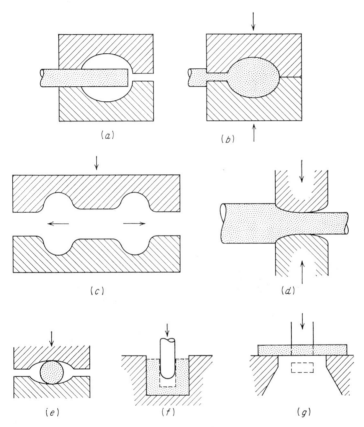

Fig. 18-2. Forging operations.   (*a, b*) Edging; (*c*) fullering; (*d*) drawing; (*e*) swaging;
(*f*) piercing; (*g*) punching.

it is forged to final shape and dimensions.   Usually the blocking cavity
and the finishing cavity are machined into the same die block.   Fullering
and edging impressions are often placed on the edges of the die block.
    It is important to use enough metal in the forging blank so that the
die cavity is completely filled.   Because it is difficult to put just the right
amount of metal in the correct places during fullering and edging, it is
customary to use a slight excess of metal.   When the dies come together

for the finishing step, the excess metal squirts out of the cavity as a thin ribbon of metal called *flash*. In order to prevent the formation of a very wide flash, a ridge, known as a *flash gutter*, is usually provided (Fig. 18-3). The final step in making a closed-die forging is the removal of the flash with a *trimming die*. Closed-die forgings made on a forging hammer are usually called *drop forgings*, while those made on a press are called *press forgings*. With press forgings each step is usually accomplished on a separate die in separate presses, in contrast to the use of multiple die cavities in a single hammer for *drop forgings*. In press forging each sequence is usually performed by a single application of pressure, while in drop forging multiple blows are used for each step.

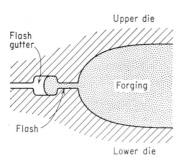

Fig. 18-3. Sectional view through closed-die forging.

18-2. Forging Equipment

In forging hammers the force is supplied by a falling weight, or *ram*. The two basic types of forging hammers are the *board hammer* and the *steam hammer* (Fig. 18-4). In the board hammer the upper die and ram are raised by rolls gripping the board. When the ram is released, it falls owing to gravity. The energy supplied to the blow is equal to the potential energy due to the weight of the ram and the height of the fall. Board hammers are rated by the weight of the falling part of the equipment. They range from 400-lb hammers with a 35-in. fall to 7,500-lb hammers with a 75-in. fall. This type of equipment is capable of producing forgings weighing up to about 100 lb.

Greater forging capacity, in the range from 1,000 to 50,000 lb, is available with the steam hammer (Fig. 18-4). Steam is admitted to the bottom of a cylinder to raise the ram, and it enters the top to drive the ram down. Since the falling ram is accelerated by steam pressure, the energy supplied to the blow is related to the kinetic energy of the falling mass.

$$W = \frac{Mv^2}{2g} \tag{18-1}$$

where M = falling weight, lb
v = velocity, ft/sec
g = acceleration of gravity, 32.2 ft/(sec)(sec)
Striking velocities in excess of 25 ft/sec may be obtained. An important feature of the steam hammer is that the striking force can be readily

controlled, whereas in the board hammer the mass and height of fall are constant. However, in the modern version of the board hammer, where the ram is raised and lowered with compressed air, it is possible to control the force of each blow. A unique type of pneumatic forging hammer

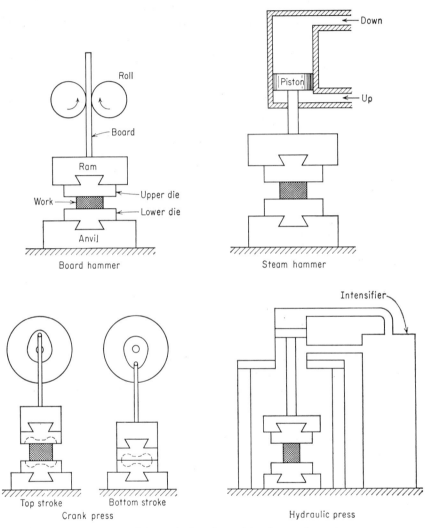

Fig. 18-4. Schematic drawings of forging equipment.

uses two horizontally opposed rams. Each ram strikes the work at high velocity, and practically all their energy is absorbed by the work.

Forging presses are of either mechanical or hydraulic design. Presses are rated on the basis of the estimated force or load developed at the bottom of the stroke.   Most mechanical presses operate from an eccentric crank (Fig. 18-4).   Loads of 100 to 7,000 tons are commercially available.   Vertical hydraulic presses usually have the pressure chamber located on top of the press (Fig. 18-4).   High pressures are built up in the intensifier cylinders by using oil or water as the hydraulic medium. Hydraulic presses are generally built to ratings of 500 to 18,000 tons, although several presses with ratings of 50,000 tons have been built.[1] Large hydraulic presses are particularly adaptable to the open-die forging of steel ingots and the closed-die forging of aluminum and magnesium.

Forging machines, also known as *upsetters,* or *headers,* are horizontal presses which are very useful for the high-production forging of symmetrical shapes from bar stock.   The machine is basically a double-acting press with dies which firmly grip the work around the circumference and forming tools which upset the metal.   Bolts, rivets, and gears are typical parts made with forging machines.   Forging machines are rated in terms of the maximum-diameter bar which can be gripped by the machine.

Forging rolls are used for initial forming prior to closed-die forging and for producing tapered sections or long, slender sections.   The rolls use only part of their circumference to reduce the metal.   The remaining portion is reduced in diameter so that the forged part can move freely between the rolls.   The operator stands at the rear of the rolls, and when the clearance space appears, he inserts the work.   When the reducing portion of the rolls comes in contact with the work, it is reduced and ejected toward the operator.   Different portions of the work can be successively fed into the rolls or fed through other grooves to produce increased reductions.   Long bolts and spring leaves are often made on forging rolls.

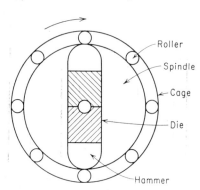

Fig. 18-5. Swaging machine.

Rotary swaging, or rotary forging, subjects a bar or tube to a series of blows from two dies which rotate around the stock so that it is hammered from all sides.   Figure 18-5 illustrates the operation of the swaging machine.   Two dies, backed up by hammers, are rotated with the spindle.   The spindle rotates in a cage containing a number of hardened steel rollers.   When the hammers contact the rollers, the dies are forced together, but when the spindle rotates the hammers to a position between the rollers, the dies fly open owing to centrifugal force.   Thus, the work is subjected to

[1] M. D. Stone, *Trans. ASME,* vol. 75, pp. 1493–1512, 1953.

several thousand blows per minute. The applied stresses are almost entirely compressive. For this reason small swaging machines have found considerable use as a laboratory method of decreasing the diameter of relatively brittle materials. On a commercial basis swaging is used for reducing the diameter of rod and tubing, for pointing rod prior to wire drawing, and for attaching sleeves to cable ends.

18-3. Deformation in Compression

The compression of a flat plate or a cylinder between two flat dies represents the simplest type of forging operation. Although at first glance this appears to be a simple type of experiment which is subject to easy analysis, in actuality a compression experiment is usually complicated by the presence of friction between the dies and the specimen.

In the absence of friction, i.e., when the dies are very well lubricated, the uniaxial compressive force required to produce yielding is

$$P_x = \sigma_0 A \tag{18-2}$$

The compressive stress p induced by a uniaxial force P is given by[1]

$$p = \frac{4Ph}{\pi D_0{}^2 h_0} \tag{18-3}$$

where h = height of cylindrical sample at any instant during compression
h_0 = original height of cylinder
D_0 = original diameter of cylinder
The engineering strain in compression is

$$e = \frac{\Delta h}{h_0} = \frac{h - h_0}{h_0} = -\left(1 - \frac{h}{h_0}\right) \tag{18-4}$$

The true, or natural, strain in compression is given by

$$\epsilon = \int_{h_0}^{h} \frac{dh}{h} = \ln \frac{h}{h_0} = -\ln \frac{h_0}{h} \tag{18-5}$$

It can be readily shown that $\epsilon = \ln (e + 1)$.

When friction is present between the dies and the specimen, the metal adjacent to these regions undergoes little or no deformation. The specimen deforms in the inhomogeneous manner shown in Fig. 18-6, and the specimen assumes a barreled shape. The shaded areas in Fig. 18-6 represent regions of little deformation owing to the presence of frictional stresses at the die interface. Under these conditions the compressive force required to cause yielding is no longer given by the simple relation-

[1] M. Cook and E. C. Larke, *J. Inst. Metals*, vol. 71, pp. 371–390, 1945.

ship of Eq. (18-2).   The force required to produce deformation will be a
function of the dimensions of the specimen (Sec. 18-6) as well as the
frictional conditions at the interface.   For the two cylinders shown in
Fig. 18-6, with the same diameter and equal frictional conditions but
different heights, the shorter cylinder will require a greater axial force to
produce the same percentage reduction in height because of the relatively
larger undeformed region.   Similarly, for cylinders of equal height but
different diameter, the larger-diameter cylinder will require a higher average axial pressure to produce the same reduction in height because it has
a greater surface area in contact with the dies.   The true flow stress or

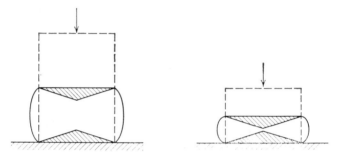

Fig. 18-6. Undeformed regions (shaded) due to friction at ends of a compression
specimen.

yield stress in compression can be found by extrapolating the measured
average stress for a number of specimens of different geometry to a
diameter-height ratio of zero.[1]   Quite reliable approximate methods of
calculating the yield stress in compression with friction present will be
given in the next two sections.   A correction factor to apply to the
measured uniaxial pressure to correct for barreling, similar to the necking
correction for the tension test, has also been determined.[2]

The plane-strain compression of a plate between platens was one of the
first problems attacked by the method of the slip-line field.   Prandtl[3]
made the first analysis, which was later extended by Hill,[4] Green,[5]
Alexander,[6] and Bishop.[7]

[1] *Ibid.;* see also N. H. Polakowski, *J. Iron Steel Inst. (London),* vol. 163, pp. 250–
276, 1949.

[2] T. A. Read, H. Markus, and J. M. McCaughey, in "Fracturing of Metals," pp.
228–243, American Society for Metals, Metals Park, Ohio, 1948.

[3] L. Prandtl, *Z. angew. Math. u. Mech.,* vol. 3, pp. 401–406, 1923.

[4] R. Hill, "The Mathematical Theory of Plasticity," pp. 226–236, Oxford University Press, New York, 1950.

[5] A. P. Green, *Phil. Mag.,* vol. 42, pp. 900–918, 1951.

[6] J. M. Alexander, *J. Mech. and Phys. Solids,* vol. 3, pp. 233–245, 1955.

[7] J. F. W. Bishop, *J. Mech. and Phys. Solids,* vol. 6, pp. 132–144, 1958.

18-4. Forging in Plane Strain with Coulomb Friction

The differential equation for the forging of a plate of constant thickness under conditions of plane strain will be developed with the aid of Fig. 18-7. This figure shows the stresses acting on an element of a flat plate which is being compressed in open dies. The two principal stresses are the compressive axial pressure on the dies, $\sigma_y = -p$, and the longitudinal compressive stress σ_x, which is the stress required to make the metal flow parallel to the dies. It is assumed that the plate has unit width normal to the plane of the paper and that this width remains constant so that the analysis can be based on the two-dimensional plane-strain condition. The shearing stresses τ_{xy} act at the die-metal interfaces as a result of friction.

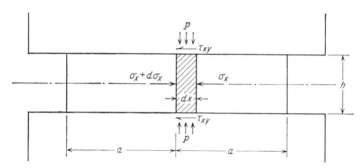

Fig. 18-7. Stresses acting on a plate forged in plane strain.

Taking the equilibrium of forces in the x direction results in

$$(\sigma_x + d\sigma_x - \sigma_x)h - 2\tau_{xy}\,dx = 0$$
$$h\,d\sigma_x - 2\tau_{xy}\,dx = 0 \tag{18-6}$$

The distortion-energy criterion of yielding for a condition of plane strain was given by Eq. (3-60).

$$\sigma_x - \sigma_y = \frac{2}{\sqrt{3}}\sigma_0 = \sigma_0' = \sigma_x + p \tag{18-7}$$

By differentiating both sides of Eq. (18-7), one finds that

$$d\sigma_x = -dp$$

and upon substituting into Eq. (18-6) and rearranging, the general differential equation of equilibrium is obtained.

$$dp + \frac{2\tau_{xy}}{h}\,dx = 0 \tag{18-8}$$

If it is assumed that the shearing stress is related to the normal pressure by Coulomb's law of sliding friction, $\tau_{xy} = fp$, then Eq. (18-8) becomes

$$dp + \frac{2fp}{h} dx = 0$$

Separating the variables results in

$$\frac{dp}{p} = -\frac{2f}{h} dx \qquad (18\text{-}9)$$

Integrating both sides gives

$$\ln p = -\frac{2fx}{h} + \ln C$$

or
$$p = C \exp \frac{-2fx}{h} \qquad (18\text{-}10)$$

The integration constant C is evaluated by the boundary condition that at a free surface $x = a$ the longitudinal stress $\sigma_x = 0$. Therefore, by Eq. (18-7) $p = \sigma_1'$ and $\ln C = \ln \sigma_1' + 2fa/h$.

$$p = \sigma_0' \exp \frac{2f(a - x)}{h} \qquad (18\text{-}11)$$

$$\sigma_x = \sigma_0' \left[1 - \exp \frac{2f(a - x)}{h} \right] \qquad (18\text{-}12)$$

Since f is usually a small number, we can make use of the expansion $\exp y = 1 + y + y^2/2! + y^3/3! + \cdots$ to simplify the above equations.

$$p = \sigma_0' \left[1 + \frac{2f}{h} (a - x) \right] \qquad (18\text{-}13)$$

$$\sigma_x = \sigma_0' \left[-\frac{2f}{h} (a - x) \right] \qquad (18\text{-}14)$$

$$p_{\text{av}} = \frac{\int_0^a p\, dx}{a} = \sigma_0' \frac{\exp (2fa/h) - 1}{2fa/h} \qquad (18\text{-}15)$$

The total forging load P can then be established, since $P = 2p_{\text{av}}aw$, where w is the width in the direction normal to the plane of the paper.

Equation (18-13) shows that, as the ratio of length to thickness, x/h, increases, the resistance to compressive deformation increases rapidly. This fact is used to advantage in closed-die forging, where the deformation resistance of the flash must be very high so that the pressure in the die will be high enough to ensure complete filling of the die cavity.

Figure 18-8 shows the pressure distribution and the variation of longi-

tudinal compressive stress over a
plate of length $2a$. The pressure
builds up to a maximum at the
center of the plate. Note also
that the longitudinal resistance to
flow, σ_x, increases rapidly with
distance from the free surface.

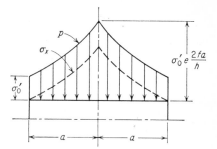

The equations described above
are strictly applicable only to open-
die forgings. While these equations have been applied with fair
accuracy to the prediction of the
pressure required for closed-die

Fig. 18-8. Distribution of normal stress
and longitudinal stress for compression
between plates.

forging,[1] a more detailed analysis[2] provides a better estimate of the
forging pressure for this situation.

18-5. Forging in Plane Strain with Sticking Friction

In the previous section we assumed that the shearing stresses at the
die-metal interfaces were related to the normal pressure on the interface
by Coulomb's law of sliding friction. Another assumption that could be
made is that the die surfaces are so rough that the metal adheres perfectly
to them. This is the limiting case known as sticking friction. For sticking friction at the die-metal interface the shearing stress at the interface
is constant and equal to the shearing strength of the metal in plane strain,
$\sigma_0'/2 = \sigma_0/\sqrt{3}$. Substituting this value for τ_{xy} in Eq. (18-8) gives, after
integration, the following relation:

$$p = \sigma_0'\left(1 + \frac{a - x}{h}\right) \tag{18-16}$$

Equation (18-16) predicts that for a situation of sticking friction the
pressure distribution over a plate of length $2a$ is linear, with the maximum pressure at the center of the plate.

18-6. Forging of a Cylinder in Plane Strain

Figure 18-9 shows the stresses acting on a volume element cut from a
thin cylinder of radius a that is compressed in the z direction. The equi-

[1] R. L. Dietrich and G. Ansel, *Trans. ASM*, vol. 38, pp. 709–728, 1947.

[2] S. Kobayashi, R. Herzog, J. T. Lapsley, and E. G. Thomsen, *Trans. ASME*, ser.
B, vol. 81, pp. 228–238, 1959; A. G. MacDonald, S. Kobayashi, and E. G. Thomsen,
Trans. ASME, ser. B, vol. 82, pp. 246–252, 1960.

librium of forces in the radial direction gives

$$\sigma_r r \, d\theta \, h - (\sigma_r + d\sigma_r)(r + dr) \, d\theta \, h - 2fpr \, dr \, d\theta + \sigma_t h \, d\theta \, dr = 0$$

which reduces to

$$\frac{d\sigma_r}{dr} + \frac{\sigma_r - \sigma_t}{r} = -\frac{2fp}{h} \tag{18-17}$$

Since the strains in the radial and transverse directions are equal, $\sigma_r = \sigma_t$. Also, $\sigma_z = p$. Substituting these three principal stresses into the equation for the distortion-energy yielding criterion results in

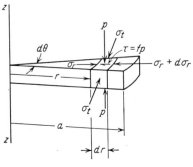

$$p - \sigma_r = \sigma_0 \tag{18-18}$$

Differentiating and substituting into Eq. (18-17) yields

$$\frac{dp}{p} = -\frac{2f}{h} dr \tag{18-19}$$

This is the same as Eq. (18-9) for the rectangular slab. Therefore, the solution is

Fig. 18.9. Stresses acting on element of cylinder.

$$p = \sigma_0 \exp\left[\frac{2f}{h}(a - r)\right] \tag{18-20}$$

The average pressure for a cylinder loaded in compression is given by[1]

$$p_{av} = \sigma_0 \frac{\exp(2fa/h) - 2fa/h - 1}{2(fa/h)^2} \tag{18-21}$$

Equation (18-20) again demonstrates the fact that higher forming pressures are required when the height of the body is small compared with its transverse dimensions. By using specimens of different a/h ratio it is possible to determine the coefficient of friction and the flow stress. Studies of this type and analytical expressions for the deformation pressure of thin cylinders under different conditions of die friction have been reported.[2]

18-7. Forging Defects

If the deformation during forging is limited to the surface layers, as when light, rapid hammer blows are used, the dendritic ingot structure will not be broken down at the interior of the forging. Incomplete forging penetration can be readily detected by macroetching a cross section

---

[1] Stone, *op. cit.*

[2] W. Schroeder and D. A. Webster, *J. Appl. Mech.*, vol. 16, pp. 289–294, 1949.

of the forging.   The examination of a deep etch disk for segregation, dendritic structure, and cracks is a standard quality-control procedure with large forgings.   To minimize incomplete penetration, forgings of large cross section are usually made on a forging press.

Surface cracking can occur as a result of excessive working of the surface at too low a temperature or as a result of hot shortness.   A high sulfur concentration in the furnace atmosphere can produce hot shortness in steel and nickel.   Cracking at the flash of closed-die forgings is another surface defect, since the crack generally penetrates into the body of the forging when the flash is trimmed off (Fig. 18-10a).   This type of crack-

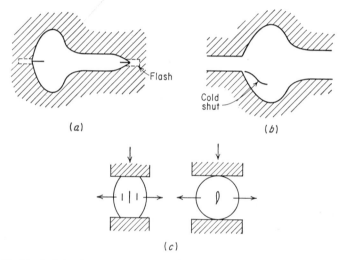

Fig. 18-10. Typical forging defects.   (a) Cracking at the flash; (b) cold shut or fold; (c) internal cracking due to secondary tensile stresses.

ing is more prevalent the thinner the flash in relation to the original thickness of the metal.   Flash cracking can be avoided by increasing the flash thickness or by relocating the flash to a less critical region of the forging.[1]

Another common surface defect in closed-die forgings is the *cold shut*, or fold (Fig. 18-10b).   A cold shut is a discontinuity produced when two surfaces of metal fold against each other without welding completely. A cold shut can occur when a flash or fin produced by one forging operation is pressed into the metal surface during a subsequent operation.

In the upsetting of bar stock on a forging machine certain precautions must be taken to prevent buckling of the bar.   For upsetting in a single operation the unsupported length should be no greater than two to three

[1] G. Sachs, *J. Inst. Metals*, vol. 64, pp. 261–283, 1939.

times the diameter of the stock.   General rules for the optimum dimensions for upsetting in forging machines have been developed.[1]

Secondary tensile stresses can develop during forging, and cracking can thus be produced.   Internal cracks can develop during the upsetting of a cylinder or a round (Fig. 18-10c), as a result of the circumferential tensile stresses.   Proper design of the dies, however, can minimize this type of cracking.   In order to minimize bulging during upsetting and the development of circumferential tensile stresses, it is usual practice to use concave dies.   Internal cracking is less prevalent in closed-die forging because lateral compressive stresses are developed by the reaction of the work with the die wall.

The deformation produced by forging results in a certain degree of directionality to the microstructure in which second phases and inclusions are oriented parallel to the direction of greatest deformation.   When viewed at low magnification, this appears as *flow lines*, or *fiber structure*. The existence of a fiber structure is characteristic of all forgings and is not to be considered as a forging defect.   However, as was discussed in Sec. 9-11, the fiber structure results in lower tensile ductility and fatigue properties in the direction normal to it (transverse direction).   To achieve an optimum balance between the ductility in the longitudinal and transverse directions of a forging, it is often necessary to limit the amount of deformation to 50 to 70 per cent reduction in cross section.

18-8. Residual Stresses in Forgings

The residual stresses produced in forgings as a result of inhomogeneous deformation are generally quite small because the deformation is usually carried out well into the hot-working region.   However, appreciable residual stresses and warping can occur on the quenching of steel forgings in heat treatment (Sec. 15-6).

Special precautions must be observed during the cooling of large steel forgings from the hot-working temperature.   Large forgings are subject to the formation of small cracks, or *flakes*, at the center of the cross section.   Flaking is associated with the high hydrogen content usually present in steel ingots of large size, coupled with the presence of residual stresses.   In order to guard against the development of high thermal or transformation residual stresses, large forgings are very slowly cooled from the working temperature.   This may be accomplished by burying the forging in ashes for periods up to several weeks or, in the controlled cooling treatment which is used for hot-rolled railroad rail and certain forgings, by transferring the hot forging to an automatically controlled cooling cycle which brings the forging to a safe temperature in a number of hours.

[1] "Metals Handbook," p. 40, American Society for Metals, Metals Park, Ohio, 1948.

BIBLIOGRAPHY

Hoffman, O., and G. Sachs: "Introduction to the Theory of Plasticity for Engineers," chap. 21, McGraw-Hill Book Company, Inc., New York, 1953.

Kyle, P. E.: "The Closed Die Forging Process," The Macmillan Company, New York, 1954.

Naujoks, W., and D. C. Fabel: "Forging Handbook," American Society for Metals, Metals Park, Ohio, 1939.

Sachs, G., and K. R. Van Horn: "Practical Metallurgy," American Society for Metals, Metals Park, Ohio, 1940.

Chapter 19

ROLLING OF METALS

19-1. Classification of Rolling Processes

The process of plastically deforming metal by passing it between rolls is known as *rolling*. This is the most widely used metalworking process because it lends itself to high production and close control of the final product. In deforming metal between rolls, the work is subjected to high compressive stresses from the squeezing action of the rolls and to surface shear stresses as a result of the friction between the rolls and the metal. The frictional forces are also responsible for drawing the metal into the rolls.

The initial breakdown of ingots into blooms and billets is generally done by hot rolling. This is followed by further hot rolling into plate, sheet, rod, bar, pipe, rails, or structural shapes. The cold rolling of metals has reached a position of major importance in industry. Cold rolling produces sheet, strip, and foil with good surface finish and increased mechanical strength, at the same time maintaining close control over the dimensions of the product.

The terminology used to describe rolled products is fairly loose, and sharp limits with respect to dimensions cannot always be made for steel-making terminology. A *bloom* is the product of the first breakdown of the ingot. Generally the width of a bloom equals its thickness, and the cross-sectional area is greater than 36 in.^{2} A further reduction by hot rolling results in a *billet*. The minimum cross section of a billet is about $1\frac{1}{2}$ by $1\frac{1}{2}$ in. It should be noted that in nonferrous metallurgical terminology a billet is any ingot which has received hot working by rolling, forging, or extrusion, or the term may refer to a casting which is suitable for hot working, as an extrusion billet. A *slab* refers to a hot-rolled ingot with a cross-sectional area greater than 16 in.^{2} and with a width that is at least twice the thickness. Blooms, billets, and slabs are known as *semifinished products* because they are subsequently formed into other mill products. The differentiation between *plate* and *sheet* is determined by the thickness of the product. In general, plate has a thickness greater than $\frac{1}{4}$ in., although there are exceptions to this limit, depending upon the width. *Sheet* and *strip* refer to rolled products which generally have a thickness less than $\frac{1}{4}$ in. In general, strip refers to the rolled product with a width no greater than 12 in., while sheet refers to the product of greater width.

Generally rolling starts with a cast ingot, but this is not a necessary requirement. A recent development is *powder rolling*. Metal powder is introduced between the rolls and compacted into a "green strip," which is subsequently sintered to high density. The advantages claimed[1] for this process are that the elimination of hot working minimizes contamination, results in a fine grain size, and produces a sheet with no preferred orientation. Powder rolling is still in its infancy, but it appears to have definite advantages for reactive metals.

In conventional hot or cold rolling the main objective is to decrease the thickness of the metal. Ordinarily little increase in width occurs, so that the decrease in thickness results in an increase in length. *Roll forming* is a special type of cold rolling in which strip is progressively bent into complex shapes by passing it through a series of driven rolls. The thickness of the metal is not appreciably changed during this process. Roll forming is particularly suited to producing long, molded sections such as irregular-shaped channels and trim. Another specialized use of rolling is *thread rolling*, in which a blank is fed between two grooved die plates to form the threads.

19-2. Rolling Equipment

A rolling mill consists basically of rolls, bearings, a housing for containing these parts, and a drive for applying power to the rolls and controlling their speed. The forces involved in rolling can easily reach many millions of pounds. Therefore, very rigid construction is needed, and very large motors are required to provide the necessary power. When these requirements are multiplied several times for the successive stands of a large continuous mill, it is easy to see why a modern rolling-mill installation demands many millions of dollars of capital investment and many man-hours of skilled engineering design and construction.

Rolling mills can be conveniently classified with respect to the number and arrangement of the rolls (Fig. 19-1). The simplest and most common type of rolling mill is the *two-high* mill (Fig. 19-1a). Rolls of equal size are rotated only in one direction. The stock is returned to the entrance, or rear, of the rolls for further reduction by hand carrying or by means of a platform which can be raised to pass the work above the rolls. An obvious improvement in speed results from the use of a *two-high reversing*

---

[1] S. Storchheim, *Metal Progr.*, vol. 70, pp. 120–126, 1956.

mill, in which the work can be passed back and forth through the rolls by reversing their direction of rotation (Fig. 19-1*b*).   Another solution is the *three-high mill* (Fig. 19-1*c*), consisting of an upper and lower driven roll and a middle roll which rotates by friction.

A large decrease in the power required for rolling can be achieved by the use of small-diameter rolls.   However, because small-diameter rolls have less strength and rigidity than large rolls, they must be supported by larger-diameter backup rolls.   The simplest mill of this type is the

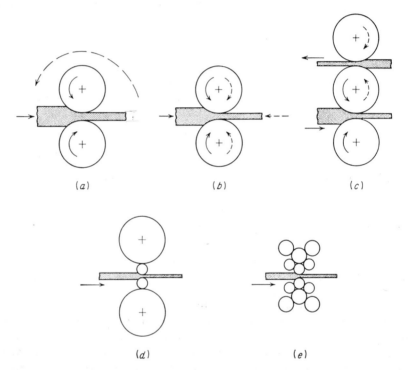

(a)   (b)   (c)

(d)   (e)

Fig. 19-1. Typical arrangements of rolls for rolling mills.   (*a*) Two-high, pull-over; (*b*) two-high, reversing; (*c*) three-high; (*d*) four-high; (*e*) cluster.

four-high mill (Fig. 19-1*d*).   Very thin sheet can be rolled to very close tolerances on a mill with small-diameter work rolls.   The *cluster mill* (Fig. 19-1*e*), in which each of the work rolls is supported by two backing rolls, is a typical mill of this kind.   The *Sendzimir mill* is a modification of the cluster mill which is very well adapted to rolling thin sheet or foil from high-strength alloys.

For high production it is common to install a series of rolling mills one after another in tandem (Fig. 19-2).   Each set of rolls is called a *stand.*   Since a different reduction is taken at each stand, the strip will be moving at different velocities at each stage in the mill. The speed of each set of rolls is synchronized so that each successive stand takes the strip at a speed equal to the delivery speed of the preceding stand. The uncoiler and windup reel not only accomplish the functions of feeding the stock to the rolls and coiling up the final product but also can be used to supply a *back tension* and a *front tension* to the strip. These added horizontal forces have several advantages that will be discussed later. In a special type of reversible mill, called the *Steckel mill*, the force is applied through the power reels, and the rolls are not driven at

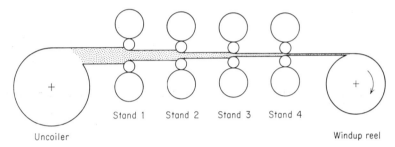

Fig. 19-2. Schematic drawing of strip rolling on a four-stand continuous mill.

all. While the amount of reduction per pass that can be accomplished by means of the Steckel mill is limited, because it uses small work rolls it can reduce hard metals to thin gages with close tolerances on thickness.

19-3. Hot Rolling

The first hot-working operation for most steel products is done in the *blooming mill* (also called cogging mill). Blooming mills are usually two-high reversing mills with 24- to 54-in.-diameter rolls. Because blooming represents the initial breakdown of the ingot structure, it is done in small, careful steps with repeated reheating. It is not unusual to require 25 passes for the blooming of a large alloy-steel ingot. To produce the size of billet required by smaller finishing mills, it is often necessary to reroll the blooms on a three-high, or continuous, billet mill. The billets may then be rolled into round bars, hexagons, special shapes, or flats on various types of finishing mills.

Sheared plate is produced by cross-rolling billets on two-high, three-high, and four-high mills and then shearing all edges to size. The other common method of rolling plate is on a *universal mill*. This type of mill consists of two rolling mills, one with two horizontal rolls and the other with four vertical rolls so arranged that they can be used for side rolling. A universal mill can take an ingot and roll it directly into plate with straight edges that need no shearing.   By this method of rolling the ingot is merely elongated in the longitudinal direction, and it thus receives no cross rolling.   Therefore, plate produced with the universal mill will have lower transverse ductility than plate produced by cross rolling.

Hot-rolled steel strip has been produced on tandem continuous mills since about 1930.   The starting material is a rolled slab which is initially heated to 2200°F.   The continuous mill consists of a *roughing train* of four to seven stands and a *finishing train* of four to eight stands. The roughing train contains two-high scale-breaking rolls and a spreading mill for spreading the slab to the desired width.   The four-high reducing stands usually are equipped with vertical edging rolls to control the width of the strip.   High-pressure water jets are usually sprayed on the strip to break up the scale.   Four-high mills are used in the finishing train.   The finishing temperature varies from 1300 to 1600°F, depending on the thickness and the desired grain size and mechanical properties.

The fact that the nonferrous-metals industry deals with a diverse product mix is responsible for the fact that nonferrous hot-rolling equipment is generally more versatile and less specialized and mechanized than the equipment used for the hot rolling of steel.   Further, the smaller ingot sizes and lower flow stresses found with nonferrous metals generally mean that smaller rolling mills can be used.   Two- and three-high mills are used for most hot rolling, although continuous four-high hot mills have been installed for rolling aluminum alloys.

19-4. Cold Rolling

Cold rolling is used to produce sheet and strip with superior surface finish and dimensional tolerances compared with hot-rolled strip.   In addition, the strain hardening resulting from the cold reduction may be used to give increased strength.   A greater percentage of rolled nonferrous metals is finished by cold rolling compared with rolled-steel products.   The starting material for cold rolled-steel sheet is pickled hot-rolled breakdown coil from the continuous hot-strip mill.   Cold-rolled nonferrous sheet may be produced from hot-rolled strip, or in the case of certain copper alloys it is cold-rolled directly from the cast state.

High-speed four-high tandem mills with three to five stands are used for the cold rolling of steel sheet, aluminum, and copper alloys.   Generally, this type of mill is designed to provide both front and back tension. A continuous mill has high capacity and results in low labor costs.   For example, the delivery speed of a five-stand continuous mill can reach 6,000 ft/min.   However, this type of equipment requires a large capital investment and suffers further from lack of versatility.   Four-high single-stand reversing mills with front and back tension are a more versatile installation. This type of mill is used often for the production of specialty items that vary widely in dimensions. However, it cannot compete with the continuous-tandem mill where large tonnages are involved.

The elimination of the yield point from annealed-steel sheet is an important practical problem since the existence of a yield-point elongation results in inhomogeneous deformation (stretcher strains) during deep drawing or forming. The usual practice is to give the annealed steel a final, small cold reduction, *temper rolling*, or *skin pass*, which eliminates the yield-point elongation. Temper rolling also results in an improved surface and in improved flatness. Other methods which are used to increase the flatness of rolled sheet are *roller leveling* and *stretcher leveling*. A roller-leveling machine consists of two sets of small-diameter rolls which are arranged so that the top and bottom rows are offset. When the sheet is passed into the leveler, it is flexed up and down and the sheet is straightened as it emerges from the rolls. The stretcher leveler consists of two jaws which grip the edges of the sheet and stretch it with a pure tensile force.

19-5. Rolling of Bars and Shapes

Bars of circular or hexagonal cross section and structural shapes like I beams, channels, and railroad rails are produced in great quantity by hot rolling with grooved rolls (Fig. 19-3). Actually, the hot breakdown of an ingot into a bloom falls in this category since grooved rolls are used to control the changes in shape during the blooming operation.

The rolling of bars and shapes differs from the rolling of sheet and strip in that the cross section of the metal is reduced in two directions. However, in any one pass the metal is usually compressed in one direction only. On the next pass it is rotated 90°. Since the metal spreads to a much greater extent in the hot rolling of bars than in cold rolling of sheet, an important problem in designing passes for bars and shapes is to provide allowance for the spreading. A typical method of reducing a square billet to a bar is by alternate passes through oval and square-shaped grooves. The design of roll passes for structural shapes is much more complicated and requires extensive experience.[1] Because different metals spread different amounts, it is not generally possible to roll metals of widely different rolling characteristics on the same set of bar rolls.

A rolling mill designed to roll bars is known as a *bar mill*, or *merchant mill*. Most production bar mills are equipped with guides to feed the billet into the grooves and repeaters to reverse the direction of the bar

[1] W. Trinks, "Roll Pass Design," 2d ed., Penton Publishing Company, Cleveland, 1933; R. Stewartson, The Rolling of Rods, Bars, and Light Sections, *Met. Reviews*, vol. 4, pp. 309–379, 1959.

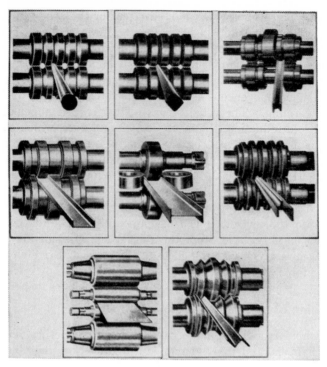

Fig. 19-3. Rolling of bars and structural shapes. (*Courtesy American Iron and Steel Institute.*)

and feed it back through the next roll pass.   Mills of this type are generally either two- or three-high.   A common installation consists of a roughing stand, a strand stand, and a finishing stand.   It is common practice to arrange bar rolls *in train;* i.e., several mills are set close together, side by side, and the rolls in one stand are driven by connecting them to those of the adjacent stand.

19-6. Forces and Geometrical Relationships in Rolling

Figure 19-4 illustrates a number of important relationships between the geometry of the rolls and the forces involved in deforming a metal by rolling.   A metal sheet with a thickness h_0 enters the rolls at the entrance plane XX with a velocity v_0.   It passes through the roll gap and leaves the exit plane YY with a reduced thickness h_f.   To a first approximation no increase in width results, so that the vertical compression of the metal is translated into an elongation in the rolling direction.   Since equal volumes of metal must pass a given point per unit time, we can write

$$bh_0v_0 = bhv = bh_fv_f \tag{19-1}$$

where b = width of sheet

v = its velocity at any thickness h intermediate between h_0 and h_f

In order that a vertical element in the sheet remain undistorted, Eq. (19-1) requires that the exit velocity v_f must be greater than the entrance velocity v_0. Therefore, the velocity of the sheet must steadily increase from entrance to exit. At only one point along the surface of contact between the roll and the sheet is the surface velocity of the roll, V, equal to the velocity of the sheet. This point is called the *neutral point*, or *no-slip point*. It is indicated in Fig. 19-4 by point N.

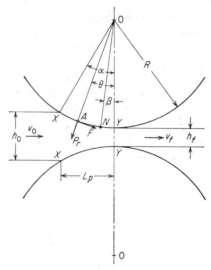

Fig. 19-4. Forces acting during rolling.

At any point along the surface of contact, such as point A in Fig. 19-4, two forces act on the metal. These are a radial force P_r and a tangential friction force F. Between the entrance plane and the neutral point the sheet is moving slower than the roll surface, and the frictional force acts in the direction shown in Fig. 19-4 so as to draw the metal into the rolls. On the exit side of the neutral point the sheet moves faster than the roll surface. The direction of the frictional force is then reversed so that it acts to oppose the delivery of the sheet from the rolls.

The vertical component of P_r is known as the *rolling load P*. The rolling load is the force with which the rolls press against the metal. Because this is also equal to the force exerted by the metal in trying to force the rolls apart, it is frequently called the *separating force*. The *specific roll pressure p* is the rolling load divided by the contact area. The contact area between the metal and the rolls is equal to the product of the width of the sheet b and the projected length of the arc of contact, L_p.

$$L_p = \left[R(h_0 - h_f) - \frac{(h_0 - h_f)^2}{4} \right]^{1/2} \approx [R(h_0 - h_f)]^{1/2} \qquad (19\text{-}2)$$

Therefore, the specific roll pressure is given by

$$p = \frac{P}{bL_p} \qquad (19\text{-}3)$$

The distribution of roll pressure along the arc of contact is indicated in Fig. 19-5. The pressure rises to a maximum at the neutral point and then falls off. The fact that the pressure distribution does not come to a sharp peak at the neutral point, as required in theoretical treatments of rolling, indicates that the neutral point is not really a line on the roll surface but an area. The area under the curve is proportional to the rolling load, which for purposes of calculation acts at the center of gravity of the pressure distribution. Therefore, the shape of the pressure distribution is important because the location of the resultant rolling load with respect to the roll centers determines the torque and power required to produce the reduction. The area shown shaded in Fig. 19-5 represents the force required to overcome frictional forces between the roll and the sheet, while the area under the dashed line AB represents the force required to deform the metal in plane homogeneous compression. A similarity should be noted between the pressure distribution in rolling shown in Fig. 19-5 and the pressure distribution for plane-strain compression between plates (Fig. 18-8). Use is sometimes made of this analogy to simplify the analysis of the rolling forces. For example, Eq. (18-15) can be used to give an approximate value for the mean rolling pressure if the factor $2a$ in Eq. (18-15) is made equal to the projected arc of contact, L_p.

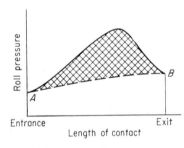

Fig. 19.5. Distribution of roll pressure along the arc of contact.

The angle α (Fig. 19-4) between the entrance plane and the center line of the rolls is called the *angle of contact*, or angle of nip. Metal will not be drawn into the rolls when $\tan \alpha$ exceeds the coefficient of friction between the rolls and the metal. Therefore, the coefficient of friction f controls the maximum bite which the rolls can take. Because of this fact, rolls are often purposely roughened to increase the coefficient of friction. Blooming rolls frequently have grooves cut in them for the same purpose.

The angle β is the angle between the neutral point and the center line of the rolls. β is usually called the *no-slip angle*. Since the horizontal forces change direction at the neutral point, the angle β can be determined from an equilibrium of forces in the horizontal direction.[1]

$$\sin \beta = \frac{\sin \alpha}{2} - \frac{\sin^2 (\alpha/2)}{f} \qquad (19\text{-}4)$$

which can be expressed in approximate form as

$$\beta \approx \frac{\alpha}{2} - \frac{1}{f}\left(\frac{\alpha}{2}\right)^2 \qquad \text{radians} \qquad (19\text{-}5)$$

However, $\sin \alpha$ equals the horizontal projection of the arc of contact divided by the roll radius.

$$\sin \alpha = \frac{[R(h_0 - h_f)]^{1/2}}{R} = \left[\frac{2(h_0 - h_f)}{D}\right]^{1/2} \qquad (19\text{-}6)$$

where D is the roll diameter. Therefore, the no-slip angle can be expressed by

$$\beta \approx \left[\frac{h_0 - h_f}{2D}\right]^{1/2} - \frac{1}{f}\frac{h_0 - h_f}{2D} \qquad (19\text{-}7)$$

In the previous equations it was assumed that the roll radius remains unchanged under the high pressures developed in rolling. Actually, as a result of these pressures the rolls undergo elastic flattening. The most widely used solution to this problem is the analysis of Hitchcock,[2] which assumes that the pressure distribution on the rolls will produce the same distortion as an elliptical pressure distribution. If it is assumed that the arc of contact remains circular and that the radius of curvature of the roll is increased from R to R', the Hertz theory for the elastic compression of two cylinders results in

$$R' = R\left[1 + \frac{CP}{b(h_0 - h_f)}\right] \qquad (19\text{-}8)$$

where $C = 16(1 - \nu^2)/\pi E$ is evaluated for the roll material ($C = 3.34 \times 10^{-4}$ in.^{2}/ton for steel rolls) and P is the rolling load based on the deformed roll radius. Since P is a function of R', the exact solution of Eq. (19-8) requires a trial-and-error procedure.[3]

[1] L. R. Underwood, "The Rolling of Metals," vol. I, pp. 15–16, John Wiley & Sons, Inc., New York, 1950.

[2] J. H. Hitchcock, "Roll Neck Bearings," American Society of Mechanical Engineers, New York, 1935; see Underwood, *op. cit.*, pp. 286–296.

[3] E. C. Larke, "The Rolling of Strip, Sheet, and Plate," pp. 325–330, Chapman & Hall, Ltd., London, 1957.

19-7. Main Variables in Rolling

The main variables which control the rolling process are (1) the roll diameter, (2) the deformation resistance of the metal, (3) the friction between the rolls and the metal, and (4) the presence of front tension and back tension. In this section the effect of these factors will be considered chiefly from the standpoint of their influence on the rolling load.

Increasing the diameter of the rolls results in a large increase in the rolling load for given reduction and frictional conditions. For a given reduction of a sheet of a certain thickness the contact area will be greater for a large-diameter roll. Equation (19-2) shows that the contact area is directly proportional to $D^{1/2}$. Therefore, for a given pressure required to deform the metal the total rolling load will increase with the roll diameter. However, the rolling load increases with roll diameter at a rate greater than $D^{1/2}$ because of the requirement to overcome the greater frictional forces acting over the larger area of contact. In the previous chapter it was shown that the average uniaxial stress required to compress cylinders of equal height but varying diameter increases with the diameter of the cylinder. The effect of roll diameter on rolling load is the direct analog for the case of rolling.

Similarly, for cylinders of constant diameter but varying thickness the average uniaxial compressive yield stress increases with decreasing height of the cylinder. The compressive force required to deform the cylinder can increase to quite high values compared with the true flow stress when the thickness is a small fraction of the diameter. A similar situation exists when the sheet thickness is small compared with the contact area of the rolls. The rolling load increases as the sheet entering the rolls becomes thinner. Eventually a point is reached where the deformation resistance of the sheet is greater than the roll pressure which can be applied and no further reduction in thickness can be achieved. When this occurs, the rolls in contact with the sheet are elastically deformed and it is easier for the rolls to deform than for the sheet to deform plastically. The roll diameter has an important influence on the limiting reduction possible with a rolling mill. Both the rolling load and the length of the arc of contact decrease for smaller-diameter rolls. Therefore, with small-diameter rolls, properly stiffened against deflection by backup rolls, it is possible to produce a greater reduction before roll flattening becomes important and no further reduction in sheet thickness occurs.

Since sheet rolling is essentially a plane-strain process, the constrained flow stress for rolling is the value obtained in tension or compression multiplied by the factor $2/\sqrt{3}$. The plane-strain flow stress can also be obtained directly from the plane compression test discussed in Sec. 17-5.

The flow stress for cold rolling does not depend much on the strain rate or roll speed. However, as has been emphasized earlier, in hot rolling changes in the strain rate can produce significant changes in the flow stress of the metal.[1]

The friction between the roll and the metal surface is of great importance in rolling. Not only does the frictional force pull the metal into the rolls, but it also affects the magnitude and distribution of the roll pressure. Reference to Fig. 19-5 shows that the larger the frictional forces the greater must be the rolling load and the more steeply the pressure builds up toward a maximum value at the neutral point. Because the roll pressure distribution is so strongly dependent on the friction, a pressure distribution like that of Fig. 19-5 is commonly called the *friction hill*. High friction results in high rolling loads and also produces greater lateral spread and edge cracking. On the other hand, very low values of friction, such as are obtained in cold rolling with lubrication and polished rolls, may lead to difficulties in feeding the metal into the rolls.

The friction varies from point to point along the contact arc of the roll. However, because it is extremely difficult to measure this pressure distribution,[2] all theories of rolling are forced to assume a constant coefficient of friction. On the basis of this assumption, coefficients of friction can be obtained from measured values of rolling load and torque.[3] If back tension is gradually applied to the strip until the neutral point is moved to the exit of the rolls, then the friction acts in one direction only. For a constant roll speed and constant reduction, the coefficient of friction f can be calculated from the total rolling load P and the torque M_T by

$$f = \frac{M_T}{PR} \qquad (19\text{-}9)$$

Another way of measuring friction in rolling is through the determination of the forward slip S_f.

$$S_f = \frac{v_f - V}{V} \qquad (19\text{-}10)$$

where v_f = velocity of metal leaving rolls
V = surface velocity of rolls
The forward slip is related to the contact angle and the coefficient of

[1] P. M. Cook, *Proc. Conf. on the Properties of Materials at High Rates of Strain*, Institution of Mechanical Engineers, London, 1957, pp. 86–97.

[2] G. T. Van Rooyen and W. A. Backofen, *J. Iron Steel Inst. (London)*, vol. 186, pp. 235–244, 1957.

[3] P. W. Whitton and H. Ford, *Proc. Inst. Mech. Engrs. (London)*, vol. 169, p. 123, 1955.

friction by the relation[1]

$$S_f = \frac{1}{4}\frac{r}{1-r}\left(1 - \frac{\alpha}{2f}\right)^2 \qquad (19\text{-}11)$$

where $r = (h_0 - h_f)/h_0$ is the reduction. An average value of the friction also can be obtained by determining the maximum contact angle for which the metal will just enter the rolls.

$$f = \tan \alpha_{max} \qquad (19\text{-}12)$$

Values of f obtained by this method are somewhat higher than those obtained by other methods.

The minimum-thickness sheet that can be rolled on a given mill is directly related to the coefficient of friction. Since the friction coefficients for hot rolling of steel can vary from 0.20 to 0.70, while for cold rolling values of 0.03 to 0.12 are more typical, it can be seen that thinner-gage sheet is obtainable with cold rolling. The thickness of the sheet produced on a cold-rolling mill can also be changed appreciably by altering the rolling speed. With increasing rolling speed the thickness of the sheet is decreased. This is directly attributable to the decrease in friction coefficient with increasing rolling speed.[2]

The presence of front and back tension in the plane of the sheet can materially reduce the rolling load. That this should be so can be seen readily by assuming that the deformation resistance of the metal is governed by a maximum-shear-stress law $\sigma_1 - \sigma_3 = \sigma_0'$. Since σ_1, the roll pressure, and σ_3, the horizontal tension stress, are opposite in sign, it becomes apparent that the deformation resistance σ_0' is reached at a lower value of σ_1 when σ_3 is present. The reduction in roll pressure due to strip tension decreases the wear of the rolls. Another important advantage of strip tension is that it improves the flatness and thickness uniformity across the width of a sheet. A study[3] of the effect of tension on rolling has shown that back tension is about twice as effective in reducing the rolling load as front tension. The rolling load when tension is applied, P_t, can be calculated from the following equation,

$$P_t = P\left(1 - \frac{\sigma_b + \sigma_f}{\bar{\sigma}_0'}\frac{\beta}{\alpha}\right) \qquad (19\text{-}13)$$

[1] M. D. Stone, *Trans. ASME*, ser. D, vol. 81, pp. 681–686, 1957.

[2] *Ibid.*; R. B. Sims and D. F. Arthur, *J. Iron Steel Inst.* (*London*), vol. 172, pp. 285–295, 1952.

[3] W. C. F. Hessenberg and R. B. Sims, *J. Iron Steel Inst.* (*London*), vol. 168, pp. 155–164, 1951.

where P = rolling load for same reduction but without front or back
     tension
   σ_b = back tension
   σ_f = front tension
   $\bar{\sigma}_0'$ = mean value of plane-strain yield stress
   α = angle of contact
   β = no-slip angle

Nadai[1] developed a theory of rolling which permits the calculation of
the effect of strip tension on the roll pressure distribution. As shown
schematically in Fig. 19-6, the addition of both front and back tension
materially reduces the area under the curve, although there is little shift
of the neutral point. If only back tension is applied, the neutral point

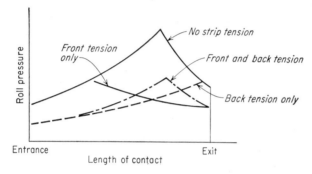

Fig. 19-6. Effect of strip tension on the distribution of roll pressure.

moves toward the roll exit. If a high enough back tension is applied,
the neutral point will eventually reach the roll exit. When this happens,
the rolls are moving faster than the metal and they slide over the surface.
On the other hand, if only front tension is used, the neutral point will
move toward the roll entrance.

19-8. Deformation in Rolling

The deformation produced by rolling can be considered to be two-
dimensional. To a good approximation in sheet rolling, the reduction in
thickness is transferred into an increase in length with little increase in
the width. Thus, there is good justification for the use of a plane-strain
model in the mathematical analysis of rolling. While the lateral spread
is usually of little importance in rolling sheet and strip, in the rolling of
bars and shapes this can result in the formation of flash, which produces
surface defects. The amount of lateral spread depends on such factors

[1] A. Nadai, *J. Appl. Mech.*, vol. 6, pp. A54–A62, 1939.

as the diameter and condition of the rolls, the flow properties of the metal, and the amount of reduction.   According to Trinks,[1] the lateral spread equals 0.25 to 0.40 times the reduction times the contact length.

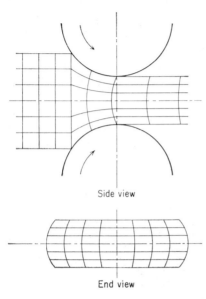

Side view

End view

Fig. 19-7. Distortion of square-grid network by rolling.

In comparison with other metal-working processes the deformation produced by rolling is relatively uniform.   However, studies with grid networks have shown that the surface layers are not only compressed but also sheared.   Figure 19-7 illustrates the typical grid distortion produced by the rolling of a flat bar.   MacGregor and Coffin[2] showed that, while the greatest shear strain occurs at the outside fibers when a bar is always rolled in one direction, when the direction of rolling is reversed after each pass the maximum shear stress occurs near the center of the thickness of the bar.   Although practically all investigations of the deformation in rolling have been based on surface strain measurements, it appears from investigations[3] of the internal strain, using the radiography of an embedded lead grid, that the surface measurements are reliable indications of the interior deformation.

19-9. Defects in Rolled Products

Defects in rolled metal products can result from defects introduced during the ingot stage of production or during rolling.   Internal defects such as fissures due to incomplete welding of pipe and blowholes are the result of ingot defects.   Also, longitudinal stringers of nonmetallic inclusions or pearlite banding in steels are related to melting and solidification practices.

Because rolled products usually have a high surface-volume ratio, the condition of the surface during all stages in the rolling process is of considerable importance.   In order to maintain high standards, the surface

---

[1] Trinks, *op. cit.*

[2] C. W. MacGregor and L. F. Coffin, Jr., *J. Appl. Mech.*, vol. 10, pp. A13–A20, 1943.

[3] B. L. Averbach, *Trans. AIME*, vol. 188, pp. 150–153, 1950.

of billets must be conditioned by grinding, chipping, or burning with an oxygen lance to remove surface defects. Typical surface defects are slivers, seams, and scabs. Laps are surface defects which resemble seams but which are caused by folded-over fins that are rolled into the surface. Occasionally pieces of refractory and oxide are rolled into the surface. Scratches due to defective rolls or guides can be a serious quality problem for certain classes of cold-rolled sheet.

The prevention of flakes or cooling cracks is an important consideration with railroad rail and other rolled shapes. Special controlled cooling schedules are used for these items to minimize the residual stresses, which are mainly responsible for this problem. Control of the thickness and flatness of rolled sheet and strip is an important problem. Most of the variation in thickness along the rolling direction is due to changes in the rolling speed or strip tension. Variation in either the thickness or hardness of the material entering the rolls will also cause a variation in thickness. Very elaborate devices for continuously measuring the sheet thickness and adjusting the mill operating conditions have been developed to control the thickness in continuous rolling mills.[1] Variation in thickness in the width direction is related to the deflection of the rolls. A set of parallel rolls will deflect under load to produce a sheet which is thicker at the center than at the edges. To compensate for this, it is customary to *camber*, or crown, the rolls so that the working surfaces are parallel when the rolls deflect under load. The proper roll crown, or camber, will depend on the rolling load,[2] and therefore, if the rolls are not operated at the conditions for which they were designed, sheet with edge or center waves will result.

19-10. Residual Stresses in Rolled Products

Two general types of residual-stress patterns can exist in rolled sheet and strip.[3] In the case of sheet which has been given a small reduction, as in temper rolling, so that the plastically deformed region does not extend much below the outer surface, the longitudinal residual-stress pattern will be compressive at the surface and tensile at the midplane of the strip (see Fig. 15-1). For the more usual case of large reductions the plastic flow penetrates completely through the strip. For this situation the longitudinal residual pattern will consist of tension on the outer surfaces and compression at the interior.

In spite of the great technological importance of rolling, there is very

[1] Larke, *op. cit.*, pp. 161–173.
[2] *Ibid.*, chap. 3.
[3] W. M. Baldwin, Jr., *Proc. ASTM*, vol. 49, pp. 539–583, 1949.

little published information on the residual stresses imposed by this process. Little information on the residual stresses in any direction except the rolling (longitudinal) direction of the strip is available, although it is likely that a biaxial state of stress exists at the surface. The greatest amount of information on the effect of rolling variables on the resulting residual stresses is available for a bearing bronze.[1]

The magnitude of the residual stress at the surface of a rolled strip depends primarily on the roll diameter, the strip thickness, and the reduction in thickness. The residual stress increases with the ratio of strip thickness to contact length. Thus, a thick strip, a light reduction, and a small-diameter roll all tend to give a high residual stress. Moreover, the larger the sheet thickness relative to the contact length, the greater the tendency for the deformation to be concentrated at the surface. Therefore, small roll diameter, light reductions, and thick strip all tend to give a residual-stress pattern which is compressive at the surface and tensile at the interior of the strip. The evidence that is available indicates that the final residual-stress pattern is determined primarily by the conditions of the last pass through the rolls. Therefore, the final skin pass which is used to provide close control of the dimensions can produce high residual stresses despite the fact that low residual stresses were produced by the previous passes.

19-11. Theories of Cold Rolling

Probably more work has been expended in developing a theoretical treatment of cold rolling than for any other metalworking process. A theory of rolling is aimed at expressing the external forces, such as the rolling load and the rolling torque, in terms of the geometry of the deformation and the strength properties of the material being rolled.

The differential equation for the equilibrium of an element of material being deformed between rolls is common to all the theories of rolling. The derivation given below is based on the following assumptions.

1. The arc of contact is circular—no elastic deformation of the rolls.

2. The coefficient of friction is constant at all points on the arc of contact.

3. There is no lateral spread, so that rolling can be considered a problem in plane strain.

4. Plane vertical sections remain plane.

5. The peripheral velocity of the rolls is constant.

6. The elastic deformation of the sheet is negligible in comparison with the plastic deformation.

---

[1] R. M. Baker, R. E. Ricksecker, and W. M. Baldwin, Jr., *Trans. AIME*, vol. 175, pp. 337–354, 1948.

7. The distortion-energy criterion of yielding, for plane strain, holds.

$$\sigma_1 - \sigma_3 = \frac{2}{\sqrt{3}} \sigma_0 = \sigma_0'$$

The stresses acting on an element of strip in the roll gap are shown in Fig. 19-8. At any point of contact between the strip and the roll surface, designated by the angle θ, the stresses acting are the radial pressure p_r and the tangential shearing stress $\tau = fp_r$. These stresses are resolved into their horizontal and vertical components in Fig. 19-8b. In

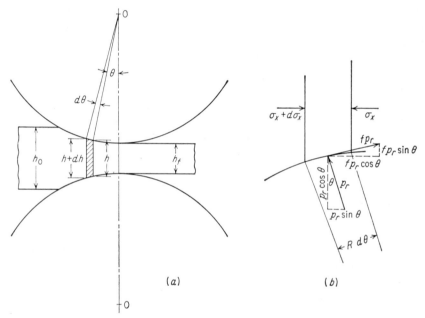

(a) (b)

Fig. 19-8. (a) Geometrical relationship for element undergoing plane-strain deformation by rolling; (b) stresses acting on an element.

addition, the stress σ_x is assumed to be uniformly distributed over the vertical faces of the element. The normal stress on one end of the element is $p_r R \, d\theta$, and the horizontal component of this force is $p_r R \sin \theta \, d\theta$. The tangential friction force is $fp_r R \, d\theta$, and its horizontal component is $fp_r R \cos \theta \, d\theta$. Taking the summation of the horizontal forces on the element results in

$$(\sigma_x + d\sigma_x)(h + dh) + 2fp_r R \cos \theta \, d\theta - \sigma_x h - 2p_r R \sin \theta \, d\theta = 0$$

which simplifies to

$$\frac{d(\sigma_x h)}{d\theta} = 2p_r R(\sin \theta \pm f \cos \theta) \qquad (19\text{-}14)$$

The minus and plus signs in Eq. (19-14) occur because the direction of the friction force changes at the neutral point. This equation was first derived by Von Kármán[1] and is usually named for him. Equation (19-14) can also be converted into the form given by Underwood[2] by considering that $dx = R\, d\theta$, $f = \tan \mu$, and assuming that $\cos \theta = 1$ for small angles.

$$\frac{d(\sigma_x h/2)}{dx} = p_r(\tan \theta \pm \tan \mu) \tag{19-15}$$

The forces acting in the vertical direction are balanced by the specific roll pressure p. Taking the equilibrium of forces in the vertical direction results in a relationship between the normal pressure and the radial pressure.

$$p = p_r(1 \pm f \tan \theta) \tag{19-16}$$

The relationship between the normal pressure and the horizontal compressive stress σ_x is given by the distortion-energy criterion of yielding for plane strain.

$$\sigma_1 - \sigma_3 = \frac{2}{\sqrt{3}} \sigma_0 = \sigma_0'$$

or
$$p - \sigma_x = \sigma_0' \tag{19-17}$$

where p is the greater of the two compressive principal stresses.[3]

The solution of problems in cold rolling consists in the integration of Eq. (19-14) with the aid of Eqs. (19-16) and (19-17). Unfortunately, the mathematics is rather formidable, and various approximations must be made to obtain a tractable solution. Trinks[4] provided graphical solutions to Von Kármán's equation, using the assumptions of constant yield stress and a parabolic arc of contact. The most complete solution of the rolling equations has been obtained by Orowan.[5] In this solution, allowance was made for the fact that the flow stress changes with θ owing to strain hardening. However, the complexity of the equations makes it necessary to obtain solutions by graphical integration.[6] Even though the equations for roll pressure have been expressed[7] in algebraic form,

---

[1] T. Von Kármán, *Z. angew. Math. u. Mech.*, vol. 5, pp. 139–141, 1925.

[2] Underwood, *op. cit.*, pp. 204–208.

[3] In agreement with the literature on rolling, compressive stresses are taken as positive.

[4] W. Trinks, *Blast Furnace Steel Plant*, vol. 25, pp. 617–619, 1937; see also Underwood, *op. cit.*, pp. 210–215.

[5] E. Orowan, *Proc. Inst. Mech. Engrs. (London)*, vol. 150, pp. 140–167, 1943.

[6] A computer solution to Orowan's equations which also incorporates corrections for the deformation of the rolls has been given by J. E. Hockett, *Trans. ASM*, vol. 52, pp. 675–697, 1960.

[7] M. Cook and E. C. Larke, *J. Inst. Metals*, vol. 74, pp. 55–80, 1947.

they are still too complicated for routine calculation of rolling problems. Some simplification to this problem has been provided by Bland and Ford.[1] By restricting the analysis to cold rolling under conditions of low friction and for angles of contact less than 6°, they were able to put $\sin \theta \approx \theta$ and $\cos \theta \approx 1$. Thus, Eq. (19-14) can be written

$$\frac{d(\sigma_x h)}{d\theta} = 2p_r R'(\theta \pm f) \tag{19-18}$$

It is also assumed that $p_r \approx p$, so that Eq. (19-17) can be written $\sigma_x = p_r - \sigma'_0$. By substituting into Eq. (19-18) and integrating,[2] relatively simple equations for the radial pressure result.

Roll entrance to neutral point

$$p_r = \frac{\sigma'_0 h}{h_0}\left(1 - \frac{\sigma_{xb}}{\sigma'_{01}}\right)\exp f(H_1 - H) \tag{19-19}$$

Neutral point to roll exit

$$p_r = \frac{\sigma'_0 h}{h_f}\left(1 - \frac{\sigma_{xf}}{\sigma'_{02}}\right)\exp fH \tag{19-20}$$

where
$$H = 2\left(\frac{R'}{h_f}\right)^{1/2}\tan^{-1}\left(\frac{R'}{h_f}\right)^{1/2}\theta$$

and σ_{xb} = back tension
σ_{xf} = front tension

Subscript 1 refers to a quantity evaluated at the roll-entrance plane, and subscript 2 refers to a quantity evaluated at the roll-exit plane.

The rolling load or total roll force P is the integral of the specific roll pressure over the arc of contact.

$$P = R'b \int_0^{\theta=\alpha} p_r \, d\theta$$

where b = width of sheet
α = contact angle

This is best evaluated by graphical integration following a point-by-point calculation with Eqs. (19-19) and (19-20). Computational methods based on the Bland and Ford solution have been published.[3]

The equations based on the Bland and Ford solution have been shown to give close agreement with Orowan's graphical solution except when there is a high back tension which produces rapid strain hardening.

[1] D. R. Bland and H. Ford, *Proc. Inst. Mech. Engrs.* (*London*), vol. 159, pp. 144–163, 1948.

[2] See *ibid.*, or H. Ford *Met. Reviews*, vol. 2, pp. 5–7, 1957.

[3] P. W. Whitton, *J. Appl. Mech.*, vol. 23, pp. 307–311, 1956.

However, a modification has been developed[1] which results in close agreement with Orowan's solution for this particular situation. In making exact calculations a correction[2] should be included for the effect of the elastic deformation of the sheet just in front of the entrance and exit to the rolls. When all the corrections are used with the Bland and Ford solution, the rolling load and torque can be calculated with high precision. It is, however, necessary to make a slight correction to the flow curve determined in plane compression in order to correct for the redundant shearing that occurs in the rolling process.

When the sheet is both thin and hard, roll flattening becomes severe and the elastic regions in the sheet at entry and exit to the rolls become important factors. Under these conditions the theory outlined above no longer applies. Although there is no really satisfactory theory of rolling for these conditions, it is possible to make a fairly reliable prediction of the minimum thickness of sheet that is obtainable under a given set of rolling conditions. Ford and Alexander[3] have shown that

$$h_{\min} = \left[\frac{14.22 f^2 R (1 - \nu_s{}^2)}{E_s} + \frac{9.05 f R (1 - \nu_r{}^2)}{E_r} \right] (\sigma'_0 - \sigma_t) \quad (19\text{-}21)$$

where R = undeformed roll radius, in.

E_s = elastic modulus for sheet material, psi

E_r = elastic modulus for roll material, psi

ν_s = Poisson's ratio for sheet material

ν_r = Poisson's ratio for roll material

σ_t = mean strip tension = $(\sigma_{xb} + \sigma_{xf})/2$

Equation (19-21) shows that the minimum sheet thickness can be obtained by increasing the modulus of the rolls or the sheet tension or by decreasing the friction, the roll diameter, and the flow stress. When equipment is not available for altering these variables in the proper way, it is often possible to achieve a reduction in rolling load and a decrease in the minimum thickness by sandwich, or pack, rolling the hard sheet between two softer sheets[4] such as copper or brass.

19-12. Theories of Hot Rolling

The theoretical treatment of hot rolling has not advanced to the state of knowledge that exists for cold rolling because of the difficulty of accu-

[1] D. R. Bland and R. B. Sims, *Proc. Inst. Mech. Engrs.* (*London*), vol. 167, pp. 371–374, 1953.

[2] D. R. Bland and H. Ford, *J. Iron Steel Inst.* (*London*), vol. 171, pp. 245–249, 1952.

[3] H. Ford and J. M. Alexander, *J. Inst. Metals*, vol. 88, pp. 193–199, 1959–1960.

[4] R. R. Arnold and P. W. Whitton, *Proc. Inst. Mech. Engrs.* (*London*), vol. 173, pp. 241–256, 1959.

mulating reliable experimental data and the added complexity of the problem. As in other hot-working processes, the flow stress for hot rolling is a function of both the temperature and the strain rate (speed of rolling).

The strain rate during rolling is a function of the position along the arc of contact, indicated by the angle θ. While precise measurement of the coefficient of friction during hot rolling has not been made, it is known that the values are higher than for cold rolling. In fact, there are indications that the tangential force fp can reach values as high as the plane-strain yield stress σ_0'. When this occurs, the sheet moves at the same peripheral speed as the rolls and a situation of "sticking friction" exists. The strain rate for rolling with sticking friction is given[1] by

$$\dot\epsilon = \frac{v}{h} = \frac{2V \sin\theta}{h} = \frac{2V \sin\theta}{h_f + D(1 - \cos\theta)} \qquad (19\text{-}22)$$

where v = velocity of a point on surface of metal

V = peripheral speed of rolls

Evaluation of the above equation will show that the maximum rate of deformation occurs at the entrance to the rolls. For equal percentage reductions thin sheet will undergo much greater rates of deformation than a thick slab. In practical calculations it is usually satisfactory to determine the mean rate of deformation, $\dot{\bar\epsilon}$.

$$\dot{\bar\epsilon} = V \left[\frac{2}{D(h_0 - h_f)} \right]^{1/2} \ln \frac{h_0}{h_f} \qquad (19\text{-}23)$$

Slipping friction, where there is a speed difference between the sheet and the rolls, occurs for cold rolling and probably during the early stages of hot rolling. For the case of slipping friction the strain rate is given by

$$\dot\epsilon = \frac{V}{h_0} \left[\frac{2(h_0 - h_f)}{D} \right]^{1/2} \qquad (19\text{-}24)$$

In general, for equal conditions, the rate of deformation with slipping friction will be lower than with sticking friction.

Although in hot working the flow stress does not increase because of strain hardening, nevertheless, since the strain rate varies along the arc of contact, the flow stress will vary and this may affect the pressure distribution. In using the theories of hot rolling, to be described shortly, it is sufficiently accurate to compute a mean deformation rate. This value should be used with published data[2] on compression tests at various strain rates to arrive at a mean flow stress.

[1] Larke, *op. cit.*, chap. 8.
[2] Cook, *loc. cit.*

When sticking friction occurs, Von Kármán's equation can be written as

$$\frac{d(\sigma_x h)}{d\theta} = 2R(p_r \sin\theta \pm \sigma_0' \cos\theta) \tag{19-25}$$

In developing what is at present the most widely accepted theory of hot rolling, Sims[1] assumed that sticking friction occurs and that the rolling process can be compared with deformation between rough inclined platens. For the latter situation Orowan[2] derived the equation

$$\sigma_x = p_r - \frac{\pi}{4}\sigma_0' \tag{19-26}$$

If the usual approximations are made, $\sin\theta \approx \theta$ and $\cos\theta \approx 1$, then Eq. (19-25) results in

$$\frac{dh}{d\theta}\left(p_r - \frac{\pi}{4}\sigma_0'\right) = 2Rp_r\theta \pm R\sigma_0' \tag{19-27}$$

Integration of Eq. (19-27) results in two equations for the branches of the pressure distribution over the arc of contact:
Roll entrance to neutral point

$$\frac{p_r}{\sigma_0'} = \frac{\pi}{4}\left(1 + \ln\frac{h}{h_0}\right) + \left(\frac{R}{h_f}\right)^{\frac{1}{2}}\left[\tan^{-1}\left(\frac{R}{h_f}\right)^{\frac{1}{2}}\alpha - \tan^{-1}\left(\frac{R}{h_f}\right)^{\frac{1}{2}}\theta\right] \tag{19-28}$$

Neutral point to roll exit

$$\frac{p_r}{\sigma_0'} = \frac{\pi}{4}\left(1 + \ln\frac{h}{h_f}\right)^{\frac{1}{2}} + \left(\frac{R}{h_f}\right)^{\frac{1}{2}}\tan^{-1}\left[\left(\frac{R}{h_f}\right)^{\frac{1}{2}}\theta\right] \tag{19-29}$$

The rolling load P can be determined by measuring the area under the curve when p_r is plotted against θ. This is stated mathematically as

$$P = Rb\int_0^{\theta = \alpha} p_r\, d\theta \tag{19-30}$$

where b = width of sheet
α = contact angle
Sims has shown that when the substitutions are made into Eq. (19-30) it reduces to the following relationship,

$$P = \sigma_0' b[R(h_0 - h_f)]^{\frac{1}{2}}Q_p \tag{19-31}$$

where Q_p is a complex function of the reduction in thickness and the ratio R/h_f. To simplify calculation, values of Q_p may be obtained from Fig. 19-9.

[1] R. B. Sims, *Proc. Inst. Mech. Engrs. (London)*, vol. 168, pp. 191–200, 1954.
[2] Orowan, *op. cit.*

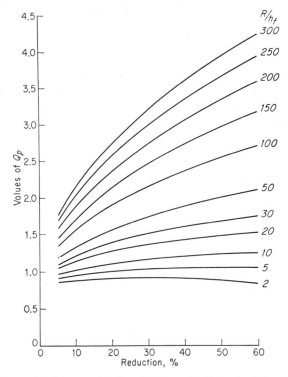

Fig. 19-9. Values of Q_p for use with Eq. (19-30).   (*E. C. Larke, "The Rolling of Strip, Sheet, and Plate," Chapman & Hall, Ltd., London,* 1957.)

Comparison with available data on hot rolling shows that Sims' equations give agreement within ± 15 per cent with the experimental rolling load about 90 per cent of the time.[1]   Better agreement is obtained with Sims' equations than with the older equations proposed by Ekelund[2] and by Orowan and Pascoe.[3]

19-13. Torque and Horsepower

Power is applied to a rolling mill by applying a torque to the rolls and by means of strip tension.   The power is expended principally in four ways, (1) the energy needed to deform the metal, (2) the energy needed to overcome frictional forces in the bearings, (3) the energy lost in the pinions and power-transmission system, and (4) electrical losses in the

[1] Larke, *op. cit.*, chap. 10.
[2] S. Ekelund, *Steel*, vol. 93, 1933.
[3] E. Orowan and K. J. Pascoe, *Iron Steel Inst. (London) Spec. Rept.* 34, 1946.

various motors and generators.   Losses in the windup reel and uncoiler must also be considered.

The total rolling load is distributed over the arc of contact in the typical friction-hill pressure distribution.   However, the total rolling load can be assumed to be concentrated at a point along the arc of contact at a distance a from the line of centers of the rolls.   In calculating the torque the problem is mainly how to calculate this moment arm.   It is usual practice[1] to consider the ratio of the moment arm a to the projected length of the arc of contact.

$$\lambda = \frac{a}{L_p} = \frac{a}{[R(h_0 - h_f)]^{1/2}} \tag{19-32}$$

For cold rolling a correction for the change in roll radius from R to R' due to elastic deformation must be made in the calculation of λ.   According to Ford,[2] λ is expressed in terms of an experimental parameter λ' as follows,

$$\lambda = 0.5\left(\frac{R}{R'}\right)^{1/2} - (0.5 - \lambda')\left(\frac{R'}{R}\right)^{1/2} \tag{19-33}$$

where λ' has a value of 0.43 for cold rolling with matte-finished rolls and λ' is 0.48 for rolls with a smooth surface.   With this information it is possible to determine the moment arm from Eq. (19-32).

The torque is equal to the total rolling load multiplied by the effective moment arm, and since there are two work rolls, the torque is given by

$$M_t = 2Pa \quad \text{lb-ft} \tag{19-34}$$

During one revolution of the top roll the resultant rolling load P moves along the circumference of a circle equal to $2\pi a$ (Fig. 19-10).   Since there are two work rolls involved, the work done is equal to

$$\text{Work} = 2(2\pi a)P \quad \text{ft-lb} \tag{19-35}$$

Since horsepower is defined as the rate of doing work at 33,000 ft-lb/min, the horsepower needed to operate a pair of rolls revolving at N rpm is given by

$$\text{hp} = \frac{4\pi a P N}{33,000} \tag{19-36}$$

The above equation expresses the horsepower required in deforming the metal as it flows through the roll gap.   The horsepower needed to overcome friction in the bearings and the pinions must be determined separately.

[1] Larke, *op. cit.*, chap. 11.
[2] H. Ford, *Proc. Inst. Mech. Engrs.* (*London*), vol. 159, pp 115, 1948.

The same basic equation for horsepower holds for hot rolling, with the important condition that the equations which were given for determining the effective moment arm in cold rolling are not applicable in hot rolling.

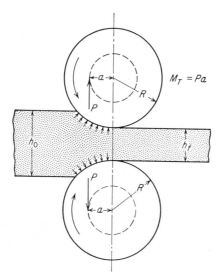

Fig. 19-10. Schematic diagram illustrating roll torque.

A procedure for determining the moment arm in hot rolling, based on the work of Sims,[1] is given in detail by Larke.[2] Although the calculations are straightforward, they are too detailed for inclusion here.

BIBLIOGRAPHY

Bibliography on the Rolling of Iron and Steel, *Iron Steel Inst. (London) Bibliog. Ser.* 15a, 1955.

Ford, H.: "The Theory of Rolling," *Met. Reviews,* vol. 2, no. 5, pp. 1–28, 1957.

Larke, E. C.: "The Rolling of Strip, Sheet, and Plate," Chapman & Hall, Ltd., London, 1957.

"The Making, Shaping, and Treating of Steel," 7th ed., chaps. 22–34, United States Steel Corp., Pittsburgh, 1957.

"Nonferrous Rolling Practice," I.M.D. Series, vol. 2, American Institute of Mining and Metallurgical Engineers, New York, 1948.

Underwood, L. R.: "The Rolling of Metals," vol. I, John Wiley & Sons, Inc., New York, 1950.

[1] Sims, *op. cit.*

[2] Larke, *op. cit.*, chap. 12.

Chapter 20

EXTRUSION

20-1. Classification of Extrusion Processes

Extrusion is the process by which a block of metal is reduced in cross section by forcing it to flow through a die orifice under high pressure. In general, extrusion is used to produce cylindrical bars or hollow tubes, but shapes of irregular cross section may be produced from the more readily extrudable metals, like aluminum. Because of the large forces required in extrusion, most metals are extruded hot under conditions where the deformation resistance of the metal is low. However, cold extrusion is possible for many metals and is rapidly achieving an important commercial position. The reaction of the extrusion billet with the container and die results in high compressive stresses which are effective in reducing the cracking of materials during primary breakdown from the ingot. This is an important reason for the increased utilization of extrusion in the working of metals difficult to form, like stainless steels, nickel-base alloys, and molybdenum.

The two basic types of extrusion are *direct extrusion* and *indirect extrusion* (also called inverted, or back, extrusion). Figure 20-1a illustrates the process of direct extrusion. The metal billet is placed in a container and driven through the die by the ram. A dummy block, or pressure plate, is placed at the end of the ram in contact with the billet. Figure 20-1b illustrates the indirect-extrusion process. A hollow ram carries the die, while the other end of the container is closed with a plate. Frequently, for indirect extrusion, the ram containing the die is kept stationary, and the container with the billet is caused to move. Because there is no relative motion between the wall of the container and the billet in indirect extrusion, the friction forces are lower and the power required for extrusion is less than for direct extrusion. However, there are practical limitations to indirect extrusion because the requirement for using a hollow ram limits the loads which can be applied.

Tubes can be produced by extrusion by attaching a mandrel to the end of the ram. The clearance between the mandrel and the die wall determines the wall thickness of the tube.   Tubes are produced either by starting with a hollow billet or by a two-step extrusion operation in which a solid billet is first pierced and then extruded.

Extrusion was originally applied to the making of lead pipe and later to the lead sheathing of cable.   Figure 20-2 illustrates the extrusion of a lead sheath on electrical cables.

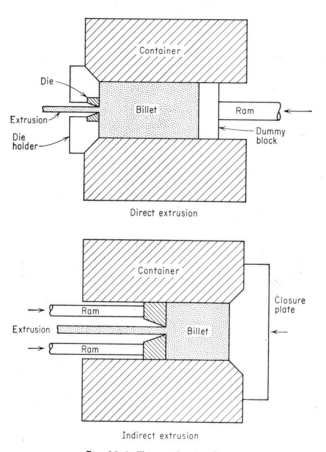

Fig. 20-1. Types of extrusion.

Impact extrusion is a process used to form short lengths of hollow shapes, such as collapsible tooth-paste tubes.   As shown in Fig. 20-3a, a metal blank is placed in a die having the correct outside diameter of the tube, and a punch having the correct inside diameter strikes the blank at a high velocity.   The punch compresses the metal into the die, and then, having no other method of escape, the metal flows up around the punch to form the tube.   In a sense, this is analogous to inverted

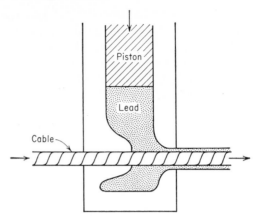

Fig. 20-2. Extrusion of lead sheath on electrical cable.

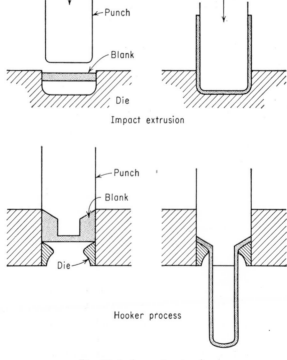

Fig. 20-3. Impact extrusion.

extrusion. In direct impact extrusion, known as the *Hooker process*, a preformed metal cup is placed in a die, and a punch, with a mandrel that fits the inside diameter of the cup, strikes the cup at high velocity. Pressure is exerted on the cup by the shoulder of the punch, and it is extruded into a tube. Impact extrusions are made on high-velocity mechanical presses. The process is generally performed cold, but it is difficult to classify it strictly as a cold-working process because considerable heating results from the high-speed deformation. Impact extrusion processes are restricted to the softer metals such as lead, tin, aluminum, and copper.

20-2. Extrusion Equipment

Most extrusions are made with hydraulic presses. Hydraulic extrusion presses are classified into horizontal and vertical presses, depending upon the direction of travel of the ram. Vertical extrusion presses are generally built with capacities of 300 to 1,000 tons. They have the advantages of easier alignment between the press ram and the tools, higher rate of production, and the need for less floor space than horizontal presses. However, they need considerable headroom, and to make extrusions of appreciable length, a floor pit is frequently necessary. Vertical presses will produce uniform cooling of the billet in the container, and thus symmetrically uniform deformation will result. In a horizontal extrusion press the bottom of the billet which lies in contact with the container will cool more rapidly than the top surface, unless the extrusion container is internally heated, and therefore the deformation will be nonuniform. Warping of bars will result, and nonuniform wall thickness will occur in tubes. In commercial operations the chief use for vertical presses is in the production of thin-wall tubing, where uniform wall thickness and concentricity are required. Horizontal extrusion presses are used for most commercial extrusion of bars and tubes. Presses with a capacity of 1,500 to 5,000 tons are in regular operation, while a few presses of 12,000-ton capacity have been constructed.

The dies and tooling used in extrusion must withstand considerable abuse from the high stresses, thermal shock, and oxidation. Highly alloyed tool steels are used to provide tough dies and tools with adequate elevated-temperature strength. Figure 20-4 illustrates the main features of a simple die, such as would be used for extruding bars. The die illustrated is a flat or square die with a 90° half-die angle. This type of die is commonly used, but it does not represent the optimum condition for all metals. The optimum die angle is a compromise which provides the lowest extrusion pressure with the longest die life. Half-die angles down to 45° are used with conical dies, depending on the flow characteristics of the metal.   The determination of the optimum die angle is a matter

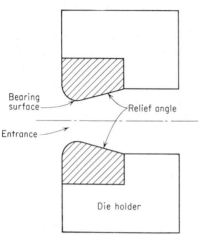

Fig. 20-4. Cross section through a flat extrusion die.

for empirical investigation, and few general rules have been developed.

In addition to the extrusion press, with its pumps and accumulators, other auxiliary equipment is required for an extrusion operation.   Since most extrusion is done hot, billet-heating facilities are needed, and for a production operation, automatic transfer equipment is needed to place the heated billet in the container.   Provision for heating the extrusion container may also be required, particularly with alloys which must be worked at low extrusion speeds.   A hot saw is needed to cut off the extrusion so that the discard, or butt, can be removed from the die.   In addition, there must be a runout table for catching the extrusion and a straightener to correct minor warpage of the extruded product.

20-3. Variables in Extrusion

The principal variables which influence the force required to cause extrusion are (1) the type of extrusion (direct vs. indirect), (2) the extrusion ratio, (3) the working temperature, (4) the speed of deformation, and (5) the frictional conditions at the die and container wall.

In Fig. 20-5 the extrusion pressure is plotted against ram travel for direct and indirect extrusion.   Extrusion pressure is the extrusion force divided by the cross-sectional area of the billet.   The rapid rise in pressure during the initial ram travel is due to the initial compression of the billet to fill the extrusion container.   For direct extrusion the metal begins to flow through the die at the maximum value of pressure.   As the

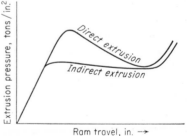

Fig. 20-5. Typical curves of extrusion pressure vs. ram travel for direct and indirect extrusion.

billet extrudes through the die, the pressure required to maintain flow progressively decreases as the frictional forces decrease with decreasing length of the billet in the container. For indirect extrusion there is no relative motion between the billet and the container wall. Therefore, the extrusion pressure is approximately constant with increasing ram travel and represents the stress required to deform the metal in the die. The curve for direct extrusion approaches the curve for indirect extrusion when the billet length approaches zero. For both processes the curves turn upward at the end of the ram travel as the ram attempts to extrude the thin disk of the billet which remains in the die. It is generally uneconomical to develop enough pressure to force the billet completely through the die, and therefore a small discard, or butt, must be removed from the container. The curve for direct extrusion will be dependent on the length of the billet and the effectiveness of lubrication at the billet-container interface.

Extrusion ratio is the ratio of the initial cross-sectional area to the cross-sectional area after extrusion, $R = A_0/A_f$. The extrusion pressure is an approximately linear function of the natural logarithm of the extrusion ratio. Therefore, the extrusion force P is given by

$$P = \sigma_0 A_0 \ln \frac{A_0}{A_f} \qquad (20\text{-}1)$$

If σ_0 is taken as the uniaxial flow stress at the conditions of temperature and strain rate used during extrusion, Eq. (20-1) will predict an extrusion force which is at least 50 per cent lower than the observed extrusion force. This is because Eq. (20-1) does not take into consideration such factors as nonhomogeneous deformation of the billet (which results in redundant work), die friction, and friction between the billet and the container (for direct extrusion). A complete analytical treatment of these factors is difficult, which prevents the accurate calculation of extrusion force and extrusion pressure.[1] Frequently the effective flow stress, or *extrusion constant*, is calculated for an extrusion operation from the observed breakthrough pressure and the extrusion ratio using Eq. (20-1).

For a given size of billet extruded under a particular set of conditions there will be an upper limit to the extrusion ratio which can be obtained with a press of a given capacity. When the change in dimensions produced by extrusion is expressed as per cent reduction in area, it is soon seen that slight increases in the per cent reduction in the region of 90 per cent result in large increases in the extrusion pressure. For example, the extrusion pressure is nearly doubled when the per cent reduction is

[1] A graphical method based on slip-field theory for estimating the upper limit of extrusion force has been proposed by W. Johnson, *Proc. Inst. Mech. Engrs. (London)*, vol. 173, pp. 61–72, 1959.

increased from 95 to 99 per cent. This corresponds to a change in extrusion ratio from 20 to 100. Easily extruded metals like brass and aluminum can be worked at extrusion ratios greater than 100, while metals more difficult to extrude like nickel-base high-temperature alloys are limited to extrusion ratios of around 20.

Most metals are extruded hot so as to take advantage of the decrease in flow stress or deformation resistance with increasing temperature. Since hot working introduces the problems of oxidation of the billet and the extrusion tools and softening of the die and tools, as well as making it more difficult to provide adequate lubrication, it is advantageous to use the minimum temperature which will provide the metal with suitable plasticity. The upper hot-working temperature is the temperature at which hot shortness occurs, or, for pure metals, the melting point. Because of the extensive deformation produced in extrusion, considerable internal heating of the metal also results. Therefore, the top working temperature should be safely below the melting-point or hot-shortness range. For a given deformation, higher working temperatures are generally possible with extrusion than can be used in forging or rolling because the high compressive stresses minimize cracking. However, cracking in extrusions of unsymmetrical shape may occur because of unequal flow in different sections.

Increasing the ram speed produces an increase in the extrusion pressure. A tenfold increase in the speed results in about a 50 per cent increase in pressure. Greater cooling of the billet occurs at low extrusion speeds. When this becomes pronounced, the pressure required for direct extrusion will actually increase with increasing ram travel because of the increased flow stress as the billet cools. The higher the temperature of the billet, the greater the effect of low extrusion speed on the cooling of the billet. Therefore, high extrusion speeds are required with high-strength alloys that need high extrusion temperatures. The temperature rise due to deformation of the metal is greater at high extrusion speeds, and therefore problems with hot shortness may be accentuated.[1]

The selection of the proper extrusion speed and temperature is best determined by trial and error for each alloy and billet size. The interdependence of these factors is shown schematically in Fig. 20-6. For a given extrusion pressure, the extrusion ratio which can be obtained increases with increasing temperature. For any given temperature a larger extrusion ratio can be obtained with a higher pressure. The maximum billet temperature, on the assumption that there are no limitations from the strength of the tools and die, is determined by the temperature at which incipient melting or hot shortness occurs in the

[1] The heat balance during extrusion has been discussed by A. R. E. Singer and J. W. Coakham, *Metallurgia*, vol. 60, pp. 239–246, 1959.

extrusion.   The temperature rise of the extrusions will be determined by
the speed of extrusion and the amount of deformation (extrusion ratio).
Therefore, the curve which represents the upper limit to the safe extrusion region slopes upward toward the left.   The worst situation is for
extrusion at infinite speed, where none of the heat produced by deformation is dissipated.   At lower extrusion speeds there is greater heat
dissipation, and the allowable extrusion ratio for a given preheat temperature increases.   The allowable extrusion range is the region under
the curve of constant pressure and extrusion speed.

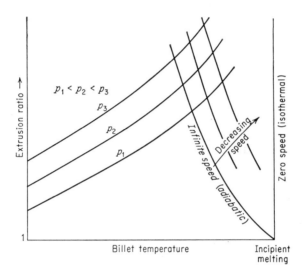

Fig. 20-6. Schematic diagram showing interdependence of temperature, pressure, and
extrusion speed.   (*After S. Hirst and D. H. Ursell, Metal Treatment and Drop Forging,
vol. 25, p. 409, 1958.*)

Although flat dies with a 90° half-die angle are used for most extrusion,
experiments[1] on extrusion through wedge-shaped dies have shown that
the extrusion pressure decreases with decreasing die angle.   More
uniform deformation of the metal results with small-angle dies.   Additional control over the deformation can be obtained by changing the
length of the bearing section in the die.   An increased bearing length
results in greater friction, and hence greater pressure is required to maintain the flow.   Careful adjustment of the bearing length is used to make
the flow through irregular-shaped dies more uniform.

Lubrication of extrusion dies and containers is often rather difficult.
Graphite dispersions are used in extruding copper and nickel-base alloys.

[1] W. Johnson, *J. Mech. and Phys. Solids.* vol. 3, pp. 218–223, 1955.

If effective lubrication can be obtained, an appreciable increase in the allowable extrusion ratio for a given capacity press can be secured. In addition, higher extrusion speeds are possible with lubrication because less heat is produced. Also, for a given extrusion ratio the loads on the tooling will be lower with effective lubrication. An outstanding example of the effectiveness of lubrication is the use of glass in the Ugine-Sejournet process.[1] This has made the extrusion of steel, stainless steel, and high-temperature alloys a commercial reality.

20-4. Deformation in Extrusion

The pressure required to produce extrusion is dependent on the way the metal flows in the container and extrusion die. Also, certain defects which occur in extrusions are directly related to the way the metal

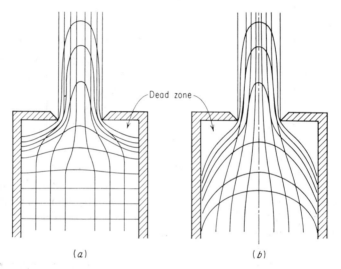

(a)   (b)

Fig. 20-7. Flow patterns in direct extrusion. (a) Lubricated billet; (b) high billet-container friction.

deforms during the process. A fairly large number of investigations of the flow characteristics of the softer metals, lead, tin, and aluminum, have been made by using the split-billet technique. Both the deformation of the metal in the container and in the die must be considered.

Figure 20-7 illustrates the flow patterns produced by the deformation of a square-grid network for direct extrusion through a flat die. Figure

[1] E. K. L. Haffner and J. Sejournet, *J. Iron Steel Inst.* (*London*), vol. 195, pp. 145–162, 1960.

20-7a represents the extrusion of a well-lubricated billet in which the billet slides along the container wall. Deformation in the billet is relatively uniform until close to the die entrance. Here the center part of the billet moves more easily through the die than the metal along the container wall. At the corners of the die there is a *dead zone* of stagnant metal which undergoes little deformation. Elements at the center of the billet undergo essentially pure elongation in the extruded rod, which corresponds to the change in cross section from billet to extrusion. Elements near the sides of the billet undergo extensive shear deformation. The shear deformation which occurs over much of the cross section of the extruded rod requires an expenditure of energy which is not related to the change in dimensions from the billet to the extrusion. This *redundant work* is chiefly responsible for the large discrepancy between the actual extrusion pressure and the extrusion pressure calculated on the basis of ideal deformation.

If there is high friction between the billet and the container wall, severe shear deformation will occur in the billet as well as in the flow of the metal through the die (Fig. 20-7b). Since the velocity of the metal at the center of the billet is higher than along the container wall, there is a tendency for metal to pile up along the wall and eventually it will move toward the center of the billet. This gives rise to the *extrusion defect*. Alternatively, if the shear resistance of the metal along the container wall is lower than the frictional stress, the metal will separate along this region and a thin skin of metal will be left in the container.

The nonhomogeneous flow through an extrusion die can be modified by changing the die angle. Decreasing the die angle of a conical die so that it approaches the natural angle for flow through a flat die results in less shear deformation.[1] However, even though more uniform flow results from smaller-angle dies, the friction forces are higher. Therefore, it does not necessarily follow that the extrusion pressure is lower when the deformation is more uniform.

In indirect extrusion there is no friction between the billet and the container wall. With a flat die a dead metal zone exists, as in Fig. 20-7a, and therefore the deformation in the extrusion is nonuniform.

A number of theoretical slip-field solutions for extrusion under plane-strain conditions have been developed.[2-5] These analyses consider a

[1] G. Sachs and W. Eisbein, *Mitt. deut. Materialprüfungsanstalt.*, vol. 16, pp. 67–96, 1931; J. Frisch and E. G. Thomsen, *Trans. ASME*, ser. B., vol. 81, pp. 207–216, 1959.

[2] R. Hill, *J. Iron Steel Inst. (London)*, vol. 158, pp. 177–185, 1948.

[3] W. Johnson, *J. Mech. and Phys. Solids*, vol. 4, pp. 191–198, 1956.

[4] A. P. Green, *J. Mech. and Phys. Solids*, vol. 3, pp. 189–196, 1955.

[5] T. F. Jordan and E. G. Thomsen, *J. Mech. and Phys. Solids*, vol. 4, pp. 184–190, 1956.

dead metal zone and result in a good approximation to observed deformation patterns.

20-5. Extrusion Defects

Because of the inhomogeneous deformation in the direct extrusion of a billet, the center of the billet moves faster than the periphery. As a result, the dead metal zone extends down along the outer surface of the billet. After about two-thirds of the billet is extruded, the outer surface of the billet moves toward the center and extrudes through the die near the axis of the rod. Since the surface of the billet often contains an oxidized skin, this type of flow results in internal oxide stringers. This defect can be considered to be an internal pipe, and it is known as the *extrusion defect*. On a transverse section through the extrusion this will appear as an annular ring of oxide. The tendency toward the formation of the extrusion defect increases as the container wall friction becomes greater. If a heated billet is placed in a cooler extrusion container, the outer layers of the billet will be chilled and the flow resistance of this region will increase. Therefore, there will be a greater tendency for the center part of the billet to extrude before the surface skin, and the tendency for formation of the extrusion defect is increased.

One way of avoiding the extrusion defect is to carry out the extrusion operation only to the point where the surface oxide begins to enter the die and then discard the remainder of the billet. This procedure may have serious economic consequences since as much as 30 per cent of the billet may remain at the point where the extrusion defect is encountered. An alternative procedure, which is frequently applied in the extrusion of brass, is to use a dummy block which is slightly smaller than the inside diameter of the extrusion container. As the ram pushes the dummy block forward, it scalps the billet and the oxidized surface layer remains in the container. A similar remedy, which is used with nickel and high-temperature alloys, is to machine the oxidized skin from the billet before placing it in the extrusion container. For this procedure to be successful, the billet should not oxidize when it is heated to the extrusion temperature.

Because of the nature of the metal flow in indirect extrusion, the oxidized surface of the billet builds up on the surface of the extrusion. This is known as *external pipe* and can be eliminated by scalping the billet with a dummy block which is smaller than the inside diameter of the container.

When extrusion is carried to the point at which the length of billet remaining in the container is about one-quarter its diameter, the rapid radial flow into the die results in the creation of an axial hole, or funnel, in the back end of the extrusion. This hole may extend for some distance into the back end of the extrusion, and therefore this metal must be discarded. The length of this defect can be reduced considerably by inclining the face of the ram at an angle to the ram axis.[1]

Surface cracking can result from extruding at too rapid a rate or at too high a temperature. A severe form of surface serrations, called the "fir-tree defect," results from the momentary sticking of the extrusion in the die land. The pressure builds up rapidly as the metal tries to extrude internally to overcome the high friction at the die wall.

Because of the nonuniform deformation produced in extrusion there will be considerable variation in structure and properties from

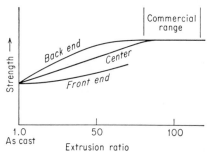

Fig. **20-8.** Schematic representation of effect of extrusion ratio on strength. (*After G. Sachs and K. R. Van Horn,* "*Practical Metallurgy,*" *p.* 373, *American Society for Metals, Metals Park, Ohio.* 1940.)

the front to the back end of the extrusion in the longitudinal direction and across the diameter of the extrusion in the transverse direction. The first metal through the die receives less deformation than the remainder of the extrusion. Therefore, the strength in this region will be lower. The variation in strength along the length of the extrusion depends on the extrusion ratio in the manner shown in Fig. 20-8. For the commercial range of extrusion ratios there is little variation in longitudinal strength beyond the front end of the extrusion. The indirect-extrusion process is particularly effective in producing uniform working in the longitudinal direction.

Because of the severe shear deformation in the surface layers of the extrusion, this region is more highly deformed than the center. Therefore, if the extrusion is heated after it leaves the press, the surface layers will generally respond differently from the interior. One result can be formation of large grains in the surface layer when the extrusion is recrystallized.

20-6. Extrusion under Ideal Conditions

An estimate of the pressure required for extrusion under ideal conditions can be made from an analysis of the dimensional changes pro-

[1] An analysis of this defect based on the slip-field theory has been given by W. Johnson, *Appl. Sci. Research*, vol. 8A, pp. 52–60, 228–236, 1959.

duced in the extrusion operation.   Consider the extrusion of a cylindrical billet of length L_0 and cross-sectional area A_0 into a rod of length L_f and cross-sectional area A_f.   On the assumption of no friction and of uniform deformation, so that there are no regions of high shear deformation and hence no redundant work, the work per unit volume required to increase the length of the extrusion by an increment dL is given by

$$dW = \sigma \, d\epsilon_1 = \sigma_0 \frac{dL}{L} \tag{20-2}$$

The total work required in deforming the metal is

$$W = \sigma_0 V \int_{L_0}^{L_f} \frac{dL}{L} \tag{20-3}$$

where $V = AL$ is the volume of the metal.   Therefore,

$$W = \sigma_0 V \ln \frac{L_f}{L_0} \tag{20-4}$$

The work produced by the ram in moving through a distance L is given by

$$W = PL = pAL \tag{20-5}$$

where P = force on ram
p = extrusion pressure

Equating the work required in deforming the metal to the work produced by the extrusion ram gives the equation for the extrusion pressure.

$$p = \sigma_0 \ln \frac{L_f}{L_0} = \sigma_0 \ln \frac{A_0}{A_f} \tag{20-6}$$

Actually, Eq. (20-6) will predict an extrusion pressure approximately 50 per cent lower than is required, because it does not consider friction and nonhomogeneous deformation.   In the derivation of Eq. (20-6) it is assumed that the maximum-shear-stress law is the criterion of yielding. If the derivation had started with Eq. (17-18), which is based on the distortion-energy yield criterion, the yield stress for plane strain would be used in the equation.

$$p = \frac{2}{\sqrt{3}} \sigma_0 \ln \frac{A_0}{A_f} \tag{20-7}$$

20-7. Extrusion with Friction and Nonhomogeneous Deformation

The flow of metal during extrusion under practical conditions is too complex to permit a precise analytical solution of the forces involved. For the case of extrusion through a flat die an expression can be developed for the effect of friction between the billet and the container on the same basis as was used in Chap. 18 for the forging of a cylinder.[1]

$$p = \sigma_0 \left[(\beta \ln R - 1) \exp \frac{4fL}{D} + 1 \right] \qquad (20\text{-}8)$$

where R = extrusion ratio
f = coefficient of friction between billet and container of diameter D
L = length of unextruded billet
$\beta \approx 1.5$ = a form factor to account for redundant work
The coefficient of friction can be evaluated by measuring the pressures required to extrude two billets of different lengths, since

$$\frac{p_1}{p_2} = \exp \frac{4f}{D} (L_1 - L_2) \qquad (20\text{-}9)$$

Other workers[2,3] have shown that the extrusion pressure for direct extrusion can be expressed in terms of the extrusion ratio by equations of the form

$$p = \sigma_0(C_1 + C_2 \ln R) \qquad (20\text{-}10)$$

where the constants C_1 and C_2 depend on the frictional conditions and the die angle. For indirect extrusion an equation of the form

$$p = \sigma_0[(C_1 - C_2 \cot \alpha) + (C_3 + C_4 \cot \alpha) \ln R] \qquad (20\text{-}11)$$

has been found valid,[4] where α is the half angle of the die.

In extruding with conical dies the flow becomes more uniform as the die angle is decreased. The equations for wire drawing which are presented in the next chapter appear to be more applicable to this situation than the previous equations for extrusion through flat dies.

20-8. Extrusion of Tubing

With modern equipment, tubing may be produced by extrusion to tolerances as close as those obtained by cold drawing. To produce tubing by extrusion, a mandrel must be fastened to the end of the extrusion ram. The mandrel extends to the entrance of the extrusion die, and the clearance between the mandrel and the die wall determines the wall thickness of the extruded tube. Generally, a hollow billet must be used so that the mandrel can extend to the die. In order to produce

[1] M. D. Stone, *Trans. ASME*, vol. 75, pp. 1493–1512, 1953.
[2] R. J. Wilcox and P. W. Whitton, *J. Inst. Metals*, vol. 87, pp. 289–293, 1958–1959.
[3] L. C. Dodeja and W. Johnson, *J. Mech. and Phys. Solids*, vol. 5, p. 281, 1957.
[4] R. J. Wilcox and P. W. Whitton, *J. Inst. Metals*, vol. 88, pp. 145–149, 1959–1960.

concentric tubes, the ram and mandrel must move in axial alignment with the container and the die. Also, the axial hole in the billet must be concentric, and the billet should offer equal resistance to deformation over its cross section.

One method of extruding a tube is to use a hollow billet for the starting material. The hole may be produced either by casting, by machining, or by hot piercing in a separate press. Since the bore of the hole will become oxidized during heating, the use of a hollow billet may result in a tube with an oxidized inside surface.

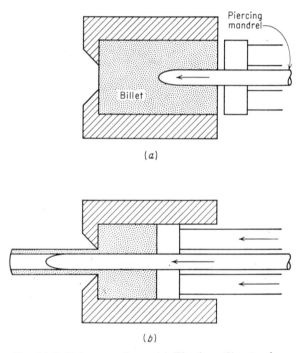

Fig. 20-9. Tube extrusion. (a) Piercing; (b) extrusion.

A more satisfactory method of extruding a tube is to use a solid billet which is pierced and extruded in one step in the extrusion press. With a modern extrusion press the piercing mandrel is actuated by a separate hydraulic system from the one which operates the ram. The piercing mandrel moves coaxially with the ram, but it is independent of its motion (Fig. 20-9). In the operation of a double-action extrusion press the first step is to upset the billet with the ram while the piercing mandrel is withdrawn. Next the billet is pierced with the pointed mandrel, ejecting a metal plug through the die. Then the ram advances and extrudes the billet over the mandrel to produce a tube.

A third method of extruding tubing, which is used with aluminum and magnesium alloys, is to use a solid billet and a porthole die with a standard extrusion ram without a mandrel. A sketch of a porthole die is shown in Fig. 20-10. The metal is forced to flow into separate streams and around the central bridge, which supports a short mandrel. The separate streams of metal which flow through the ports are brought together in a welding chamber surrounding the mandrel, and the metal exits from the die as a tube. Because the separate metal streams are

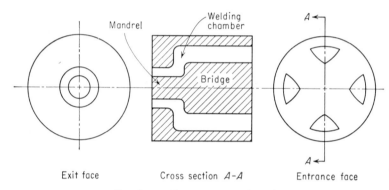

Fig. 20-10. Porthole extrusion die.

joined within the die, where there is no atmospheric contamination, a perfectly sound weld is obtained. In addition to tubing, porthole extrusion is used to produce hollow unsymmetrical shapes in aluminum alloys.

20-9. Production of Seamless Pipe and Tubing

Pipe and tubing may be classified as seamless or welded, depending on the method of manufacture. Extrusion is an excellent method of producing seamless pipe and tubing, particularly for metals which are difficult to work. However, there are other well-established processes for producing seamless pipe and tubing which are generally more economical than extrusion.

The *Mannesmann mill* (Fig. 20-11*a*) is used in the rotary piercing of steel and copper billets for the production of seamless pipe and tubes. Rotary piercing takes advantage of the fact that tensile stresses are developed at the center of a bar when it is subjected to forces around its periphery. In the operation of the Mannesmann mill a heated cylindrical billet is placed between rotating rolls which, in the horizontal plane, are inclined at an angle. Guide rolls (not shown in Fig. 20-11*a*) prevent the billet from dropping through the work rolls in the vertical plane. Because the work rolls are set at an angle to each other, the billet is given a helical motion which drives it forward toward the *piercing plug*. The roll pressure acting around the periphery of the billet opens up cracks at the center of the billet just in front of the piercing point. The plug assists in further opening up the center of the billet and forms the inside diameter of the tube. Piercing is the most severe forming operation that is customarily applied to metals. Only the highest-quality steel can be

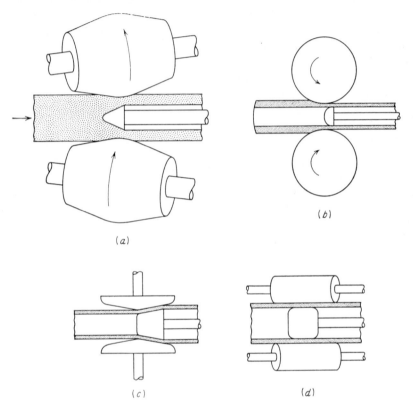

Fig. 20-11. (*a*) Mannesmann mill; (*b*) plug rolling mill; (*c*) rotary mill; (*d*) reeling mill.

used in this operation, and there are many alloys which cannot be satisfactorily pierced. In making large-sized pipe double piercing is frequently used. A small hole is pierced in the first operation, and in a second piercing operation the wall thickness is reduced and the inside diameter enlarged.

Pipe produced on a Mannesmann mill usually requires subsequent processing to its final dimensions. This is usually accomplished by means of a *plug rolling mill* (Fig. 20-11*b*), which is basically a two-high

rolling mill with a plug mandrel.   In this operation the wall thickness
and diameter are reduced, and the pipe is lengthened.   To make large-
sized pipes from the product of a plug rolling mill, the pipe is passed
through a *rotary mill* (Fig. 20-11c).   In this operation the wall thickness
is decreased, and the diameter is increased.   Then the pipe is passed
through a *reeling mill* (Fig. 20-11d), which burnishes the outside and
inside surfaces and removes the slight oval shape produced by the previous forming processes.   The final operation in the production of seamless
steel pipe is to pass it through a two-high mill with grooved rolls which
produce the final outside diameter.

BIBLIOGRAPHY

Bishop, J. F. W.: The Theory of Extrusion, *Met. Reviews*, vol. 2, pp. 361–390, 1957.
Chadwick, Richard: The Hot Extrusion of Non-ferrous Metals, *Met. Reviews*, vol.
    4, pp. 189–255, 1959.
Haffner, E. K. L., and R. M. L. Elken: Extrusion Presses and Press Installations,
    Met. Reviews, vol. 2, pp. 263–303, 1957.
Pearson, C. E., and R. N. Parkins: "The Extrusion of Metals," 2d ed., John Wiley &
    Sons, Inc., New York, 1960.
Sachs, G., and K. R. Van Horn: "Practical Metallurgy," American Society for Metals,
    Metals Park, Ohio, 1940.
"Tube Producing Practice," American Institute of Mining and Metallurgical Engi-
    neers, New York, 1951.

Chapter 21

ROD, WIRE, AND TUBE DRAWING

21-1. Introduction

Drawing operations involve the forcing of metal through a die by means of a tensile force applied to the exit side of the die. Most of the plastic flow is caused by compression force which arises from the reaction of the metal with the die. Usually the metal has a circular symmetry, but this is not an absolute requirement. The reduction in diameter of a solid bar or rod by successive drawing is known as *bar, rod,* or *wire drawing,* depending on the diameter of the final product. When a hollow tube is drawn through a die without any mandrel to support the inside of the tube, this is known as *tube sinking.* When a mandrel or plug is used to support the inside diameter of the tube as it is drawn through a die, the process is called *tube drawing.* Bar, wire, and tube drawing are usually carried out at room temperature. However, because large deformations are usually involved, there is considerable temperature rise during the drawing operation.

21-2. Rod and Wire Drawing

The principles involved in the drawing of bars, rod, and wire are basically the same, although the equipment that is used is different for the different-sized products. Rods and tubes, which cannot be coiled, are produced on drawbenches (Fig. 21-1a). The rod is pointed with a swager, inserted through the die, and clamped to the jaws of the drawhead. The drawhead is moved either by a chain drive or by a hydraulic mechanism. Drawbenches with 300,000 lb pull and 100 ft of runout are available. Draw speeds vary from about 30 to 300 ft/min.

The cross section through a typical conical drawing die is shown in Fig. 21-1b. The entrance angle of the die is made large enough to allow room for the lubricant that adheres to the die. The *approach angle* is the section of the die where the actual reduction in diameter occurs. The

532

bearing surface serves to guide the rod or wire as it exits from the die. An important characteristic of a drawing die is the *half-die angle*, denoted by α. At the present time most drawing dies are made from tungsten carbide because it provides long die life.

Wire drawing starts with hot-rolled *wire rod*. The rod is first cleaned by pickling to remove any scale which would lead to surface defects and excessive die wear. For the production of steel wire the next step consists in coating the wire rod with lime or plating it with a thin layer of copper or tin. The lime serves as an absorber and carrier of the lubricant during *dry drawing*, and it also serves to neutralize any acid remaining from pickling. In dry drawing the lubricant is grease or soap powder, while in *wet drawing* the entire die is immersed in a lubricating fluid of

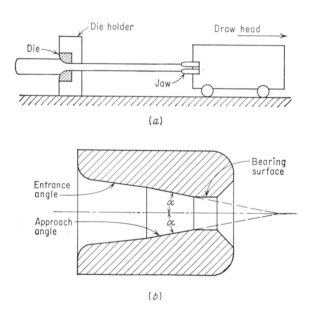

Fig. 21-1. (*a*) Schematic drawing of a drawbench; (*b*) cross section of a drawing die.

fermented rye-meal liquor or alkaline soap solution. The electroplated coating of copper or tin is used in the wet drawing of steel wire. No coating is generally used for drawing copper wire. After surface preparation of the wire rod, it is pointed, passed through the die, and fastened to the *draw block* (Fig. 21-2). For coarse wire, with a final diameter greater than $\frac{1}{4}$ in., a single draw block, called a *bull block*, is used. For fine wire a large number of draw blocks are used, with the wire passing through a number of dies until it is reduced to its final size in one continuous operation.   For fine wires reductions per pass of 15 to 25 per cent are used, while for coarse wires the reduction per pass may be 20 to 50 per cent.   Drawing speeds of modern wire-drawing equipment may be over 5,000 ft/min.

Nonferrous wire and low-carbon steel wire are produced in a number of tempers ranging from dead soft to full hard.   Depending on the metal and the reductions involved, intermediate anneals may be required. Steel wire with a carbon content greater than 0.25 per cent is given a special *patenting* heat treatment.   This consists in heating above the upper critical temperature and then cooling at a controlled rate or transforming in a lead bath at a temperature around 600°F to cause the

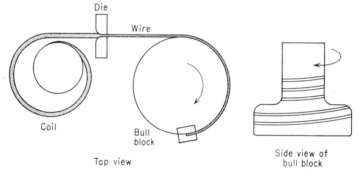

Fig. 21-2. Wire-drawing equipment (schematic).

formation of fine pearlite.   Patenting produces the best combination of strength and ductility for the successful drawing of high-carbon music and spring wire.

21-3. Defects in Rod and Wire

Internal defects in rod and wire[1] include internal cracks due to seams or pipe in the hot-rolled starting material and a defect known as *cupping*. Cupping is the rupturing of the center of the wire when it is subjected to a tensile force.   It can be recognized by a localized necking during drawing or by a cup-and-cone type of fracture when the wire is broken.   Problems from cupping are more frequent with large die angles and high friction.   Surface checking may result from improper surface lubrication. Longitudinal scratches are caused by a scored die, by improper lubrication, or by abrasive particles being drawn into the die with the wire. Slivers and seams result from cold shuts and blowholes in the hot-rolled

[1] G. Earnshaw, *Wire Ind.*, vol. 27, pp. 683–685, 706–707, 1960.

starting material. Surface discoloration and ground-in oxide result from improper cleaning of the hot-rolled bar and rod.

21-4. Variables in Wire Drawing

The force required to draw a wire through a die is the summation of the force required to decrease the diameter uniformly (as in tensile elongation), the force required to produce nonuniform shear deformation of the surface layers at the entry to and exit from the die (redundant work), and the force required to overcome the friction between the wire and the die wall. The first and last factors can be included without too much difficulty in an analysis of the wire-drawing process, but the nonhomogeneous deformation presents a problem which has not yet been ade-

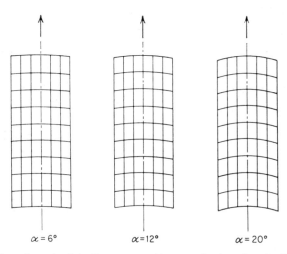

$\alpha = 6°$ $\alpha = 12°$ $\alpha = 20°$

Fig. 21-3. Distortion of originally square-grid network along longitudinal axis of a drawn bar as a function of die angle. Total reduction approximately 30 per cent.

quately solved. The total force required for wire drawing can be considered to depend on the following factors: (1) the die angle; (2) the percentage reduction; (3) the flow stress of the material; (4) the die friction, which is a function of the die material, the lubrication, and the drawing speed.

Studies of the deformation of grids scribed on the longitudinal axis of drawn bars have demonstrated the nonhomogeneous deformation produced by drawing.[1] Figure 21-3 shows that for a given reduction in

[1] E. Siebel, *Steel*, vol. 94, no. 94, pp. 28–30, 1934; G. I. Taylor and H. Quinney, *J. Inst. Metals*, vol. 49, p. 187–202, 1932.

diameter the amount of shear deformation in the direction opposite to the draw pull increases with increasing half-die angle. Only the elements on the axis of the bar undergo pure elongation. For large die angles the large shear deformation results in an increased longitudinal tensile stress at the center of the wire which can exceed the fracture stress and can thereby result in the cupping type of failure. For a given die angle the shear deformation becomes less important with increasing percentage reductions. For this reason, theoretical treatments of wire drawing which neglect the nonuniform deformation have greater validity at high reductions. Because of the increased surface shear deformation, the yield and tensile strengths of drawn wires are higher for larger die angles. This effect is greater for lower reductions.

Although the nonuniform shear deformation is lower with smaller die angles, the wall friction is higher. Since the draw force depends in a complicated way on the die angle, reduction, the flow stress, and the friction, there will be an optimum die angle which results in the minimum draw force for a given reduction. This optimum die angle will depend on the reduction, the lubrication, and the materials involved. All other factors being constant, the optimum die angle increases with amount of reduction. The drawing speed has little effect on the drawing force. However, there is greater temperature rise with high drawing speeds, and lubrication becomes more difficult.

Another factor to consider is the existence of a *back pull* in the direction opposite to the draw pull. A back pull of considerable magnitude can arise from frictional forces acting on the draw blocks of multiple drawing machines, or it may be purposely applied for the reasons given below. A back pull materially increases the drawing force. On the other hand, it reduces the wall pressure in the die and reduces the friction, and therefore die wear is appreciably decreased.

21-5. Wire Drawing without Friction

A simplified theory of wire drawing can be developed[1] on the basis of the assumption that the metal flow in a conical die can be represented by the inward radial flow of a segment of a sphere. The presence of friction and shear (redundant) deformation is neglected in this analysis, so that it represents the ideal situation. In Fig. 21-4, the principal stresses are the longitudinal draw stress σ_r and the tangential compressive stress (die pressure) σ_θ. The stress situation shown here represents a cylindrical state of stress, for which the distortion-energy yield criterion

---

[1] O. Hoffman and G. Sachs, "Introduction to the Theory of Plasticity for Engineers," pp. 166–168, McGraw-Hill Book Company, Inc., New York, 1953.

can be written

$$\sigma_r - \sigma_\theta = \sigma_0 \tag{21-1}$$

The differential equation of equilibrium is given by

$$\frac{d\sigma_r}{dr} + \frac{2\sigma_0}{r} = 0 \tag{21-2}$$

where r is the radial distance of a particle from the surface of the sphere. Equation (21-2) integrates into

$$\sigma_r = C - \sigma_0 \ln r^2 \tag{21-3}$$
$$\sigma_\theta = C - \sigma_0(1 + \ln r^2) \tag{21-4}$$

The constant of integration can be evaluated by the boundary condition that at the entrance to the die, $r = r_0$, the longitudinal stress σ_r equals zero.

$$0 = C - \sigma_0 \ln r_0{}^2$$

or $$C = \sigma_0 \ln r_0{}^2$$

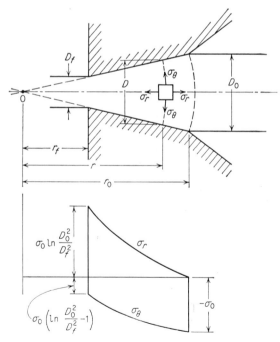

Fig. 21-4. Stresses in wire drawing without friction. (*O. Hoffman and G. Sachs, "Introduction to the Theory of Plasticity for Engineers," McGraw-Hill Book Company, Inc., New York, 1953.*)

The equations for the principal stresses now become

$$\sigma_r = \sigma_0 \ln \frac{r_0^2}{r^2} \tag{21-5}$$

$$\sigma_\theta = \sigma_0 \left(\ln \frac{r_0^2}{r^2} - 1 \right) \tag{21-6}$$

These equations can be expressed more conveniently in terms of the wire diameter D, since $r_0/r = D_0/D$.

$$\sigma_r = \sigma_0 \ln \frac{D_0^2}{D^2} \tag{21-7}$$

$$\sigma_\theta = \sigma_0 \left(\ln \frac{D_0^2}{D^2} - 1 \right) \tag{21-8}$$

The largest value of the longitudinal stress occurs at the exit of the die. When Eq. (21-7) is evaluated at $r = r_f$, it is equal to the *draw stress*. Figure 21-4 illustrates the trends in σ_r and σ_θ with radial position from the apex of the die.

For an ideal plastic material the draw stress cannot exceed the yield stress.

$$\sigma_0 \ln \frac{D_0^2}{D_f^2} = \sigma_0 \tag{21-9}$$

The reduction in area, q, produced by drawing the wire through the die is given by

$$q = 1 - \frac{D_f^2}{D_0^2} \tag{21-10}$$

Solving Eq. (21-9) for D_f^2/D_0^2 results in

$$\frac{D_f^2}{D_0^2} = \frac{1}{e} = 0.37 \tag{21-11}$$

where $e = 2.718$ is the base of the natural system of logarithms, and

$$q_{max} = 1 - \frac{1}{e} = 0.63 \tag{21-12}$$

Therefore, the maximum reduction in area which can be produced by drawing a rod or wire through a die is 63 per cent, on the assumption that the metal behaves as an ideal plastic material. (An exactly similar analysis can be used to derive the equations for the extrusion of an ideal plastic material.)

21-6. Wire Drawing with Friction

Friction occurs in even the best-lubricated die, and therefore it must be considered in the analysis of the forces required for wire drawing. The friction force at any point in the die is assumed proportional to the normal pressure at that point (Coulomb's law of friction) and acts in a direction to oppose relative motion between the die and the wire.

An analysis which considers the effect of friction on the stresses in wire drawing was made by Sachs.[1] The coefficient of friction is assumed constant over the entire die-metal interface, and a cylindrical state of stress is assumed throughout the wire. Figure 21-5 illustrates the state of stress acting on an element of wire perpendicular to the axis of the wire. The equilibrium of forces acting along the axis of the wire is made

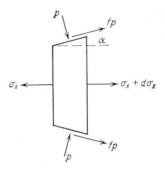

Fig. 21-5. Stresses acting on element of wire.

up of the longitudinal tensile stress σ_x, the longitudinal component of the pressure p between the die and the wire, and the longitudinal component of the total frictional force on this interface. The equilibrium of forces results in the following differential equation for the axial stress σ_x as a function of the wire diameter D,

$$\frac{d\sigma_x}{\sigma_x B - \sigma_0(1 + B)} = \frac{2\,dD}{D} \tag{12-13}$$

where $B = f/(\tan \alpha)$. In integrating this equation consideration is given to the possibility that a back pull σ_{xb} may be present. The boundary condition that, at $D = D_0$, $\sigma_x = \sigma_{xb}$ results in the following expressions for σ_x and p:

$$\frac{\sigma_x}{\sigma_0} = \frac{1 + B}{B}\left[1 - \left(\frac{D^2}{D_0{}^2}\right)^B\right] + \frac{\sigma_{xb}}{\sigma_0}\left(\frac{D^2}{D_0{}^2}\right)^B \tag{21-14}$$

$$\frac{p}{\sigma_0} = \frac{1}{B}\left[1 + (1 + B)\left(\frac{D^2}{D_0{}^2}\right)^B\right] - \frac{\sigma_{xb}}{\sigma_0}\left(\frac{D^2}{D_0{}^2}\right)^B \tag{21-15}$$

The draw stress σ_{xf} is the axial stress at the die exit where $D = D_f$.

$$\sigma_{xf} = \sigma_0\frac{1 + B}{B}\left[1 - \left(\frac{D_f{}^2}{D_0{}^2}\right)^B\right] + \sigma_{xb}\left(\frac{D_f{}^2}{D_0{}^2}\right)^B \tag{21-16}$$

---

[1] G. Sachs, *Z. angew. Math. u. Mech.*, vol. 7, pp. 235–236, 1927; see also Hoffman and Sachs, *op. cit.*, pp. 176–186.

When there is no back pull, Eq. (21-16) reduces to

$$\sigma_{xf} = \sigma_0 \frac{1+B}{B} \left[1 - \left(\frac{D_f{}^2}{D_0{}^2}\right)^B \right] \tag{21-17}$$

Equation (21-16) indicates that the draw stress increases with increasing back pull by an amount which is less than the value of the back pull. The greater the reduction and the value of the constant B, the smaller the influence of the back pull on the draw stress. Since for a given reduction the presence of a back pull increases the draw stress, the condition which limits the maximum reduction, $\sigma_{xf} = \sigma_0$, will be reached sooner when there is back pull. Therefore, the maximum possible reduction decreases with increasing back pull. However, back pull has the advantage that the die pressure is reduced, and therefore the die life is materially increased.

To account for strain hardening in Sachs's equation, an average value of the yield stress before and after passing through the die should be used. An analytical treatment of wire drawing which accounts for strain hardening by expressing the stress-strain curve as a power function has been developed by Davis and Dokos.[1]

Sachs's analysis of wire drawing does not take into account the redundant work which results from shear deformation. Shear deformation is not great for small die angles or for large deformations with larger die angles. These factors can be related by the parameter Δ.

$$\Delta = \sin \alpha \frac{D_0 + D_f}{D_0 - D_f} \tag{21-18}$$

For values of Δ less than about 0.9 the redundant work is not significant, and Sachs's equation adequately describes the draw stress.[2] It has been determined[3] that Sachs's equation agrees within ± 10 per cent of experimental results for all reductions when α is less than about 6°, and for α up to 20° the equation is valid within ± 10 per cent for reductions greater than about 25 per cent. Whitton has developed an empirical correction for redundant work which allows the prediction of draw stress for half-die angles of 5 to 25° for reductions of 10 to 50 per cent.

$$\sigma_{xf} = \sigma_0 \frac{1+B}{B} \left[1 - \left(\frac{D_f{}^2}{D_0{}^2}\right)^B \right] + \frac{2}{3}\left(\frac{\pi}{4}D_f{}^2\right)\sigma_0 \frac{\alpha^2(1-q)}{q} \tag{21-19}$$

where α = half-die angle
q = reduction in area

[1] E. A. Davis and S. J. Dokos, *J. Appl. Mech.*, vol. 11, pp. 193–198, 1944.
[2] J. G. Wistreich, *Met. Reviews*, vol. 3, pp. 97–142, 1958.
[3] P. W. Whitton, *J. Inst. Metals*, vol. 86, pp. 417–421, 1957–1958.

So far no theoretical analyses based on slip-field theory have been directly applicable to wire drawing. Solutions have been obtained[1,2] for the two-dimensional (plane-strain) analog to wire drawing, which consists in the drawing of a rectangular strip through a tapered die. Calculations of the effect of die angle, amount of reduction, and friction have been made for an ideally plastic material which obeys the distortion-energy criterion of yielding.

21-7. Tube-drawing Processes

Hollow cylinders, or tubes, which are made by hot-forming processes such as extrusion or piercing and rolling (see Chap. 20), are often cold-finished by drawing. Cold drawing is used to obtain closer dimensional tolerances, to produce better surface finishes, to increase the mechanical properties of the tube material by strain hardening, to produce tubes with thinner walls or smaller diameters than can be obtained with hot-forming methods, and to produce tubes of irregular shapes.

Tube drawing is essentially the same as wire drawing. Tubes are produced on a drawbench and with dies similar to those employed in wire drawing. However, in order to reduce the wall thickness and accurately to control the inside diameter, the inside surface of the tube must be supported while it passes through the die. This is usually accomplished by inserting a *mandrel*, or *plug*, inside the tube. The mandrel is often fastened to the end of a stationary rod attached to one end of the draw-bench and is positioned so that the mandrel is located in the throat of the die. The mandrel may have either a cylindrical or a tapered cross section (Fig. 21-6a and b). Tube drawing may be accomplished also with a moving mandrel, either by pulling a long rod through the die with the tube (Fig. 21-6c) or by pushing a deep-drawn shell through the die with a punch (Fig. 21-6d). Because of difficulties in using long rods for mandrels, tube drawing with a rod usually is limited to the production of small-sized tubing, where the rod supporting the stationary mandrel would be too thin to have adequate strength. Another tube-producing method is *tube sinking*, in which no mandrel is used to support the inside surface of the tube as it is drawn through the die. Since the inside of the tube is not supported in tube sinking, the wall thickness will either increase or decrease, depending on the conditions imposed in the process. On a commercial basis tube sinking is used only for the production of small tubes. However, it represents an important problem in plastic-forming theory because it occurs as the first step in tube drawing with a mandrel. In order that the tube dimensions can be controlled by the

---

[1] R. Hill and S. J. Tupper, *J. Iron Steel Inst.* (*London*), vol. 159, pp. 353–359, 1948.
[2] A. P. Green, *Phil. Mag.*, vol. 42, pp. 900–918, 1951.

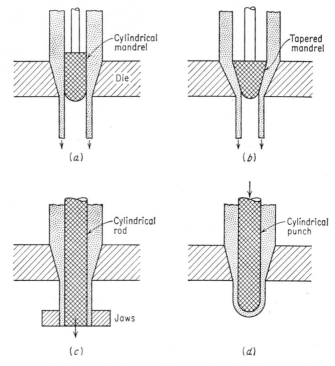

Fig. 21-6. Tube-drawing methods. (a) Stationary cylindrical mandrel; (b) conical (tapered) stationary mandrel; (c) moving rod; (d) pushed with a punch.

dimensions of the mandrel, it is necessary that the inside diameter of the tube be reduced to a value a little smaller than the diameter of the mandrel by a tube-sinking process during the early stages of its passage through the die.

21-8. Tube Sinking

The stresses involved in tube sinking have been analyzed by Sachs and Baldwin[1] on the assumption that the wall thickness of the tube remains constant. The equation for the draw stress at the die exit is analogous with the equation describing the draw stress in wire drawing. The cross-sectional area of the tube is related to the midradius r and the wall thickness h by $A \simeq 2\pi rh$.

$$\sigma_{xf} = \sigma_0'' \frac{1 + B}{B} \left[1 - \left(\frac{A_f}{A_b} \right)^B \right] + \sigma_{xb} \left(\frac{A_f}{A_0} \right)^B \qquad (21\text{-}20)$$

[1] G. Sachs and W. M. Baldwin, Jr., *Trans. ASME*, vol. 68, pp. 655–662, 1946; also see Hoffman and Sachs, *op. cit.*, pp. 252–255.

where $\sigma_0'' = 1.10\sigma_0$ and $B = f/(\tan \alpha)$. Experiments confirm the prediction of Eq. (21-20) that, for equal reduction, die angle, and frictional conditions, the draw stress for tube sinking is about 10 per cent higher than the draw stress for wire drawing. A more complete analysis of tube sinking has been made by Swift.[1] This analysis considers changes in wall thickness of the tube, but the complexity of the relationship makes it advisable to refer to graphical relationships presented in the original paper.

Experimental measurements of the changes in wall thickness produced by tube sinking have been made by Baldwin and Howald.[2] Changes in wall thickness during tube sinking depend on the degree of strain hardening of the metal, the reduction per pass, and the ratio of the wall thickness to the outside diameter of the tube. For reductions in outside diameter up to 40 per cent a straight-line relationship is obtained between the wall-thickness ratio and the reduction in the outside diameter.

21-9. Tube Drawing with a Stationary Mandrel

The state of stress on an element of a tube being drawn with a stationary mandrel is shown in Fig. 21-7. The axial draw stress σ_x is one of the principal stresses. The same die pressure p is assumed to act at both the interface between the die and the tube and the interface between the tube and the mandrel at any point along the axis of the die. In the analysis of the stresses[3] provision is made for the facts that different coefficients of friction may exist at the two interfaces and that the half-die angle α and the half angle of the mandrel, β, are not necessarily equal. It is possible to assume that plane-strain conditions exist for tube drawing since the strain in the circumferential direction is negligible compared with the longitudinal

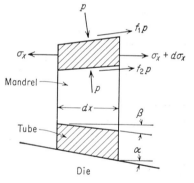

Fig. 21-7. Stresses acting on element of tube drawn with a stationary mandrel.

and radial strains. Therefore, the distortion-energy criterion for yielding can be written

$$\sigma_x + p = \frac{2\sigma_0}{\sqrt{3}} = \sigma_0'$$

[1] H. W. Swift, *Phil. Mag.*, vol. 40, ser. 7, pp. 883–902, 1949.

[2] W. M. Baldwin, Jr., and T. S. Howald, *Trans. ASM*, vol. 33, pp. 88–102, 1944.

[3] Hoffman and Sachs, *op. cit.*, pp. 190–195.

The equilibrium of forces acting along the axis of the tube is made up of the longitudinal stress σ_x, the longitudinal components of the normal pressure on the die and on the mandrel, and the longitudinal components of the friction forces between the die and the tube and the tube and the mandrel. This equilibrium of forces results in the following differential equation for the axial stress σ_x as a function of the thickness of the tube wall, h:

$$\frac{d\sigma_x}{\sigma_x B' - \sigma_0'(1 + B')} = \frac{dh}{h} \tag{21-21}$$

where

$$B' = \frac{f_1 + f_2}{\tan \alpha - \tan \beta} \tag{21-22}$$

and f_1 = coefficient of friction along die-tube interface
f_2 = coefficient of friction along tube-mandrel interface
α = one-half apex angle of die
β = one-half apex angle of mandrel

The solution of Eq. (21-21) results in the following equation for the draw stress at the exit section of the die, where $h = h_f$:

$$\sigma_{xf} = \sigma_0' \frac{1 + B'}{B'} \left[1 - \left(\frac{h_f}{h_0}\right)^{B'} \right] \tag{21-23}$$

Different values of the constant B' must be used in Eq. (21-23) for different physical situations. Usually the coefficients of friction along the die-tube and tube-mandrel interfaces can be assumed equal so that $f_1 = f_2 = f$.

$$B' = \frac{2f}{\tan \alpha - \tan \beta} \qquad \text{for a tapered mandrel}$$

If the mandrel has a cylindrical shape, $\beta = 0$.

$$B' = \frac{2f}{\tan \alpha} \qquad \text{for a cylindrical mandrel}$$

Drawing a wide strip through a wedge-shaped die is known as *strip drawing*. For strip drawing, $\beta = \alpha$, and $f_1 = f_2 = f$.

$$B' = \frac{f}{\tan \alpha} = B \qquad \text{for strip drawing}$$

The constant B' is always positive for strip drawing and tube drawing with a stationary mandrel.

The maximum axial stress occurs at the die exit. At the exit the metal is no longer in a plane-strain condition because it is free to undergo circumferential strains. Therefore, the limiting stress at the exit is the uniaxial flow stress σ_0. Equation (21-23) can then be written

$$\frac{\sigma_{xf}}{\sigma_0'} = \frac{\sqrt{3}}{2} \frac{\sigma_{xf}}{\sigma_0} = 0.866 = \frac{1 + B'}{B'} \left[1 - \left(\frac{h_f}{h_0}\right)^{B'} \right]$$

By rearranging, the maximum reduction per pass can be expressed as follows:

$$q_{max} = 1 - \frac{h_f}{h_0} = 1 - \left(\frac{1 + 0.133B'}{1 + B'}\right)^{1/B'} \qquad (21\text{-}24)$$

The above equation shows that the maximum reduction per pass decreases as B' increases. The highest reduction of about 58 per cent is obtained for frictionless drawing, where $B' = 0$. Figure 21-8 shows the maximum theoretical reduction plotted against the constant B'. A curve for tube drawing with a moving mandrel (Sec. 21-10) is also given in this figure.

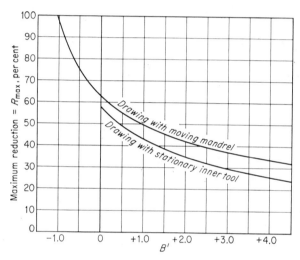

Fig. 21-8. Theoretical maximum reductions in tube drawing. (*O. Hoffman and G. Sachs, "Introduction to the Theory of Plasticity for Engineers," McGraw-Hill Book Company, Inc., New York,* 1953.)

It should be realized that these curves are based on a theoretical equation for an ideal plastic metal with a constant flow stress. Strain hardening will allow a higher tensile stress at the die exit, and therefore the maximum reduction may be somewhat higher.

21-10. Tube Drawing with a Moving Mandrel

In tube drawing with a moving mandrel, as when a rod or punch is used (Fig. 21-6c and d), the draw force is transmitted to the metal partly by the pull on the exit section and partly by the friction forces acting along the tube-mandrel interface. The frictional forces in any forming operation always tend to oppose relative motion between the metal and the forming tools. In drawing with a moving mandrel the frictional forces at the die-tube interface act toward the die entrance, as was the case for wire drawing and tube drawing with a stationary mandrel.

However, for the case of tube drawing with a moving mandrel the mandrel is moving with a velocity equal to that of the tube on the exit side of the die, and this is higher than the velocity of the metal confined between the die and the mandrel. Therefore, there is relative motion between the metal in the die and the mandrel toward the entrance end of the die, and as a result the frictional forces are directed toward the die exit. Therefore, the direction of the friction force $f_2 p$ in Fig. 21-7 must be reversed for drawing with a moving mandrel, and the constant B' must be rewritten as follows:

$$B' = \frac{f_1 - f_2}{\tan \alpha - \tan \beta} \quad \text{for a moving mandrel}$$

Either positive or negative values of B' can be obtained, depending on the relative magnitudes of f_1 and f_2. Equation (21-23) again expresses the draw stress at the die exit when the proper value of B' is used. Examination of this equation indicates that when B' is less than -1 the axial stress will be compressive; i.e., the metal is extruded by the frictional forces developed between the mandrel and the inner surface of the tube. This condition represents an instability which leads to damage to the tube or breakage of the tools. For the specific case of tube drawing with a moving cylindrical mandrel ($\beta = 0$) where $f_1 = f_2 = f$ the average unit draw stress can be written as follows:[1]

$$\sigma_x = \frac{P}{\pi D_f h_f} = \sigma_0'(1 + B) \ln \frac{h_0}{h_f} + \sigma_{xb} \left[1 - B \left(\ln \frac{h_0}{h_f} - 1 \right) \right] \quad (21\text{-}25)$$

where σ_{xb} is a back pull resulting from elastic reactions at the die entrance and $B = f/(\tan \alpha)$. Experimental measurements[2] of the forces involved in tube drawing provide good agreement with the above equation.

The determination of the theoretical maximum reduction per pass for drawing with a moving mandrel depends upon a different criterion from that for the situation with a stationary mandrel. Because the mandrel is in contact with the metal after exiting from the die, the metal cannot undergo circumferential strain. Therefore, a plane-strain condition exists, and the forming limit is given by the condition that $\sigma_{xf} = \sigma_0'$. Equation (21-23) then becomes

$$\sigma_{xf} = \sigma_0' = \sigma_0' \frac{1 + B'}{B'} \left[1 - \left(\frac{h_f}{h_0} \right)^{B'} \right]$$

---

[1] *Ibid.*, pp. 197–199.

[2] G. Espey and G. Sachs, *J. Appl. Mech.*, vol. 14, pp. 81–87, 1947.

and on rearranging the expression for the maximum reduction is obtained.

$$q_{max} = 1 - \frac{h_f}{h_0} = 1 - \left(\frac{1}{1+B'}\right)^{1/B'} \qquad (21\text{-}26)$$

A maximum reduction of about 63 per cent is obtained when $B' = 0$. This corresponds to the situation where $f_1 = f_2$ or the frictionless situation where $f_1 = f_2 = 0$. Higher values of reduction are possible with negative values of B', but these have little practical significance.

21-11. Residual Stresses in Rod, Wire, and Tubes

Two distinct types of residual-stress patterns are found in cold-drawn rod and wire, depending upon the amount of reduction. For reductions per pass of less than about 1 per cent the longitudinal residual stresses are compressive at the surface and tensile at the axis, the radial stresses are tensile at the axis and drop off to zero at the free surface, while the circumferential stresses follow the same trend as the longitudinal residual stresses. For larger reductions of commercial significance the residual-stress distribution is completely reversed from the first type of stress pattern. In this case the longitudinal stresses are tensile at the surface and compressive at the axis of the rod, the radial stresses are compressive at the axis, and the circumferential stresses follow the same pattern as the longitudinal stresses. The first type of residual-stress pattern is characteristic of forming operations where the deformation is localized in the surface layers.

The effect of die angle and the amount of reduction per pass on the longitudinal residual stress in cold-drawn brass wire was investigated by Linicus and Sachs.[1] Figure 21-9 shows that for a given reduction the longitudinal residual stress increases with the half-die angle. Maximum values of residual stress are obtained for reductions in the region of 15 to 35 per cent.

For tubes produced by tube sinking, under conditions where the deformation is relatively uniform throughout the tube wall, the longitudinal residual stresses are tensile on the outer surface and compressive on the inner surface of the tube. The residual stresses in the circumferential direction follow the same pattern, while the stresses in the radial direction are negligible. Approximate measurements[2] of the circumferential stresses on the outer surface of sunk tubes indicate that the stresses increase with increasing reduction in diameter at the same rate at which the yield stress is increased by the cold work. No detailed investigations

[1] W. Linicus and G. Sachs, *Mitt. deut. Materialprüfungsanstalt.*, vol. 16, pp. 38–67, 1932.

[2] D. K. Crampton, *Trans. AIME*, vol. 89, pp. 233–255, 1930.

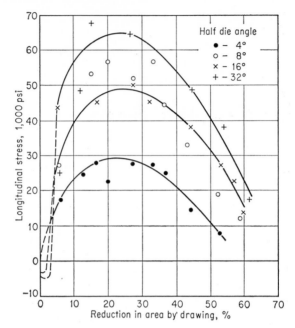

Fig. 21-9. Longitudinal residual stresses in cold-drawn brass wire. (*W. Linicus and G. Sachs.*)

of the residual-stress patterns in drawn tubes have been made, but from the available data it appears that the stress distributions are approximately the same as for tube sinking.[1]

BIBLIOGRAPHY

Hoffman, O., and G. Sachs: "Introduction to the Theory of Plasticity for Engineers," chaps. 15–17, McGraw-Hill Book Company, Inc., New York, 1953.

Sachs, G., and K. R. Van Horn: "Practical Metallurgy," American Society for Metals, Metals Park, Ohio, 1940.

"Tube Producing Practice," American Institute of Mining and Metallurgical Engineers, New York, 1951.

Wistreich, J. G.: The Fundamentals of Wire Drawing, *Met. Reviews*, vol. 3, pp. 97–142, 1958.

[1] W. M. Baldwin, Jr., *Proc. ASTM*, vol. 49, pp. 539–583, 1949.

Chapter 22

SHEET-METAL FORMING

22-1. Introduction

The ability to produce a variety of shapes from flat sheets of metal at high rates of production has been one of the real technological advances of the twentieth century. This transition from hand-forming operations to mass-production methods has been an important factor in the great improvement in the standard of living which occurred during the period.

In essence, a shape is produced from a flat blank by stretching and shrinking the dimensions of all its volume elements in the three mutually perpendicular principal directions. The resulting shape is then the result of the integration of all the local stretching and shrinking of the volume elements. Attempts have been made to classify the almost limitless number of shapes which are possible in metal forming into definite categories depending upon the contour of the finished part. Sachs[1] has classified sheet-metal parts into five categories.

1. Singly curved parts
2. Contoured flanged parts—including parts with stretch flanges and shrink flanges
3. Curved sections
4. Deep-recessed parts—including cups and boxes with either vertical or sloping walls
5. Shallow-recessed parts—including dish-shaped, beaded, embossed, and corrugated parts

Typical examples of these parts are shown in Fig. 22-1. Another classification system, developed in the automotive industry, groups sheet-steel parts into categories depending on the severity of the forming operation.[2] Severity of the operation is based on the maximum amount of bending or stretching in the part.

[1] G. Sachs, "Principles and Methods of Sheet-metal Fabricating," pp. 9–14, Reinhold Publishing Corporation, New York, 1951.

[2] The Selection of Sheet Steel for Formability, ASM Metals Handbook Supplement, 1955.

(a)   (b)

(c)   (d)

(e)   (f)

Fig. 22-1. Typical formed shapes. (a) Singly curved; (b) stretch flange; (c) shrink flange; (d) curved section; (e) deep-drawn cup; (f) beaded section.

Still another way of classifying sheet-metal forming is by means of specific operations such as bending, shearing, deep drawing, stretching, ironing, etc. Most of these operations have been illustrated briefly in Fig. 17-1, and they will be discussed in considerably greater detail in this chapter.

22-2. Forming Methods

The old method of hand forming of sheet metal is today used primarily as a finishing operation to remove wrinkles left by forming machines. In the metalworking industries hand forming is primarily limited to experimental work where only a few identical pieces are required.

Most high-production-volume sheet-metal forming is done on a press, driven either by mechanical or by hydraulic action. In mechanical presses energy is generally stored in a flywheel and is transferred to the movable slide on the downstroke of the press. Mechanical presses are usually quick-acting and have a short stroke, while hydraulic presses are slower-acting but can apply a longer stroke. Presses are usually classified according to the number of slides which can be operated independently of each other. In the *single-action press* there is only one slide, generally operating in the vertical direction. In the *double-action press* there are two slides. The second action is ordinarily used to operate the *hold-down*, which prevents wrinkling in deep drawing. A *triple-action press* is equipped with two actions above the die and one action below the die.

The basic tools used with a metalworking press are the *punch* and the *die*.[1] The punch is the convex male tool which mates with the concave female die. Generally the punch is the moving element. Because accurate alignment between the punch and die is usually required, it is common practice to mount them permanently in a *subpress*, or *die set*, which can be quickly inserted in the press. An important consideration in tooling for sheet-metal forming is the frequent requirement for a clamping pressure, or hold-down, to prevent wrinkling of the sheet as it is being formed. Hold-down can be best provided by a *hold-down ring*, which is actuated by the second action of a double-action press. However, by using mechanical springs or an auxiliary air cylinder hold-down can be provided in a single-action press.

Frequently punches and dies are designed so that successive stages in the forming of the part are carried out in the same die on each stroke of the press. This is known as *progressive forming*. A simple example is a progressive blanking and piercing die to make a plain, flat washer (Fig. 22-2). As the strip is fed from left to right, the hole for the washer is first punched and then the washer is blanked from the strip. At the same time as the washer is being blanked from the strip, the punch A is piercing the hole for the next washer. The stripper plate is used to prevent the metal from separating from the die on the up stroke of the punch. The die materials depend on the severity of the operation and the required production run.[2] In aircraft work, where production runs are often small, tooling is frequently made from a zinc-base alloy called Kirksite or from wood or epoxy resins. For long die life, however, tool steel is required.

A forging hammer can be used for sheet-metal forming in place of a mechanical press. Drop-hammer forming differs from forming with a conventional press in that usually many blows of varying force will be applied rather than a single stroke of fixed length or pressure. While a

[1] F. A. Stanley, "Punches and Dies," 2d ed., McGraw-Hill Book Company, New York, 1936.

[2] The Selection of Material for Press Forming Dies, ASM Metals Handbook Supplement, 1955.

drop hammer is equivalent only to a single-action press, hold-down action can usually be provided by auxiliary devices.   Because of the flexibility of the drop hammer, it is often used on short production runs in the air-craft industry.   However, since the force cannot be controlled as accurately as in the double-action mechanical or hydraulic press, the drop hammer is not particularly well suited to the most severe forming operations.

The *press brake* is a single-action press with a very long and narrow bed. The chief purpose of a press brake is to form long, straight bends in pieces

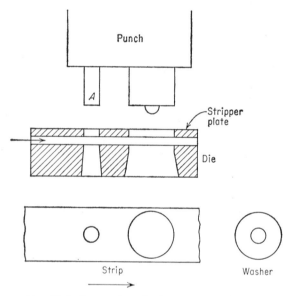

Fig. 22-2. Progressive piercing and blanking die.

such as channels and corrugated sheets.   *Roll forming* (Chap. 19) is another common method of producing bent shapes in long lengths.   The roll-forming process is also used to produce thin-wall cylinders from flat sheet.

Rubber hydroforming is a modification of the conventional punch and die in which a pad of rubber serves as the female die.   Rubber forming, or the *Guerin process*, is illustrated in Fig. 22-3.   A form block (punch) is fastened to the bed of a single-action hydraulic press, and a thick blanket of rubber is placed in a retainer box on the upper platen of the press.   When a blank is placed over the form block and the rubber forced down on the sheet, the rubber transmits a nearly uniform hydrostatic pressure against the sheet. A unit pressure of around 1,500 psi is sufficient for most parts, and higher local pressures can be provided by auxiliary tooling.[1] Rubber forming is used extensively in the aircraft industry. Shallow flanged parts with stretch flanges are readily produced by this method, but shrink flanges are limited because the rubber provides little resistance to wrinkling. Another limitation is that the blank tends to move on the form block unless holes for positioning pins are provided in the part. A modification to this process known as *Marforming*[2] provides a controlled hold-down pressure that results in deeper, wrinkle-free draws. The hydraulic analog of rubber forming is the *hydroforming process*. In this proc-

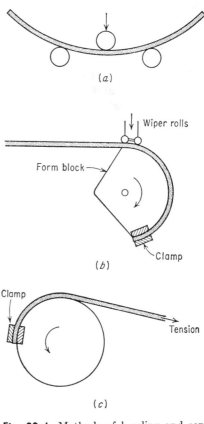

(a)

(b)

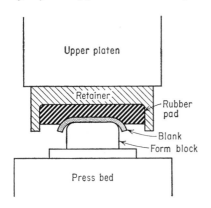

Fig. 22-3. Rubber forming.

Fig. 22-4. Methods of bending and contouring. (a) Three-roll bender; (b) wiper-type bender; (c) wrap forming.

ess the rubber pad is replaced by a flexible diaphragm backed up by hydraulic fluid with pressures as high as 15,000 psi.

A variety of methods are used to bend or to contour-form straight sections.[3] Cylindrical- and conical-shaped parts are produced with *bending rolls* (Fig. 22-4a). A three-roll bender is not very well suited to pre-

[1] Sachs, *op. cit.*, pp. 424–455.

[2] R. B. Schulze, *Metal Progr.*, vol. 57, pp. 769–772, 1950.

[3] Sachs, *op. cit.*, pp. 476–493.

venting buckling in thin-gage sheet.   Often a fourth roll is placed at the
exit to provide an extra adjustment in curvature.   In three-point loading the maximum bending moment is at the midpoint of the span.   This
localization of strain can result, under certain circumstances, in the forming limit being reached at the midpoint before the rest of the part is bent
to the proper contour.   More uniform deformation along the length of
the part is obtained with *wiper-type equipment.*   In its simplest form this
consists of a sheet which is clamped at one end against a form block; the
contour is progressively formed by successive hammer blows, starting
near the clamp and moving a short distance toward the free end with
each blow.   A wiper-type bender is sketched in Fig. 22-4*b.*   In this case

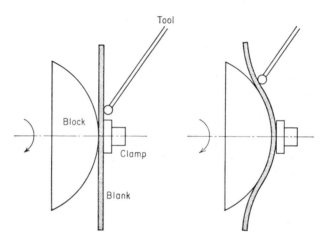

Fig. 22-5. Manual spinning.

the form block or die has a nonuniform contour so that the wiper rolls
must be pressed against the block with a uniform pressure supplied by a
hydraulic cylinder.   For a form block of constant radius, as in a power-
driven tube bender, the clearance between the die and the wiper rolls
remains constant, and there is no need for the hydraulic-actuated rolls.
Still a third method of producing contours is by *wrap forming.*   In wrap
forming the sheet is compressed against a form block, and at the same
time a longitudinal tensile stress is applied to prevent buckling and
wrinkling (Fig. 22-4*c*).   A simple example of wrap forming is the coiling
of a spring around a mandrel.   The stretch forming of curved sections
is a special case of wrap forming.

   A method of making tank heads, television cones, and other deep parts
of circular symmetry is *spinning* (Fig. 22-5).   The metal blank is clamped
against a form block which is rotated at high speed.   The blank is pro-

gressively formed against the block, either with a manual tool or by means of small-diameter work rolls.

22-3. Shearing and Blanking

Shearing is the separation of metal by two blades moving as shown in Fig. 22-6a. In shearing, a narrow strip of metal is severely plastically deformed to the point where it fractures at the surfaces in contact with the blades. The fracture then propagates inward to provide complete separation. The depth to which the punch must penetrate to produce complete shearing is directly related to the ductility of the metal. The penetration is only a small fraction of the sheet thickness for brittle materials, while for very ductile materials it may be slightly greater than the thickness.

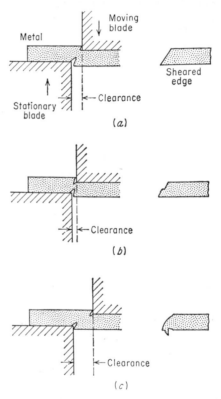

The clearance between the blades is an important variable in shearing operations. With the proper clearance the cracks that initiate at the edges of the blades will propagate through the metal and meet near the center of the thickness to provide a clean fracture surface (Fig. 22-6a). Note that even with proper clearance there is still distortion at a sheared edge. Insufficient clearance will produce a ragged fracture (Fig. 22-6b) and also will require more energy to shear the metal than when there is proper clearance. With excessive clearance there is greater distortion of the edge, and more energy is required because more metal must plastically deform before it fractures.

Fig. 22-6. Shearing of metal. (a) Proper clearance; (b) insufficient clearance; (c) excessive clearance.

Furthermore, with too large a clearance, burrs or sharp projections are likely to form on the sheared edge (Fig. 22-6c). A dull cutting edge also increases the tendency for the formation of burrs. The amount of plastic deformation that can be withstood in brittle metals without extensive edge cracking when the metal is sheared is small, and therefore the clearance should be small for hard and brittle metals. On the other hand, soft, ductile metals require extensive plastic deformation before fracture, and therefore the clearance must be larger.

Neglecting friction, the force required to shear a metal sheet is the product of the length of cut, the sheet thickness, and the shearing strength of the metal. The shearing force can be reduced appreciably by making the edges of the cutting tool at an inclined angle (Fig. 22-7), so that only a short part of the total length of cut is made at one time. The inclination of the cutting edge is called *shear*. The amount of shear should be equal to the metal thickness. Since shear on the tool produces some distortion of the sheet metal in contact with it, the shear should be applied to the tool which acts on the scrap. Therefore, in punching a hole the face of the punch should be inclined at an angle, but when blanks are cut from the sheet, the die should be given a shear angle and the punch should be flat.

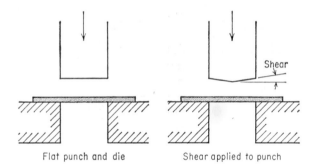

Flat punch and die   Shear applied to punch

Fig. 22-7. Illustration of use of shear in blanking.

A whole group of press operations are based on the process of shearing. The shearing of closed contours, when the metal inside the contour is the desired part, is called *blanking*. If the material inside the contour is discarded, then the operation is known as *punching*, or *piercing*. Punching indentations into the edge of the sheet is called *notching*. *Parting* is the simultaneous cutting along at least two lines which balance each other from the standpoint of side thrust on the parting tool. *Slitting* is a shearing cut which does not remove any metal from the sheet. *Trimming* is a secondary operation in which previously formed parts are finished to size, usually by shearing excess metal around the periphery. The removal of forging flash in a press is a trimming operation. When the sheared edges of a part are trimmed or squared up by removing a thin shaving of metal, the operation is called *shaving*. The interior of a punched hole can be squared up by *broaching* with a punch containing a series of shearing edges.

22-4. Bending

Bending is the process by which a straight length of metal is transformed into a curved length. The definitions of the terms used in bending are illustrated in Fig. 22-8. The bend radius R is defined as the radius of curvature on the concave, or inside, surface of the bend. The neutral axis is the circumferential fiber across the thickness at which the strain passes through zero. In plastic bending the neutral axis does not remain at the half thickness, as is the case for elastic bending. For a sharp bend the neutral axis is closer to the inside than the outside of the bend. To estimate the change in length produced by bending, the neutral axis is usually taken at a distance of 0.45 times the sheet thickness from the inside surface of the bend.

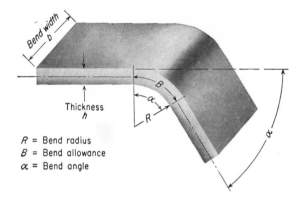

R = Bend radius
B = Bend allowance
α = Bend angle

Fig. 22-8. Definition of terms used in bending.

When metal is bent, its final length is increased over its original length in the blank because the metal thickness is decreased. As the bend radius becomes smaller, the decrease in thickness increases. The initial or developed length of the center line of the bent section is called the *bend allowance B*. The bend allowance is useful for determining the length of the blank required for making a bend. If it is assumed that the neutral axis has a radius of curvature equal to $R + 0.45h$, the bend allowance can be determined from the following equation,

$$B = (R + 0.45h)\frac{2\pi\alpha}{360} \tag{22-1}$$

where the bend angle α is expressed in degrees.

The principal directions in bending are shown in Fig. 22-9. The strain in the circumferential or longitudinal direction is the greatest principal strain, and most experimental data on bending are concerned with this strain. The elementary theory of the bending of rectangular beams considers only the circumferential strain, which is considered to vary only in the direction perpendicular to the surface of the sheet. However, experiment[1] shows that the distribution of strain in bending is considerably more complicated. The circum-

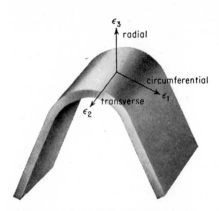

Fig. 22-9. Principal directions in bending.

ferential strain distribution depends significantly on the method of bending. Three-point bending in a die produces rather nonuniform distribution of strain. In bending by wiping or wrapping the metal against a form block, the bend angle increases progressively. However, since the distribution of circumferential strain in the circumferential direction becomes uniform only after the bend angle exceeds a minimum value of about 90°, the strain introduced by these bending methods is not uniform until appreciable deformation has been produced. The distribution of circumferential strain ϵ_1 across the width is quite uniform except at the edges, where it is about 20 per cent higher than at the center. This is explained by the fact that an initially rectangular cross section is distorted into a trapezoidal cross section with curled edges during bending. The distribution of the transverse strain ϵ_2 is usually rather nonuniform. Since the stress normal to a free surface is always zero, the edges of a bent specimen are subjected to uniaxial tension. Therefore, because of the Poisson effect a transverse compressive strain is set up. The transverse compressive strain decreases with distance in from the edge in the transverse direction. If the ratio of width to thickness is greater than 8, the transverse strain at the center of the width of the sheet is equal to 0. Because of this the transverse strain is important only for narrow pieces.

According to the theory of bending[2] the strain increases with decreasing radius of curvature. If the change in thickness is neglected, the neutral axis will remain at the center fiber and the circumferential stretch on the top surface, e_a, will be equal to the shrink on the bottom surface, e_b. The

[1] G. S. Sangdahl, E. L. Aul, and G. Sachs, *Proc. Soc. Exptl. Stress Anal.*, vol. 6, pp. 1–18, 1948.

[2] J. D. Lubahn and G. Sachs, *Trans. ASME*, vol. 72, pp. 201–208, 1950; B. W. Shaffer and E. E. Unger, *Trans. ASME*, ser. E, *J. Appl. Mech.*, vol. 27, pp. 34–40, 1960.

conventional strain at the outer and inner fibers is given by

$$e_a = -e_b = \frac{1}{2R/h + 1} \tag{22-2}$$

Experiments show that the circumferential strain on the tension surface is considerably greater than that given by Eq. (22-2) for large values of h/R, while the strain on the compression surface is not very different from the strain predicted by the simplified equation.

For a given bending operation the bend radius cannot be made smaller than a certain value, or the metal will crack on the outer tensile surface. The *minimum bend radius* is usually expressed in multiples of the sheet thickness. Thus, a $3T$ bend radius indicates that the metal can be bent without cracking through a radius equal to three times the sheet thickness. Therefore, the minimum bend radius is a forming limit. It varies considerably between different metals and always increases with cold working. Although some very ductile metals have a minimum bend radius of zero, indicating that they can be flattened upon themselves, it is general practice to use a bend radius of not less than $\frac{1}{32}$ in. in order to prevent damage to punches and dies. For high-strength sheet alloys the minimum bend radius may be $5T$ or higher. The minimum bend radius is not a precise material parameter because it depends, among other things, on the geometry of the bending conditions.

The minimum bend radius for a given thickness of sheet can be predicted[1] fairly accurately from the reduction of area measured in a tension test, q. If q is less than 0.2, then the shift in the neutral axis can be neglected and R_{min} is given simply by

$$\frac{R_{min}}{h} = \frac{1}{2q} - 1 \qquad \text{for } q < 0.2 \tag{22-3}$$

When q is greater than 0.2, the shift in the neutral axis must be taken into consideration and the minimum bend radius is given by

$$\frac{R_{min}}{h} = \frac{(1-q)^2}{2q - q^2} \qquad \text{for } q > 0.2 \tag{22-4}$$

The ductility of the outer fiber in bending is a function of the stress state acting on the surface. It is a well-established fact that the occurrence of a biaxial state of tension produces a decrease in the ductility of the metal. The biaxiality ratio σ_2/σ_1 of the transverse stress to the circumferential stress increases with increasing ratio of width to thickness, b/h. Figure 22-10 indicates that for low values of b/h the biaxiality is low because the stress state is practically pure tension, but as the width of the sheet increases relative to its thickness, the ratio σ_2/σ_1 increases

[1] J. Datsko and C. T. Yang, *Trans. ASME*, ser. B, vol. 82, pp. 309–314, 1960.

until at approximately $b/h = 8$ the biaxiality reaches a saturation value of approximately ½. Correspondingly, the strain to produce fracture in bending is a reverse function of the width-thickness ratio. In bending sheets with a high width-thickness ratio the cracks will occur near the

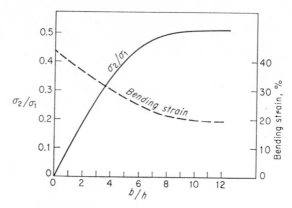

Fig. 22-10. Effect of ratio of width to thickness on biaxiality and bend ductility in bending. (*G. S. Sangdahl, E. L. Aul, and G. Sachs, Proc. Soc. Exptl. Stress Analy., vol. 6, no. 1, p. 1, 1948.*)

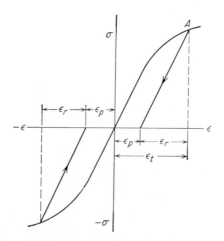

Fig. 22-11. Elastic recovery of a plastically loaded body.

center of the sheet when the ductility is exhausted. However, if the edges of the sheet are rough, edge cracking will occur. Frequently the minimum bend radius can be increased by polishing or grinding the edges of the sheet. In bending narrow sheets the failure will occur at the edges because the biaxiality is quite low at the center of the width.

In addition to cracking on the tensile surface of a bend another common forming difficulty is springback. *Springback* is the dimensional change of the formed part after the pressure of the forming tool has been released. It results from the changes in strain produced by elastic recovery (Fig. 22-11). When the load is released, the total strain ϵ_t is reduced to ϵ_p owing to the elastic recovery ϵ_r. The elastic recovery, and therefore the springback, will be greater the higher the yield stress and flow curve of the metal, the lower the elastic modulus, and the greater the plastic strain. For a given material and strain the springback increases with the ratio between the lateral dimensions of the sheet and its thickness.

Springback is encountered in all forming operations, but it is most easily recognized and studied in bending (Fig. 22-12). The radius of

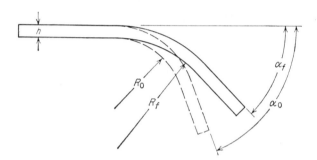

Fig. 22-12. Springback in bending.

curvature before release of load, R_0, is smaller than the radius after release of the load, R_f. Since the bend allowance is the same in both conditions, the radius of curvature and bend angle are related as follows:

$$B = \left(R_0 + \frac{h}{2}\right)\alpha_0 = \left(R_f + \frac{h}{2}\right)\alpha_f$$

This equation results in the *springback ratio K*.

$$K = \frac{\alpha_f}{\alpha_0} = \frac{R_0 + h/2}{R_f + h/2} \tag{22-5}$$

The springback ratio defined in this way is independent of sheet thickness and depends only on the ratio of bend radius to sheet thickness. Values are available[1] for aluminum alloys and austenitic stainless steels in a number of cold-rolled tempers. Other data,[2] which include a number of high-temperature alloys, indicate that to a first approximation the

---

[1] Sachs, *op. cit.*, p. 100.

[2] F. J. Gardiner, *Trans. ASME*, vol. 79, pp. 1–9, 1957.

springback in bending can be expressed by

$$\frac{R_0}{R_f} = 4\left(\frac{R_0\sigma}{Eh}\right)^3 - 3\frac{R_0\sigma}{Eh} + 1 \tag{22-6}$$

The commonest method of compensating for springback is to bend the part to a smaller radius of curvature than is desired so that when springback occurs the part has the proper radius. The trial-and-error procedure of finding the proper die contour to correct for springback can be shortened somewhat by the use of the above equation, but the calculation is by no means a precise procedure. Furthermore, the correction to the die is valid only over a rather narrow range of yield stress. Other methods of compensating for springback are to bottom the punch in the die so as to produce a coining action and the use of high-temperature forming so as to reduce the yield stress.

22-5. Stretch Forming

Stretch forming is the process of forming by the application of primarily tensile forces in such a way as to stretch the material over a tool or form block.[1] The process is an outgrowth of the stretcher leveling of rolled sheet. Stretch forming is used most extensively in the aircraft industry to produce parts of large radius of curvature, frequently with double curvature. An important consideration is that springback is largely eliminated in stretch forming because the stress gradient is relatively uniform. On the other hand, because tensile stresses predominate, large deformations can be obtained by this process only in materials with appreciable ductility.

Stretch-forming equipment consists basically of a hydraulically driven ram (usually vertical) which carries the punch or form block and two jaws for gripping the ends of the sheet (Fig. 22-13). No female die is used in stretch forming. The grips may be pivoted, so that the tension force is always in line with the edge of the unsupported sheet, or they can be fixed, in which case a large radius is needed to prevent tearing the sheet at the jaws. In using a stretch-forming machine the sheet-metal blank is first bent or draped around the form block with relatively light tensile pull, the grips are applied, and the stretching load is increased until the blank is strained plastically to final shape. This differs from wrap forming (Sec. 22-2) in that in the latter process the blank is first gripped and then while still straight is loaded to the elastic limit before wrapping around the form block.

For the stretch forming of simple shapes the forming limit is the uni-

---

[1] R. D. Edwards, *J. Inst. Metals*, vol. 84, pp. 199–209, 1956; Sachs, *op. cit.*, pp. 456–475.

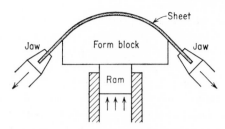

Fig. 22-13. Stretch-forming operation.

form elongation in tension.   Generally the elongations involved are much less than the uniform elongation.   The main type of failure is tearing of the sheet at the location of the maximum stretch.   In parts with large radius of curvature, failure usually occurs between the jaws and the form block, but in sharply curved parts the tearing occurs midway between the jaws.   Edge cracking will occur in sheet with sheared edges, and this will decrease appreciably the allowable stretch.   Another forming defect is the occurrence of wrinkles due to buckling of the sheet.   The tendency to form wrinkles increases with increasing width and decreasing thickness, increasing radius of curvature, and increasing strength of the metal.

22-6. Deep Drawing

Deep drawing is the metalworking process used for shaping flat sheets into cup-shaped articles such as bathtubs, shell cases, and automobile fenders.   This is done by placing a blank of appropriate size over a shaped die and pressing the metal into the die with a punch (Fig. 22-14).   Generally a clamping or hold-down pressure is required to press the blank

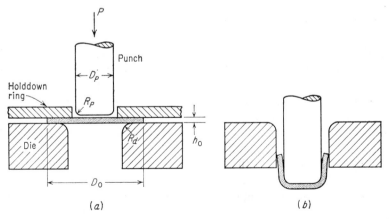

Fig. 22-14. Deep drawing of a cylindrical cup.   (a) Before drawing; (b) after drawing.

against the die to prevent wrinkling. This is best done by means of a *blank holder* or *hold-down ring* in a double-action press. Although the factors which control the deep-drawing process are quite evident, they interact in such a complex way that precise mathematical description of the process is not possible in simple terms. The greatest amount of experimental and analytical work has been done on the deep drawing of a cylindrical cup from a flat circular blank. The discussion of deep drawing which follows will be limited to this relatively simple situation.

In the deep drawing of a cup the metal is subjected to three different types of deformations. Figure 22-15 represents the deformation and stresses developed in a pie-shaped segment of the circular blank during

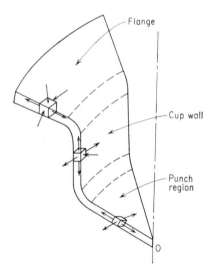

Fig. 22-15. Stresses and deformation in a section from a drawn cup.

deep drawing. The metal at the center of the blank under the head of the punch is wrapped around the profile of the punch, and in so doing it is thinned down. The metal in this region is subjected to biaxial tensile stress due to the action of the punch. Metal in the outer portion of the blank is drawn radially inward toward the throat of the die. As it is drawn in, the outer circumference must continuously decrease from that of the original blank, πD_0, to that of the finished cup, πD_p. This means that it is subjected to a compressive strain in the circumferential, or hoop, direction and a tensile strain in the radial direction. As a result of these two principal strains there is a continual increase in the thickness as the metal moves inward. However, as the metal passes over the die radius, it is first bent and then straightened while at the same time being subjected to a tensile stress. This plastic bending under tension results in considerable thinning, which modifies the thickening due to the circumferential shrinking. Between the inner stretched zone and the outer shrunk zone there is a narrow ring of metal which has not been bent over either the punch or the die. The metal in this region is subjected only to simple tensile loading throughout the drawing operation.

The resulting thickness changes depend on the total reduction from blank to cup and the punch and die radii. Generally, the greatest increase in thickness occurs at the outer edge of the cup, where only a circumferential compression acts. From the constancy-of-volume relationship it can be shown that the thickness at the outer edge after cupping, h, is related to the original thickness and blank diameter by the simple relationship $h = h_0(D_0/D)^{1/2}$. The greatest decrease in thickness occurs at the punch radius. Thinning may also occur at the bottom of

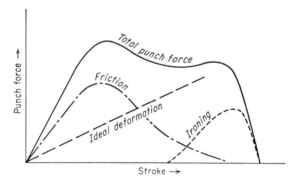

Fig. 22-16. Punch force vs. punch stroke for deep drawing.

the cup under the punch if the tensile stresses become high enough. This occurs for large reductions and small values of punch radius.

If the clearance between the punch and the die is less than the thickness produced by free thickening, the metal in these regions will be squeezed, or *ironed*, between the punch and the die to produce a uniform wall thickness. In commercial deep drawing clearances about 10 to 20 per cent greater than the metal thickness are common. Ironing operations in which appreciable uniform reductions are made in the wall thickness use much smaller clearances.

The force on the punch required to produce a cup is the summation of the ideal force of deformation, the frictional forces, and the force required to produce ironing (if present). Figure 22-16 illustrates the way in which these components of the total punch force vary with the length of stroke of the punch. The ideal force of deformation increases continuously with length of travel because the strain is increasing and the flow stress is increasing owing to strain hardening. A major contribution to the friction force comes from the hold-down pressure. This force component peaks early and decreases with increasing travel because the area of the blank under the hold-down ring is continually decreasing. Any force required to produce ironing occurs late in the process after the cup wall has reached maximum thickness. An additional factor is the force required to bend and unbend the metal around the radius of the die. One measurement[1] of the work required in cupping showed that 70 per cent of the work went into the radial drawing of the metal, 13 per cent into overcoming friction, and 17 per cent into the bending and unbending around the die radius.

From an analysis of the forces in equilibrium during the formation of a deep-drawn cup Sachs[2] has developed the following approximate equation for the total punch force as a function of the diameter of the blank, D_0, at any stage in the process,

$$P = \left[\pi D_p h (1.1\sigma_0) \ln \frac{D_0}{D_p} + f\left(2H \frac{D_p}{D_0} \right) \right] \exp\left(f\frac{\pi}{2} \right) + B \qquad (22\text{-}7)$$

where P = total punch load
  σ_0 = average flow stress
  D_p = punch diameter
  D_0 = blank diameter
  H = hold-down force
  B = force required to bend and restraighten blank
  h = wall-thickness
  f = coefficient of friction

In Eq. (22-7) the first term expresses the ideal force required to produce the cup, and the second term is the friction force under the blank holder. The exponential term considers the friction at the die radius, and the quantity B accounts for the force required to bend and unbend the sheet around this radius. A more complete and accurate analysis of the stresses and strains in the deep drawing of a cup has been presented by Chung and Swift.[3] Considerable computation is required for a solution according to this method, and it is too detailed for inclusion here.

The success of a deep-drawing operation depends primarily on whether or not the tensile stresses in the wall of the cup, parallel to its longitudinal

[1] H. W. Swift, *J. Inst. Metals*, vol. 82, p. 119, 1952.

[2] G. Sachs, "Spanlose Formung," pp. 11–38, Springer-Verlag OHG, Berlin, 1930; G. Sachs and K. R. Van Horn, "Practical Metallurgy," pp. 430–431, American Society for Metals, Metals Park, Ohio, 1940.

[3] S. Y. Chung and H. W. Swift, *Proc. Inst. Mech. Engrs.* (*London*), vol. 165, pp. 199–228, 1951; this theory has been reviewed in detail by J. M. Alexander, *Met. Reviews*, vol. 5, pp. 349–411, 1960.

axis, remain below the tensile strength of the metal in the cup wall. The maximum load which a cup can withstand is given approximately by the following equation,

$$P_{\max} = 1.1\sigma_u \pi D_m h \qquad (22\text{-}8)$$

where D_m = mean cup diameter

σ_u = tensile strength

For a successful drawing operation the punch load determined by Eq. (22-7) should not exceed the cup strength given by Eq. (22-8). A number of geometrical factors, which are considered below, have as much influence on the punch load and the cup strength as the strength of the metal and its cross-sectional area.

The *drawability* of a metal is related primarily to the ratio of the initial blank diameter to the punch diameter, D_0/D_p. Depending upon geometrical factors, this draw ratio will fall within the limits 1.6 to 2.3. The punch load increases approximately linearly with initial blank diameter. Other important factors which influence the drawability are the die radius and the punch radius. If the die radius is greater than about ten times the metal thickness, it has little effect on the punch load. There is no advantage in increasing the die radius much above this limit because the increased radius results in an appreciable unsupported area under the hold-down ring, and buckling may occur. For a die radius less than ten times the sheet thickness, the punch load and the drawability can be appreciably affected. As an example,[1] increasing the die radius from 0.05 to 0.20 in. decreases by 50 per cent the force required to draw a cup in 0.040-in.-thick brass. The punch radius does not affect the punch load, but it may determine whether or not a cup can be produced at all. The sharper the punch radius, the greater the thinning at this region and the greater the likelihood of the cup tearing. Therefore, a sharp punch radius results in severe plastic bending and a low cup strength. On the other hand, a very large punch radius may result in areas of unsupported metal which can wrinkle.

The clearance between the punch and the die determines the amount of ironing, and hence its effect on the punch load. In ordinary cupping operations ironing does not affect the maximum punch load because it occurs late in the process after the punch load has started to decrease.

Unless the blank is comparatively thick and the draw ratio small, it is necessary to use hold-down pressure to prevent the formation of radial wrinkles in the outer region of the blank. The wrinkles are produced by the buckling of the thin sheet under the action of the compressive circumferential stresses. It is important to prevent the formation of wrinkles, since once they have formed they are almost impossible to iron out.

[1] L. Hermann and G. Sachs, *Metallwirtschaft*, vol. 13, pp. 687, 705, 1934.

Sachs[1] suggests that the hold-down pressure should be between one-fiftieth and one two-hundredth the sum of the yield strength and tensile strength of the sheet metal.

Frictional forces occur between the blank and the hold-down ring, around the die radius, and between the punch and the die. An appreciable reduction in the punch load, and hence an increase in the drawability, can be obtained by applying lubricants to the die side of the blank. Lubricating the punch may actually reduce drawability[2] because it redistributes a large percentage of the drawing force to the center of the base of the cup, where the cross-sectional area is small.

22-7. Redrawing Operations

The reduction obtained in a single draw is given by

$$q = 1 - \frac{D_p}{D_0} \tag{22-9}$$

The average maximum reduction is about 50 per cent, and even under the most favorable conditions the obtainable reduction in a single draw does not exceed 60 per cent. Therefore, even under such conditions, it is impossible in a single drawing operation to produce a cup that is much higher than its diameter. To make tall, slender cups, such as cartridge cases and closed-end tubes, it is necessary to use successive drawing operations. Reducing a cup or drawn part to a smaller diameter and increased height is known as *redrawing*.

The two basic methods of redrawing are *direct*, or *regular*, redrawing and *reverse*, or *indirect*, redrawing (Fig. 22-17). In direct redrawing the

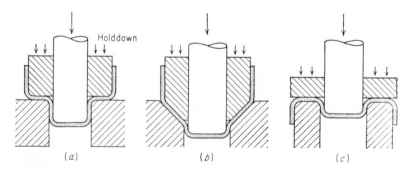

Fig. 22-17. Redrawing methods. (a) Direct redrawing; (b) direct redrawing with tapered die; (c) reverse redrawing.

[1] G. Sachs. "Principles and Methods of Sheet-metal Fabricating." pp. 191–194, Reinhold Publishing Corporation. New York. 1951.

[2] W. Johnson, *J. Inst. Metals*, vol. 84. p. 168. 1956.

original outside surface of the cup remains the outside surface of the redrawn cup. Figure 22-17a illustrates direct redrawing by means of a hold-down ring. Note that the metal must bend twice and that it is bent and unbent at the punch and die radii. The high strain hardening that is encountered in the process shown in Fig. 22-17a is reduced somewhat by the design shown in Fig. 22-17b. Although the metal still goes through the same number of bends, the angle through which it bends is less than 90° and the punch load is reduced. The disadvantage of the design shown in Fig. 22-17b is that the first-stage drawn cup must be made with a tapered corner. This type of drawn cup cannot be produced in all metals without buckling. The thickness of the hold-down ring used in direct redrawing is determined by the percentage reduction of the redraw. For small reductions a hold-down ring cannot be used.

In reverse redrawing (Fig. 22-17c) the cup is turned inside out so that the outside surface of the drawn cup becomes the inside surface of the redrawn shell. The bending is always in the same direction, rather than in opposite directions as for direct redrawing, and therefore there is less strain hardening of the walls of the shell. Better control of wrinkling can be obtained in reverse redrawing because of the snug control of the metal around the die radius and the fact that there are no geometrical limitations to the use of a hold-down ring. Although the forces required to overcome the bending resistance are lower for reverse redrawing, this does not necessarily mean that this method always requires a lower punch load than direct redrawing. With reverse redrawing there is obviously a minimum reduction determined by the thickness of the die needed to provide adequate strength. For reductions somewhat larger than the minimum the design limitations dictated by die strength favor direct redrawing because a more generous die radius can be used.

The reduction obtained by redrawing is always less than that obtainable on the initial draw because of the higher friction inherent in the redrawing process. Generally the reduction is decreased for each successive redrawing operation to allow for strain hardening. Greater reductions are, of course, possible if annealing is carried out between redraws. Most metals will permit a total reduction of 50 to 80 per cent before annealing.

22-8. Ironing and Sinking

Redrawing operations may also be classified into drawing with appreciable decrease in wall thickness, called *ironing*, and drawing with little change in wall thickness, called *sinking*. The ironing process is basically the same as tube drawing with a moving mandrel (Sec. 21-10). The predominant stress in ironing is the radial compressive stress developed by the pressure of the punch and the die.   Redrawing without reduction in wall thickness is basically the same as tube sinking or tube drawing without a mandrel (Sec. 21-8).   The predominant stresses are an axial tensile stress from the action of the punch and a circumferential compression from the drawing in of the metal.

Ironing is accomplished by restricting the clearance between the punch and the die so that the wall thickness is thinned out by a radial pressure.

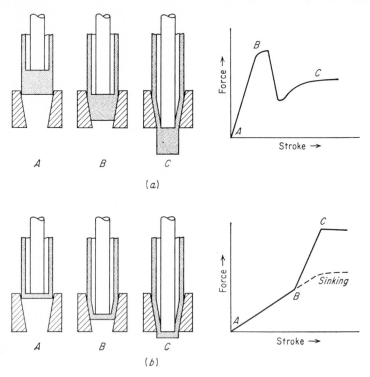

Fig. 22-18. Stages in ironing process.   (a) Thick-bottom cup; (b) thin-bottom cup.

If the cup has a thick bottom relative to its diameter, the first stage in the ironing process consists in a radial upsetting of the bottom (Fig. 22-18a).   Then, as the tube wall begins to draw in, it is first sunk onto the punch without any decrease in thickness and then the wall thickness is reduced by ironing.   Depending upon the geometry of the die,[1] the force-stroke diagram can have a number of different shapes.   The curve shown in Fig. 22-18a is typical of the case where the radial upsetting of the bottom of the cup determines the maximum force.

[1] G. Sachs, "Principles and Methods of Sheet-metal Fabricating," pp. 223–247, Reinhold Publishing Corporation, New York, 1951.

The simpler case of the ironing of a cup with a thin bottom is shown in Fig. 22-18b. The first step is the sinking of the cup onto the punch. When the punch comes in contact with the inside wall of the part, a rapid decrease in the wall thickness begins and the deformation force rises rapidly. As the part begins to emerge from the die, this force reaches its maximum value.

According to Sachs, the maximum force required to deform the bottom of the cup, P_B, is given by

$$P_B = (\pi D_f h_f)\sigma_0(\tan \alpha + f) \tag{22-10}$$

where D_f = final cup diameter
$\quad\ h_f$ = final thickness of bottom of cup
$\quad\ \alpha$ = half angle of die
The punch force P_s required for sinking a tube having a wall thickness h is given by

$$P_s = \pi(D_0 - h)h\sigma_0 \ln \frac{D_0}{D_f}\left(1 + \frac{f}{\tan \alpha}\right) \tag{22-11}$$

Finally, the punch force required for ironing is expressed by

$$P_i = 1.15\sigma_0 A_0 \ln \frac{A_0}{A_f}\left(1 + \frac{f}{\tan \alpha}\right) \tag{22-12}$$

where A_0 = cross-sectional area at entrance to die
$\quad\ A_f$ = corresponding value at die exit

22-9. Defects in Formed Parts

The ultimate defect in a formed sheet-metal part is the development of a crack which destroys its structural integrity. The usefulness of the part may also be destroyed by local necking or thinning or by buckling and wrinkling in regions of compressive stress. Another troublesome defect is the failure to maintain dimensional tolerances because of springback.

In the deep drawing of a cup the most common failure is the separation of the bottom from the rest of the cup at the location of greatest thinning near the punch radius. This defect may be minimized either by reducing the thinning by using a larger punch radius or by decreasing the punch load required for the drawing operation. If radial cracks occur in the flange or the edge of the cup, this indicates that the metal does not have sufficient ductility to withstand the large amount of circumferential shrinking that is required in this region of the blank. This type of failure is more likely to occur in redrawing without annealing than on the initial draw.

Wrinkling of the flange or the edges of the cup results from buckling of the sheet as a result of the high circumferential compressive stresses. In analyzing this type of failure each element in the sheet can be considered as a column loaded in compression. If the blank diameter is too large, the punch load will rise to high values, which may exceed the critical buckling load of the column. Since column stability decreases with an increasing slenderness ratio, the critical buckling load will be achieved at lower loads for thin sheet. To prevent this defect, it is necessary to use sufficient hold-down pressure to suppress the buckling.

Since sheet-metal formed parts usually present a large surface area, they are particularly susceptible to surface blemishes which detract from

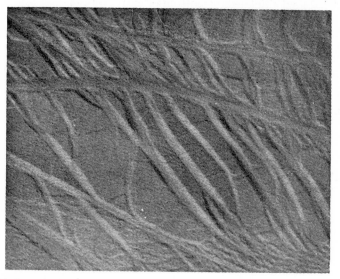

Fig. 22-19. Stretcher strains in low-carbon steel sheet. (*Courtesy E. R. Morgan and Metal Progress, June,* 1958, *p.* 89.)

the appearance of the part. Pronounced surface roughness in regions of the part which have undergone appreciable deformation is usually called *orange peeling.* The orange-peel effect occurs in sheet metal of relatively large grain size. It results from the fact that the individual grains tend to deform independently of each other, and therefore the grains stand out in relief on the surface. This condition is best corrected by using finer-grain-size sheet metal so that the grains deform more nearly as a whole and the individual grains are difficult to distinguish with the eye.

Another serious surface defect that is commonly found in low-carbon sheet steel is the presence of *stretcher strains,* or "worms." This defect shows up as a flamelike pattern of depressions in the surface (Fig. 22-19).

The depressions first appear along planes of maximum shear stress, and then, as deformation continues, they spread and join together to produce a uniform rough surface. The existence of stretcher strains is directly associated with the presence of a yield point in the stress-strain curve and the nonuniform deformation which results from the yield-point elongation (Fig. 22-20). The metal in the stretcher strains has been strained an amount equal to B in Fig. 22-20, while the remaining metal has received essentially zero strain. The elongation of the part is given by some intermediate strain A. As the deformation continues and the number of stretcher strains increase, the strain will increase until when the entire part is covered it has a strain equal to B. Beyond this strain the deformation is uniform and homogeneous. The main difficulty with stretcher strains, therefore, occurs in regions of the part where the strain

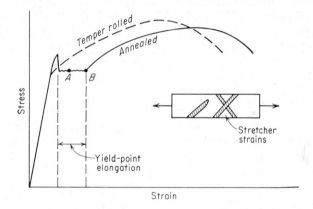

Fig. 22-20. Relation of stretcher strains to stress-strain curve.

is less than the yield-point elongation. The usual solution to this problem is to give the sheet steel a small cold reduction, usually ½ to 2 per cent reduction in thickness. Such a temper-rolling or skin-rolling treatment cold-works the metal sufficiently to eliminate the yield point. However, if the steel strain-ages during storage, the yield point will return and difficulties with stretcher strains will reappear.

The directionality in mechanical properties produced by rolling and other primary working processes can have an important effect on the fabricability of the metal. Mechanical fibering has little effect on formability, whereas crystallographic fibering or preferred orientation may have a large effect. Ordinarily, bending is more difficult when the bend line is parallel to the rolling direction than when the bend is made perpendicular to the rolling direction. In the deep drawing of cups, directionality shows up in the phenomenon of *earing*. Earing is the formation of a wavy edge on the top of the cup. Usually two, four, or six ears will be formed, depending on the preferred orientation of the sheet.[1] Allowance for trimming the ears from the cup must be made in determining the size of the blank. The height of the ears varies directly with the degree of preferred orientation in the sheet. This, in turn, is strongly dependent on the deformation characteristics of the metal and the cold-work–anneal cycle to which it has been subjected.

The directionality just discussed occurs in the plane of the sheet. However, even when there is no directionality in the plane of the sheet, so that earing does not occur, there is likely to be a difference between the properties measured in the direction normal to the sheet and in the plane of the sheet. Measurements of properties in the thickness direction are difficult to make, although it is possible to measure the strain in the width and thickness directions. There are indications (see Sec. 22-10) that the ratio of the width and thickness strains, called the *strain ratio*, has a constant value at any strain level. A material with a strain ratio equal to unity is completely isotropic, while a material with a strain ratio greater than unity is more resistant to thinning during plastic forming.

22-10. Tests for Formability

Because of the variety of shapes and stress distributions which are possible in the forming of metals, it is not surprising that formability cannot be predicted on the basis of simple mechanical properties, such as elongation or tensile strength, or that there are no simple evaluation tests which are applicable to all forming operations. It can be stated in very general terms that a high uniform elongation, so as to forestall local plastic instability, and a low yield stress and high tensile strength, so as to make flow easy but fracture difficult, are the combination of mechanical properties most conducive to good formability. The greater the spread between the yield strength and the tensile strength, the greater the strain-hardening capacity of the material. It is generally considered that a high capacity for strain hardening is conducive to good fabricability since the metal in critically stressed regions can strain-harden and pass along the deformation to the adjoining metal. Any retardation in the localization of deformation reduces failures by permitting a larger area of metal to contribute to the deformation process. The capability for strain hardening is described most precisely by the strain-hardening coefficient n determined from a true stress-strain curve.

The plastic-strain ratio, described in the previous section, has been found to be a sensitive parameter for rating the press performance of sheet materials. In cupping tests, which are a pure deep-drawing oper-

[1] A. J. McEvily, Jr., *NACA Tech. Note* 3439, May, 1955.

ation, a direct correlation has been found between a high value of strain ratio and drawability.[1] Excellent correlation has also been obtained between the formability of automobile fenders and the product of the strain ratio and the strain-hardening coefficient.[2] The reason for a different correlation parameter for this latter case is probably that considerable stretching as well as drawing is required in the forming of a fender. The greater the amount of stretching required in a forming operation, the more important the strain-hardening capacity of the material.

For more reliable prediction of formability, short of actual production forming, it is necessary to perform laboratory tests[3] which duplicate as closely as possible the strains found in the forming operation. One of the simplest tests is the determination of the minimum bend radius. The value of minimum bend radius depends somewhat on the dimensions of the bend specimen and the method of bending. Unfortunately, these testing details have never been sufficiently standardized to permit really useful comparison of bend-test data.

The Olsen and Erichsen *cupping tests* have been used for many years for evaluating the deep-drawing characteristics of sheet materials. In these tests the sheet is clamped between two ring dies while a punch, usually a ball, is forced against the sheet until fracture occurs. The height of the dome that is produced before fracture of the sheet is taken as the measure of drawability. Although the tests will generally differentiate between poor and good material, there are often major differences in the press performance of materials which are not detected. However, the tests are still widely used because of their simplicity and speed of operation.

A standardized drawability test, known as the Swift cup-forming test, has been developed in England.[4] Cylindrical cups 32 or 50 mm in diameter are deep-drawn under standard conditions with standardized tooling. The drawability is expressed in terms of the *limiting draw ratio*, which is the ratio of the largest blank diameter that can be drawn without failure to the punch diameter.

A *hydraulic bulge test*, in which a sheet-metal blank is clamped over a circular or oval die and bulged into a dome by the application of hydraulic pressure, has been used for evaluating drawability. This test is a good method of producing biaxial states of stress. The strain distribution produced in the blank during this test is more like that encountered in the stretch forming of a shallow, recessed part than the strain distribution

[1] R. L. Whiteley, *Trans. ASM*, vol. 52, pp. 154–169, 1960.
[2] W. T. Lankford, S. C. Snyder, and J. A. Bauscher, *Trans. ASM*, vol. 42, pp. 1192–1235, 1950.
[3] Sachs, "Principles and Methods of Sheet-metal Fabricating," pp. 26–39.
[4] O. H. Kemmis, *Sheet Metal Inds.*, vol. 34, pp. 203, 251, 1957.

produced in deep drawing. The bulge test has been shown[1] to correlate with press performance under conditions where the Olsen cupping test and Rockwell hardness gave poor correlation with performance.

BIBLIOGRAPHY

Alexander, J. M.: An Appraisal of the Theory of Deep Drawing, *Met. Reviews*, vol. 5, pp. 349–411, 1960.

Crane, E. V.: "Plastic Working of Metals and Non-metallic Materials in Presses," 3d ed., John Wiley & Sons, Inc., New York, 1944.

Eary, D. F., and E. A. Reed: "Techniques of Pressworking Sheet Metal," Prentice-Hall, Inc., Englewood Cliffs, N.J., 1958.

Hinman, C. W.: "Die Engineering Layouts and Formulas," McGraw-Hill Book Company, Inc., New York, 1943.

Jevons, J. D.: "The Metallurgy of Deep Drawing and Pressing," 2d ed., Chapman & Hall, Ltd., London, 1941.

Krivobok, V. N., and G. Sachs: "Forming of Austenitic Chromium-Nickel Steels," International Nickel Co., Inc., New York, 1948.

Sachs, G.: "Principles and Methods of Sheet-metal Fabricating," Reinhold Publishing Corporation, New York, 1951.

Willis, J.: "Deep Drawing," Butterworth & Co. (Publishers) Ltd., London, 1954.

Yoshida, K.: Classification and Systematizing of Sheet Metal Press Forming Process, *Inst. Phys. Chem. Research (Tokyo) Sci. Papers*, vol. 53, pp. 125–187, 1959. (In English.)

[1] W. N. Lambert, E. S. Madrzyk, and F. E. Gibson, *J. Metals*, November, 1960 pp. 857–860.

APPENDIX

CONSTANTS AND CONVERSION FACTORS

1 angstrom unit, $A = 10^{-8}$ cm

1 micron, $\mu = 10^{-3}$ mm $= 10^4$ A

1 centimeter $= 0.39370$ in.

1 inch $= 2.5400$ cm

1 foot $= 30.480$ cm

1 radian $= 57.29°$

1 pound $= 453.59$ g

1 kilogram $= 2.204$ lb

1 dyne $= 2.24 \times 10^{-6}$ lb

1 erg $= 1$ dyne-cm $= 10^{-7}$ joule

1 foot-pound $= 1.3549$ joules

1 calorie $= 4.182$ joules

1 kilocalorie $= 10^3$ cal

1 electron volt, ev $= 1.602 \times 10^{-12}$ erg

Avogadro's number $n = 6.02 \times 10^{23}$ molecules per mole

Universal gas constant $R = 1.987$ cal/(deg)(mole) $= 8.34 \times 10^7$ ergs/(deg)(mole)

Boltzmann's constant $k = 1.380 \times 10^{-16}$ erg/(deg)(mole)

Planck's constant $h = 6.6234 \times 10^{-27}$ erg-sec

1 atmosphere $= 14.697$ psi

1 pound per square inch $= 7.04 \times 10^{-4}$ kg/mm² $= 6.93 \times 10^4$ dyne/cm²

1 square inch $= 6.4516$ cm²

1 square foot $= 929.03$ cm²

1 cubic inch $= 16.387$ cm³

$\ln x = \log_e x = 2.3026 \log_{10} x$

The base of the natural system of logarithms $= 2.718$

PROBLEMS

Chapter 1

1-1. An annealed-steel tensile specimen ($E = 30 \times 10^6$ psi) has a 0.505-in. minimum diameter and a 2-in.-gage length. Maximum load is reached at 15,000 lb, and fracture occurs at 10,000 lb. (a) What is the tensile strength? (b) Why does fracture occur at a lower load than maximum load? (c) What is the deformation when a tensile stress of 15,000 psi is applied? (d) At what deformation will the 0.2 per cent offset yield strength be obtained?

1-2. A wire 100 ft long elongates by 1 in. when a tensile force of 1,000 lb is applied. What is the modulus of elasticity if its cross-sectional area is 0.05 in.²?

1-3. Show that the deformation of a bar subjected to an axial load P is $\delta = PL/AE$.

1-4. The deflection of a cantilever beam of length L subjected to a concentrated load P at one end is given by $\delta = PL^3/3EI$, where I is the moment of inertia. Compare the relative deflections of steel, titanium, and tungsten beams. See Table 2-1 for necessary data.

1-5. A hollow copper cylinder (OD = 10 in., and ID = 5 in.) contains a solid steel core. Determine the compressive stresses in the steel and the copper when a force of 200,000 lb is applied with a press.

1-6. Discuss the relative factor of safety to be applied to the following situations: (1) boxcar coupling; (2) pressure vessel for nuclear reactor; (3) missile nose cone; (4) flagpole; (5) automobile leaf spring. Consider each case in terms of the following factors: (a) material reliability; (b) type of loading; (c) reliability of stress analysis; (d) fabrication factors; (e) influence of time; (f) consequences of failure.

1-7. A cylinder of cast iron 0.50 in. in diameter by 2 in. long is tested in compression. Failure occurs at an axial load of 50,000 lb on a plane inclined 40° to the axis of the cylinder. Calculate the shearing stress on the plane of failure. The same cylinder of cast iron is pulled in tension. Give your estimate of the failure load and the plane of failure.

Chapter 2

2-1. Find the principal stresses and the orientation of the axes of principal stress with the x, y axes for the following situations:

(a) $\sigma_x = +50,000$ psi   (b) $\sigma_x = -60,000$ psi
      $\sigma_y = +5,000$ psi $\sigma_y = +5,000$ psi
      $\tau_{xy} = -8,000$ psi $\tau_{xy} = +25,000$ psi

2-2. Construct a Mohr's circle of stress for each of the plane-stress conditions given in Prob. 2-1.

2-3. The three-dimensional state of stress is given by

$$\sigma_x = +8{,}000 \text{ psi} \qquad \tau_{xy} = +2{,}000 \text{ psi}$$
$$\sigma_y = -4{,}000 \text{ psi} \qquad \tau_{yz} = +3{,}000 \text{ psi}$$
$$\sigma_z = +6{,}000 \text{ psi} \qquad \tau_{xz} = -5{,}000 \text{ psi}$$

Determine (a) the total stress (magnitude and direction with x, y, z axes) on plane described by direction cosines $l = +1/\sqrt{2}$, $m = +\frac{1}{2}$, n = negative; (b) magnitude of normal and shear stresses on this plane; (c) principal stresses and direction cosines of the principal planes; (d) maximum shear stress.

2-4. The three-dimensional state of strain is given by

$$e_x = 4 \times 10^{-4} \qquad \gamma_{xy} = 3 \times 10^{-4}$$
$$e_y = -6 \times 10^{-4} \qquad \gamma_{yz} = -3 \times 10^{-4}$$
$$e_z = 2 \times 10^{-4} \qquad \gamma_{xz} = -5 \times 10^{-4}$$

Determine (a) the direction cosines of the three principal axes; (b) the greatest axial strain; (c) the volume expansion per unit volume.

2-5. The following strain-gage readings are obtained from the delta rosette shown in Fig. 2-11b: $e_a = 1.4 \times 10^{-3}$; $e_b = 0.2 \times 10^{-3}$; $e_c = -0.6 \times 10^{-3}$. (a) Find the maximum and minimum principal strains and the angle that e_{max} makes with gage a. (b) Calculate the principal stresses from the strain readings, and compare with the results given by the equations in Table 2-2.

2-6. For the strain-gage arrangement shown in Fig. 2-12, $\alpha = 30°$, and $\beta = 40°$. If $e_a = 2.6 \times 10^{-3}$, $e_b = 0.4 \times 10^{-3}$, and $e_c = 1.4 \times 10^{-3}$, determine the principal strains by means of Mohr's circle.

2-7. On a plate of material ($E = 25 \times 10^6$ psi, $\nu = 0.25$) strain gages are arranged as shown. When the plate is loaded, the gages read $e_1 = 1{,}860 \times 10^{-6}$, $e_2 = 185 \times$

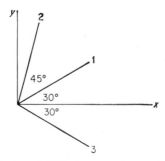

10^{-6}, and $e_3 = 1{,}330 \times 10^{-6}$. (a) What is the largest normal stress? (b) What is the smallest normal stress? (c) What is the largest shear stress?

2-8. For a thin-wall cylindrical pressure vessel of internal diameter D and wall thickness h show that the stress in the circumferential direction is related to the internal pressure p by the equation $\sigma_t = pD/2h$. If the ends of the vessel are welded shut, what is the average longitudinal stress in the walls? Determine the ratio of circumferential to longitudinal stress. Why would these equations not hold for a thick-wall pressure vessel?

2-9. Show that for an isotropic crystal $S_{44} = 2(S_{11} - S_{12})$.

2-10. Strain gages on the outer surface of a pressure vessel read $e_l = 0.002$ in the longitudinal direction and $e_t = 0.005$ in the circumferential direction. Compute the stresses in these two principal directions: $E = 30 \times 10^6$ and $\nu = 0.3$.   What is the error if the Poisson effect is not taken into consideration?

2-11. It is found experimentally that a certain material does not change in volume when subjected to an elastic state of stress.   What is Poisson's ratio for this material?

2-12. Determine the volume of a 6-in.-diameter solid copper sphere that is subjected to a fluid pressure of 20,000 psi.

2-13. Determine the ratio of the yield stress in torsion and tension if the amount of strain energy per unit volume that can be stored without producing permanent set is the same in both states of stress.

2-14. Show that the elastic strain energy per unit volume is the same under uniaxial loading as under hydrostatic tension if $\nu = \frac{1}{3}$.

Chapter 3

3-1. Plot a curve of conventional linear strain vs. true strain from zero to $e = 3.0$.

3-2. A 2-in.-diameter forging billet is decreased in height (upset) from 5 to 2 in. (a) Determine the average axial strain and the true strain in the direction of compression.   (b) What is the final diameter of the forging (neglect bulging)?   (c) What are the transverse plastic strains?

3-3. A 1-in.-thick plate is decreased in thickness according to the following schedule: 0.50, 0.25, 0.125 in.   Compute the total strain on the basis of initial and final dimensions and the summation of the incremental strains, using (a) conventional strain and (b) true strain.   How does this show an advantage for the use of true strain in metalforming work?

3-4. Show that constancy of volume results in $e_1 + e_2 + e_3 = 0$ and $\epsilon_1 + \epsilon_2 + \epsilon_3 = 0$. Why is the relationship for conventional strain valid only for small strains but the relationship for true strains is valid for all strains?

3-5. A steel shaft ($\sigma_0 = 100,000$ psi) is subjected to static loads consisting of a bending moment of 200,000 in.-lb and a torsional moment of 500,000 in.-lb.   Using a factor of safety of 2, determine the diameter of the shaft based on (a) maximumshear-stress theory and (b) distortion-energy theory.

3-6. Prove that the distortion-energy criterion for a generalized x, y, z system of axes is given by

$$2\sigma_0{}^2 = (\sigma_x - \sigma_y)^2 + (\sigma_y - \sigma_z)^2 + (\sigma_z - \sigma_x)^2 + 6(\tau_{xy}^2 + \tau_{yz}^2 + \tau_{xz}^2)$$

3-7. Show that Poisson's ratio equals $\frac{1}{2}$ for a perfectly plastic body.

3-8. If the yield strength of the steel used in the vessel in Prob. 2-8 is 30,000 psi, D is 12 in., and h is $\frac{1}{4}$ in., what will be the value of internal pressure at which the tank will yield?

3-9. Draw a flow curve for simple tension similar to Fig. 3-6.   On the same figure superimpose the flow curve that you would get if you measured σ_1 and ϵ_1 as the material was being drawn through a die where the state of stress is $\sigma_1 = \sigma_L$; $\sigma_2 = \sigma_3 = \sigma_T$; $\sigma_L > \sigma_T$.

3-10. On the assumption that there is no change in width during the rolling of a sheet derive the expression for the significant strain in terms of the change in thickness of the sheet.   Also express in terms of percentage reduction.

3-11. A steel shaft transmits 400 hp at 200 rpm.   The maximum bending moment is 8,000 ft.-lb.   The factor of safety is 1.5.   Find the minimum diameter of solid shaft on the basis of (a) maximum-shear-stress theory and (b) distortion-energy theory.   ($\sigma_0 = 40,000$ psi, $E = 30 \times 10^6$, $\nu = 0.30$.)

3-12. A steel with a yield strength in tension of 42,000 psi is tested under a state of stress where $\sigma_2 = \sigma_1/2$, $\sigma_3 = 0$. What is the stress at which yielding will occur if it is assumed that (a) the maximum-normal-stress theory holds, (b) the maximum-shear-stress theory holds, and (c) the distortion-energy theory holds?

3-13. A material is tested under the state of stress $\sigma_1 = 3\sigma_2 = -2\sigma_3$. Yielding is observed at $\sigma_2 = 20,000$ psi. (a) What is the yield stress in simple tension? (b) If the material is used under conditions such that $\sigma_1 = -\sigma_3$, $\sigma_2 = 0$, at what value of σ_3 will yielding occur? (Assume distortion-energy criterion of yielding.)

Chapter 4

4-1. (a) Interstitials in the fcc lattice occupy the tetrahedral positions $(\frac{1}{4},\frac{1}{4},\frac{1}{4})$ and the octahedral positions $(\frac{1}{2},\frac{1}{2},\frac{1}{2})$. Indicate these interstitial positions on a sketch of the structure cell. (b) In the bcc lattice interstitials occupy sites at $(\frac{1}{2},\frac{1}{4},0)$ and smaller sites at $(\frac{1}{2},\frac{1}{2},0)$ and $(\frac{1}{2},0,0)$. Show these sites on a sketch. Compare the number of available interstitial sites in the fcc and bcc lattices.

4-2. For what geometrical conditions can a single crystal be deformed but not show slip lines on its surface?

4-3. Prove that the c/a ratio for an ideal hcp structure is $\sqrt{8/3}$.

4-4. How many atoms per square millimeter are there on a (100) face of a copper crystal? ($a_0 = 3.60$ A.)

4-5. How many atoms per square millimeter are there on a (111) face of a copper crystal?

4-6. Verify the values for the distance between planes for fcc and bcc lattices given in Table 4-2.

4-7. (a) Show by means of a model or sketch that the intersection of $\{111\}$ in an fcc structure cell produces an octahedron. (b) How many favorable slip systems are there for tensile straining along a [001] axis? (c) How many for deformation along [111]?

4-8. The following data for zinc single crystals were obtained by Jillson:[1]

$90 - \phi$	λ	P, g
6.5	18	20,730
19.5	29	7,870
30	30.5	5,280
40	40	4,600
61	62.5	5,600
85	85.5	28,500

$$A = 122 \text{ mm}^2$$

(a) Establish that Schmid's law is obeyed. (b) Demonstrate the orientation dependence of the yield stress by plotting σ_0 versus $\cos \phi \cos \lambda$.

Chapter 5

5-1. Calculate the number of grains in the top surface of the head of a pin (0.1 in. diameter) if the pin is made from steel with ASTM grain size 6.

5-2. What is the grain-boundary area in 1 in.^{3} of steel with ASTM grain size 6? Assume that the grains have a cubic shape.

[1] D. C. Jillson, *Trans. AIME*, vol. 188, p. 1129, 1950.

5-3. If the grain boundaries of an iron sample (ASTM grain size 6) are completely covered with a monatomic layer of oxygen, how much oxygen, in ppm, is present? (Radius of the oxygen atom is 0.6 A.)

5-4. For a steel with ASTM grain size 3, what reduction in grain size would double the yield stress? Express as both average grain diameter and ASTM number.

5-5. For a unit cube containing a dispersed second phase of uniform spherical particles of radius r, the number of particles per unit volume, N_v, is related to the volume fraction of particles, f, by $N_v = f/\frac{4}{3}\pi r^3$. The average distance between particles is given by $\Lambda = 1/(N_v)^{1/3} - 2r$. (a) Show that $\Lambda = 2r[(1/1.91f)^{1/3} - 1]$. (b) For $f = 0.001, 0.01, 0.1$ and $r = 10^{-6}, 10^{-5}, 10^{-4}$, and 10^{-3} cm calculate Λ. Plot f versus Λ on log-log paper.

5-6. Calculate the modulus of elasticity for a two-phase alloy composed of 50 volume per cent cobalt, and 50 volume per cent tungsten carbide on the basis of (a) equality-of-strain and (b) equality-of-stress hypotheses. $E_{Co} = 30 \times 10^6$ psi; $E_{WC} = 100 \times 10^6$ psi. Compare the calculated values with the measured modulus of 54×10^6 psi.

5-7. From the theory of elasticity, the radial and tangential stresses due to thermal stress developed in a spherical inclusion in an infinite plate are given by[1]

$$\sigma_R = \sigma_T = \frac{2E_1 E_2 (\alpha_2 - \alpha_1) \Delta T}{(1 + \nu_2)E_1 + 2(1 - 2\nu_1)E_2}$$

where subscript 1 refers to the inclusion and subscript 2 refers to the matrix. α is the coefficient of thermal expansion. Apply this equation to the situation of WC particles in a Co matrix, and plot the variation of stress on the particle with volume per cent cobalt. Use a temperature range of 800°C. $E_{Co} = 30 \times 10^6$ psi; $E_{WC} = 100 \times 10^6$ psi; $\alpha_{Co} = 12.3 \times 10^{-6}$ in./in.; $\alpha_{WC} = 5.4 \times 10^{-6}$ in./in.; $\nu_{Co} = 0.3$; $\nu_{WC} = 0.22$.

5-8. The energy of a low-angle boundary is given by $E = E_0\theta(A - \ln \theta)$, where E is the energy per unit boundary area, E_0 is the elastic strain energy of a dislocation, θ is the angle of misfit, and A is a constant. (a) Plot E/θ versus $\ln \theta$. (b) Plot E versus θ.

5-9. The dislocation density ρ is the total length of dislocation line in the crystal volume. The units are number per square centimeter. Show that the relationship between ρ and the radius of curvature of a bent crystal, R, is given by $\rho = 1/Rb$. (HINT: Use Fig. 5-5.)

Chapter 6

6-1. (a) Prove that the dislocation reaction $(a/2)[10\bar{1}] \rightarrow (a/6)[2\bar{1}\bar{1}] + (a/6)[11\bar{2}]$ is vectorially correct. (b) Show that this reaction results in a decrease in strain energy.

6-2. Construct a two-dimensional drawing of the (110) plane of a bcc lattice. By means of vector addition show that $(a/2)[\bar{1}11] + (a/2)[111] \rightarrow a[001]$ and that $(a/2)[\bar{1}11] + (a/2)[\bar{1}\bar{1}1] \rightarrow a[\bar{1}\bar{1}0]$. Show that the last reaction is not energetically favorable.

6-3. Define the following: (a) perfect dislocation; (b) glissile dislocation; (c) cross slip; (d) Frank partial dislocation; (e) Shockley partial dislocation; (f) extended dislocation.

6-4. Using Fig. 6-9, show that the y components in Cottrell's equation $(a/2)[\bar{1}11] + (a/2)[111] \rightarrow a[001]$ cancel each other with a release of elastic energy. Show that this equals the energy gained by the x components of the reaction.

[1] J. Gurland, *Trans. ASM*, vol. 50, pp. 1063–1070, 1958.

6-5. Express Eq. (6-4) in terms of the polar coordinates r and θ. By letting $\theta = 0$ show that the shear stress on the slip plane in the direction of the Burgers vector is equal to $\tau = \tau_0 b/r$.

6-6. Plot the shear stress vs. distance (in atomic distances a_0) from a straight edge dislocation in a copper crystal. Let $G = 5 \times 10^{11}$ dynes/cm^2, $b = 2.5 \times 10^{-8}$ cm, and $\nu = \frac{1}{3}$. Show that the stress falls to about 10^7 dynes/cm^2 at a distance of 1 μ.

6-7. Using Eqs. (6-1) and (6-2) map out the stress distribution around an edge dislocation lying along the z axis. Start $2a_0$ from the dislocation line.

6-8. The yield stress of most single crystals is $10^{-4}G$ or less. By using the concept of the Frank-Read source, develop an argument in which the yield stress is determined by the spacing of sources initially present in the crystal. Show that this leads to a reasonable estimate for the dislocation density. Give some alternative explanations for the yield stress.

6-9. (a) Estimate the strain energy of an edge dislocation where $r = 1$ cm, $r_0 = 10^{-7}$ cm, $G = 5 \times 10^{11}$ dynes/cm^2, $b = 2.5 \times 10^{-8}$ cm, and $\nu = \frac{1}{3}$. Express the result in electron volts per atomic plane. How much energy (electron volts) is required to produce 1 cm of dislocation line? (b) Show that more than one-half the strain energy resides outside the core of the dislocation in the region $r = 10^{-4}$ to $r = 1$ cm.

6-10. (a) Show that the shear stress produced on a slip plane by an edge dislocation on a parallel plane at coordinates r, θ is given by

$$\tau_{xy} = \frac{Gb}{8\pi(1 - \nu)} \frac{1}{h} \sin 4\theta$$

where h is the perpendicular distance between two parallel planes.

(b) What is the shear stress required for two edge dislocations to pass on parallel slip planes that are 1,000 A apart in an annealed copper crystal? (Use the data in Prob. 6-9.)

6-11. Derive an expression for the stress-strain curve, using G. I. Taylor's assumption that the dislocations are arranged in the crystal in alternate rows of positive and negative edge dislocations. Explain why this concept is no longer valid.

6-12. If the interaction energy between an impurity atom and a dislocation can be approximated by $U_i = A/b$ when the atmosphere is saturated, calculate the interaction energy and the temperature below which the strongest binding occurs for the case of iron containing 0.01 weight per cent carbon. Let $A = 1.8 \times 10^{-20}$ dyne cm^2 and $b = 2.5 \times 10^{-8}$ cm. Also, calculate the breakaway stress, and compare with the average yield stress of 20 kg/mm^2 at room temperature.

Chapter 7

7-1. Estimate the theoretical fracture stress of iron if $\gamma = 1,200$ ergs/cm^2. How does this compare with the highest observed strength of heat-treated steel?

7-2. Using Griffith's equation for plane stress, determine the critical crack length for (a) iron, (b) zinc, and (c) NaCl if the following constants apply:

	σ_c, dynes/cm^2	γ, ergs/cm^2	E, dynes/cm^2
Iron..........	9×10^9	1,200	20.5×10^{11}
Zinc..........	2×10^7	800	3.5×10^{11}
NaCl.........	2×10^7	150	5.0×10^{11}

7-3. What is the critical crack length in iron according to the Griffith-Orowan equation if $p \approx 10^6$ ergs/cm^2?

7-4. Show that the Cottrell mechanism for the creation of a microcrack by slip on intersecting planes is not energetically favorable in an fcc lattice.

7-5. A ship steel has a value of $\mathcal{G}_c = 200$ lb/in. (a) What is the fracture stress in a thin plate that is 12 in. wide and that contains a central crack 0.5 in. long? (b) If the crack is 2 in. long, what is the fracture stress? (c) Increasing the plate thickness to 5 in. reduces $\mathcal{G}_c$ to 100 lb/in. What is the fracture stress for a 0.5-in.-long crack?

7-6. A steel plate is 12 in. wide and $\frac{1}{4}$ in. thick. There is a 1-in.-long crack along each edge. (a) Calculate the force required to propagate the crack the remaining 10 in. across the width of the plate. (b) Calculate the force required to break the plate in tension if there were no crack. Assume that the fracture strength is 100,000 psi. (c) Calculate the force required to break the plate in tension if the steel had the theoretical cohesive strength.

7-7. Using Eqs. (7-28) and (7-29), discuss how they qualitatively predict the effect of the following factors on the ductile-to-brittle transition: (a) material composition; (b) impurities; (c) melting practice; (d) temperature; (e) grain size; (f) state of stress; (g) rate of loading.

7-8. Analyze the data[1] below for the ductile-to-brittle transition of columbium in tension in terms of the Cottrell theory of the transition temperature. Estimate the effective surface energy. Why is it quite a bit larger than the true surface energy of about 3×10^3 ergs/cm^2?

Test temp, °K	Strain rate, sec^{-1}	τ_i, psi	k_y, cgs $\times 10^6$	Grain diam, cm	Type of fracture
77	6.18×10^{-2}	56,500	7.25	0.1414	Brittle
20	2.02×10^{-4}	58,000	5.87	0.1414	Brittle
77	2.02×10^{-4}	48,000	5.18	0.1414	Ductile
77	6.18×10^{-2}	56,500	7.25	0.0312	Ductile
20	2.02×10^{-4}	58,000	5.87	0.0312	Ductile

7-9. If at a low temperature it takes about 1 sec for yielding to occur, how long would it take to produce yielding at the same value of applied stress if the temperature were raised 100°K? What significance does this have in the theory of brittle fracture?

Chapter 8

8-1. The internal-friction peak due to carbon in iron occurs at 35°C for $f = 0.65$ cps. If $D_0 = 2 \times 10^{-2}$ cm^2/sec and $\Delta H = 20.1$ kcal/mole, what is the relaxation time at 0, 100, and 500°C?

8-2. Explain how you would determine the solubility of carbon in alpha iron by internal friction.

8-3. How can internal friction be used to study strain aging?

8-4. A steel beam 15 in. long, 1.5 in. wide, and 0.25 in. thick is loaded as a cantilever beam. The following amplitude readings were observed at a point 12 in. from the loaded end of the beam for the cases of no end load and when the beam is damped

[1] M. A. Adams, A. C. Roberts, and R. E. Smallman, *Acta Met.*, vol. 8, pp. 328–337, 1960.

with a 3-lb weight at the free end:

No load		Damped with 3-lb load	
Cycles	Amplitude, μ in.	Cycles	Amplitude, μ in.
0	563	0	464
10	420	4	390
20	300	8	360
30	240	12	328
40	185	16	270
50	160	20	243
60	135	24	205
70	115	28	165
80	100	32	125
90	85	36	97
100	78	40	63
120	60	44	33

(a) Plot ln A versus cycles.   (b) Plot the logarithmic decrement vs. amplitude.

Chapter 9

9-1. The following data were obtained during the tension test of a low-carbon steel with a specimen having a 0.505-in. diameter and a 2-in. gage length.

Load, lb	Elongation, in.	Load, lb	Elongation, in.
500	0.00016	6,300	0.020
1,000	0.00032	7,000	0.060
1,500	0.00052	7,500	0.080
2,000	0.00072	8,500	0.12
2,500	0.00089	9,600	0.18
3,000	0.00105	10,000	0.26
3,500	0.00122	10,100	0.30
4,000	0.00138	10,200	0.50
4,500	0.00154	10,050	0.58
5,000	0.00175	9,650	0.62
5,500	0.00191	9,100	0.70
6,000	0.00204	8,100	0.76

Yield point, 6,200 lb; breaking load, 6,800 lb; final gage length, 2.87 in.; final diameter, 0.266 in.

(a) Plot the engineering stress-strain curve.   (b) Determine the (1) proportional limit; (2) modulus of elasticity; (3) lower yield point; (4) tensile strength; (5) fracture stress; (6) percentage elongation; (7) reduction of area.   (c) Plot the true stress-strain curve up to maximum load.

9-2. Derive the relationship for the toughness of a metal whose true stress-strain curve obeys the power law $\sigma = K\epsilon^n$.

9-3. (a) Show that $q = 1 - \exp(-\epsilon_f)$, where q is the reduction of area and ϵ_f is the true strain at fracture.   (b) If the true stress-strain curve is given by $\sigma = K\epsilon^n$, derive a relationship between the yield stress and the reduction in cross-sectional area.

9-4. A useful measure of ductility for evaluating formability is the *zero-gage-length elongation* e_0. This represents the maximum possible elongation on the minimum possible gage length. Show that $e_0 = q/(1 - q)$. If q is measured at some point on the tensile specimen other than the neck, it gives a value of uniform reduction. Why?

9-5. The following data were obtained during the true stress-strain test of a nickel specimen:

Load, lb	Diameter, in.	Load, lb	Diameter, in.
0	0.252	3,570	0.210
3,440	0.250	3,500	0.200
3,580	0.245	3,350	0.190
3,670	0.240	3,150	0.180
3,710	0.235	2,950	0.170
3,720	0.230	2,800	0.149

(a) Plot the true stress-strain curve. (b) For the data beyond the maximum load correct for necking by means of Bridgman's correction (Fig. 9-7). (c) Determine the following: (1) true stress at maximum load; (2) true fracture stress; (3) true fracture strain; (4) true uniform strain; (5) true necking strain; (6) ultimate tensile strength; (7) strain-hardening coefficient.

9-6. The true stress-strain curve is sometimes expressed by $\sigma = \sigma_{0.2}(\epsilon/0.2)^n$, where $\sigma_{0.2}$ is the true stress at $\epsilon = 0.2$. Show how this equation is equivalent to $\sigma = K\epsilon^n$, and explain why the new relationship may be preferable.

9-7. For a material with a true-stress–true-strain curve of the form $\sigma = K\epsilon^n$, show that the ratio of the yield strength σ_0 to the tensile strength σ_u is a direct function of the strain-hardening exponent n.

9-8. The variation of percentage elongation X with gage length has been found empirically to follow the relationship $X = c\sqrt{A}/L_0 + b$, where c and b are constants. The following data were obtained for a steel plate that is 2 in. wide and $\frac{1}{2}$ in. thick:

L_0, in........	2	4	6	10	12	14
X..........	40.0	30.6	27.5	25.7	25.0	24.3

Find b and c, and determine the percentage elongation for a 2- by $\frac{7}{8}$-in. steel plate with a 10-in. gage length.

9-9. The true stress-strain curve of a material can be expressed by the equation $\sigma = 200,000\epsilon^{0.33}$, where stress is in units of pounds per square inch. What is the ultimate tensile strength of this material?

Chapter 10

10-1. A 1-in.-diameter hot-rolled steel bar was tested in torsion, with the following results:

Torque, in.-lb	Number of $\frac{1}{4}$ turns of bar	Torque, in.-lb	Number of $\frac{1}{4}$ turns of bar
6,700	1	10,600	12
7,400	2	11,000	15
8,200	3	11,400	18
8,700	4	11,800	24
9,100	5	12,400	32
9,700	7	12,600	38
10,200	9	12,800	39

If the length of the bar between chucks is 18 in., determine (a) shear-stress–shear-strain curve; (b) modulus of rupture; (c) shear-stress–shear-strain curve corrected for inelastic strain. (d) If the twisting moment at the yield point was 4,500 in.-lb and the angle of twist was 2.6°, determine the torsional yield stress, the modulus of elasticity, and the modulus of resilience. (e) What is Poisson's ratio if $E = 29.0 \times 10^6$ psi?

10-2. Compare the torsional strength, stiffness, and weight of two steel shafts, one solid, the other hollow. The hollow shaft has twice the diameter of the solid shaft, but the cross-sectional area is the same.

10-3. Assume that a certain brittle material will fail at a tensile stress of 30,000 psi. (a) For a bar with a ¼-in. diameter, what torsional moment will cause failure? Sketch the failure. (b) If this is an ideal brittle material ($\nu = \frac{1}{4}$), show that greater strain will be achieved in torsion than tension before failure occurs.

10-4. The following data were obtained for the same low-carbon steel when tested in tension and in torsion:

Tension		Torsion	
True normal stress, psi	True strain, in./in.	Shear stress, psi	Shear strain, in./in.
55,000	0.05	24,000	0.05
63,000	0.10	30,000	0.10
73,000	0.20	36,000	0.20
80,000	0.30	39,000	0.30
85,000	0.40	41,000	0.40
90,000	0.50	42,000	0.50
95,000	0.60	44,000	0.60
100,000	0.70	45,000	0.70
105,000	0.80	45,500	0.80
116,000	1.00	47,000	1.00
126,000	1.20	48,500	1.20
131,000	1.30	50,000	1.50

(a) Plot the tension stress-strain curve and the torsion stress-strain curve on the same axes. (b) Apply Bridgman's correction for necking to the tension data. (c) Plot both tension and torsion data as significant stress and significant strain. (d) Plot both sets of data as maximum shear stress vs. maximum shear strain.

10-5. Explain why necking is observed in the tension test of a ductile material but not in the torsion test of the same material.

Chapter 11

11-1. Estimate the Mohs hardness for the following materials: (a) steel file; (b) chalk; (c) pine plank; (d) ball bearing; (e) sapphire.

11-2. (a) Show by means of a sketch that in order to produce geometrically similar indentations in a Brinell test d/D must remain constant.

(b)

Diam of indenter, mm	Diam of indentation, mm	Load, kg
10	4.75	3,000
7	3.33	1,470
5	2.35	750
1.2	0.57	425

P/D^2 is constant for the above data.   Determine the BHN, and show that it is approximately constant with load.

11-3. The following hardness data were obtained on copper by using a 10-mm ball indenter:

Load, kg	Diam of indentation, mm		
	Annealed	$\frac{1}{4}$ hard	$\frac{1}{2}$ hard
500	4.4	3.2	2.9
1,000	5.4	3.9	3.7
1,500	6.2	4.6	4.5
2,000	. . .	5.4	5.3
2,500	. . .	5.9	5.7

(a) Determine whether or not Meyer's law is obeyed.   (b) Determine the Meyer's law constants k, n', and C.   (c) Plot the BHN and Meyer hardness as a function of load for the $\frac{1}{4}$ hard copper.

11-4. If a $\frac{1}{4}$-in.-diameter ball is used for the annealed copper in Prob. 11-3, calculate what the indentation would be at 500-, 1,000-, and 1,500-kg loads.   Compare with the observed values.

Load, kg	Diam of indentation, mm
500	4.0
1,000	4.6
1,500	5.5
2,000	5.9

Determine k and n', and compare with the values for a 10-mm ball.

11-5. Tabor[1] has shown that the relationship between Rockwell C and Brinell hardness should be expressed by an equation of the form $R_C = C_1 - C_2/\sqrt{BHN}$. Using the hardness-conversion tables for steel, evaluate the constants, and see whether or not this equation provides a good fit.

Chapter 12

12-1. Peterson has shown that for an average value of $K_t = 2$ the notch sensitivity index is given by $q = 1/(1 + a/r)$, where a is a "particle size" dependent on

[1] "The Hardness of Metals," pp. 111–112, Oxford University Press, New York, 1951.

the material and r is the notch radius. Kuhn and Hardrath[1] have related a with the tensile strength of the steel.

σ_u, ksi	200	160	100	50
a	0.0004	0.001	0.0042	0.012

Using these data, plot a curve of q versus r for steels of different strengths.

12-2. Show by sketches that the stress gradient across a grain is higher with a small-notch-radius specimen for geometrically similar notches and equal grain size. Show by a sketch how the same volume at peak stress can be obtained in two specimens of different size.

12-3. Show that increasing the size of a fatigue specimen tested in bending decreases the stress gradient.

12-4. Eckert[2] found that the cold straightening of steel axles had no effect on the torsional fatigue strength but that this procedure could appreciably lower the fatigue strength in bending. Give an explanation of this effect.

12-5. Torsional fatigue tests on solid bars show no influence of static torque on the fatigue limit. Would this be true if the bar contained a small transverse hole? Explain.

12-6. Why are the notched fatigue properties of ordinary gray cast iron about equal to the unnotched properties?

12-7. Using the ideas about stress gradient developed in Sec. 12-7, show that the increase in fatigue limit due to nitriding the surface of a steel shaft is given approximately by $1/(D/2\delta - 1)$, where δ is the depth of the nitrided layer and D is the diameter of the shaft. Would this equation be applicable for axial loading? Explain why nitriding is an effective means of counteracting stress raisers.

12-8. A steel shaft is subjected to a completely reversed bending moment of 6,000 in.-lb. A transition section at one end contains a fillet with a 0.10-in. radius. The steel has a tensile strength of 100,000 psi, and the fatigue limit is 45,000 psi. K_t for the fillet is about 2, and the dynamic factor of safety is 2.5. What is the minimum allowable diameter of the shaft?

12-9. Derive an expression for the bending stress in an R. R. Moore type of fatigue specimen as a function of the angle of rotation of the specimen.

12-10. A 2-in.-diameter shaft is subjected to a static axial load of 25,000 lb. If the yield strength is 50,000 psi and the fatigue limit ($R = -1$) is 38,000 psi, what is the largest completely reversed bending moment that can be applied? The factor of safety is 2, and K_f due to notches is 1.8.

12-11. A threaded bolt experiences a completely reversed axial load of 60,000 lb. The static factor of safety is 2.0, and the dynamic factor of safety is 3.0. $K_t = 2.0$. The root radius of the threads is 0.020 in. (a) Compare the root area required for static and dynamic service for a high-strength bolt ($\sigma_0 = 180,000$ psi, $\sigma_u = 200,000$ psi). (b) Repeat for a low-strength bolt ($\sigma_0 = 30,000$ psi, $\sigma_u = 50,000$ psi). Use data in Prob. 12-1. (c) Determine the ratio of the areas for low-strength and high-strength bolts for the static and dynamic conditions.

12-12. In completely reversed bending a steel has a fatigue limit of 60,000 psi. Under a repeated stress cycle of zero to maximum stress in tension the same steel can withstand 90,000 psi without failure in 10^7 cycles. Evaluate the constants in Eq. (12-11).

12-13. A pressure vessel with a 4-in. inside diameter and a $\frac{1}{4}$-in. wall thickness is

[1] *NACA Tech. Note* 2805, 1952.
[2] *ASTM Spec. Tech. Publ.* 216, p. 21, 1958.

subjected to an internal pressure that varies from $-p/4$ to p. If the fatigue properties of the steel are given in Prob. 12-12, what is the maximum pressure that can be
withstood in fatigue?

12-14. A 2-in.-diameter shaft is subjected to a static bending moment of 8,000 in.-lb.
What is the value of the maximum twisting moment varying from 0 to M_T to produce
failure in 10^7 cycles? The yield strength is 90,000 psi, and the fatigue limit at
10^7 cycles in completely reversed stress is 60,000 psi.

Chapter 13

13-1. Construct a three-dimensional plot showing the relationship between stress,
strain, and time, for $T = T_m/2$.

13-2. Assuming that the mechanical equation of state is completely valid, show
how creep curves could be constructed from stress-strain curves.

13-3. The following rupture times[1] were obtained for stress rupture tests on a
steel alloy:

Stress, psi	Temperature, °F	Rupture time, hr
80,000	1080	0.43
80,000	1030	6.1
80,000	1000	22.4
80,000	975	90.8
10,000	1400	1.95
10,000	1350	6.9
10,000	1300	26.3
10,000	1250	84.7

Establish the validity of the Larson-Miller and Manson-Haferd parameters.

13-4. By means of sketches, show how isochronous stress-strain curves are derived
from creep data.

13-5. Draw a typical three-stage creep curve for a single-phase alloy determined
at constant temperature and load. (a) On the same graph draw the creep curve for
the same temperature and load after the material has been reduced by cold rolling.
(b) On the same graph draw the creep curve at the same temperature and load if
5 volume per cent of fine-precipitate particles are uniformly dispersed in the matrix.

13-6. The following data[2] were obtained in creep tests at 1500°F on an austenitic high-temperature alloy.

Stress, psi	Minimum creep rate, %/hr
10,000	0.00008
15,000	0.0026
20,000	0.025
30,000	2.0
40,000	30
50,000	320

[1] S. S. Manson, G. Succop, and W. F. Brown, Jr., *Trans. ASM*, vol. 51, p. 924, 1959.
[2] N. J. Grant and A. G. Bucklin, *Trans. ASM*, vol. 42, p. 720, 1950.

Establish the validity of Eq. (13-16), and determine the constants.

13-7. A tie rod 10 ft long is made from the austenitic alloy whose creep properties are given in Prob. 13-6.   At 1500°F it is subjected to an axial load of 8,000 lb.   The yield stress at 1500°F is 60,000 psi, and the stress for rupture in 1,000 hr is 20,000 psi. Using a factor of safety of 3.0, establish the necessary cross-sectional area of the tie rod based on the following considerations: (a) yield stress at 1500°F; (b) 1,000 hr rupture life at 1500°F; (c) an allowable creep rate of 1 per cent/10,000 hr.

13-8. A thin-wall pressure vessel of an austenitic alloy has a 1-in. wall thickness and an 18-in. inside diameter.   The vessel operates at 1500°F.   Find the allowable internal pressure if the maximum allowable increase in diameter is 0.2 in. over a 2-year period.   Assume steady-state conditions, and use the values of B and n' derived from the data in Prob. 13-6.

13-9. A steel bolt is loaded in tension to 10,000 psi and rigidly attached at both ends.   After 3 years of service at 800°F what is the stress in the bolt? $E = 22.5 \times 10^6$ psi; $B = 3 \times 10^{-40}$ per cent/(hr)(psi); $n' = 8.0$.

Chapter 14

14-1. Sketch the transition-temperature curves for a plain carbon steel tested in tension, torsion, and notched impact.

14-2. A mild-steel pipe is bent cold to a radius of eight times its diameter on a day when the temperature is 70°F.   After fabrication it accidentally falls to the concrete floor and breaks in a brittle manner.   Describe in detail the factors responsible for the failure, and prescribe remedies to prevent this type of failure.

14-3. For the introduction of a given amount of hydrogen into a steel, would an annealed or cold-worked steel suffer the greatest embrittlement?   Explain on the basis of dislocation theory.

14-4. The weight of the pendulum of an impact tester is 45 lb, and the length of the pendulum arm is 32 in.   If the arm is horizontal before striking the specimen, what is the potential energy of the tester?   What is the striking velocity?

14-5. A weight W falls vertically downward (without friction) along a thin rod of area A and length L until it is brought to rest by striking a flange at the end of the rod.   Using energy considerations, derive an expression for the maximum stress in the rod produced by the weight falling through a distance h.   Assume perfectly elastic impact.   Show that the sudden release of load from a height $h = 0$ produces twice the stress that would result from a gradual application of load.

14-6. Compare the loads required to produce yielding in an annealed steel rod ($E = 30 \times 10^6$ psi, $\sigma_0 = 30,000$ psi) and a cold-worked copper rod ($E = 16 \times 10^6$ psi, $\sigma_0 = 30,000$ psi) when a weight is dropped from a height of 12 in.   The cross-sectional area in both cases is 1 in.^{2}, and the lengths are both 18 in.   How does the dependence of tensile stress on area and length differ on impact loading from static loading?

14-7. The critical impact velocity for a steel is 160 ft/sec, and the longitudinal sound velocity is 19,500 ft/sec.   If $E = 30 \times 10^6$ psi and the density is 0.32 lb/in.^{3}, what is the fracture stress under these impulsive-loading conditions?

Chapter 15

15-1. A solid shaft is cooled with liquid nitrogen and shrunk into a solid disk. After the shaft has warmed up to room temperature, residual stresses are developed, due to the interference fit.   Sketch the distribution of tangential and radial stress in the disk and shaft.

15-2. A spot weld is made in a wide sheet of metal.   Sketch the distribution of tangential and radial residual stress due to thermal stresses.

15-3. A solid steel cylinder is examined for residual stresses by turning off layers from the outside diameter.

Diameter, in.	Length, in.
2.000	20.0200
1.800	20.0150
1.600	20.0050
1.400	20.0002
1.200	20.0100

Calculate and graph the residual stresses present, if it is assumed that only longitudinal stresses are present.

15-4. The residual stresses adjacent to a long butt weld between two deck plates in a Liberty ship were determined by an X-ray technique. The average lattice parameters in the three principal directions were found to be

$$a_0 = 2.8617 \text{ parallel to the weld bead}$$
$$a_0 = 2.8611 \text{ perpendicular to the weld bead}$$
$$a_0 = 2.8611 \text{ in the plate-thickness direction}$$

Find the values of the residual stresses if $a_0 = 2.8610$ for the unstrained steel $E = 30 \times 10^6$ psi, and $\nu = 0.30$.

15-5. The spacing between the (310) planes in ferrite were used to measure residual stresses in a steel plate ($E = 30 \times 10^6$ psi, $\nu = 0.25$). The lattice spacing perpendicular to the plate was 0.90584 A. One X ray shot at 45° from the vertical gave 0.90735 A. Another shot, also at 45° from the vertical but 90° counterclockwise away looking down on the plate, gave 0.90584 A. What is the largest normal stress present in the plate?

Chapter 16

16-1. The following data[1] were obtained for the transverse reduction of area (RAT) of a steel gun tube:

RAT, % class interval	Midpoint of class interval, X_i	Frequency f_i	$X_i f_i$
29–31	30	2	60
31–33	32	3	96
33–35	34	6	204
35–37	36	4	144
37–39	38	10	380
39–41	40	21	840
41–43	42	27	1,134
43–45	44	46	2,024
45–47	46	61	2,806
47–49	48	62	2,976
49–51	50	32	1,600
51–53	52	2	104
53–55	54	1	54
		$\Sigma f_i = 277$	$\Sigma f_i X_i = 12,422$

[1] E. G. Olds and Cyril Wells, *Trans. ASM*, vol. 42, p. 851, 1950.

(a) Plot a frequency histogram from these data.   (b) Plot the cumulative frequency distribution on regular coordinate paper.   (c) Determine the mean, median, and mode.   (d) Determine the range and standard deviation.   (e) Plot the cumulative frequency distribution on normal-probability paper, and determine the mean and standard deviation.

16-2. (a) For the data given in Prob. 16-1, what are the 95 per cent confidence limits on the mean of the population?   (b) What are the odds that the mean of the population will be outside the region 44.84 ± 0.76?

16-3. Eight fatigue specimens were tested at the same stress.   The number of cycles to failure, expressed as log N, were as follows:

i	$log\ N_i$
1	4.8388
2	4.9243
3	4.9445
4	4.9542
5	4.9731
6	4.9777
7	5.0334
8	5.0828

(a) What are the mean fatigue life and its standard deviation?   (b) What are the 95 per cent confidence limits on the mean of the population?

16-4. In an experiment to determine whether or not there is an effect of specimen diameter on RAT the following data were obtained:

0.505-*in. diam*	0.252-*in. diam*
$\overline{X} = 40.156$	$\overline{X} = 40.544$
$s^2 = 5.7850$	$s^2 = 3.2765$
$n = 16$	$n = 16$

Is the difference in the means for the two tests statistically significant?   (Note that the variances are not significantly different.)

16-5. Fatigue tests from two presumably identical bars of steel gave the following results for tests at 60,000 psi:

Bar 1	Bar 2
$\overline{\log N} = 5.0631$	$\overline{\log N} = 4.8306$
$s = 0.00615$	$s = 0.00315$
$n = 10$	$n = 12$

The F test shows that the variances are significantly different.   Establish whether or not the two samples are from the same population.

16-6. The following data[1] were obtained on the effect of specimen diameter on the value of RAT.   (a) Establish the regression equation, and determine the correlation coefficient.   (b) Is this a good correlation?

---

[1] E. G. Olds and Cyril Wells, *Trans. ASM*, vol. 42, p. 860, 1950.

Specimen number i	Specimen diameter	
	0.505-in. RAT, %, X_i	0.252-in. RAT, %, Y_i
1	36.4	44.1
2	42.0	41.0
3	42.6	41.8
4	41.4	39.7
5	43.7	41.3
6	40.8	36.8
7	38.9	40.2
8	41.4	39.7
9	36.1	38.2
10	40.8	39.7
11	37.6	43.7
12	37.6	41.6
13	43.7	41.0
14	38.0	41.1
15	39.2	39.1
16	42.3	39.7

16-7. The following data[1] were obtained from an experimental measurement of the fatigue limit using the probit technique:

Stress, psi	Per cent surviving 10^7 cycles
40,000	93.33
41,500	75.0
43,000	60.0
44,500	25.0
46,000	6.67

Determine the mean fatigue limit.

16-8. The following data were obtained in a determination of the fatigue limit by the staircase method. What are the mean fatigue limit and the standard deviation?

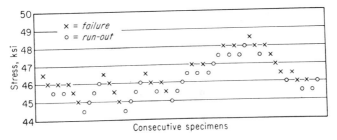

[1] *ASTM Spec. Tech. Publ.* 91A, pp. 29–30, 1958.

Chapter 17

17-1. Discuss the relative ease of hot work and cold work for the following metals: aluminum, zirconium, lead, SAE 4340 steel, molybdenum. Consider the following factors: melting point, flow stress, oxidation behavior, brittleness.

17-2. Derive an expression for the ideal work of deformation in extrusion.

17-3. Calculate the ideal work of deformation per unit volume in drawing a wire through a die. Express in terms of the strain in the longitudinal direction.

17-4. The reduction per pass is given by $q_n = (h_{n-1} - h_n)/h_{n-1}$, where n is the number of the pass. Derive an expression between the total reduction $Q_n = (h_0 - h_n)/h_0$ and the summation of the reductions per pass, q_n.

17-5. The change in shape during the flat-die forging of a steel billet of initial height h_0, width w_0, and length l_0 can be expressed[1] in terms of the coefficient of spread, s, by the relations $w_1/w_0 = (h_0/h_1)^s$ and $(l_1/l_0) = (h_0/h_1)^{1-s}$. If the coefficient of spread is defined by $s = -[\ln(w_1/w_0)]/[\ln(h_1/h_0)]$, derive the preceding relationships.

Chapter 18

18-1. Plot a curve of p_{av}/σ_0 versus the parameter $2fa/h$ for a rectangular slab and a cylinder for values of the parameter from 0 to 5.

18-2. Calculate the ideal work of deformation for pure (frictionless) compression. With this result, how is the reduction per blow related to the velocity of the forging hammer?

18-3. By means of sketches illustrate the Cook and Larke method for determining the true compression stress-strain curve.

18-4. What would be the effect of the section thickness h on the forging load if the friction were reduced to zero?

18-5. Assuming that an average forging pressure of 50,000 psi is required, what is the largest closed-die forging that could be made on a 35,000-ton press (the largest available)?

18-6. Show that the strains in the transverse and radial directions are equal for a thin circular disk compressed in the z direction.

18-7. Compare the average pressure needed to compress a cylinder 1 in. in thickness and 2 ft in diameter with one $\frac{1}{8}$ in. in thickness and 2 ft in diameter.

18-8. An SAE 1040 steel at the forging temperature has a yield stress of 6,000 psi. A right-circular cylinder 3 in. high and 1 in. in diameter is to be upset to half height between flat dies. (*a*) If the coefficient of friction is 0.4, what is the maximum force required for the upsetting? (*b*) How much extra force is required over what would be needed if no friction were present? (*c*) If it takes 3 sec to produce the forging and the efficiency is 40 per cent, how much power must be available in order to do the job?

Chapter 19

19-1. The mean rolling pressure can be expressed in simplified terms by Eq. (18-15), where $2a$ is the length of contact arc. Using this relation, plot curves for the variation of rolling load with roll diameter, coefficient of friction, and mean strip thickness.

[1] A. Tomlinson and J. D. Stringer, *J. Iron Steel Inst. (London)*, vol. 193, pp. 157–162, 1959.

19-2. Sheet steel is reduced from 0.160 to 0.140 in. with 20-in.-diameter rolls having a coefficient of friction equal to 0.04. The mean flow stress in tension is 30,000 psi. Neglect strain hardening and roll flattening. (a) Calculate the roll pressure at the entrance to the rolls, the neutral point, and the roll exit. (b) If $f = 0.40$, what is the roll pressure at the neutral point? (c) If 5,000 psi front tension is applied in Prob. 19-2a, what is the roll pressure at the neutral point?

19-3. Calculate the minimum gage possible in hot rolling low-carbon steel strip at 1700°F on a 23-in. mill with steel rolls. ($\sigma_0' = 35,000$ psi, $f = 0.4$, $E = 20 \times 10^6$ psi.) What is the minimum gage for cold rolling on the same mill? ($\sigma_0' = 60,000$ psi, $f = 0.10$, $E = 30 \times 10^6$ psi.)

19-4. The geometry of rolling is uniquely defined by the ratios h_f/R, h_f/h_0, or R/h_0 and q. Show that h_f/R is independent of the scale of the operation and that equivalent stress states are produced for equal values of h_f/R.

19-5. In hot rolling with an 18-in. rolling mill a groove was placed on the roll so as to put an imprint on the sheet every revolution. If the distance between marks on the sheet was 62.1 in., what was the forward slip? What is the coefficient of friction in rolling from 0.30 to 0.20 in. in thickness?

19-6. List three basic requirements for a good rolling lubricant.

19-7. The residual stresses produced in rolling are proportional to $(h_f/L)^2$, where L is the length of the arc of contact.[1] From the geometry of rolling show that $(h_f/L)^2 = (h_f/R)[(100 - q)/q]$, where $q = [(h_0 - h_f)/h_0]100$.

19-8. On a certain mill the rolling load for a 30 per cent reduction is 19.5 tons/in. of width. What is the rolling load when a back tension of 10 tons/in.^{2} and a front tension of 8 tons/in.^{2} are applied? Assume that $\sigma_0' = 35$ tons/in.^{2} and $\alpha = 2\beta$.

19-9. Show how the mean rate of deformation varies with the reduction for 0.3-in.-thick strip rolled on 28-in. rolls at 500 ft/min. Determine separate curves for sticking friction and slipping friction. Use $q = 0.10, 0.20, 0.30,$ and 0.50.

Chapter 20

20-1. Derive Eq. (20-8).

20-2. If p_d is the breakthrough pressure in direct extrusion and p_b is the maximum pressure for indirect extrusion, derive an expression which gives the container wall friction.

20-3. In the hot extrusion of aluminum at 600°F, $\sigma_0 = 12,000$ psi. (a) For a 12-in.-diameter billet, 36 in. long, what is the breakthrough pressure required to extrude a 3-in.-diameter bar if $f = 0.10$? (b) What is the required extrusion pressure at the end of the stroke? (c) What capacity press would be needed for this extrusion?

20-4. For extrusion through a flat die the strain rate is given approximately by $\dot{\epsilon} = (6v/D) \ln R$, where v is the ram velocity, D is the billet diameter, and R is the extrusion ratio.[2] For the conditions given in Prob. 20-3 compare the strain rates and the time the metal is in the die for a 2 in./sec and 10 in./sec ram speed.

20-5. What would be the form of Eq. (20-8) for the extrusion of a tube with $OD = D$ and $ID = d$?

20-6. The following equation[3] expresses the pressure for the extrusion of aluminum

[1] R. McC. Baker, R. E. Ricksecker, and W. M. Baldwin, Jr., *Trans. AIME*, vol. 175, pp. 337–354, 1948.

[2] P. Feltham, *Metal Treatment and Drop Forging*, vol. 23, pp. 440–444, 1956.

[3] S. Hirst and D. H. Ursell, *Metal Treatment and Drop Forging*, vol. 25, pp. 409–413, 1958.

bars:

$$p = \sigma_0(0.47 + 1.2 \ln R) \exp \frac{4fL}{D}$$

Billets 8 in. in diameter and 16 in. long are extruded into $\frac{3}{4}$-in.-diameter bars. In order to increase the length of the product by 10 ft, would it be more economical in terms of pressure to increase the billet length or the diameter? (Assume that $f = 0.10$.)

Chapter 21

21-1. Plot a curve of the ratio of draw stress to yield stress versus reduction in area for $B = 0$, 1, and 2.

21-2. Plot a curve of the ratio of draw stress to yield stress for $f = 0.10$, $q = 0.40$, and $D_f = 0.25$. Compare Sachs's analysis with Whitton's.

21-3. For a value of $B = 1$, plot a graph similar to that of Prob. 21-1 which shows the effect of back pull on draw stress. Use $\sigma_{xb}/\sigma_0 = 0$, 0.4, 0.6, and 0.8. Plot a curve that shows the effect of back pull on the maximum theoretical reduction.

21-4. Show that the strain rate of wire being pulled through a die can be expressed by $\dot{\epsilon} = \frac{2 \tan \alpha}{r} \frac{dx}{dt}$. What is the maximum strain rate for a 0.040-in.-diameter wire pulled at 2,000 ft/min through a 10° semiangle die?

21-5. Compare the force required to give a 30 per cent reduction in a 0.5-in.-diameter wire in a 10° semiangle die with the force required to produce the same reduction in a tube blank of 0.500 in. outside diameter, 0.400-in. inside diameter using a cylindrical mandrel. Assume that $f = 0.08$ for both cases.

Chapter 22

22-1. On the assumption that the fracture strain in the outer fiber in bending is equal to the fracture strain in the tension test derive Eq. (22-3) for the situation where the neutral axis does not shift.

22-2. Discuss the state of stress during the deep drawing of a cup at the following locations: (1) outer edge of the blank; (2) under the punch; (3) in the cup wall.

22-3. Estimate the punch load required for a deep-drawn cup with a 2-in. diameter and 0.040-in. wall if it is made from low-carbon steel, $\sigma_0 = 30,000$ psi, $\sigma_u = 50,000$ psi. The blank diameter is 4 in., and the over-all coefficient of friction is 0.08. Estimate the hold-down pressure and force required for bending and unbending, from other considerations.

22-4. How would you distinguish between the formability of different heats of low-carbon sheet steel?

22-5. L. R. Jackson[1] has suggested that a good general formability index is the ratio of the maximum uniform strain to the true stress at this strain. Use this criterion to estimate the formability of the following materials: H-11 tool steel; beta brass; titanium; Armco iron.

[1] *TML Rept.* 12, July 20, 1955.

ANSWERS TO SELECTED PROBLEMS

Chapter 1

1-1. (a) 75,000 psi   (b) Necking
(c) 0.001 in.   (d) 0.004 in.
1-2. 24×10^6 psi   **1-4.** W:Fe:Ti 1.72:3.44:5:88
1-5. Copper 2,110 psi; steel 3,830 psi   **1-7.** 195,000 psi

Chapter 2

2-1. (a) $\sigma_1 = 51,100$ psi, $\sigma_3 = 3,900$ psi
(b) $\sigma_1 = 13,500$ psi, $\sigma_3 = -68,500$ psi
2-3. (a) $S = 10,620$ psi; $l = 0.862$, $m = -0.196$, $n = -0.473$
(b) $\sigma_n = 7,940$ psi, $\tau = 7,100$ psi
(c)

	l	m	n
$\sigma_1 = 12,100$ psi	∓ 0.764	± 0.022	± 0.640
$\sigma_2 = -5,760$ psi	∓ 0.261	± 0.900	∓ 0.341
$\sigma_3 = +3,580$ psi	± 0.586	± 0.427	± 0.688

(d) $\tau_{\max} = 8,930$ psi

2-4. (a)

	l	m	n
$e_1 = 6.05 \times 10^{-4}$	0.810	0.171	0.563
$e_2 = -6.38 \times 10^{-4}$	0.111	0.985	0.143
$e_3 = 0.33 \times 10^{-4}$	0.577	0.056	0.812

(b) -6.38×10^{-4} (c) $\Delta = 0$
2-6. $e_1 = 5.5 \times 10^{-3}$, $\theta = 48°$, $e_2 = 0.25 \times 10^{-3}$
2-7. (a) 58,000 psi   (b) 9,300 psi   (c) 29,000 psi
2-8. $\sigma_T : \sigma_L = 2:1$
2-10. $\sigma_L = 115,000$ psi, 48% error; $\sigma_T = 185,000$ psi, 19% error
2-12. 112.86 in.^{3}

Chapter 3

3-2. (a) $e = -0.60$, $\epsilon = -0.915$ (b) $D = 3.16$ in.   (c) $\epsilon_1 = \epsilon_2 = 0.457$
3-5. (a) 4.78 in.   (b) 4.59 in.   **3-8.** 1,460 psi

3-10. $\bar{\epsilon} = -\dfrac{2}{\sqrt{3}}\ln\dfrac{h}{h_0} = -\dfrac{2}{\sqrt{3}}\ln\,(1-q),$ where $q = \dfrac{h_0 - h}{h_0}$

3-11. (a) 3.93 in. (b) 3.83 in.

3-12. (a) 42,000 psi (b) 42,000 psi (c) 48,700 psi

3-13. (a) 78,000 psi (b) 45,000 psi

Chapter 4

4-1. bcc lattice has more but slightly smaller interstitial sites

4-4. 1.54×10^{13} atoms/mm^2 **4-5.** 1.78×10^{13} atoms/mm^2

4-7. (b) 8; (c) 6

Chapter 5

5-1. 2,500 grains   **5-2.** 1,780 in.^{2}/in.^{3} of metal

5-3. 20 ppm   **5-4.** 0.031 mm (ASTM No. 7)

5-6. Equality of strain, $E = 65 \times 10^6$ psi; equality of stress, $E = 46 \times 10^6$ psi

Chapter 6

6-1. (b) $\dfrac{a^2}{2} > \frac{1}{6}a^2 + \frac{1}{6}a^2$ **6-2.** (b) $\frac{3}{4}a^2 + \frac{3}{4}a^2 < 2a^2$

6-8. Dislocation density about 2×10^7

6-9. 9.4 ev/atom plane   **6-10.** (b) 7.4×10^7 dynes/cm^2

6-11. $\tau = \dfrac{G}{8\pi(1-\nu)}\left(\dfrac{\gamma b}{L}\right)^{\frac{1}{2}}$

6-12. (a) $U_i = 0.5$ ev, $T \approx 750°$K; (b) 700 kg/mm^2

Chapter 7

7-1. 5×10^6 psi theoretical strength; about a factor of 10 greater

7-2. (a) $2c = 3.8 \times 10^{-5}$ cm; (b) $2c = 8.9 \times 10^{-1}$ cm; (c) $2c = 2.4 \times 10^{-1}$ cm

7-3. $2c = 5 \times 10^{-2}$ cm

7-4. The dislocation reaction would be $\dfrac{a}{2}[\bar{1}01] + \dfrac{a}{2}[101] \rightarrow a[001]$

7-5. (a) 91,600 psi; (b) 14,300 psi; (c) 65,000 psi

7-6. (a) 35,800 lb; (b) 300,000 lb; (c) 15,000,000 lb

7-8. 1.36×10^4 ergs/cm^2

Chapter 8

8-1. $0°$C $-$ 13.4 sec; $100°$C $- 7.5 \times 10^{-4}$ sec; $500°$C $- 5.74 \times 10^{-10}$ sec

Chapter 9

9-1. (b) (1) 30,000 psi; (2) 29.4×10^6 psi; (3) 31,000 psi
(4) 51,000 psi; (5) 34,000 psi; (6) 43.5%; (7) 72%

9-2. $U_T = \dfrac{Kn^{n+1}}{n+1}$ **9-3.** (b) $\sigma_0 = K\left(\ln\dfrac{1}{1-q}\right)^n$

9-5. (c) (1) 89,000 psi; (2) 136,000 psi; (3) 1.05; (4) 0.182; (5) 0.87; (6) 74,700 psi
(7) $n = 0.15$, $K = 116,000$ psi

9-7. $\ln \dfrac{\sigma_0}{\sigma_u} = n \ln \dfrac{\epsilon_0}{\epsilon_u} + \epsilon_u$ 　　　　**9-8.** $b = 22.0,\ c = 36;\ X = 26.7\%$

9-9. 100,000 psi

Chapter 10

10-1. (b) 49,000 psi; (d) $\tau_0 = 22,900$ psi, $G = 11.2 \times 10^6$ psi
$U_0 = 11.7$ in.-lb/in.^{3}; (e) $\nu = 0.29$

10-2. Hollow shaft will be 3.5 times stronger; $\theta_{\text{hollow}} = 0.14\theta_{\text{solid}}$
Both shafts will be the same weight

10-3. (a) 92 in.-lb; (b) torsion $\epsilon_{\max} = 1.5 \times 10^{-3}$, tension $\epsilon_{\max} = 1.2 \times 10^{-3}$

Chapter 11

11-1. (a) 8; (b) 1; (c) 1.5; (d) 7; (e) 9

11-3. Annealed: $k = 5.0$, $n' = 3.2$, $C = 79.5$
$\frac{1}{4}$ hard: $k = 26.3$, $n' = 2.52$, $C = 86.8$
$\frac{1}{2}$ hard: $k = 40.0$, $n' = 2.42$, $C = 105$

11-4. (a)

Load, kg	Indentation, mm	
	Observed	Calculated
500	4.0	3.55
1,000	4.6	4.4
1,500	5.5	5.1
2,000	5.9	5.5

(b)

Diam of ball, mm	n'	k	C
10	3.2	5.0	79
6.35 ($\frac{1}{4}$ in.)	3.25	6.0	60

11-5. $R_C = 124 \left(1 - \dfrac{12.2}{\sqrt{\text{BHN}}} \right)$

Chapter 12

12-8. 1.88 in. 　　　　**12-10.** 5,600 in.-lb

12-11. (a) Static: 0.67 in.^{2}; dynamic: 3.56 in.^{2}
(b) Static: 4.0 in.^{2}; dynamic: 11.7 in.^{2}
(c) Static 6.0; dynamic 3.3

12-12. $\sigma_e = 60,000$ psi; $C_2 = \frac{1}{3}$ 　　　**12-13.** 11,000 psi

Chapter 13

13-3. Manson-Haferd $= \dfrac{T - 880}{\log t - 5.65}$ 　　**13-6.** $B = 1.28 \times 10^{-43}$; $n' = 9.6$

13-7. (a) 0.40 in.^{2}; (b) 1.20 in.^{2}; (c) 1.94 in.^{2}

13-8. 1,380 psi 　　　　**13-9.** 6,900 psi

Chapter 14

14-4. $\mathrm{PE} = 120$ ft-lb; 13.2 ft/sec   **14-5.** $\sigma = \dfrac{W}{A}\left(1 + \sqrt{1 + 2h\,\dfrac{AE}{WL}}\right)$

14-6. Steel: 22.5 lb; copper: 42.2 lb   **14-7.** $370{,}000$ psi

Chapter 15

15-3. 1st layer: $-31{,}800$ psi; 4th layer: $+70{,}400$ psi
15-4. $\sigma_1 = 11{,}100$ psi; $\sigma_2 = \sigma_3 = 6{,}250$ **15-5.** $80{,}000$ psi

Chapter 16

16-1. (c) Mean—44.84%, median—46%, mode—48%
     (d) range—24%, standard deviation—4.21%
16-2. (a) 44.34 to 45.34%; (b) 3 in $1{,}000$
16-3. (a) $\overline{\log N} = 4.9661$, $s = 0.0726$
     (b) 4.9053 to 5.0269
16-4. $t = 0.516$; not statistically significant
16-8. $\bar{X} = 46{,}270$ psi; $s = 2{,}920$ psi

Chapter 17

17-2. $W_d = \sigma_0 V \ln (A_0/A_f)$ **17-3.** $W_d = \tfrac{3}{2}\sigma_0 \epsilon_1$

17-4. $Q_n = 1 - \exp\left(-\Sigma \ln \dfrac{1}{1 - q_n}\right)$

Chapter 18

18-2. $\dfrac{h}{h_0} = \exp\left(\dfrac{1}{2}\dfrac{mv^2}{\sigma_0 V}\right)$ **18-5.** 10 ft^2 cross-sectional area

18-8. (c) 4.9 hp

Chapter 19

19-2. (a) $34{,}700$ psi at roll entrance; $38{,}000$ psi at neutral point
     (b) $109{,}000$ psi
     (c) $32{,}600$ psi
19-5. $f = 0.5$ **19-8.** 14.5 tons/in.

Chapter 20

20-2. $f = \dfrac{D}{4L}\ln\dfrac{p_d}{p_b}$

20-3. a) $138{,}000$ psi; (b) $50{,}000$ psi; (c) $7{,}800$ tons

20-5. $p = \sigma_0\left[(\beta \ln R - 1)\exp\dfrac{4fL}{D-d} + 1\right]$

20-6. Increase the diameter

Chapter 21

21-4. 3.5×10^3 sec^{-1}

Chapter 22

22-3. $8{,}700$ lb

NAME INDEX

SUBJECT INDEX

5470-14
A

34